NATIONAL GEOGRAPHIC SOCIETY

Research Reports

NATIONAL GEOGRAPHIC SOCIETY

Research Reports

On research and exploration
supported by grants from the
National Geographic Society
during the year

1970

Compiled and edited by Paul H. Oehser and John S. Lea
under the direction of the
Committee for Research and Exploration

NATIONAL GEOGRAPHIC SOCIETY

WASHINGTON, D.C.

NATIONAL GEOGRAPHIC SOCIETY

Washington, D.C.

Organized "for the increase and diffusion of geographic knowledge"

GILBERT HOVEY GROSVENOR (1875–1966)

Editor, 1899–1954; President, 1920–1954

Chairman of the Board, 1954–1966

THE NATIONAL GEOGRAPHIC SOCIETY is chartered in Washington, D.C., in accordance with the laws of the United States, as a nonprofit scientific and educational organization for increasing and diffusing geographic knowledge and promoting research and exploration. Since 1890 the Society has supported more than 1,500 explorations and research projects, adding immeasurably to man's knowledge of earth, sea, and sky. It diffuses this knowledge through its monthly journal, NATIONAL GEOGRAPHIC, more than 50 million maps distributed each year; its books, globes, atlases, and filmstrips; National Geographic WORLD, a magazine for 8- through 12-year-olds; information services to press, radio, and television; technical reports; timely exhibits from around the world in Explorers Hall; and a nationwide series of programs on television.

• • •

Standard Book No. 087044-292-9

Library of Congress Catalog Card No. 68-26794

Contents

Editor's Note

The following accounts published in *National Geographic Society Research Reports, 1968 Projects* and *1969 Projects*, pertain in part to projects that continued into 1970, and no further treatment of them is required in the present volume:

"Preliminary Investigation of Artifact Association in an Arikara Cemetery (Larson Site), Walworth County, South Dakota," by William M. Bass, *1968 Projects*, pp. 33–38.

"Excavation at the Sutton Hoo Site, England," by Rupert L. S. Bruce-Mitford, *1968 Projects*, pp. 49–52.

"The 'Acropolis' of Aphrodisias in Caria: Investigations of the Theater and the Prehistoric Mounds, 1968–1970," by Kenan T. Erim, *1968 Projects*, pp. 79–114.

"Behavior and Ecology of the Giant Sable," by Richard D. Estes, *1968 Projects*, pp. 115–130.

"An Archeological Study of the Eskimo Thule Culture in the Northwest Hudson Bay Area," by Charles F. Merbs, *1968 Projects*, pp. 247–254.

"Mesozoic and Tertiary Vertebrates of Baja California, 1968–1971," by William J. Morris, *1968 Projects*, pp. 305–316.

"Excavation of Monte Alto, Escuintla, Guatemala," by Lee A. Parsons, *1968 Projects*, pp. 325–332.

"Development and Behavior of the White Gorilla," by Arthur J. Riopelle, *1968 Projects*, pp. 355–367.

"Biology and Ecology of Outer Reef Faces in the Western Caribbean and Bahama Islands," by Walter A. Starck II, *1968 Projects*, pp. 411–416.

"Studies of the Avifauna of Some Rift Valley Lakes of Ethiopia," by Emil K. Urban, *1968 Projects*, pp. 425–435.

"Religious Symbolism in a New Guinea Tribe," by Wilson G. Wheatcroft, *1968 Projects*, pp. 493–502.

"Reproduction Dynamics and Behavior of the Torrent Duck," by Marvin C. Cecil, *1969 Projects*, pp. 65–72.

"Ecological Studies in Southwest Florida," by Frank C. Craighead, Sr., *1969 Projects*, pp. 89–102.

"The Development of an Archeomagnetic Chronology for the New World," by Robert L. DuBois, *1969 Projects*, pp. 115–120.

"Exploring Subbottom Features of a Harbor with Sonar and Magnetometer," by Harold E. Edgerton and Peter Throckmorton, *1969 Projects*, pp. 133–139.

"Archeological and Paleobiological Studies at Stanton's Cave, Grand Canyon National Park, Arizona—a Report of Progress," by Robert C. Euler, *1969 Projects*, pp. 141–162.

"Mountain-gorilla Research, 1969–1970," by Dian Fossey, *1969 Projects*, pp. 173–186.

"Geophysical and Geologic Investigations of Some 'Accidents Circulaires' in Mauritania," by Robert F. Fudali, *1969 Projects*, pp. 195–202.

"Archeological Research in Colima, Mexico," by Isabel T. Kelly, *1969 Projects*, pp. 307–311.

"Population Ecology of Key Deer," by Willard D. Klimstra, James W. Hardin, and Nova J. Silvy," *1969 Projects*, pp. 313–321.

"Reproductive Performance of Ospreys (*Pandion haliaetus*) at Flathead Lake, Montana," by James R. Koplin *1969 Projects*, pp. 323–332.

"Studies of the Natural History of the American Bison," by Dale F. Lott, *1969 Projects*, pp. 399–404.

"Underwater Research in *Sublimnos*," by Joseph B. MacInnis and Alan R. Emery, *1969 Projects*, pp. 405–410.

"Excavation of the Phoenician and Roman Cities at Sarepta (Modern Sarafand, Lebanon)," by James B. Pritchard, *1969 Projects*, pp. 455–472.

"Archeological Investigations in the Grand Canyon," by Douglas W. Schwartz, *1969 Projects*, pp. 545–555.

Foreword

The National Geographic Society was founded in 1888 by a group composed largely of Washington scientists to increase and diffuse geographic knowledge and to promote research and exploration. The Society's activities toward achieving its second objective date from 1890, when the society sponsored a geographic and geologic expedition to study the Mount St. Elias Range of Alaska. Since then it has made more than 1,900 grants in support of approximately 1,500 projects in research and exploration. The work has encompassed the broad scope of geography, including such scientific disciplines as geology, paleontology, astronomy, geophysics, oceanography, biology, anthropology, archeology, ethnology, and geographical exploration. The research program has increased as the Society has grown, until today the budget of the Society provides $2,000,000 annually in support of the program.

This is the eleventh in a series of volumes that as projected will eventually contain abstracts and reviews of the results of all the research and exploration projects sponsored by the Society since it was established. These are being published volume by volume, as rapidly as the material can be assembled. The present volume contains 58 accounts covering work done under grants made during the year 1970. In some instances, when a continuing research program has been supported by grants over a number of years, and a breakdown of results by year is found impracticable, it has seemed best to include only one résumé for the entire project, with cross references to the main account inserted in other volumes as appropriate. Volumes now in print (1979) cover the following years: 1890–1954, 1955–1960, 1961–1962, 1963, 1964, 1965, 1966, 1967, 1968, 1969, 1970.

In presenting the résumés no attempt has been made to standardize the style and specific approach of the investigator, other than to confine each account to reasonable space limitations. In many cases fuller but scattered reports on the work have been, or will be, published elsewhere—in the technical scientific journals, occasionally in the *National Geographic*, or in book form. Published accounts emanating from the research projects are included in the literature references, which each author has been encouraged to supply.

Although the editors of these Reports make every reasonable effort to obtain a report from every grantee, so that the results of all projects supported in a given year will be accounted for in the volume for that year, circumstances occasionally interfere. In rare instances of delayed reports they will be published in later volumes as appropriate. Grantees generally have been most cooperative in this publication project, and the Committee for Research and Exploration takes this opportunity to thank them for their support. In the years to come we shall be calling on them in similar fashion, and we solicit their continued help.

Experience with the previous volumes of this series has convinced us that the presentation of research findings as given in these books is of real value to the scientific community. Scholars the world over find this record of the accumulating results of National Geographic Society research grants of real assistance in their own investigations and in the preparation of scientific publications. The general reader also gains new and important knowledge about the current state of research related to geography from each of these volumes.

MELVIN M. PAYNE
Chairman, Committee for Research and Exploration
National Geographic Society

Archeological Excavations at Cadbury-Camelot, South Cadbury, Somerset, England

Principal Investigator: Leslie Alcock, University of Glasgow, Scotland.

Grant No. 825: For archeological research at Cadbury-Camelot.

The excavations at Cadbury-Camelot started in 1966 as a modest reconnaissance; they were continued on a scale more appropriate to the importance of Cadbury in 1967–69; and the final season in 1970 was continued until all the major outstanding problems had been cleared up. The initial impetus for the work came from the collection, by the late Mrs. Mary Harfield, of pottery turned up in plowing, and the recognition by Dr. C. A. Ralegh Radford that some of this pottery belonged to the period of the historic Arthur. This seemed to give weight to the traditional identification of Cadbury Castle with the legendary or fabulous Camelot.

But this was not the only inspiration for the excavations. Pottery and flints collected by Mrs. Harfield and others revealed that the hilltop had a long and rich occupation in the Iron Age, as well as vestiges of an Early Neolithic settlement. Numismatic evidence showed that Cadbury had been the site of an emergency mint and fortified town in the last years (A.D. 1010–16) of King Ethelred the Unready. Air photographs indicated very dense occupation in the Iron Age, to judge from the number of pits that appeared on them. In brief, Cadbury Castle was known to be a hill fort with an exceptionally long, rich, and complex history, thoroughly worthy of excavation even without the Camelot connection. The fundamental policy of research was, therefore, to give full weight to every period of that history.

Prehistoric Cadbury

The first activity on the Cadbury hilltop, in the Early Neolithic period, remains enigmatic. Characteristic pottery, dated by the thermoluminescence technique, shows that occupation begins before 3000 B.C. On the crown of the hill, and more rarely on the southern slopes, there are pits with pottery, waste flakes of flint and rare implements of flint, burnt hazelnuts, animal bones, and occasional human bones. One pit had a radiocarbon age of 2825 ± 115 B.C. The general character of the pits suggests ritual rather than domestic use, and there are no traces of contemporary dwellings.

Apart from a little Late Neolithic pottery and characteristic arrowheads, Cadbury was deserted from shortly after 2500 to a little after 1000 B.C. It was then reoccupied by people using Late Bronze Age pottery and metalwork. The pottery consists principally of large plain storage jars and cooking pots, some of which were found in oven pits. The metalwork ranges from a gold bracelet of the 8th or 7th century B.C., indicating a wealthy element in the community, through weapons to simple tools like knives and gouges. however, pottery and coins demonstrate renewed activity. It is probable that this was associated with a Romano-Celtic temple. The coins and general set-ramparts of the hill were not built at this time, and the inference is that defense was not the motive for the location of this hilltop settlement. It is more likely that climatic deterioration had driven a group of farmers up from the Somerset swamps.

The Late Bronze Age culture of Cadbury exhibits some features that are not native to Britain, and in the 7th and 6th centuries B.C. continental bronzes appear, notably razors and pins derived from the Central and West European Hallstatt culture. New types of pottery also occur, characteristically decorated with fingertip impressions on strips of clay applied to the neck of the pot. Similar vessels are known in Hallstatt graves, for instance, in Bavaria. It seems likely that the pottery and bronzes reflect a movement of peoples bringing Celtic speech and an impoverished Hallstatt culture from West Central Europe to southern Britain. They also introduced an iron-using technology and therefore usher in the Iron Age.

Cadbury in the Iron Age

From small beginnings, Cadbury grew in the Iron Age to be a heavily defended and densely occupied town. The earliest inhabitants may have lived in small rectangular houses, but the dominant house type was the medium-sized circular house, with a floor area of about 1,200 square feet. Between the houses were rock-cut pits, used principally to store grain. Once the pits became sour, they were filled with trash, and they therefore provided a rich haul of pottery, metal, bone, and stone objects.

Some of the pits, however, appear to have been primarily ritual, for they contain carefully buried animal skulls. There are also deliberate burials of young animals, presumably sacrifices, on the approach to a porched shrine that stood on the crest of the hill. Like a medieval cathedral town, then, Iron Age Cadbury was a religious center. It was also the scene of industrial activity, especially the manufacture of bronze and iron weapons and armor for the Celtic warrior aristocracy.

The ramparts that are so striking a feature of Cadbury today do not go back to the earliest Iron Age, but once they had been founded in the 5th or 4th century B.C., their strength and complexity were increased, as the town itself grew in population. Enormous quantities of wood and stone were used in their construction, and a large and well-organized labor force is also implied. Starting with a single rock-cut ditch and a timber-revetted bank, the defenses were modified at least four times until, by the end of the Iron Age, the town was surrounded by four, or in places five, ramparts.

Total exploration of the southwest gate showed that this too had been modified several times. The early gate had a single wooden guard chamber; that of the middle periods has paired guardrooms facing each other across the entrance; while in the final phase there was a single stone-walled chamber. A further point of great importance is that between the penultimate and final phases the gate was completely derelict. It is possible that this implies that the town as a whole had been abandoned.

Roman Activity at Cadbury

The flourishing Celtic culture of Iron Age Cadbury was brought to an abrupt end by the sack of the town and the massacre of its inhabitants at the hands of Roman soldiery apparently in the 60s–70s of the first century A.D. A large collection of pottery, bronze brooches, and iron weapons dating to this time was recovered. But the most spectacular find was a bronze plaque with a human or divine head in Romano-Celtic style. A small quantity of Roman military equipment shows that the fort was occupied briefly by a detachment engaged in demolishing the defenses.

Thereafter the town lay derelict for a couple of centuries, and the hilltop was given over to farming. In the late 3d and 4th centuries A.D., however, pottery and coins demonstrate renewed activity. It is probable that this was associated with a Romano-Celtic temple. The coins and general setting are certainly consistent with this, even though no structural remains of a temple were found. The destruction witnessed by antiquaries in the 17th and 18th centuries A.D. could account for the disappearance of temple buildings.

Cadbury-Camelot in the Arthurian Period

Early in the 5th century A.D. Cadbury was abandoned yet again; but the clear evidence of pottery imported from Gaul and the Mediterranean shows that it was reoccupied for a century or more after 470. In the southwest gate of this period there are two structural phases. The second is dated to the late 6th century A.D. by a stratified silver buckle, suggesting that the defenses were refurbished to provide a base for the defense of southwest England against aggression from the young kingdom of Wessex.

The earlier structural phase, datable broadly by the imported pottery, would mark the creation of a fortified base against the earlier Saxon aggression which was halted (in A.D. 490 or 518) by the British victory of Badon. This phase is strictly contemporary with the historical Arthur. When we bear in mind his probable role as commander of a force drawn from several British kingdoms, it is significant that Cadbury alone among British forts of that period is capable of accommodating a large army. This gives symbolic value to the traditional identification with the fabulous Camelot.

Size apart, Cadbury-Camelot is interesting because of the very thorough way in which its 1,200 yards of rampart were rebuilt. The new defense was in the form of a timber fighting platform, anchored down and walled at the front with rubble, much of it quarried from derelict Roman buildings. The gateway had a square tower, raised on massive corner posts above the general level of the sentry walk. While the rampart has a distinctly Celtic, pre-Roman look, the gate tower is based on Roman models.

The principal building of the Arthurian fort was a large timber feasting hall, which stood on the very summit of the hill. The discovery of such a building had been an important aim of the excavations, but the odds against it were clearly high, and our success is all the more noteworthy.

The Cadanbyrig of Ethelred the Unready

On the Saxon conquest of Somerset, the British fort of Cadbury was abandoned once more. But in the last years of Ethelred the Unready, when southern England was ravaged by Viking armies, the hilltop provided a natural strong point on which to place a fortified town and an emergency coin-mint, dated A.D. 1010–1016. Excavation showed that the town had been defended by a mortared stone wall, with monumental arched gateways. It had been intended to build a church in the center, but only the foundations had been dug when Ethelred's successor, Cnut, abandoned Cadanbyrig altogether about A.D. 1020. In the defenses and southwest gate there are traces of yet another building phase, but its historical context is unknown. Thereafter, the history of the site is one of agriculture, antiquarian speculation, and, finally, the excavations of 1966–70.

Supplementary Excavation, 1973

Although the main work of excavation was brought to a close in 1970, intensive study continued on the tens of thousands of potsherds, hundreds of metal objects and other artifacts, and on the large number of site drawings and photographs which resulted from the excavation. In April 1973 the opportunity was taken to test by means of a small supplementary excavation some of the hypotheses based on the site evidence. This led to some minor modifications in detail, but the main history of the defenses remains substantially unmodified.

The opportunity was taken also to obtain carbon samples from critical positions in the rampart. When these have been dated by the radiocarbon technique, it should prove possible to place the chronology of the defenses on a sound basis.

REFERENCES

ALCOCK, LESLIE

1971a. Arthur's Britain, 415 pp., illus., St. Martin's Press, New York.

1971b. Excavations at South Cadbury Castle 1970. Antiq. Journ., vol. 51, pt. 1, pp. 1–7, illus.

1972. "By South Cadbury is that Camelot...": Excavations at Cadbury Castle 1966–70, 224 pp., illus. Thames & Hudson, London. (Published by Stein & Day, New York, 1972, under title "Was This Camelot? Excavations at Cadbury Castle 1966–70.")

LESLIE ALCOCK

National Geographic Society–Tulane University Program of Archeological Research on the Yucatán Peninsula, Mexico

Principal Investigator: E. Wyllys Andrews IV, Middle American Research Institute, Tulane University, New Orleans, Louisiana.[1]

Grant Nos. 835, 898: For archeological excavation and reconnaissance in the Río Bec area, Campeche, Mexico, 1970 and 1971.

Background

Until recent years the central Maya lowlands, home of the Río Bec and Chenes architectural styles, remained covered by almost impenetrable high forest. In the 1960s, when logging companies and a new transpeninsular highway began to open the abandoned but exceedingly important Río Bec area, Maya archeology was not slow to take advantage of the new possibilities for research. In 1968, with a concession from the Instituto Nacional de Antropología e Historia of Mexico and a grant from the National Geographic Society (no. 679), E. Wyllys Andrews IV, director of the Middle American Research Institute Program of Research on the Yucatán Peninsula, began reconnaissance in the vicinity of Xpuhil, about halfway across the base of the peninsula, near the center of the Río Bec archeological area. The 1968–69 field season, devoted to survey, limited excavations at the sites of Becan and Chicanna, and construction of a base camp, has been reported in this series by Joann M. Andrews (1976) and need not be described here. Figure 1 in the 1968 report shows a map of the Yucatán Peninsula.

The present report outlining the activities of the 1970 and 1971 field seasons includes also a description of research and analysis continuing since 1971, a brief and preliminary summary of the major results, and references to publications deriving from the excavations in Campeche. Many of the graduate students who participated in the three years of field work were supported by Ford Foundation Traineeships in Archaeology.

---

[1]Dr. Andrews died on July 3, 1971.

1970 Season

The 1970 season saw a significant increase in the size of the project, both in personnel and in the scope of the excavations. The staff, including local workers and 16 masons trained in archeological consolidation, totaled 94. As a consequence, problems of supplying food, water, building materials, and other necessities also grew. Joann M. Andrews again handled the continuous purchase and delivery of material from Mérida.

Becan. Richard E. W. Adams joined the project during its second season. As field director at Becan, he supervised the various excavations at this site and helped with the analysis of ceramics from here and elsewhere.

Excavations at Str. IV, begun in the previous year, continued under the direction of David F. Potter as the principal architectural investigation at Becan. Str. IV is an unusual Late Classic building, of a kind unknown in other parts of the Maya lowlands. The south face is formed of a wide stairway leading to what was probably a large, collapsed, serpent-mouth doorway in the Chenes-Río Bec style. The complex at top consists of an open courtyard surrounded by seven large vaulted rooms. Two small stairways toward the rear lead down into a 4-story series of vaulted rooms ranging from the level of the courtyard above to a low, open plaza behind Str. IV. Over half of this complex structure was excavated in 1970, many of the north ranges were cleared and consolidated, and the central portion of the main stairway was repaired. Above the room floors in this Chintok-phase building (ca. A.D. 730/750–830) lay thick residential deposits of refuse, rich in pottery dating to the Terminal Classic and Early Postclassic Periods.

One of the most distinctive features at Becan is its elaborate defensive fortifications, the largest known in the Maya lowlands. The entire central ceremonial complex of about 46 acres is surrounded by a kidney-shaped ditch, 1,890 meters long and averaging 5.3 meters deep and 16 meters wide. The ditch cuts through 2 meters of hard limestone bedrock into deep areas of the soft, granular lime known as *sascab*. The hard-surface rock was probably brought inside the perimeter to be used as building material or plaza fill; the *sascab* was mounded on the interior rim of the ditch to form a tall parapet averaging 5 meters high. At seven points thin strips of original surface were left as causeways, sometimes built up with excavated material to the height of the parapet. At some later date, the central portions of at least two and possibly four of these approachways were severed by deep excavations, presumably to simplify defense at a time of military stress. At least one of these was subsequently restored to use during the late Early Classic Period.

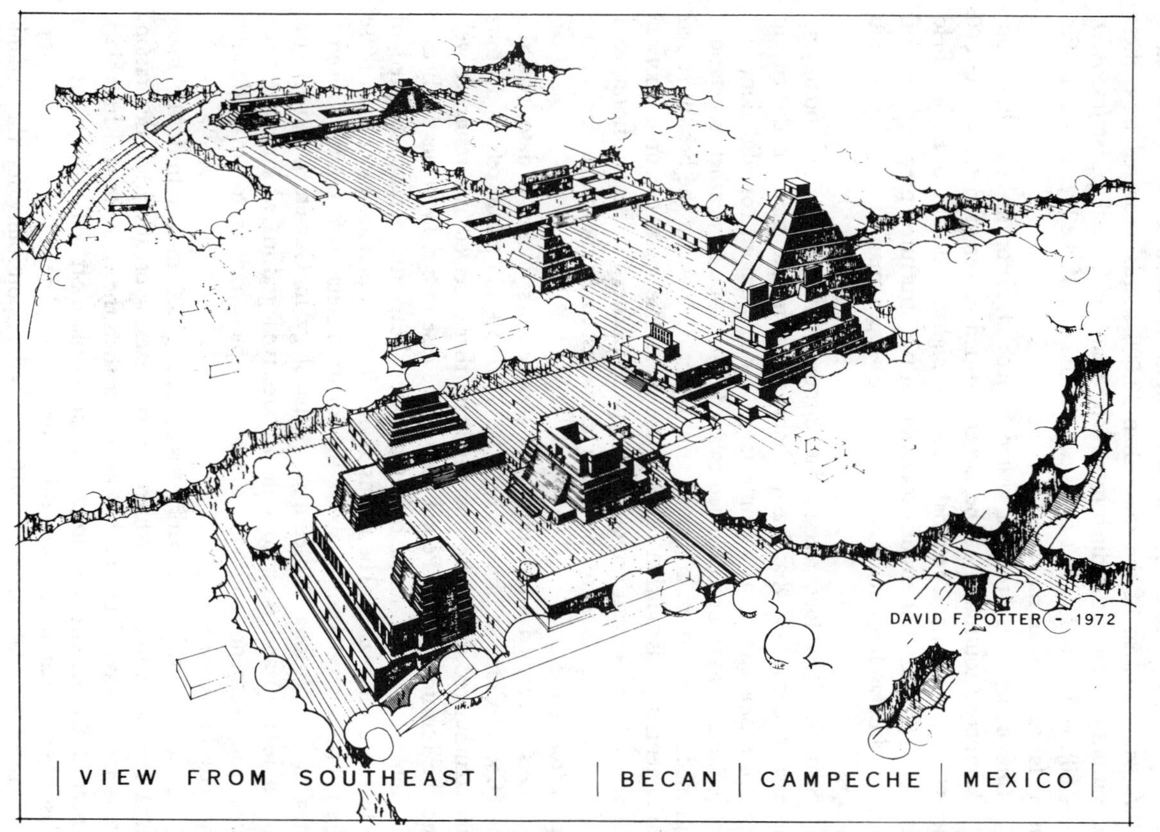

FIG. 1. Becan, Campeche, Mexico, from the southeast. Restoration drawing by David F. Potter.

David L. and Jinx Webster investigated the huge ditch, placing almost 40 test pits in and around it and excavating seven small associated structures. J. W. Ball's analysis of the more than 30,000 sherds recovered from these excavations has dated the ditch to no later than the Chacsik phase (ca. A.D. 250–500), and it may in fact be as early as the end of the Preclassic Pakluum phase, far earlier than had been guessed.

Chicanna. This site, first visited by Jack D. Eaton in 1967, lies about 2½ kilometers southwest of the larger fortified center of Becan, some 800 meters south of the Chetumal-Escarcega highway. In 1970 Eaton, field director at this site, undertook excavations at two structures, prepared detailed plans of all standing architecture, and drew up a map of the various ruin groups.

Structure II, a low, rectangular, 8-room, range-type edifice occupying the eastern border of what was probably the principal plaza of the city in late times, was chosen as a prime target for excavation, consolidation, and repair. Much of its front façade had escaped destruction by weather, vegetation, and modern marauders, and now, after repair, it is one of the best-preserved monuments in this portion of the Maya area. The massive central doorway is framed by a serpent's mouth in typical Chenes-Río Bec tradition, and elaborately carved stucco and stone elements cover the remainder of the upper front façade.

Ceramics sealed under the floors and benches of Str. II date it to the Late Classic Chintok phase (ca. A.D. 730/750–830), but refuse deposits that accumulated over these floors indicate that it served as a residence well into the Terminal Classic Period, as was the case in Str. IV at nearby Becan.

Interior walls of Maya buildings often bear crude graffiti painted or etched into the plaster. The rooms at Str. II retain perhaps more than those of any building yet known, about 100 square meters. José Antonio Oliveros, artist of the National Museum of Archaeology in Guatemala, joined the project in 1970 and drew to scale all preserved graffiti, which range from huge, long serpents and tall, stepped temple-pyramids to small doodles and recording devices.

Structure XI, in a separate group about 100 meters from the main plaza, represents an earlier architectural style lacking ornate façade decoration. Walls are of heavy slabs and blocks, rather than the concrete and fine block veneer of Str. II. Architecture and ceramics place Str. XI early in the Late Classic Period. Eaton excavated this structure completely.

Joseph W. Ball, who in 1970 assumed responsibility for the ceramic analysis, processed over 150,000 sherds by the end of this season, establishing the outlines of a sequence running from the Middle Preclassic (ca. 600 B.C.)

FIG. 2. Structure II, Chicanna, Campeche, Mexico, before (top) and after repair.

until shortly before the Spanish Conquest. Preliminary analysis indicated that during the Preclassic and Classic Periods the local Río Bec ceramic column was closely tied to that of the southern Maya lowlands, in Guatemala. By the end of Classic times, however, coinciding roughly with the downfall of the southern sites, the Río Bec region was increasingly influenced by northern Maya lowland pottery traditions.

Of great importance for future work were the early ceramic remains. Late Preclassic pottery was clearly associated with architecture in three test pits, and expansion of these excavations was planned for the following year.

The region around Becan, Chicanna, and Xpuhil is a frontier area, largely abandoned for almost a millennium, and is now being rapidly resettled by farmers. Ingolf Vogeler, an ecologist, spent the 1970 season surveying the modern cultural ecology of the region, concentrating on its agricultùral potential.

Additional staff members in 1970 included Michael P. and Ellin Simmons, who remained in Mérida, continuing the analysis of pottery from Dzibilchaltun, Yucatán. Richard H. Stewart, National Geographic Society staff photographer, spent four months in the field.

1971 Season

During the final season of the project, excavations continued at Becan, but, with the exception of limited test-pitting, work at Chicanna ended in the spring of the previous year, freeing Eaton for resumption of reconnaissance started in 1968–69. Adams did not return for a second year, and illness prevented E. Wyllys Andrews IV from spending much time in the field. Anthony P. Andrews, who was part of the final year's staff, assumed much of the responsibility for logistics.

Becan. David Potter returned to Str. IV, spending most of the season at this building. Like many large Maya pyramidal platforms, Str. IV contained within it an earlier structure, a 15-meter-high pyramid with traces of an unvaulted superstructure. Ceramics date the huge inner construction to the Late Preclassic Pakluum phase, indicating that even by this early time Becan was an important ceremonial center.

Three other excavations contributed to our knowledge of Becan in the Late Preclassic. Str. XI, a Late Classic ballcourt, was cleared and test-pitted in 1969. Below it appeared several floors, associated with Late Preclassic pottery. Adams enlarged this pit in 1970, and in 1971 A.P. Andrews greatly expanded the excavation, unearthing sections of two small Preclassic platforms.

As part of the excavations associated with his investigation of the fortifications, David Webster tested Str. XXVII, buried under the parapet, and came upon the remains of an additional Preclassic platform. Ball returned to it in 1971, completely uncovering the intact building. Str. XXVII is the best-preserved example of Pakluum phase architecture at Becan, showing a

FIG. 3. Structure IV, Becan, showing architectural detail.

small platform supporting a stone-walled room with a perishable roof. Under the platform floor were sealed several Pakluum caches. The bright red paint of the structure faded hours after being exposed. The pristine condition of this paint suggests that the building could not have been subject to long weathering before the *sascab* of the parapet covered it.

Mundo Perdido, a typical Late Classic suburban courtyard a few hundred meters north of the Becan ditch, was originally tested by Adams in 1970. A. P. Andrews excavated the complex in 1971, uncovering the outlines of an Early Classic structure and, below it, a small Late Preclassic platform overlying Middle Preclassic refuse. As Xcocom phase (Terminal Classic and Early Postclassic) middens covered the Late Classic structures, the small group provided an essentially unbroken sequence of architectural and ceramic remains.

Str. XXV, another small Late Classic building first tested in 1970, produced a complete ceramic column extending back to the Late Preclassic. The range of rooms was cleared in 1971 and the excavation through it enlarged, to increase the ceramic sample from early sealed contexts.

David Potter, in addition to his work at Str. IV, investigated several other large buildings around the main plazas at Becan (Strs. I, II, VIII, and X). His test pits indicated that most—or possibly all—large, visible buildings at the site date to the Late Classic Period. He and Ball also tested some of the major standing architecture at Chicanna, which, with the exception of a few later and earlier structures, also appears to date to the Late Classic.

Reconnaissance. Jack Eaton, assisted by A. P. Andrews, resumed the survey of the central Río Bec area south of Becan, finding many sites first reported by Merwin (1913) and Ruppert and Denison (1943) and recording several new ones. One goal of this season was to find the famous ruins of Río Bec B, which no archeologist had visited since the early 20th century. Although time restrictions prevented Eaton from reaching the ruins, his gridded trail system came within a few hundred meters of them, and the following year a private team did in fact extend the trails to the important temple (Kelly and Kelly, 1974).

The survey discovered new sites to the east and west of Becan and Chicanna. One very important ruin lies about 9 kilometers east of Chicanna, south of the main highway. Called Manos Rojas, the large, 2-towered building shows the recent depredations of looters that are taking such a heavy toll in this still poorly recorded area.

In the course of reconnaissance, Eaton noticed many hillsides covered by ancient terraces, as well as many lower fields crossed by agricultural ridges. His observations, along with those of Prentice Thomas during the 1969 season, provided impetus for future work in the Río Bec area specifically concerned with prehistoric agricultural practices. An additional result of the survey will be a new archeological map of the Río Bec area.

Irwin Rovner joined the staff in 1971 to study the lithic artifacts from the Campeche project, undertaking also the final report on lithic materials from Dzibilchaltun, Yucatán. At the end of the season, Jennifer Taschek arrived in Yucatán to undertake a study of the nonlithic artifacts from Becan, Chicanna, and Dzibilchaltun. Dolores Skaer deSilver, who replaced Oliveros as staff artist, spent the season drawing pottery, artifacts, and sculptured stucco from Becan.

In May 1971, when field work ended, the project officially turned over Becan and Chicanna to the Instituto Nacional de Antropología e Historia. Permanent guardians were placed at these two sites, at Xpuhil and nearby ruins, and at Río Bec. The field camp at the Xpuhil crossroads was also transferred to the Mexican Government, with a guardian, and has subsequently been used by I.N.A.H. projects in the area as well as by several National Geographic Society-sponsored research teams.

Continuing Research: 1971–1975

The excavations and survey in the central Maya lowlands resulted in accumulation of a vast amount of data, most of which remained to be sifted and analyzed after field operations ended. Many of these studies are now complete, although some are still in preparation. Five students have used portions of the material for doctoral dissertations. The Middle American Research Institute at Tulane is publishing the final reports, which are expected to fill six volumes, in addition to several shorter monographs. The Institute has published a brief compilation of preliminary reports (Adams, 1974).

Joseph W. Ball completed the ceramic analysis in 1973, and his final report is now in press (Ball, 1971, 1972, 1973, 1974a, 1974b, 1977). David F. Potter submitted an analysis of the Chenes-Río Bec architectural style as a doctoral dissertation, concentrating heavily on his excavations at Becan (Potter, 1973, 1974, 1977). The defensive fortifications at Becan and their significance are the subject of David L. Webster's final report, now published (1972, 1974, 1976). Irwin Rovner has finished, and Jennifer Taschek is completing, dissertations on the lithic and nonlithic artifacts, respectively, both of which are combined with their analyses of artifacts from Dzibilchaltun, Yucatán. For the first time in the Maya lowlands, Rovner's analysis has established detailed sequences of stone artifact types that rely heavily on technology of

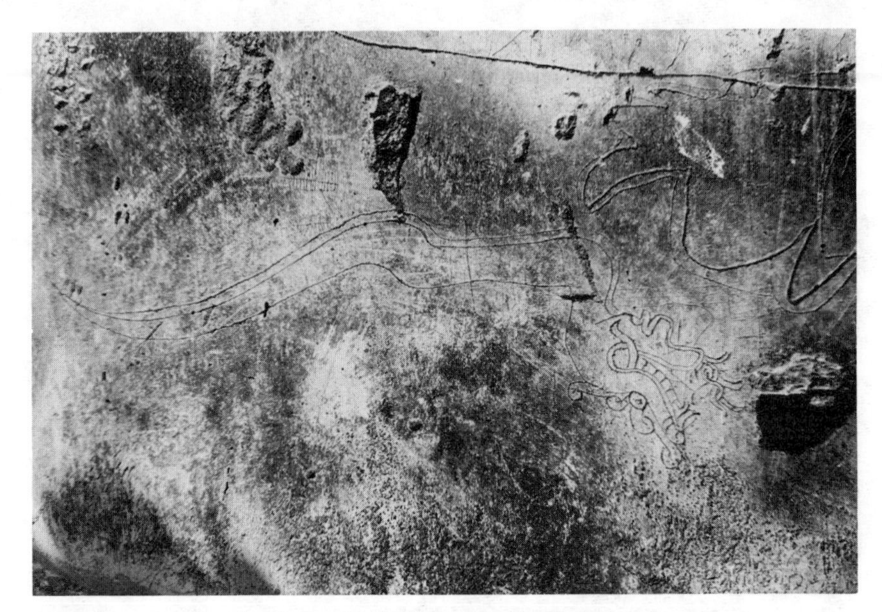

FIG. 4. Structure II, Chicanna. Graffito of a serpent.

manufacture (Rovner, 1974, 1975). Jack D. Eaton, in addition to his report on excavations at Chicanna, will submit a more comprehensive work on the Río Bec survey (Eaton, 1972, 1974).

A description and comparative analysis of the important Preclassic architecture at Becan, not treated in Potter's manuscript on the Late Classic remains, has appeared as a separate short monograph (Ball and Andrews V, 1978). A visit by E. Wyllys Andrews IV and others to the Río Bec site of El Chorro, first reported in 1938 by the Carnegie Institution of Washington as Pasión del Cristo, resulted in drawings and partial analysis of new hieroglyphic inscriptions on two very late monuments (see J. M. Andrews, 1976, fig. 2). This discovery will also be presented in a future publication.

Andrews IV had planned to continue consolidation of severely weakened sections of Str. IV at Becan. This was not possible during the final season, but in 1974 the funds set aside for this obligatory project were made available to the Instituto Nacional de Antropología e Historia. Lewis C. Messenger, from the University of the Americas in Cholula, and Juan Chablé, the I.N.A.H. master mason who worked for Andrews during the long years at Dzibilchaltun, Becan, and Chicanna, oversaw the task.

Another major responsibility to the Mexican Government was the preparation of extensive type collections of ceramic and lithic material deriving from the past 15 years of the National Geographic Society-Tulane University Program of Research, as well as delivery of all entire ceramic vessels and artifacts. These collections, which approximately double the useful study collections for the ancient Maya on the Yucatán Peninsula, were officially delivered to I.N.A.H. in the summer of 1974.

By the end of 1973, laboratory work had drawn to a close. Eduardo Toro, the project ceramic technician since 1956, following years in the same capacity for the Carnegie Institution of Washington, was employed by the Mérida center of the I.N.A.H., to which he is a valuable addition.

The National Geographic Society has sponsored subsequent expeditions in the Becan area. As these have depended on the groundwork laid by the Middle American Research Institute, they merit mention here. Andrews IV was unable to supervise the settlement pattern study planned for 1971, and this crucial aspect of the project remained for others to complete. In 1972 and 1973, Prentice M. Thomas, Jr., a member of the 1968–69 staff, surveyed the area around Becan, giving us the first intensive settlement study in the central Maya lowlands (Thomas, 1974, n.d.).

The 1973 research at Becan directed by R. E. W. Adams was oriented toward ecological reconstruction. William L. Turner, who was associated with it, followed up earlier indications of intensive farming practices in the Becan region and has contributed significantly to our understanding of ancient central lowland subsistence (Turner, 1974). A monograph on the lithic artifacts and debitage from the 1973 project has been published by James B. Stoltman (1978).

Summary of Results

The earliest inhabitants of the Becan area appear to have arrived about 550 B.C., bringing with them a ceramic tradition closely related to that of the Petén Maya. Remains of this Acachen phase are limited to refuse deposits underlying structures of later periods, as no platforms of the time have been found.

The Late Preclassic Pakluum phase, to judge from vastly increased ceramic debris and from several excavated platforms, saw a great population expansion within the ceremonial and civic center and apparently in outlying areas as well. The 15-meter-high Str. IV-sub is one of the largest Preclassic structures known in the Maya lowlands. Becan even then must have been the ceremonial and administrative focus for a large zone, which presumably included less important centers. Chicanna at this early time was a far more modest settlement than Becan.

The rapid growth of Becan in the early centuries of our era and its increasing importance in the central Maya lowlands must have been directly related to construction of the defensive fortifications in the first part of the Early Classic Period. Vogeler has suggested that the land around Becan has a relatively high carrying capacity, compared to northern Yucatán and the Petén (1970:17–18; 1974:111), and this may have permitted a higher population density under shifting agriculture. If this is so, the zone may have been an especially desirable one, coveted by neighboring groups. Webster wonders if the site might not have been located astride important trade routes, and this may in part explain the early and rapid growth of the settlement (Webster, 1976: 296–97).

The Early Classic Period seems to have been a time of population contraction and possibly decrease. Archeological remains of the Chacsik phase at Becan appear only within the defensive ditch and include relatively little in the way of architecture. Chicanna was apparently uninhabited at this time.

Green obsidian from the mines at Pachuca, Hidalgo, probably traded into the Maya lowlands by way of the central Mexican city of Teotihuacán, appears in limited quantity during the Chacsik phase, as do projectile point types reminiscent of Teotihuacán II (ca. A.D. 150–200) (Rovner, 1974:128–29). Central Mexican lithic material may in fact appear at Becan as early as the late Pakluum phase.

A late Early Classic Sabucan phase cache in Str. XIV with Teotihuacán-style figurines in a tripod cylinder jar covered with Classic Maya figures indicates that contact with the central highlands, direct or indirect, continued throughout this period (ca. A.D. 450–600). The ditch and parapet, however, probably reflect local stress and conflict, rather than a need for protection against Teotihuacán-inspired aggression.

The first half of the 7th century, like the preceding years, saw stable or decreased population at Becan, a trend possibly in some way related to the Classic Maya sculptural and architectural hiatus observed in the southern lowlands through most of the 6th century. The only sizable building dated to the early Bejuco phase is Str. XI at Chicanna, a multiroom edifice with a narrow central stairway facing east. Interestingly, Str. XI shows none of the specialized masonry or elaborate façade decoration of the Chenes-Río Bec architectural style, which, therefore, likely did not emerge until some time after A.D. 600.

This Late Classic style, which represents one of the truly great achievements of the Maya, characterizes all the major standing buildings at Becan, Chicanna, and Xpuhil. Multiroom structures with flanking templelike

towers, huge monster-mouth doorways, massive openwork roofcombs, temple-pyramids, and extensive range-type "palaces" are frequent at these sites and throughout the Chenes-Río Bec region. Although masonry varies, walls usually include finely cut, well-coursed block veneer. Long slabs tenoned deeply into a rubble and mortar hearting form most vaults. The characteristic rounded bevel of the outer slab faces leaves a rough soffit, covered by a fine, smooth plaster coat. Façades bear elaborately sculptured motifs carved in stone and rounded out with lime stucco, many of which are clearly related to Pure Florescent façade decoration in the northern Maya lowlands.

Architecture in the Río Bec tradition at Becan and Chicanna dates to the 7th, 8th, and probably early 9th centuries A.D. Radiocarbon dates available from structural contexts cluster between A.D. 600 and 720. The style is unlikely to have appeared much before A.D. 650, and by the end of the Chintok phase (ca. A.D. 830) structural activity at Chicanna was coming or had come to a halt. Str. XX at Chicanna, the latest known building of importance at either site, is a 2-story, multiroom construction with superimposed series of corner masks (Eaton, 1974:138). A ceramic cache from the upper story ties the building to the end of the Chintok or the beginning of the Xcocom phase.

From the Middle Preclassic until the end of the Late Classic Period, the pottery at Becan was closely linked to ceramic traditions in the southern lowlands. At the end of the Classic, however, local styles begin to predominate, and by the Terminal Classic the early pattern is reversed, with a strong influx of northern lowland pottery types. The Xcocom phase, if we are to rely on the depth and wide distribution of middens dating to this period, must have "witnessed an explosive revitalization of the regional ceramic tradition and an apparently major increase in population" (Ball, 1974:116). Whether this trend held for the surrounding countryside, or whether it instead represented a concentration of previously more dispersed groups in the ceremonial and administrative center, is not yet certain. Ball believes the northern influence was accompanied by movements of people from northwestern Yucatán (ibid.:116–17). Whatever the extent of such an immigration, cessation of building at Becan and Chicanna at this time does raise the possibility of foreign control over the local population.

By A.D. 1000 these two sites were on the wane, although northern-related pottery types appear for a time afterward. Tohil Plumbate, an Early Postclassic horizon marker, was an important constituent of late middens. The Late Postclassic Period is represented only by isolated finds of Mayapan-type censers, left by a scattered rural population which continued to worship at the once powerful cities.

Table 1. Selected Cultural Chronologies from the Southern, Central, and Northern Maya Lowlands

Christian Calendar*	Maya Lowland Periods	Uaxactún, Guatemala	Becan, Campeche	Dzibilchaltun, Yucatán
A.D. 1500				
1400	Late Postclassic		?	Chechem (Decadent)
1300			Lobo	
1200				
1100	Early Postclassic			Zipche (Modified Florescent)
1000				
900	Terminal Classic	Tepeu 3	Xcocom	Copo 2 (Pure Florescent)
800				
700	Late Classic	Tepeu 2	Chintok	Copo 1 (Early Period II)
		Tepeu 1	Bejuco	
600				
500	Early Classic		Sabucan	
400		Tzakol	Chacsik	Piim (Early Period I)
300				
200				
100	Proto-Classic			Xculul
0		Chicanel	Pakluum	
100	Late Preclassic			
200				Komchen
300				
400	Middle Preclassic			Nabanche
B.C. 500		Mamom	Acachen	

* Correlation of Maya and Christian calendars at 11.16.0.0.0.

REFERENCES

ADAMS, RICHARD E. W., compiler

1974. Preliminary reports on archaeological investigations in the Río Bec Area, Campeche, Mexico. Tulane Univ., Middle Amer. Res. Inst. Publ. 31, pp. 103–146, illus.

ANDREWS IV, E. WYLLYS

1973. The development of Maya civilization after abandonment of the southern cities. Pp. 243–265 *in* "The Classic Maya Collapse," 549 pp., illus. T. Patrick Culbert, ed. University of New Mexico Press, Albuquerque.

ANDREWS, JOANN M.

1976. Reconnaissance and archeological excavations in the Río Bec area of the Maya lowlands. Nat. Geogr. Soc. Res. Rpts., 1968 Projects, pp. 19–27.

BALL, JOSEPH W.

1971. A preliminary report on the ceramic sequence at Becan, Campeche, Mexico. Cerámica de Cultura Maya, no. 7, pp. 16–30.

1972. Ceramic sequence at Becan, Campeche, Mexico. Second (final) preliminary report: 1972. Cerámica de Cultura Maya, no. 8, pp. 34–41.

1973. Ceramic sequence at Becan, Campeche, Mexico, xxi + 427 pp., illus. Ph.D. dissertation, University of Wisconsin. University Microfilms, Ann Arbor, Michigan.

1974a. A regional ceramic sequence for the Río Bec area. *In* Adams, op. cit., pp. 113–117, illus.

1974b. A Teotihuacán-style cache from the Maya lowlands. Archaeology, vol. 27, pp. 2–9, illus.

1977. The archaeological ceramics of Becan, Campeche, Mexico. Tulane Univ., Middle Amer. Res. Inst. Publ. 43, 190 pp., illus.

BALL, JOSEPH W., AND ANDREWS V, E. WYLLYS

1978. Preclassic architecture at Becan, Campeche, Mexico. Tulane Univ., Middle Amer. Res. Inst., Occasional Paper 3, 17 pp., illus.

BUCKLEY, JAMES

1976. Isotope's radiocarbon measurements XI. Radiocarbon, vol. 18, pp. 172–189.

BUCKLEY, JAMES, AND WILLIS, ERIC H.

1972. Isotopes' radiocarbon measurements IX. Radiocarbon, vol. 14, pp. 114–139.

EATON, JACK D.

1972. A report on excavations at Chicanna, Campeche, Mexico. Cerámica de Cultura Maya, no. 8, pp. 42–61.

1974. Chicanna: An elite center in the Rio Bec Region. *In* Adams, op. cit., pp. 133–138.

KELLY, JOYCE, AND KELLY, JERRY

1974. The rediscovery of Río Bec B. Dixie Roto Mag., March 10, pp. 14–17. New Orleans.

MERWIN, RAYMOND E.

1913. The ruins of the southern part of the Peninsula of Yucatán, with special reference to their place in the Maya area. Ph.D. dissertation, Harvard University.

PERIGNY, MAURICE DE

1909. Ruines de Río Bec. La Nature, vol. 38, pp. 300–301.

POTTER, DAVID F.

1973. Maya architecture style in central Yucatán. Ph.D. dissertation, Tulane University. University Microfilms, Ann Arbor, Michigan.

1974. Architectural style at Becan during the Maya Late Classic Period. *In* Adams, op. cit., pp. 118–122.

1977. Maya architecture of the central Yucatán Peninsula, Mexico. Tulane Univ., Middle Amer. Res. Inst. Publ. 44, 118 pp., illus.

ROVNER, IRWIN

1974. Implications of the lithic analysis at Becan. *In* Adams, op. cit., pp. 128–132.

1975. Lithic sequences from the Maya lowlands. Ph.D. dissertation, University of Wisconsin. University Microfilms, Ann Arbor, Michigan.

RUPPERT, KARL, AND DENISON, JOHN H., JR.

1943. Archaeological reconnaissance in Campeche, Quintana Roo, and Petén. Carnegie Inst. Washington Publ. 543, 156 pp., illus.

STOLTMAN, JAMES B., JR.

1978. Lithic artifacts from a complex society: the chipped stone tools of Becan, Campeche, Mexico. Tulane Univ., Middle Amer. Res. Inst. Occ. Pap. 2, 30 pp., illus.

THOMAS, PRENTICE M., JR.

1974. Prehistoric settlement at Becan: A preliminary report. *In* Adams, op. cit., pp. 139–146, illus.

____. Prehistoric Maya settlement patterns at Becan, Campeche, Mexico. Tulane Univ., Middle Amer. Res. Inst. Publ. 45, illus.

TURNER, WILLIAM L., 2D

1974. Prehistoric intensive agriculture in the Maya lowlands. Science, vol. 185, pp. 118–124, illus.

VOGELER, INGOLF K.

1970. Frontier settlements in south-eastern Campeche: Report for the 1970 National Geographic Society–Tulane University archaeological project at Becan, Campeche, Mexico.

1974. The cultural ecological setting of southeastern Campeche. *In* Adams, op. cit., pp. 110–112.

WEBSTER, DAVID L.

1972. The fortifications of Becan, Campeche. Ph.D. dissertation, University of Minnesota. University Microfilms. Ann Arbor, Michigan.

1974. The fortifications of Becan, Campeche, Mexico. *In* Adams, op. cit., pp. 123–127, illus.

1976. Defensive earthworks at Becan, Campeche, Mexico: Implications for Maya warfare. Tulane Univ., Middle Amer. Res. Inst. Publ. 41, 134 pp., illus.

E. WYLLYS ANDREWS V
ANTHONY P. ANDREWS

Dating of Fossil Bone from Cave Deposits by Means of Amino-acid Racemization Rates

Principal Investigators: Jeffrey L. Bada, Scripps Institution of Oceanography, La Jolla, California; Sydney P. Clark, Jr., John H. Ostrom, and Karl K. Turekian, Yale University, New Haven, Connecticut.

Grant No. 910: For controlled, uncontaminated sampling of fossil bone and collection of stratigraphic and geophysical data from Muleta Cave, Soller, Mallorca, Spain.

Until recently direct age determinations of organic remains have been limited to C^{14} measurements. Hare and Mitterer (1967, 1969), Hare and Abelson (1968), Bada, Luyendyk, and Maynard (1970), and Wehmiller and Hare (1971) showed that degree of racemization of amino acids in ancient biogenic marine deposits can also be used to estimate lapsed time since death of the organism.

Artificially synthesized amino acids consist of equal portions (racemic mixture) of two mirror-image molecules termed the "L" form and the "D" form. Biogenic amino acids, on the other hand, consist only of the L-forms. Following death, biogenic amino acids are subject to degradation with time, as are all other organic compounds. The L-amino acids gradually undergo change with time to produce the "D" form, and this process, called racemization, continues until equal amounts of both L and D amino acids are present.

Most studies of the amino-acid racemization reaction in fossil marine materials until recently have concentrated on isoleucine. The racemization of L-isoleucine produces the nonprotein amino acid D-alloisoleucine. L-isoleucine and D-alloisoleucine are directly separable on an automatic amino analyzer. In contrast to this ease of separation and measurement, the determination of the amount of racemization of other amino acids requires the synthesis of a suitable diastereomeric derivative.

The racemization reaction for isoleucine can be written as

$$\text{L-isoleucine} \underset{k_{allo}}{\overset{k_{iso}}{\rightleftharpoons}} \text{D-alloisoleucine},$$

where k_{iso} and k_{allo} are the rate constants for the interconversion of isoleucine and alloisoleucine, respectively.

The amino-acid racemization reaction is a function of both time and temperature; thus, if one of these variables is known, the reaction can be used to calculate the other. By determining the extent of racemization of isoleucine in fossil materials from the deep sea where temperature has been constant for millions of years, the authors cited above have shown that the age of the materials can be deduced. Conversely, if the age of the fossil is known, then the racemization can be used to estimate the average temperature a sample has experienced since it was deposited.

The present investigation was undertaken to test the applicability of using amino-acid racemization to date organic remains from another paleoenvironment, namely, vertebrate-fossil remains from cave deposits. Cave environments would seem to fulfill the requirement of a long-term, nearly constant thermal regime as a best first approximation. A stratigraphic sampling from such an environment that could be tested against other dating techniques applicable to cave deposits would provide the best test of the potential of the method in dating fossil materials on land.

Muleta Cave (Mallorca) was selected as the test site because (a) the cave had been extensively excavated (by W. H. Waldren) during the period 1962 to 1970; (b) these excavations had recovered a very large sample of fossil bone, most of which is referable to the extinct goatlike artiodactyl *Myotragus balearicus*; (c) ample fossil bone was still available in situ and could easily be collected for amino-acid analysis, under the aseptic conditions required; also, sufficient cave deposits remained to provide at least some of the critical stratigraphic data, as well as matrix samples for paleomagnetic analysis; and (d) the island of Mallorca is situated in the western Mediterranean, well south of the maximum southern limit of Pleistocene glaciation; accordingly, temperature fluctuations within Muleta Cave, as a consequence of glacial and interglacial episodes, may be assumed to have been minimal.

There were other, unusual facts about the Muleta Cave that favored its selection. Existing collections of *Myotragus balearicus* from Muleta represent a natural, random sampling of a now extinct island species accumulated during the last several hundred thousand years of the species' existence. The cave apparently acted as a natural trap, randomly sampling the island population by accidental in-fall. Preliminary estimates indicate that Muleta in-fall may have averaged about one individual every 50 years over a period of at least 100,000 years prior to extinction some 6,000 years ago. No other fossil sample of this kind is known. Consequently, that sample provides an extraordinary opportunity to assess minute anatomical changes that probably occurred during the final 25,000 to 50,000 generations prior to extinction. Conceivably, evidence may be preserved that indicates genetic or ecological factors that may have contributed to the extinction of *Myotragus*. Preliminary examination of the sample seems to show an unusually high frequency of pathologic ossification, which may have been genetic in origin. High frequency of such an unfavorable allele could have resulted from small population size and its isolated setting, together with the apparent absence of natural predators prior to the arrival of man.

During January 1971, we visted Muleta Cave and took controlled samples of *Myotragus* bones from in situ over the entire stratigraphic sequence (as it was then exposed by Waldren's earlier excavations). Temperature variations within the cave were recorded during collecting operations and subsequently were monitored periodically by Waldren after our departure. Present-day cave temperature is virtually constant at 19 °C. The samples for amino-acid analysis were collected from all available levels, placed in sterile, air-tight plastic bags, and sealed for transport to San Diego and subsequent analysis by Bada. Additional, small collections of *Myotragus* were made for paleontologic study.

The stratigraphic section sampled represents a composite section consisting of six subsections occurring in six different sectors of the cave. It is improbable that none of these subsections are at least partial equivalents of another local section. The bone-bearing sediments were examined in an attempt to reconstruct the general sequence of deposition among the six cave sectors that were accessible. The final analysis proved inconclusive because the full extent of upper cave levels could not be determined and most of the sedimentary fill from the uppermost cave levels had been removed, thereby destroying primary sedimentary structures and stratigraphic relationships. The total composite section sampled measured 6.5 meters, but only that portion of the cave deposits that had already been excavated could be sampled. No reliable evidence is available to indicate how much fill may exist below the deepest excavations to date. At the time of our visit, excavation had been terminated because of a massive travertine floor. The cave entrance is close to 100 meters above present sea level and only a few hundred meters from the shore line. In all probability the Muleta Cave system extends down to, and possibly even below, present sea level. The principal source of the animal remains recovered from the upper levels of Muleta appears to have been via a narrow, vertical chimney located approximately 7 meters inside the cave entrance. Other access routes may have existed, but none were apparent to us. The chimney may also have been the primary entry source of sediment, but the presence of fine silt and clay strata indicates slow, nearly horizontal sediment transport as well. Similarly, the occurrence of several travertine strata indicates intermittent ponding. At the time excavations were initiated, the chimney was filled with sediment and animal remains to within 0.5 meter of the entrance level. At present, the chimney sector has been excavated to a depth of nearly 6 meters.

In addition to the bone samples a continuous suite of oriented matrix samples was collected along a section that accumulated in contact with a large stalagmite in a remote sector of the cave to be used for paleomagnetic analysis (determination of paleomagnetic reversals as preserved by remnant magnetism). The samples were transferred to Prof. N. D. Watkins at the Graduate School of Oceanography of the University of Rhode Island, who made the paleomagnetic measurements. The results indicated that although the magnetic signature was noisy there was no evidence of reversals in magnetic polarity, a result compatible with the age of the deposit determined by the other methods.

A core from the stalagmite in the cave was previously obtained by Waldren and transported to Yale where a Th^{230}-U^{234}-U^{238} age of the outer layer was obtained to compare with a racemization date on an adjacent bone.

The preliminary results for the Muleta Cave racemization ages as compared with radiocarbon ages on bone and the uranium decay series age on coterminus stalagmite and bone have been reported by Turekian and Bada (1972), and a general discussion of the use of isoleucine racemization ages to date fossil bones including those at Muleta Cave is given by Bada (1972). Since then additional work has continued in Bada's laboratory including the analyses of fossil bones from many different sites and using additional amino acids (Bada and Schroeder, 1972; Bada, Protsch, and Schroeder, 1973; Bada and Protsch, 1973; Schroeder and Bada, 1973).

Clearly this project has demonstrated the utility of a multidisciplinary approach to the problem of the age and environmental history of ancient vertebrate deposits on land.

REFERENCES

BADA, JEFFREY L.

1972. The dating of fossil bones using the racemization of isoleucine. Earth Planet. Sci. Letters, vol. 15, pp. 223–231.

BADA, JEFFREY L.; LUYENDYK, BRUCE P.; AND MAYNARD, J. BARRY

1970. Marine sediments: Dating by the racemization of amino acids. Science, vol. 170, pp. 730–732.

BADA, JEFFREY L. AND PROTSCH, REINER
1973. Racemization reaction of aspartic acid and its use in dating fossil bones. Proc. Nat. Acad. Sci., vol. 70, pp. 1331–1334.
BADA, JEFFREY L.; PROSCH, REINER; AND SCHROEDER, ROY A.
1973. The racemization reaction of isoleucine used as a palaeotemperature indicator. Nature, vol. 241, pp. 394–395.
BADA, JEFFREY L., AND SCHROEDER, ROY A.
1972. Racemization of isoleucine in calcareous marine sediments: Kinetics and mechanism. Earth Planet. Sci. Letters, vol. 15, pp. 1–11.
HARE, P. EDGAR, AND ABELSON, PHILIP H.
1968. Racemization of amino acids in fossil shells. Carnegie Inst. Washington Yearb. 66, pp. 526–528.
HARE, P. EDGAR, AND MITTERER, RICHARD M.
1967. Non-protein amino acids in fossil shells. Carnegie Inst. Washington Yearb. 65, pp. 362–364.
1969. Laboratory simulation of amino acid diagenesis in fossils. Carnegie Inst. Washington Yearb. 67, pp. 205–208.
SCHROEDER, ROY A., AND BADA, JEFFREY L.
1973. Glacial-Postglacial temperature difference deduced from aspartic acid racemization in fossil bones. Science, vol. 182, pp. 479–482.
TUREKIAN, KARL K., AND BADA, JEFFREY L.
1972. The dating of fossil bones. Pp. 171–185 *in* "Calibration of Hominoid Evolution," W. W. Bishop and J. A. Miller, eds. Scottish Academic Press.
WEHMILLER, JOHN, AND HARE, P. EDGAR
1971. Racemization of amino acids in marine sediments. Science, vol. 173, pp. 907–911.

JEFFREY L. BADA
SYDNEY P. CLARK, JR.
JOHN H. OSTROM
KARL K. TUREKIAN

An Ecological Study of the Pika (*Ochotona princeps*) in the Western United States

Principal Investigator: Richard D. Bates, Santa Ana College, Santa Ana, California.[1]

Grant Nos. 877, 1000: In support of field observations of the natural history and ecology of the pika in the Western United States.

Pikas (*Ochotona princeps*) are distributed throughout the higher mountains of western North America. This little-known mammal of the order Lagomorpha is classified in a family (Ochotonidae) separate from the other rabbits and hares. It is believed that they migrated into North America from Asia across the Bering Land Bridge. Fossil remains of these animals have been found in Nevada and Oregon, as well as farther east in Nebraska, Pennsylvania, and West Virginia. As pikas live in cool climates, indications are that the climate of North America was once much cooler than today. As the climate warmed after the last glacial period, pikas retreated to the cooler mountain ranges of western North America. Today there are 35 isolated subspecies of *Ochotona princeps* found from the Rocky Mountains of west-central Canada southward through the higher elevations of the Rocky Mountains to northern New Mexico, and southward down the Cascade and Sierra Nevada ranges to southern California. There are also isolated subspecies in the small ranges of eastern Oregon and central Nevada (Hall and Kelson, 1959).

---

[1] Grateful acknowledgment is extended to a number of individuals who contributed to this study: L. J. Colton, district ranger of Kamas District, Wasatch National Forest, for providing facilities for my use at the Duschesne Guard Station; Karl Urban, ranger, naturalist, National Park Service, for his assistance in locating pikas at Craters of the Moon National Monument; the library staff at park headquarters, Rocky Mountain National Park, for the use of their library facilities; Andrew T. Smith, for his help at Bodie; Douglas B. Herr, for his assistance with photography; Mary Griswold Smith and other staff members of the National Geographic Society for help and encouragement in my photographic work; and finally to my wife, Anita, for assistance and moral support.

The prime area of research was the Uinta Mountains of eastern Utah. From a base camp in the Uintas, pikas were studied in the following locations: Rocky Mountain National Park, Colorado; Craters of the Moon National Monument, Idaho; the Columbia River Gorge of northern Oregon; the Ruby Mountains of northeastern Nevada; and Bodie, California, a ghost town. A brief study was also conducted during August 1972 at Lake Ediza in the Sierra Nevadas of California.

A total of 125 days were spent on the project from August 1 to September 8, 1970, and from June 12 to September 6, 1971. During this period 66 days were devoted to research; the remainder to travel, outfitting, and planning.

The basic purpose of this study was to compare several subspecies of pikas living under varied climatic and ecological conditions and to investigate the effect of geographical isolation on the species *Ochotona princeps*. Although the taxonomy of pikas has been studied quite extensively, little research has been done on their ecology. The project was designed to cover a wide range of altitudes and of habitats varying from cool, moist coniferous forests, through semi-arid deserts to the high alpine tundra. Six subspecies of *Ochotona princeps* were studied.

Methods and Procedures

Observations of pika activities were made with a pair of Bushnell 6 × 25 binoculars. A Canon TL 35-millimeter SLR camera and two telephoto lenses (200 and 350 millimeter) were used to photograph the animals. A Craig 2102 tape recorder was utilized to record pika calls as well as field notes.

A previously established grid system consisting of brightly colored surveyor's stakes was used as boundary markers for study areas in the Uinta Mountains. Boundaries of study areas at other locations were marked by small piles of rocks or natural landmarks.

Observations lasted from a minimum of 2 hours to a maximum of 6 or 7. No attempt was made to build a blind or otherwise conceal myself from the animals. Observations were made at various times of the day, from the predawn hours until 10 p.m. The most frequent observation periods were from dawn until about 10 a.m. and from 5 p.m. until dark.

Study Areas

During August 1970 six study areas were established and potential pika colonies located for further study (table 1). Because of time limitations

TABLE 1. PIKA STUDY AREAS

Ochotona princeps subspecies	Location	Elevation (in feet)	Habitat
1. *uinta*	Uinta Mountains, Summit County, Utah: (4 study areas)		
	Shady Dell East	8,000	Lodgepole pine–aspen forest
	Shady Dell West	8,000	Lodgepole pine–aspen forest
	Steiner	10,300	Spruce-fir forest
	Murdock Mountain	11,000	Alpine tundra
2. *saxatilis*	Rock Cut, Rocky Mountain National Park, Larimer County, Colorado	12,110	Alpine tundra
3. *nevadensis*	Lamoille Canyon, Ruby Mountains, Elko County, Nevada	8,500	Mixed shrub forest
4. *brunnescens*	Columbia River Gorge, Multnomah County, Oregon	100	Pacific conifer forest
5. *goldmani*	Craters of the Moon National Monument, Butte County, Idaho	5,800	Lava flow in semiarid desert
6. *muiri*	Bodie, Mono County, California	8,300	Semi-arid desert
	Lake Ediza, Madera County, California	9,300	Margin of alpine tundra

and inaccessibility, the study area in the Ruby Mountains was not used during the summer of 1971. In August 1972 a pika colony was observed for five days at Lake Ediza, California.

Study areas were located in a wide range of altitudes ranging from 100 feet to over 12,000 feet and were in such widely diversified habitats as the Douglas-fir forests of the Pacific Northwest, the Great Basin Desert, lava flows, montane forests, and the alpine tundra. A brief description of each study area follows.

Uinta Mountains, Utah

The focal point of the study was the Uinta Mountains of eastern Utah. During the summer of 1968 four study areas were established at varying elevations. Two of these were located on a south-facing slope at 8,000 feet in the Upper Provo River Canyon approximately 17 miles east of Kamas, Utah, and were designated Shady Dell East and Shady Dell West Study Areas, and both were in an aspen–lodgepole-pine forest. A third area was on a south-facing slope at an elevation of 10,300 feet, approximately a mile northeast of Mirror Lake, and was in a spruce-fir forest. A fourth area was in the alpine tundra on a north slope of Murdock Mountain at an elevation of approximately 11,000 feet.

Rock Cut, Colorado

The Rock Cut Study Area was in a large rock outcropping in the otherwise smooth undulating terrain of the Trail Ridge area of Rocky Mountain National Park. The elevation here was 12,110 feet, the highest at which pikas have been studied. The predominant type of vegetation was grasses, sedges, and various species of alpine wildflowers.

As part of a National Science Foundation Biology Institute held at nearby Pingree Park, a study of pikas was conducted at this area from June 25 to July 10, 1970 (Bates, 1970). Observations of the subspecies *O. p. saxatilis* were made at this area from August 3 to 6, 1971.

Ruby Mountains, Nevada

Isolated in the Great Basin Desert in northeastern Nevada, the Ruby Mountains are a steep, glaciated range surrounded by semi-arid deserts. The vegetation here varies from desert shrub to lodgepole pine and aspen groves at higher elevations. The subspecies *O. p. nevadensis* living here is more isolated than any other population of pikas. The nearest subspecies is *O. p. tutelata*, which lives in the Monitor Range, 100 miles to the southwest. The Great Salt Lake Desert to the east and the desert areas stretching north about 200 miles and west about the same distance totally isolate this subspecies. Ancestors to present-day pikas probably crossed these now impenetrable deserts when the climate was once much cooler. As the climate warmed, members of this subspecies became effectively isolated.

In August 1970, a study area was established at 8,500 feet in Lamoille Canyon, 25 miles southeast of Elko. Because of time limitations and the impassability of the road, no study of this subspecies was made during 1971.

Columbia River Gorge, Oregon

Pikas have long been thought to be alpine mammals restricted to the higher elevations of North America (Morris, 1965; Burt and Grossenheider, 1952). In 1925 Horsfall reported that pikas were seen in the Columbia River Gorge at an elevation of 200 feet. By following his published encounter with these animals, I located several small colonies on the steep, heavily vegetated south wall of the Columbia River Gorge at elevations from 100 to 200 feet.

The steep canyon walls were covered with several species of conifers, the understory with various species of fern and mosses. Even the rocks in the talus slides were covered with thick mats of algae, lichens, and mosses. Owing to the steepness of the canyon walls and the density of undergrowth, the south wall of the Columbia River Gorge can be penetrated only on trails. Pikas of the subspecies *O. p. brunnescens* were found to live in widely scattered, small talus slides along the gorge. Small colonies were located in August 1970 along the Larch Mountain and Oneonta Falls trails. In July 1971, six days were spent observing colonies in both of the aforementioned areas. However, unusually high temperatures during this time somewhat curtailed pika activity.

Craters of the Moon National Monument, Idaho

The most bleak and forbidding area in which pikas were studied was the lava deserts of south-central Idaho. Howell (1924) described a new subspecies of pika, *O. p. goldmani*, from Craters of the Moon National Monument. Elevations in this bleak lava plain range from about 5,400 feet to about 5,900 feet, with some cinder cones as high as 6,500 feet.

Vegetation is very sparse and is found mostly in small crevices scattered throughout the broken lava flows. Several species of wildflowers thrive on cinder gardens, and scattered specimens of limber pines are found in areas where soil has developed. A study area was established in the North Crater Flow at about 5,800 feet. The lava of this flow is pahoehoe, a billowy, ropy type that has produced many subterranean caverns, some of which have collapsed and formed sinkholes or miniature canyons. Pikas are widely scattered in this jumbled rock mass and do not seem to live in colonies. Pikas were found on the cinder cones or in the aa lava. This latter type of lava is jagged and spiny and resembles clinkers.

Temperatures on the surface may be over 100°F. in the summer, while a few feet below the surface ice may remain throughout the year. Known waterholes are few and widely scattered.

This subspecies is isolated within the boundaries of the Monument, and the nearest subspecies occurs about 20 miles to the northwest in the Pioneer Mountains.

Bodie, California

Located at 8,300 feet in a high semi-arid valley east of the Sierra Nevadas, Bodie is a 19th-century gold camp with an infamous reputation. Gold was first discovered here in 1859. The town prospered in the late 19th century, but after a couple of disastrous fires in 1892 and 1932 the population dwindled and it became a ghost town. The area is now covered by sagebrush, rabbitbrush, and other species of low-growing northern desert vegetation.

Pikas were first studied here by J. H. Severaid [1955] from 1951 to 1955. His unpublished account of pika activity in the old mines surrounding the town and within the ruins of the town itself was a deciding factor in selecting Bodie as a study area. The Bodie pikas are an isolated population of the subspecies *O. p. muiri*. It is believed that these pikas somehow migrated across approximately 15 miles of open, brush-covered hills to a few rock outcroppings on Bodie Bluff, a hill overlooking the old town. As waste rock from mining activities accumulated on Bodie Bluff and on nearby hills, the pika population grew and spread throughout the mine tailings.

It has been reported (Smith, 1970, pers. comm.) that pikas have also inhabited the ruins of the ghost town of Aurora, Nevada (6,000 feet), eight miles northeast of Bodie, and also live in the tailings of the abandoned mines there.

Discussion of Results

TAMENESS

Pikas exhibit a wide range of variation in the degree to which they can be approached. Most individuals were shy and difficult to stalk. However, after I had been observing a colony of pikas for a few days, some of them lost their fear and became somewhat accustomed to my presence. Often their curiosity brought them to within a few feet of me.

At some study areas all the pikas observed seemed to be quite shy and easily spooked. This was true of pikas at the Columbia River Gorge, Craters of the Moon, and the Ruby Mountains study areas. At the Columbia River Gorge Study Area, pikas would dart out of sight at the least sound or movement and would often not reappear for several hours. Pikas at Craters of the Moon were extremely hard to approach. They were not curious about my presence and usually gave me a wide berth. Approaching these animals was difficult as there were many sinkholes and subterranean passageways underneath the jumbled surface of the lava for them to hide in. Only twice was I able to approach to within 15 or 20 feet of pikas that were perching on rocks. In the Ruby Mountains, although several pikas were heard, only two were seen on rock slides, and they disappeared as soon as they detected me.

As pikas began their haypile-building activities in midsummer and early fall, they became more tolerant of my presence. Often they became so preoccupied in carrying food back to their haypiles that they completely ignored me. At the lower elevation study areas in the Uinta Mountains (Shady Dell East and Shady Dell West), haying pikas would completely disregard me as I sat within a few feet of their haypiles. A pika at the Rock Cut Study Area would approach to within a foot or two of me to collect grasses and wildflowers for its haypile. On one occasion this animal allowed me to pet it while it was yanking up flowers. Another haying animal at Lake Ediza in the Sierra Nevadas was completely unperturbed as three persons photographed its haying activities. These latter animals, however, were the exception rather than the rule.

CALLS

Recordings were made of the vocalizations of all but one of the pika subspecies studied. These showed that the call of the pika varies considerably among the subspecies.

Members of the subspecies *O. p. uinta* utter a distinctive low-pitched *ank* sound (Bates, 1969). Individuals of *O. p. saxatilis* found in the Front Range of Colorado have a higher-pitched call that sounds somewhat like *cheep-ep*. Both the pikas of the Columbia River Gorge (*O. p. brunnescens*) and Craters of the Moon (*O. p. goldmani*) have a high-pitched call, almost a whistle. In the Ruby Mountains, pikas of the subspecies *nevadensis* sound somewhat like those of *goldmani*, except that their call has a unique rasping sound. The Bodie pikas, and other members of the subspecies *muiri* found in the Sierra Nevadas, have a very distinct two-note call that sounds like *check-ick*.

All subspecies of pikas observed had a short call and a long call. The latter was a series of short calls, often as many as 15 or 20, made in rapid-fire succession. Both the long and short calls seemed to be used as a method of exhibiting territoriality.

PREDATION

The primary predator of the pika is the longtail weasel (*Mustella frenata*). Several observations were made of these animals in the vicinity of pikas during the 1968 study in the Uinta Mountains (Bates, 1969). Weasels were seen only on one occasion during this study. On August 5, 1971, a weasel was observed for an hour and a half at Rock Cut Study Area. During this time the pikas were unusually quiet and were not seen on top of the rock slide. There was no evidence that the weasel captured any pikas.

Two other experiences with possible predators were noted. On July 30, 1971, a bobcat (*Lynx rufus*) was observed on the Shady Dell East Study Area in the Uinta Mountains. It had just killed a young marmot and was still carrying the fresh carcass. Although a bobcat would probably have a difficult time capturing a pika on a talus slide, it may well be able to seize one that is away from the protection of the talus slide. A wildlife photographer, Doug Herr, observed a marten (*Martes americana*) capture a pika in the vicinity of Lake Ediza in the Sierra Nevadas during the summer of 1971 (Herr, pers. comm.).

On July 31, 1971, two red-tailed hawks (*Buteo jamaicensis*) tried unsuccessfully to capture a young marmot on the Shady Dell West Study Area. Beyond this one incident, no predatory birds were seen in the vicinity of any of the study areas during the course of my study, although they were observed during my 1968 study in the Uinta Mountains (Bates, 1969).

TERRITORY AND HOME RANGE

The size of both territory and home range varied widely among the subspecies of pikas studied. Territories were losely defined until the commencement of the haying season in midsummer. Then pikas became vigorously defensive, with the haypile being the focal point of each individual's territory. These domains were defended by calling, depositing scent on a rock, and, as a last resort, chasing the intruder.

Territoriality was best observed at the study areas in the Uinta Mountains during the summer of 1968 (Bates, 1969). During that year territoriality was especially strong at the Shady Dell West Study Area and was still very apparent among members of the colony during the haying season of 1970 and 1971.

To a lesser degree territoriality was observed also at the Rock Cut, Bodie, and Lake Ediza areas. At Rock Cut the population density of pikas was not as great as that in the Uintas, and haying animals defined their territories only by calling. The same could be said for the Lake Ediza colony. At Bodie, Andrew Smith (1970, pers. comm.) described an experiment that he performed in which an adult pika was trapped and removed from its territory. Within a few hours a juvenile member of the colony had moved into the unoccupied territory and proclaimed its residency by calling. A few days later this second juvenile was trapped and removed, and within a few hours another juvenile pika occupied the territory. This experiment seemed to indicate that the adult pikas are established in more favorable locations in a colony, while juvenile animals are pushed to the more undesirable areas. If an adult's territory was vacated, it was soon occupied by one of the juveniles. Observations made in 1968 at Shady Dell West seem to bear this out. The choice locations for haypiles were occupied by adults, while the inexperienced juveniles were most often harassed by adults and forced to occupy small substandard areas of the talus slides that had poor access to feeding areas.

Territoriality was not observed in pika colonies in the Columbia River Gorge, Craters of the Moon National Monument, or the Ruby Mountains. Calling among pikas in these areas was very infrequent.

The size of home ranges among the subspecies varied considerably. In more inhospitable environments, such as the alpine tundra of the Uinta and Rocky Mountains, the semi-arid deserts of Bodie, or Craters of the Moon National Monument, home ranges were larger and the pikas were widely scattered. However, in comparatively lush areas such as the Columbia River Gorge, or the subalpine areas of the Uinta and Sierra Nevadas, pikas did not range as far away from their haypiles in search of food, as it was quite plentiful either on their rockslide or very close to it. Population densities were highest in these latter two areas, the highest density being at the Shady Dell West Study Area in the Uintas.

Activity Patterns

Pikas are diurnal mammals that favor cool temperatures. They are generally active on top of their rockslides in the morning from dawn until about 10 or 11 a.m., and from just prior to sunset until dark. They avoid the high temperatures of midday by retiring into the cooler areas beneath the talus slide.

Activity patterns were best studied in the 1968 study in the Uintas. It was found that pika colonies generally were more active at 8,000 than at 11,000 feet. This phenomenon was generally attributed to stronger winds and colder temperatures at the higher elevations (Bates, 1969). Pikas in the Uintas followed a daily activity pattern similar to the one mentioned above. However, at study areas in other locations, a wide variety of patterns was found. At the Rock Cut Study Area (12,110 feet), pikas were seldom seen before sunrise or after sunset and were most active in the cool morning or afternoon hours. They were never active at midday on a warm day, but when temperatures were cooler they were active throughout most of the day. In the verdant forest of the Columbia River Gorge (100 feet), pikas were never active before sunrise and were seldom seen until about 10 or 11 a.m. They were active for about an hour or two and then would retreat beneath the rocks until evening. Their most active period was from late afternoon to nightfall. At Craters of the Moon National Monument (5,800 feet), activity among pikas began about half an hour before dawn and continued for up to 2 hours. Pikas were not seen again on the lava flows until sunset, and their peak activity period was from this time until nightfall. At the Bodie Study Area (8,300 feet), pikas followed about the same pattern as those at Craters of the Moon. They were seldom seen here in the day, even though the temperatures were cool in the morning or late afternoon. At Lake Ediza (9,300 feet) to the west in the Sierra Nevadas, pikas followed a daily activity pattern similar to the ones in the Uinta Mountains. They were active from just prior to sunrise until about 10 or 11 a.m. and from late afternoon until dark. A similar pattern was observed among pikas in the Ruby Mountains (8,500 feet). From these observations it appears that pikas avoid the high temperatures of midday, and at high altitudes they tend to avoid also the cold temperatures before sunrise and after sunset.

Pikas tended to be more active where population densities were the highest. The most active group studied (and the one that had the highest population density) was the Shady Dell West colony in the Uinta Mountains. Contrastingly, the least active (and least dense) group of pikas were those of Craters of the Moon National Monument. Individuals here were widely scattered, and other than an occasional call no social interchange was observed.

Pikas are considered to be diurnal animals, yet members of some subspecies are so seldom seen above their rockpiles during the day that it is possible that they are nocturnal. Campers at Bodie, and at locations in the Sierra Nevadas, have occasionally heard pikas calling during the night. Andrew Smith (pers. comm.) studied pikas for several nights in the Bodie area during a full moon and found that they were almost as active during these nights as they were during the daylight hours.

HAYING

Pikas have the peculiar habit of storing food in haystacks or haypiles, built on top of or beneath the rockslides they live in. As a general rule they begin storing food in these haypiles in late summer and continue until a heavy snowfall buries their food source. The animals then move beneath the talus slides, and rather than hibernating they remain active under the snow and live off their cache of food during the winter.

During the summer of 1968 in the Uinta Mountains, 80 percent of the pikas began building their haypiles between August 15 and September 1. There were two exceptions. One pika at Shady Dell West began its haypile the last week of June 1968. The next year this pika began its haypile on June 27, and in 1971 haypile construction began on June 29. Another pika at Shady Dell East began its haypile during the last week of July in 1968, 1969, and 1971. Haypiles were begun at the Rock Cut, Bodie, and Lake Ediza Study Areas about mid-August. Andrew Smith (pers. comm.) reported that one pika at Bodie began haypile construction in mid-June.

No haypiles were found, nor were any pikas observed storing food, at the Columbia River Gorge Study Area. In 1970 observations were made during the haying season, and this activity was not found in the pikas observed. As the rocks here are covered with numerous species of mosses and lichens, and because of the verdant undergrowth and comparatively mild winters, perhaps there is no need to store food. Further observation is needed to determine this for all colonies in this area.

At Craters of the Moon no haypiles or haying activities were observed. Karl Urban (pers. comm.) reported seeing a small haypile near a cinder cone during the summer of 1970. The remains of two old haypiles were located in the North Crater Lava Flow, but no other evidence of haying activities was noted.

Types of food stored in the haypiles varied greatly. Pikas showed no particular food preference but seemed to collect plants that were most accessible. Bates (1969) surveyed some types of food stored by Uinta pikas. Pikas living on the tundra at the Rock Cut Study Area stored various species of grasses and sedges and of wildflowers such as alpine avens (*Geum rossii*) and alpine sandwort (*Arenaria obtusiloba*). Pikas at Bodie stored mostly rabbitbrush (*Chrysothamnus nauseosus*), sagebrush (*Artemisia tridentata*), and other assorted species of desert shrub, while those at Lake Ediza stored only grasses and sedges. At haypiles in the Uintas, Colorado Rockies, and the Sierra Nevadas, animal scats were stored by pikas in addition to plant species. Fecal droppings of deer, marmots, and coyotes were found interspersed among the dried plant material in some haypiles.

It has been written (Orr, 1972; Cahalane, 1961; Carrington, 1963; Eberhard, 1960) that pikas spread their hay out on rocks to dry and then move it under the rocks to a subterranean cache after the sun has dried it thoroughly. Supposedly, a sudden rainstorm will make a pika move this drying food beneath the rockslide to keep it from getting wet. During considerably study over a five-year period, no pikas have been observed laying their collected hay out to dry on a rock before storing it or carry it under a talus slide during a rainstorm. Some pikas build conical haypiles on top of the talus, which are exposed to the weather. Perhaps these small exposed haypiles have given observers the impression that pikas spread their hay out to dry.

Winter Survival

It is generally believed that during winter pikas live off food they have stored during the previous summer and fall. However, at higher elevations heavy snow may cover their rockslides from seven to nine months. With the small amount of hay stored by some pikas, it is doubtful they could survive for this length of time.

Although pikas were not studied during the wintertime as part of this study, inferences were obtained as to their ability to survive the prolonged winter season. During the summer of 1968 six pikas lived within the boundaries of the Steiner Study Area, and four or five individuals were found there during the summer of 1970. None of them survived the winter of 1970–71. This area was observed frequently during the summer of 1971 and no signs of pikas were noted. Populations were also lower at the nearby Murdock

Mountain Study Area. As compared to the summer of 1970, pika populations in the summer of 1971 were lower at both the Rock Cut and Bodie Study Areas.

Summary and Conclusions

Six subspecies of *Ochotona princeps* were studied during August 1970 and from June 12 to September 6, 1971 (*uinta, saxatilis, goldmani, brunnescens*, *nevadensis*, and *muiri*). Study areas were established at the following locations: Uinta Mountains, Utah (8,000–11,000 feet); Rock Cut, Rocky Mountain National Park, Colorado (12,110 feet); Ruby Mountains, Nevada (8,500 feet); Columbia River Gorge, Oregon (100 feet); Craters of the Moon National Monument, Idaho (5,800 feet); and Bodie, California (8,300 feet). Brief observations were also made at Lake Ediza, California (9,300 feet). Habitats studied included alpine tundra, subalpine forests, semiarid deserts and moist, coniferous forests. Tameness, colony populations, calls, haying activities, territoriality, and general activity patterns were studied among the various populations.

Population density was greatest at the Shady Dell West Study area (*uinta*) and least at Craters of the Moon National Monument (*goldmani*). Between the summer of 1970 and 1971 populations declined at study areas above 8,000 feet. This may have been due to the especially long winter of 1970–71. At one study area in the Uintas (Steiner) a pika colony died out during this winter, and at another (Murdock Mountain) the population was drastically reduced. In 1971 populations were also reduced at the Bodie and Rock Cut Study Areas. At the Columbia River Gorge Study Area, populations appeared to be about the same in 1970 and 1971. No comparisons were made of colonies in the Ruby Mountains or Craters of the Moon National Monument.

Activity patterns differed among the subspecies. At the high-altitude study areas (above 10,000 feet) pikas were seldom seen prior to dawn or after sunset. On cool days they were often seen during the entire day. At middle altitudes (5,000 to 10,000 feet), pikas were most active from before sunrise until about 10 or 11 a.m. and from about an hour before sunset until dark. At lower altitudes (100–200 feet) pikas were not too active until late morning, and were most active from late afternoon until dark.

Not all pikas store food in haypiles. In the Uintas during the summer of 1968, only 38 percent of the pikas constructed haypiles of dried food. It was estimated that during the summers of 1970 and 1971 fewer than a fourth of the population at the Rock Cut, Bodie, and Lake Ediza study areas built haypiles. No haypiles or haying activities were observed at study areas in Craters of the Moon National Monument and the Columbia River Gorge. Heavy undergrowth coupled with mild winters at this latter area may have precluded the necessity of storing food.

Pikas live under some of the least favorable ecological conditions known. Extremes of temperature vary from well below 0° to 100° F. Snow often buries their talus slides for 7 to 9 months of the year, and even though some animals store a fairly large cache of food it is believed that many of them starve to death during a prolonged winter.

From this study it can be concluded that pikas are a polytypic species that has adapted to a wide range of habitats from the alpine tundra to the cool, moist forests of the Pacific Northwest. They are even starting to extend themselves into the fringes of the Great Basin desert. They have become geographically isolated into 35 subspecies, and distinctions can be made among these as to the sound of their calls, their coloration, and perhaps even their instinct to store food. Further study among other subspecies is needed to determine the extent of these conditions among other isolated groups.

REFERENCES

BATES, RICHARD D.

1969. Ecology of the pika (*Ochotoma princeps uinta*) in the Uinta Mountains, Utah, 54 pp. Unpublished master's thesis, Brigham Young University, Provo, Utah.

1970. An ecological study of the pika (*Ochotona princeps saxatilis* Bangs) in the vicinity of Rock Cut, Rocky Mountain National Park, Colorado, 14 pp. Unpublished paper, Colorado State University, Fort Collins, Colorado.

BURT, WILLIAM H., and GROSSENHEIDER, RICHARD P.

1952. A field guide to the mammals, 200 pp., illus. Houghton Mifflin Co., Boston.

CAHALANE, VICTOR H.

1961. Mammals of North America, 682 pp., illus. Macmillan Co., New York.

CARRINGTON, RICHARD

1963. The mammals, 192 pp., illus. Life-Time Nature Library, New York.

EBERHARD, THOMAS

1960. Colorado's alpine hay cutter. Audubon Mag., vol. 62, pp. 58–60, illus.

HALL, E. RAYMOND, and KELSON, KEITH R.

1959. The mammals of North America, 1,083 pp., illus. Ronald Press, New York.

HORSFALL, R. BRUCE
1925. The pika at sea level. Journ. Mamm., vol. 6, pp. 201–202.
HOWELL, ARTHUR H.
1924. Revision of the American pikas. North Amer. Fauna, no. 47, 48 pp., illus.
MORRIS, DESMOND
1965. The mammals, 448 pp., illus. Harper & Row, New York.
ORR, ROBERT T.
1972 Pikas. Pacific Discovery, vol. 25, no. 6, pp. 9–11, illus.
SEVERAID, J. H.
1955. The natural history of the pikas (mammalian genus *Ochotona*), 820 pp., Unpublished Ph.D. dissertation, University of California, Berkeley, California.
SMITH, ANDREW T.
1974. The distribution and dispersal of pikas: Consequences of insular population structure. Ecology, vol. 55, pp. 1112–1119.
1974. The distribution and dispersal of pikas: Influences of behavior and climate. Ecology, vol. 55, pp. 1368–1376.

RICHARD D. BATES

The Metamorphic Rocks of New Caledonia

Principal Investigator: Philippa M. Black, University of Auckland, New Zealand.

Grant No. 843: In support of an expedition for a petrographic study and mapping of metamorphic rocks of New Caledonia.

During the past decade there has been considerable interest among petrologists and geologists in the high-pressure "blueschist" metamorphism that characterizes the Pacific margin and the relationship between the geological environment and physical conditions of formation of "blueschists" and the concepts of the "new global" or plate tectonics.

Compared with other circum-Pacific countries New Caledonia is ideally suited for a study of the processes of metamorphism because its geology is not complicated either by Upper Tertiary and Quaternary volcanism or by tectonic activity. Little work had ever been done on the metamorphic rocks of north-central New Caledonia, and although both high-pressure ("blueschists") and low-pressure ("greenschists") metamorphics had been recorded nothing was known about the relationship between the two regimes of metamorphism, the distribution of the two types of metamorphic rocks, or the ages of the lithologies involved in the metamorphisms.

The purpose of the expedition was to make reconnaissance traverses through the metamorphic belt to try to elucidate the relationship between the Cretaceous-Eocene rocks and the "blueschist" metamorphism on one hand and the basement Permian-Mesozoic sediments with their "greenschist"-type metamorphism on the other and to equate the processes of tectonism and metamorphism with those of the plate tectonics theory.

Members of the expedition in addition to myself were R. N. Brothers, and A. R. Lillie, all of Auckland University, and Dr. M. C. Blake, Jr., who was temporarily at Auckland University on leave from the United States Geological Survey. However, only Blake and I were directly financed by the present grant.

Account of the Expedition

Members of the expedition left Auckland on Friday, October 2, 1970, and arrived in Nouméa late the same afternoon. We spent the weekend in

Nouméa unraveling logistic and supply problems and collecting information on access routes to the interior of the island. Over the previous few years there had been a very marked upsurge of interest in the nickeliferous laterite deposits of New Caledonia, and several of the ultrabasic massifs in the north and central part of the area were being opened for production and new mining roads had been pushed from the west coast into the interior of the island. This proved a great boon for the expedition as it meant that we were able to cover a good deal of country quickly and efficiently. Unfortunately, none of the roads north of Bourail completely transected the island, and so to save the time involved in the 300-kilometer drive around the island needed to complete each traverse we decided to work systematically from north to south along the west coast, doing a number of west-to-east traverses and pushing as far east by foot as we could. The routes taken by the expedition are shown on the accompanying schematic geological map of New Caledonia (fig. 1).

On Monday, October 5, after having gathered together all our equipment, we drove along the length of the island from Nouméa to Koumac, where we split temporarily into two parties. Lillie and I went farther north to Arama to collect some unusual "granites" that had been recorded from ultrabasic rocks near Arama, while Brothers and Blake stayed in Koumac to collect schists near a contact with an ultrabasic massif before coming north to Arama for us all to make a combined traverse from north to south through high-pressure lawsonite-bearing schists into weakly metamorphosed Eocene sediments.

The following weekend we left Arama and moved south into the Diahôt Valley where wet set up a base camp in a delightful old colonial house on the outskirts of Ouégoa, and from this locality we made day traverses, collecting along tracks and roads in the upper Diahôt Valley. Later in the week we drove as far up the Diahôt Valley as we could and then set out on a 4-day foot traverse collecting a sequence of specimens from the high-grade amphibolites in the Témélé River east of Ouénia across the stratigraphic and metamorphic sequence almost to the west coast near Kaala-Gomen. In spite of an equinoctial storm, which poured 61 centimeters of rain down on us in two days, we were able to complete the traverse, obtain a good sequence of specimens, and return to base camp where we spent a day waiting for the rain to stop and drying ourselves out.

On Saturday the 17th we shifted camp from Ouégoa to Kaala-Gomen to collect metasediments and volcanics from adjacent to the Kaala ultrabasic massif and on Sunday moved to Ouéholle to set up camp for three nights on the bank of the Ouémou River while we did a series of day traverses from Ouéholle to Ouénia up the Ouémou River and back along the road from Ouéholle toward Gomen.

October is the height of the fruit season in the fertile northern New Caledonia valleys, and so, rather reluctantly we left Ouéholle with its groves of orange and mandarin trees, and its generous natives, and moved south to Voh, where we planned to work a major west-to-east section across the Paleocene Basalts and Cretaceous formations into Jurassic and Triassic sediments and a series of metamorphic rocks of unknown age and metamorphic grade. We camped for five days inland from Voh at the junction of the Congo and Kamendoua Rivers while we worked along mining roads in the center of the island, making extensive collections and structural observations. Our major

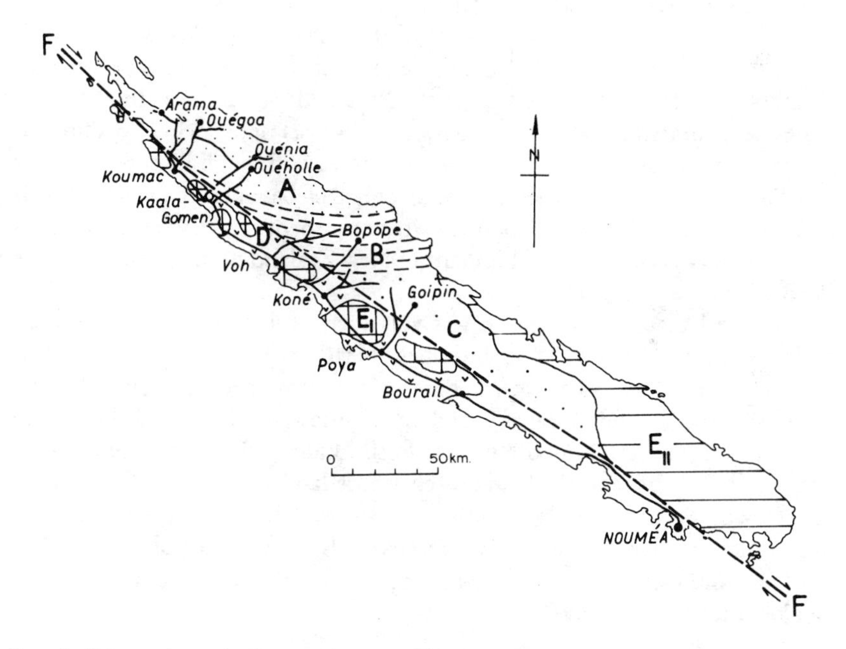

FIG. 1. Schematic geologic-tectonic map of New Caledonia simplified from Brothers and Blake (1973, figs. 2, 3). The route taken by the expedition is shown as a solid line.

A = Tertiary high-pressure metamorphic belt.
B = "Melange" zone.
C = Mesozoic low-pressure metamorphic belt.
D = Paleocene Basalts.
E_I and E_{II} = Two parts of Eocene ultrabasic nappe offset by F.
F = Major transcurrent fault.

find in this traverse was a Jurassic *Inoceramus* sp. in sediments associated with Paleocene Basalts, which indicates the sediments are, in part, older than had previously been thought.

Early in the last week of October we drove from Voh to Koné, made camp near the village of Poindas on the Koné River, and from this location worked along the Koné and adjacent Pouembout River valleys. In the Koné-Pouembout district we had the opportunity to look closely at a large area of what had been previously mapped as Paleocene Basalts and were able to observe that there were really two groups of rocks, a western coastal strip composed largely of basalts and volcanic debris and, in the east, a sequence of alternating sandstones and argillites. The Koné Valley provided good access to the basement schists, and we made fine collections from roadcuts and stream sections as far east as Bopope.

The last traverses attempted were in the Poya district. We set up a base camp at the Grottes d'Adio in the picturesque limestone country west of Goipin and worked one section along the Poya and Goipin rivers from Eocene shales and limestones through Cretaceous schists into richly fossiliferous Mesozoic sediments and a second section from Poya through Paleocene basalts and Eocene sediments to the edge of an inlier of basement greenschists. On November 3 we returned to Nouméa, where we spent two days packing specimens and arranging for their shipment to New Zealand prior to our departure for Auckland on November 5.

We feel that the expedition was very successful. Over the 5-week field period we lost only one day to inclement weather. We collected more than 500 specimens along with relevant data on lithology, bedding, graded structures, schistocity, and lineation, and in addition we discovered and made collections from several important new fossil localities. District administrative heads, tribal chiefs, and the land owners whose land we worked on and whose access roads we used were without exception friendly, interested in what we were doing, and cooperative. We received also a considerable amount of assistance and useful information from members of the Bureau des Recherches Geologique et Minière in Nouméa.

Summary of Geological and Petrological Results

Laboratory examination of material collected on the expedition has involved thin-section identification, X-ray diffractometry, chemical analysis of rocks and minerals, and some stable-isotope geochemistry. The results of laboratory studies and syntheses of field and laboratory studies have been published in papers by Black (1973a, b; 1974a, b; 1975, 1977), Brothers and Blake (1973), and Brothers (1974) listed at the end of this report. The following summaries of results are largely abridged from these papers.

General stratigraphic observations. We made extensive collections of Mesozoic sediments and from areas mapped as Paleocene Basalts and collected from a number of fossil localities including new localities that we had discovered in the course of our expedition. We have collected Triassic *Monotis* sp., Jurassic *Inoceramus* sp., and Mesozoic ammonites from various areas mapped previously as Paleocene Basalts, which indicate that this group of rocks contains units that cover a much wider time range than had earlier been appreciated. In many places also these "basalts" appear to be an association of mafic and ultramafic igneous rocks and indurated sediments and may be a structural rather than a stratigraphic unit (Brothers and Blake, 1973).

Metamorphism. Examination of specimens collected from the Paleocene Basalts and the basic igneous and sedimentary mixed rocks outcropping along the west coast of New Caledonia (unit D, fig. 1) indicated that these rocks contain only zeolites; that is, they have reached only zeolite facies grade of metamorphism. Study of our extensive collection of Mesozoic rock specimens (unit C, fig. 1) has shown that the highest grade of pre-Tertiary metamorphism reached is generally only prehnite-pumpellyite facies although locally very schistose slivers may have reached lower greenschist facies in terms of both mineralogical content and foliation.

Nowhere within the older metagreywackes and related rocks of early Mesozoic age does the grade of metamorphism approach that of the Cretaceous-Eocene rocks that have been affected by the Tertiary (Oligocene) metamorphism. This Tertiary metamorphism is most clearly seen in northern New Caledonia where Cretaceous-Eocene sediments and minor interbedded volcanics (unit A, fig. 1) show a continuous metamorphic sequence from weakly metamorphosed metasediments in the west near Koumac to a maximum grade of coarse gneissic amphibolites along the east coast. Typical high-pressure mineral assemblages such as lawsonite-albite and omphacite-almandine-epidote have been developed in these rocks. Laboratory examination of the weakly metamorphosed Cretaceous-Eocene sediments prior to the crystallization of the high-pressure minerals has shown them to contain finely crystalline chlorite, paragonite, pyrophyllite, and phengite. Crystallization of some of these minerals at such low metamorphic grades had not previously been recorded. The results of detailed mineralogical and geochemical studies on specimens collected on the expedition have been incorporated with other data in a series of publications by Black (1973a, b; 1974a, b; 1975, 1977).

Separating the northern regional high-pressure Tertiary metamorphism from the low-pressure Mesozoic metamorphic belt in the south is an approximately 30-kilometer-wide zone of faulting and exotic rocks (Brothers and Blake, 1973). This "melange" zone (unit B, fig. 1) consists of serpentinites, ultrabasic rocks, slivers of high-grade schists, metamorphosed dolerites, basalts, and fine-grained siliceous sediments, which have been thrust into position along steeply dipping faults. Prior to the work resulting from our expedition, it had been thought that the Tertiary high-pressure metamorphism and its associated high-pressure minerals (lawsonite, sodic amphiboles, and sodic pyroxenes) were confined to the Cretaceous-Eocene sequence. However, detailed sampling has shown that the high-pressure assemblage lawsonite-albite is locally developed also in country rocks (both basement Mesozoic and Cretaceous-Eocene) adjacent to the ultrabasic massifs and along planes of tectonic movement in the "melange" zone. In such locations the Tertiary metamorphism appears to have been "overprinted" on the preexisting Mesozoic metamorphism and Tertiary lawsonite, in contrast to the granular Mesozoic calc-silicates, occurs as well formed prismatic crystals standing at high angles to the preexisting mineral foliation and schistocity (Brothers and Blake, 1973; Brothers, 1974).

Metamorphism and tectonism in New Caledonia related to the plate tectonics theory. In terms of the plate tectonics theory the regional structural setting for New Caledonia is unusual when compared with the rest of the Southwest Pacific because the geological record in New Caledonia essentially stops in the Miocene; there has been no Upper Tertiary or Recent volcanism and the region at present seems to be aseismic.

Based on field observations collected in the course of our expedition and on other evidence it has been possible to elucidate the relationship of New Caledonia to the major tectonic features of the Southwest Pacific and to explain the metamorphic and tectonic history of New Caledonia according to the concepts of the plate tectonics (Brothers and Blake, 1973).

New Caledonia lies along one of a number of north-trending ridges and basins between the Australian Continent and the system of island arcs and fracture zones extending south from New Guinea through the New Hebrides and New Zealand. Geophysical studies indicate that these ridges are underlain by continental rock, and it seems that although New Caledonia is now aseismic it was once part of a series of active continental margins.

During the Permian to Eocene the New Caledonian area was apparently part of a trench system lying to the east of an active island arc. Sediments shed from the island arc and deposited in the trench and basin system were metamorphosed in the Upper Mesozoic by what appears in part to be typical

load metamorphism and in part due to underthrusting deformation in the trench. Sedimentation, however, appears to have continued in the shallowing basin system through into the Eocene when it was finally interrupted by a series of major tectonic disturbances.

Previous workers on New Caledonian Tertiary tectonics had been very concerned with the problem of the emplacement of the New Caledonian ultrabasic massif (the largest in the world) but had generally concluded that the ultramafic bodies covering much of New Caledonia were remnants of a formerly continuous sheet emplaced during a single Oligocene-Early Miocene event contemporaneous with the high-pressure metamorphism of the Cretaceous-Eocene sediments. However, important results emerging from our expedition (Brothers and Blake, 1973) were the recognition that the serpentinites and ultrabasic rocks associated with the "melange" zone are not identical with those of the ultrabasic massifs elsewhere on the island (units E_I and E_{II}, fig. 1) and the interpretation of the "melange" zone as the site of a major zone of "subduction" (crustal consumption) along a former lithospheric plate boundary. The ultramafic rocks and associated pillow basalts, siliceous schists, and high-grade metamorphic rocks thrust into place along the "melange" zone are believed to represent slivers of ocean floor caught up in the "subduction" zone.

The sequence of Mid-Tertiary tectonism now appears to have been rather complex and to have taken place in three distinct phases (Brothers and Blake, 1973).

(1) During the late Eocene a large sheet of ultramafic oceanic mantle material (unit E) was thrust ("obducted") on top of the Cretaceous-Eocene sediments and basalts without producing any significant metamorphism in the underlying rocks.

(2) In the Oligocene, a period of compressive thrust tectonics, which accompanied the formation of the "melange" zone along the site of the "subduction" zone, produced primary high-pressure metamorphism in the Cretaceous-Eocene sequence and "overprinted" high-pressure metamorphic assemblages on to the Mesozoic low-pressure rocks adjacent to thrust surfaces in the "melange" zone.

(3) Finally, in the early Miocene, differential uplift and transcurrent faulting along a major fault (F in fig. 1) parallel to the west coast cut out the "melange" zone to the west, divided the Eocene ultramafic nappe, and offset the two portions (E_I and E_{II}) by at least 150 kilometers.

Since this last Tertiary event the focus of tectonic activity has moved eastward and away from the New Caledonian area, which has, from that time, existed as a tectonically stable land mass subjected only to the ravages of deep tropical weathering.

Work in Progress

At the time of writing this report (1975) work was still in progress on some aspects of the material collected during the expedition, specifically on the petrography of the Mesozoic sediments and the detailed mineralogy of the low-pressure metamorphic belt. It is hoped that further results and publications will be forthcoming.

REFERENCES

BLACK, PHILIPPA M.

1973a. Mineralogy of New Caledonian metamorphic rocks, I: Garnets from the Ouégoa district. Contr. Min. and Petr., vol. 38, pp. 221–235.

1973b. Mineralogy of New Caledonian metamorphic rocks, II: Amphiboles from the Ouégoa district. Contr. Min. and Petr., vol. 39, pp. 55–64.

1974a. Mineralogy of New Caledonian metamorphic rocks, III: Pyroxenes and major element partitioning between coexisting pyroxenes, amphiboles and garnets from the Ouégoa district. Contr. Min. and Petr., vol. 45, pp. 281–288.

1974b. Oxygen isotope study of metamorphic rocks from the Ouégoa district, New Caledonia. Contr. Min. and Petr., vol. 47, pp. 197–206.

1975. Mineralogy of New Caledonian metamorphic rocks, IV: Sheet silicates from the Ouégoa district. Contr. Min. and Petr., vol. 49, pp. 269–284.

1977. Regional high-pressure metamorphism in New Caledonia: phase equilibria in the Ouégoa district. Tectonophysics, vol. 43, pp. 89–107.

BROTHERS, R. N.

1974. High-pressure schists in northern New Caledonia. Contr. Min. and Petr., vol. 46, pp. 109–127.

BROTHERS, R. N., and BLAKE, MILTON C., JR.

1973. Tertiary plate tectonics and high-pressure metamorphism in New Caledonia. Tectonophysics, vol. 17, pp. 337–358.

PHILIPPA M. BLACK

The Fresh-water Shark in Nicaragua

Principal Investigator: Jack D. Burke, Medical College of Virginia, Virginia Commonwealth University, Richmond, Virginia.

Grant No. 826: For a study of speciation of bull sharks in Lake Nicaragua.

Sharks have been known to exist in Lake Nicaragua since Spanish colonial times. The first historical record, of sharks in fresh water was given by Oviedo (1526). He stated that sharks "go up the rivers" in the "mainland" of the New World. In 1535 Oviedo reported that sharks existed in Lake Nicaragua. However, the first scientific study was not reported until 1877, by Gill and Bransford. They described the lake shark as being a distinct, landlocked species and named it *Eulamia nicaraguensis*. Ten years later, Jordan (1887) renamed their shark *Carcharhinus nicaraguensis*. The checklists, catalogues, and reports appearing later referred to the lake shark by one or the other of these two scientific names (Gill, 1884, 1893; Eigenmann, 1893, 1909; Smith, 1893; Jordan and Evermann, 1896; Meek, 1907; Regan, 1908; Jordan et al., 1930; Anonymous (H.U.), 1943; Marden, 1944). In 1948 Bigelow and Schroeder reported that their morphological study of four preserved lake sharks indicated a close relationship with the Atlantic marine bull shark *Carcharhinus leucas*, and they proposed keeping *nicaraguenis* as the scientific name for the lake shark. But a further morphological study on one other lake shark and a jaw led Bigelow and Schroeder (1961) to place *C. nicaraguenis* in synonymy with the marine bull shark *C. leucas*.

Molecular biology has been used to study variations in animal populations. Primarily, these types of studies seek to identify stable genetic traits. In 1969 Peterson and Smith found a variation in protein patterns of *Carcharhinus milberti* (= *C. plumbeus*) collected around Lanai, Molokai, and Oahu in Hawaii. They used extracts from the eye-lens nucleus, which has a small protein turnover rate, as a basis for their electrophoresis studies. They were able to identify variations in protein patterns, and these they interpreted as representing separate breeding populations in the sandbar sharks. Cowan (1971), also using electrophoresis, reported serum protein variation in *C. leucas* during different stages of development. He observed that serum proteins were not valuable as species indicators in elasmobranchs, and that this view might be applied to other fishes as well.

However, it is a different story with hemoglobin. Characteristically, fishes have polymorphic hemoglobins (Buhler and Shanks, 1959; Chandrasekhar, 1959; Manwell, 1963; Burke, 1965; Wilkins and Iles, 1966; Riggs, 1970). Since hemoglobin is a stable genetic character, it has been used to identify subspecific populations which are isolated reproductively within species (Sick, 1961; Gorman and Dessauer, 1965; Mourant, 1970). Therefore, if bull sharks taken in fresh and salt water possess identical hemoglobin, then Bigelow and Schroeder's (1961) synonymy, as based on morphometric data, is confirmed at a molecular level. Also, nonvariable hemoglobin would indicate no drift toward subspeciation and reproductive isolation.

Methods and Materials

Hemoglobin in bull sharks was investigated by two methods, (1) starch gel (Smithies, 1959) and cellulose acetate electrophoresis (Burke, 1965), and (2) oxyhemoglobin affinity (Burke, 1966).

Sharks were caught on large shark hooks baited with cut fish. Sometimes it was feasible to hire local fishermen to aid our efforts in collection. Sharks were stunned by head blows, and blood samples were removed by cardiac puncture into vacutainers (National Clinic Services Laboratories, Arlington, Virginia), placed in NCSL mailing containers, packaged in ice, and air-mailed to the Medical College of Virginia for study. Hemoglobin solutions were prepared according to Dementi and Burke (1972). Sometimes hemoglobin samples were shipped to MCV from Nicaragua. At the most, only three days elapsed from blood collection to sample determination.

The map of Nicaragua (fig. 3) shows the locations where sharks were collected for this study. Eighteen sharks were captured and identified as *C. leucas*: 4 from the lake; 2 at Los Cocos and 2 at San Carlos; 4 from the El Castillo rapids; 4 from the lagoon at San Juan del Norte; and 2 taken from the sea 1 kilometer off the coast of Barra del Colorado, Costa Rica.

Results

In figure 1 a typical electrophoreogram on a cellulose acetate membrane is shown of bull-shark hemoglobin. This pattern was developed from a fresh hemoglobin sample less than 12 hours old. The hemoglobin solution was prepared in Managua, where the sample was electrophoresed. The pattern was repeated on hemoglobin samples shipped to MCV where they were resolved on starch-gel also. It can be seen that the hemoglobin resolved into two fractions at a pH of 8.7 in borate buffer. The minor fraction migrated 16 percent slower than the major fraction. Densitometer records were made of the two hemoglobins at 560 mμ. After planimetry of the two hemoglobin

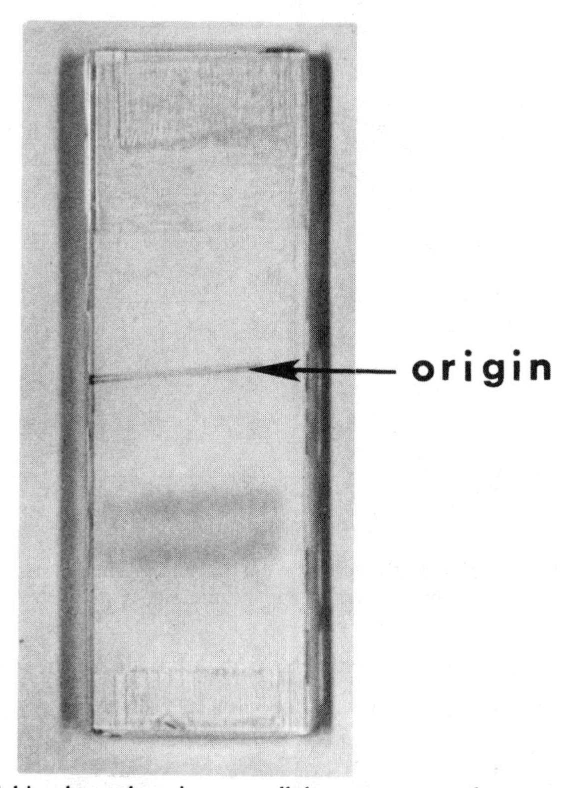

FIG. 1. Hemoglobin electrophoresis on a cellulose acetate membrane resolves into two fractions of bull shark hemoglobin (*C. leucas*).

records, it was determined that the minor fraction comprised 46 percent of the total hemoglobin and the major fraction, 54 percent. A benzidine stain (Baur, 1963) was used to identify hemoglobin.

In figure 2 is shown a typical oxyhemoglobin affinity curve for a bull shark whether or not the specimen was collected in Lake Nicaragua, Río San Juan, or the Caribbean Sea. The P_{50}, the oxygen pressure at which Hb = HbO_2, did not vary more than 1–2 millimeters Hg from one animal to another, or in duplicate analyses. At pH 7.4, the P_{50} was 11 millimeters Hg; at pH 6.8, it was 17 millimeters Hg as shown in figure 2. Of course, not all blood samples collected from bull sharks arrived in condition for analyses; they were discarded if methemoglobin was indicated. All oxyhemoglobin affinity curves were determined on 3–4 percent dilute hemoglobin solutions in phosphate buffer with an ionic strength of 0.3, and a pH of either 7.4 or 6.8. Spectrophotometric readings were made at a wavelength where the largest optical density

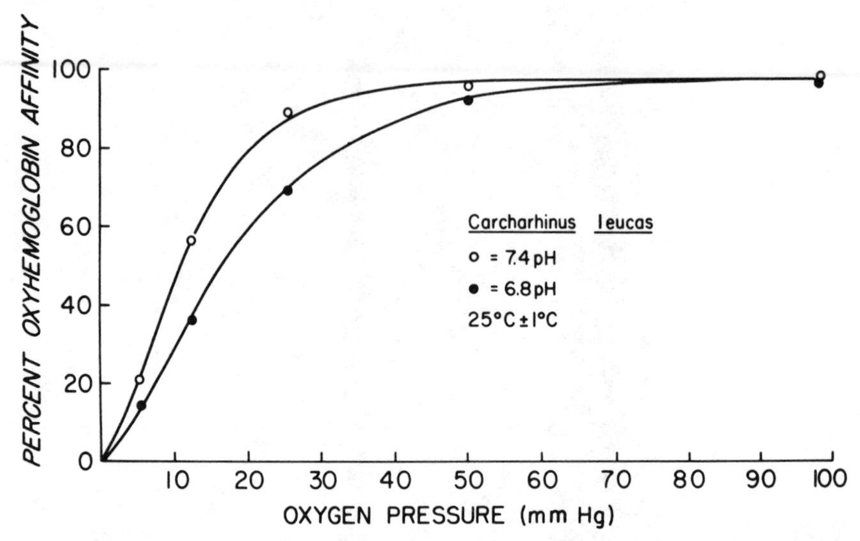

FIG. 2. Oxyhemoglobin affinity curves for *C. leucas*. The P_{50} determined at pH 7.4 and pH 6.8 was 11 and 17 mm Hg, respectively.

difference existed between reduced hemoglobin and oxyhemoglobin as shown on an OD-mμ plot.

Discussion

The synonymy proposed by Bigelow and Schroeder (1961) was confirmed by a morphometric investigation on the bull sharks (Thorson et al., 1966). Their morphological data were obtained from measurements made on 19 sharks: 4 from Los Cocos, 8 from San Carlos, 3 from El Castillo, and 4 captured in the mouth of the Río San Juan at San Juan del Norte (fig. 3). The body measurements made on these bull sharks compared favorably with similar measurements made by Schwartz (1960) and by Clark and von Schmidt (1965) on pelagic bull sharks. In the meantime, Urist (1962) had made radiographs of calcium deposits in lumbar vertebrae of bull sharks collected at El Castillo rapids in the Río San Juan and compared them with radiographs of bull shark lumbar vertebrae collected in the Atlantic Ocean off Placida, Florida. The radiographs of the two vertebrae sets showed exactly the same configurations of calcium deposits.

Carcharhinus leucas occurs in a worldwide distribution, i.e., the species is found in the Atlantic, Pacific, and Indian Oceans. Garrick (1967) has re-

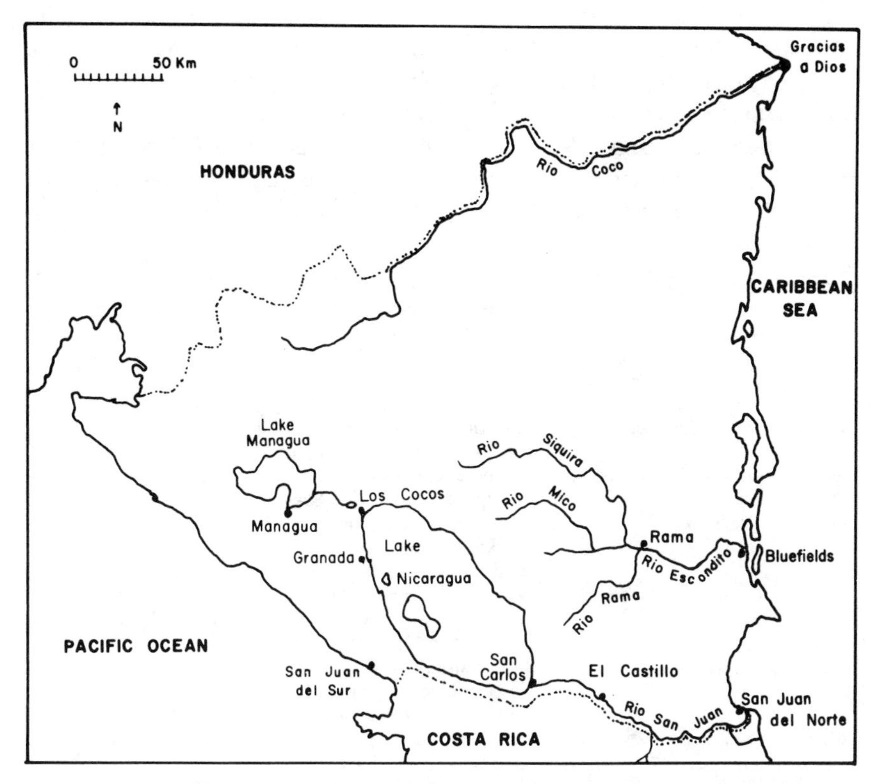

FIG. 3. Localities in Nicaragua where bull sharks were collected for this study.

evaluated the 103 nominal species of *Carcharhinus*, and he recognized that 28 species were valid. As Bass et al. (1973) have pointed out, "many of these species have wide distribution and have been described under several names in different parts of the world." It seems apparent now that *C. leucas* regularly inhabits fresh-water systems, and species previously described as other than the bull shark in inland water systems might well be *C. leucas* (table 1). Certainly, a clarification is needed.

In table 1 are records of specimens of *C. leucas* from rivers, lake systems, and bays as reported in the literature. Additionally in the table are references to older literature reports of *Carcharhinus* species which may have been identified erroneously. Our present knowledge indicates that the bull shark, *C. leucas*, is the only species of shark occurring in fresh water with regularity; it is not isolated reproductively in fresh-water systems (Burke, 1974), but seemingly it must return to the ocean to breed (Herre, 1955; Jensen, 1972). There is no doubt that, as shown by tagging, *C. leucas* migrates into fresh-water lakes and river systems and returns to the ocean (Thorson, 1971).

The 18 bull sharks collected for molecular studies of their hemoglobin in this investigation represent a sample selection extending more than 200 miles from the north end of Lake Nicaragua to the Caribbean Sea. If a variation

TABLE 1.—OCCURRENCE OF *Carcharbinus leucas* IN INLAND WATER SYSTEMS

Eulamia nicaraguensis[1]	Lake Nicaragua and/or Río San Juan, Nicaragua	Gill & Bransford, 1877
Carcharhinus nicaraguensis[1]	Lake Nicaragua and/or Río San Juan, Nicaragua	Jordan, 1887
Carcharhinus nicaraguensis[1]	Lake Nicaragua and/or Río San Juan, Nicaragua	Bigelow & Schroeder, 1948
Carcharhinus leucas	Lake Nicaragua and/or Río San Juan, Nicaragua	Bigelow & Schroeder, 1961
Carcharhinus leucas	Lake Nicaragua and/or Río San Juan, Nicaragua	Thorson et al., 1966
Carcharhinus leucas	Río Escondito (Rama), Nicaragua	Smith, 1893
Carcharhinus leucas	Lake Izabal, Guatemala	Thorson, 1966
Carcharhinus leucas	Río Amazona (Iquitos), Peru	Meyers, 1952
Carcharhinus leucas	Rio Amazona (Manaus), Brazil	Thorson, 1972
Carcharhinus leucas	Río Amazona (Leticia), Colombia	Thorson, 1972
Carcharhinus leucas	Río Magdalena (Maganque-Zambrano), Colombia	Dahl, 1971
Carcharhinus leucas	Lake Pontchartrain, Louisiana	Darnell, 1958
Carcharhinus leucas	Chesapeake Bay, Maryland	Schwartz, 1959, 1960
Carcharhinus leucas	Caloosahatchee Canal, Florida	Francis, 1961
Carcharhinus leucas	Lake Jamoer, Dutch New Guinea	Boeseman, 1964
Carcharhinus leucas	Zambezi River System, Africa	Bass et al., 1973
Carcharhinus leucas	Sabi River, Africa	Bass et al., 1973
Carcharhinus leucas	Limpopo River System, Africa	Bass et al., 1973
Carcharhinus leucas	Pongola River, Africa	Bass et al., 1973
Carcharhinus leucas	Kosi Bay, Africa	Bass et al., 1973
Carcharhinus leucas	St. Lucia Lake System, Africa	Bass et al., 1973
Carcharhinus leucas	Umfolozi River, Africa	Bass et al., 1973
Carcharhinus leucas	Richards Bay, Africa	Bass et al., 1973
Carcharhinus leucas	Umlalazi River, Africa	Bass et al., 1973
Carcharhinus leucas	Tugela River, Africa	Bass et al., 1973
Carcharhinus leucas	Durban Bay, Africa	Bass et al., 1973
Carcharhinus gangeticus?	Hooghly River (Calcutta), India	Hamilton, 1822
Carcharhinus gangeticus?	Tigris River (Baghdad), Iraq	Day, 1899
Carcharhinus gangeticus?	Philippines (all accessible rivers)	Herre, 1955
Carcharhinus borneensis?	Baram River, Borneo	Fowler, 1905
Carcharhinus zambesensis?	Zambezi River, Africa	Boulenger, 1909
Carcharhinus zambesensis?	Gambia River, Africa	Svensson, 1933
Carcharhinus melanopterus?	Perak River, Malaya	Smith, 1931

[1]Synonym of *Carcharinas leucas*.

occurred in the hemoglobin pattern for the sharks, separate breeding populations would be expected and indicated. However, such was not the case. There were only two identifiable fractions of hemoglobin found by electrophoresis in each of the bull sharks (fig. 1). Therefore, the results indicate that *C. leucas* in fresh water and salt water possesses hemoglobin which appears to be a stable genetic trait. In addition, oxyhemoglobin affinity curves (fig. 2), determined in duplicate for each of the bull sharks whose hemoglobin was identified by electrophoresis, were not different from each other. The P_{50} at a pH of 7.4 was 11 millimeters Hg, and at Ph 6.4 it was 17 millimeters Hg. This condition indicates that bull sharks have hemoglobin which can pick up and release oxygen quickly. McCutcheon (1947) also found a high oxyhemoglobin affinity in 3 species of sharks. He reported that P_{50} was about 7 millimeters Hg (pH 7.4 and 25.5 °C) in the bonnet-nose shark (*Sphyrna tiburo*), dogfish shark (*Mustelus mustelus*), and the sand shark (*Hypoprion brevirostris*).

Conclusion

With the techniques of electrophoresis and oxyhemoglobin affinity used to study hemoglobin in the bull shark *C. leucas*, the data indicate that a separate breeding population of bull sharks does not exist in Lake Nicaragua, and indicate no tendency toward speciation. These conclusions are based on the fact that hemoglobin, a stable genetic trait, showed no variation in specimens of *C. leucas* taken in fresh water from Lake Nicaragua and the Río San Juan, and from the Caribbean Sea.

Acknowledgments

My appreciation is extended to the many people who gave generously of their time in order to aid this investigation; without their help this program would have foundered. In particular, I thank the following: The National Geographic Society for support during the first year; the Virginia Academy of Science Research Committee, the MCV Foundation, and the A. D. Williams Research Committee of the Medical College of Virginia for aid in the second year; Dr. Edward Kline (MCV) and Dr. Peter Jezyk (MCV), who assisted in the shark collection program; Dr. Francis Bush (MCV) for electrophoresis of the starch-gel hemoglobin samples; Mrs. Jewell Burke for aid in determining the oxyhemoglobins affinity curves and preparing the map of Nicaragua; the officials of the Banco Nacional de Nicaragua, Dr. José Castillo (president), Sr. Alejandro Argüello, and Sr. Manuel Pilarte, for solving so easily many difficult transportation problems; Sra. Melida C. de Sansón-Román of the

Embassy of Nicaragua in Washington, D.C.; officials of the Instituto de Fomento Nacional de Nicaragua (INFONAC) in Managua, Dr. Guillermo Lugo (deputy manager) for lake transportation, Dr. Antonio Flores (chief, Fisheries Division), and Dr. Robert Ellis (UN-FAO fisheries consultant); Sr. Alfredo Bequillard, Tarpon Camp, Río San Juan; Sr. Robert Bartlett (manager), Booth Shrimp Co. (Chicago) at El Puerto Bluff, Bluefields; and those who aided in the sharking expeditions: Kurt Koenig, Tom Emerson, Gary Fleming, and Dick Beatty (USA Peace Corps); Aldo Zepeda and César Arburola (INFONAC); and Leo Brown Piter, San Juan del Norte (Greytown).

REFERENCES

ANONYMOUS (HARVARD UNIVERSITY)
1943. Fresh-water sharks of Nicaragua. Sci. Monthly, vol. 57, pp. 186–188, illus.

BASS, A. J.; D'AUBREY, J. D.; and KISTNASAMY, N.
1973. Sharks of the east coast of southern Africa, I: The genus *Carcharhinus* (Carcharhinidae). Oceanogr. Res. Inst. Rpt. no. 3, pp. 1–168.

BAUR, E. W.
1963. Thin layer starch-gel electrophoresis and plastification method. Journ. Lab. Clin. Med., vol. 61, pp. 166–173.

BIGELOW, HENRY B., and SCHROEDER, WILLIAM C.
1948. Sharks. *In* "Fishes of the Western North Atlantic." Mem. Sears Found. Mar. Res. Yale Univ., vol. 1, pp. 59–576.
1961. *Carcharhinus nicaraguensis*, a synonym of the bull shark, *C. leucas*. Copeia, 1961, p. 359.

BOESEMAN, M.
1964. Notes on the fishes of western New Guinea, III: The fresh-water shark of Jamoer Lake. Zool. Meded., vol. 40, pp. 9–22.

BOULENGER, GEORGE ALBERT
1909. Catalogue of the freshwater fishes of Africa in the British Museum (Natural History), illus. London.

BUHLER, DONALD R., and SHANKS, WARREN E.
1959. Multiple hemoglobins in fishes. Science, vol. 129, pp. 899–900.

BURKE, JACK D.
1962. A simple technique for immobilizing fish to remove blood. Copeia, 1962, pp. 852–854.
1965. Oxygen affinities and electrophoretic patterns of hemoglobins in trout and basses from Virginia. Med. Coll. Virginia Quart., vol. 1, pp. 16–21.
1966. A simple rapid method for determining oxyhemoglobin affinity: Illustration using blood from the Rhesus monkey. Med. Coll. Virginia Quart., vol. 2, pp. 219–221.
1974. Hemoglobin stability in bull sharks. Amer. Journ. Anat., vol. 139, pp. 425–430.

CHANDRASEKHAR, N.
1959. Multiple haemoglobins in fish. Nature, vol. 184, pp. 1652–1653.
CLARK, EUGENIE, and VON SCHMIDT, K.
1965. Sharks of the central Gulf Coast of Florida. Bull. Marine Sci., vol. 15, pp. 13–83.
COWAN, C. MICHAEL
1971. Serum protein variation in the bull shark, *Carcharhinus leucas* Müller and Henle, 1841. Int. Journ. Biochem., vol. 2, pp. 691–696.
DAHL, G.
1971. Los pisces del Norte de Colombia. Inderena, Bogotá, Colombia, pp. 17–18.
DARNELL, REZNEAT M.
1958. Food habits of fishes and larger invertebrates of Lake Pontchartrain, La. An estuarine community. Publ. Inst. Marine Sci. Univ. Texas, vol. 5, pp. 353–416.
DAY, FRANCIS
1889. Fishes. *In* "The Fauna of British India, including Ceylon and Burma," 2 vols. London.
DEMENTI, P. L., and BURKE, JACK D.
1972. Oxyhemoglobin affinity in the armadillo. Amer. Journ. Anat., vol. 134, pp. 509–514.
EIGENMANN, CARL H.
1893. Catalogue of the fresh water fishes of Central America and southern Mexico. Proc. U.S. Nat. Mus., vol. 16, pp. 53–60.
1909. Catalogue of the fresh water fishes of tropical and south temperate America. Rpt. Princeton Univ. Exped. to Patagonia (1896–9), pt. 2 (Zoology), vol. 3, pp. 375–511.
FOWLER, HENRY W.
1905. Some fishes from Borneo. Proc. Acad. Nat. Sci. Philadelphia, vol. 57, pp. 455–523.
FRANCIS, P.
1961. Florida ditch fishing. Florida Wildlife, vol. 15, pp. 12–15.
GARRICK, J. A. F.
1967. A broad view of *Carcharhinus* species, their systematics and distribution. Pp. 85–91 *in* "Sharks, Skates and Rays," P. W. Gilbert, R. F. Mathewson, and D. P. Hall, eds. Johns Hopkins Press, Baltimore.
GILL, THEODORE N.
1884. Salt water fish types in fresh water. Nature, vol. 29, p. 573.
1893. Sharks in fresh water. Science, old ser., vol. 22, p. 165.
GILL, THEODORE N., and BRANSFORD, JOHN F.
1877. Synopsis of the fishes of Lake Nicaragua. Proc. Acad. Nat. Sci. Philadelphia, 1877, pp. 175–191.
GORMAN, GEORGE C., and DESSAUER, HERBERT C.
1965. Hemoglobin and transferrin electrophoresis and relationships of island populations of *Anolis* lizards. Science, vol. 150, pp. 1454–1455.
HAMILTON, FRANCIS
1822. An account of the fishes found in the river Ganges and its branches, 405 pp., illus. Edinburgh.

HERRE, ALBERT W. C. T.
1955. Sharks in fresh water. Science, vol. 122, p. 417.
JENSEN, N. H.
1972. The reproduction and development of the bull shark, *Carcharhinus leucas,* in the Lake Nicaragua—Río San Juan system. Dissert. Abstr. Internat., vol. 33, pp. 2861–B.
JORDAN, DAVID STARR
1887. A preliminary list of the fishes of the West Indies. Proc. U.S. Nat. Mus., vol. 9, pp. 554–608.
JORDAN, D. S., AND EVERMANN, B. W.
1896. The fishes of North and Middle America. U.S. Nat. Mus. Bull. 47, pt. 1, lx + 1240 pp., illus.
JORDAN, D. S.; EVERMANN, B. W.; AND CLARK, HOWARD W.
1930. Check list of the fishes and fishlike vertebrates of North and Middle America north of the northern boundary of Venezuela and Colombia. Rpt. U.S. Comm. Fish., App. 10, pp. 1–670.
MCCUTCHEON, F. H.
1947. Specific oxygen affinity of hemoglobin in elasmobranchs and turtles. Journ. Cell Comp. Physiol., vol. 29, pp. 333–344.
MANWELL, C.
1963. Fetal and adult hemoglobins of the spiny dog fish, *Squalus suckleyi.* Arch. Biochem. Biophys., vol. 101, pp. 504–511.
MARDEN, LUIS
1944. A land of lakes and volcanoes. Nat. Geogr. Mag., vol. 86, no. 2, pp. 161–192, illus.
MEEK, SETH E.
1907. Synopsis of the fishes of the great lakes of Nicaragua. Publ. Field Columbian Mus. (Zool.), vol. 7, pp. 97–132.
MOURANT, A. E.
1970. Fish stocks: Biochemical and serological identification. Science, vol. 167, pp. 1760–1761.
MYERS, GEORGE S.
1952. Sharks and sawfishes in the Amazon. Copeia, 1952, pp. 268–269.
OVIEDO Y VALDES, GANZALO F. DE
1526. De la natural historia de la Indias. Toledo, Spain, (Translation: S. A. Stoudemire, ed., Univ. North Carolina Studies in the Romance Languages No. 32, Chapel Hill, North Carolina: Univ. of North Carolina Press, 1959.)
1535. Historia general de las Indias. Sevilla, Spain. pt. 1, 1535. (Chapters 1–13, Book 42, *in* "Histoire du Nicaragua," Paris: A Bertrand, 1840.)
PETERSON, G. L., AND SMITH A. C.
1969. Intraspecific variation in the soluble eye lens proteins of the sandbar shark, *Carcharhinus milberti* (Müller and Henle). Comp. Biochem. Physiol., vol. 31, pp. 679–684.
REGAN, CHARLES TATE
1908. Pisces. Pp. 1–203 *in* "Biologia Centrali-Americana," vol. 8, illus.

RIGGS, A.
1970. Properties of fish hemoglobins. Pp. 209–252 *in* "Fish Physiology," vol. 4, ch. 6, illus.
SCHWARTZ, F. J.
1959. Two eight-foot cub sharks *Carcharhinus leucas* (Müller and Henle) captured in Chesapeake Bay, Maryland. Copeia, 1959, pp. 251–252.
1960. Additional comments on adult bull sharks *Carcharhinus leucas* (Müller and Henle) from Chesapeake Bay, Maryland. Chesapeake Sci., vol. 1, pp. 68–71.
SICK, KNUD
1961. Haemoglobin polymorphism in fishes. Nature, vol. 192, pp. 894–896, illus.
SMITH, HUGH M.
1893. Sharks in Lake Nicaragua. Science, old ser., vol. 22, pp. 166–167.
SMITH, H. W.
1931. The absorption and excretion of water and salts by the elasmobranch fishes, I: Fresh-water elasmobranchs. Amer. Journ. Physiol., vol. 98, pp. 279–295.
SMITHIES, O.
1959. Zone electrophoresis in starch gels and its application to studies of serum proteins. Adv. Protein Chem., vol. 14, pp. 65–113.
SVENSSON, G. S. O.
1933. Fresh water fishes from the Gambia River. Kongl. Svenska Vet. Akad. Handl., vol. 12, no. 3, 102 pp.
THORSON, THOMAS B.
1966. Sharks and sawfish in the Lake Izabal-Rio Dulce system, Guatemala. Copeia, 1966, pp. 620–622.
1971. Movement of bull sharks, *Carcharhinus leucas,* between Caribbean Sea and Lake Nicaragua demonstrated by tagging. Copeia, 1971, pp. 336–338.
1972. The status of the bull shark, *Carcharhinus leucas*, in the Amazon River. Copeia, 1972, pp. 601–605.
THORSON, T. B.; WATSON, D. E.; AND COWAN, C. M.
1966. The status of the fresh water shark of Lake Nicaragua. Copeia, 1966, pp. 385–402.
URIST, MARSHALL R.
1962. Calcium and other ions in blood and skeleton of Nicaraguan fresh-water shark. Science, vol. 137, pp. 984–986, illus.
WILKINS, N. P., AND ILES, T. D.
1966. Haemoglobin polymorphism and its ontogeny in herring (*Clupea harengus*) and sprat (*Sprattus sprattus*). Comp. Biochem. Physiol., vol. 17, pp. 1141–1158.

JACK D. BURKE

Desert Studies in Tunisia, 1970–1971

Principal Investigator: Ian A. Campbell, University of Alberta, Edmonton, Alberta, Canada.

Grant No. 832: In support of investigations on the spread of desert conditions in central Tunisia.

The investigations lasted from July 1970 to May 1971 and covered a region from Gabes on the Tunisian coast to Ouagla, Algeria. Most of the detailed work was undertaken north of the Chott Djerid, in particular in the mountains of the Gafsa chain. The study was carried out with some cooperation from UNESCO, the Tunisian Government, and the French scientific organization ORSTOM, in their joint study—Projet Régional de Développement Intégré des Régions Pré-Sahariennes de la Tunisie.

The objectives of the research were to identify and if possible determine the rate at which the Saharan fringe areas in central Tunisia are becoming more desertlike in character. This process is referred to as "desertization." Centuries of overgrazing and other forms of land misuse, including the gathering of woody species for fuel, have contributed much to the presently rapidly deteriorating conditions observable along the Saharan fringe.

In addition to these immediate problems, studies were made of the longer-term geomorphic evidences of climatic fluctuations. Episodic channel cutting and alluviation and phases of planation and entrenchment are evidenced in the present landscape. Many of these features represent glacial and immediate postglacial fluctuations in climate and runoff characteristics. Ancient habitation sites with their datable materials serve as time indicators for many of these events.

Summary of Results

In association with a rapidly expanding population and an increase in the area of episodic cereal cultivation, soil deterioration and removal of the native vegetation cover have now attained critical limits in parts of central Tunisia. The continued and accelerating pressures on the land by grazing animals, farmers, and fuel gatherers cannot be sustained. Field observations during extensive travel and photographic evidence support the views expressed by authorities such as Le Houerou (1970). The present situation represents an imbalance between the capacity of the population to grow and the capability of the land to support this growth. Land-use statistics and crop-yield data reveal almost constant, or even declining, productivity per capita. Two disastrous floods within five years have added further serious effects. These problems have become especially acute since the early twentieth century. These are essentially man-induced.

Geomorphic evidence from earlier periods reveals the effects of climatic fluctuations. Detailed mapping of stream terrace deposits serves to illustrate the varying phases of erosion and deposition evident in North Africa as a result of Quaternary climatic patterns. Surveys in the Djebel Orbata region west of Gafsa in the Oued el Kebir drainage basin have provided evidence of three major depositional surfaces according with those identified by Coque (1962) elsewhere in Tunisia. The discovery of a hearth-site in one of these terraces enabled carbon-14 dating to be obtained, giving a date of 6000 ± 320 ^{14}C yr. B.P. and identifying the deposit as Neolithic of Capsian tradition. This provides a convenient datum for relating the other terrace deposits and thus helps establish a sequence of geomorphic events in the region during a climatically variable period.

Two papers on the research (Campbell, 1972, 1973) have been published; a third is in preparation.

REFERENCES

CAMPBELL, IAN A.

1972. Dated Capsian deposit near Gafsa, Tunisia. Nature, Phys. Sci., vol. 240, pp. 94–95.

1973. Ephemeral towns on the desert fringe. Geogr. Mag., vol. 45, no. 9, pp. 669–673, illus.

COQUE, ROGER

1962. La Tunisie presaharienne, 476 pp., illus. Armand Colin, Paris.

LE HOUEROU, H. N.

1970. North Africa: Past, present, future. Pp. 227–278 *in* "Arid Lands in Transition," H. E. Dregna, ed., Amer. Assoc. Adv. Science Publ. 90, 524 pp., illus.

IAN A. CAMPBELL

Lower Triassic Vertebrates from Tasmania

Principal Investigator: John W. Cosgriff, Jr., Wayne State University, Detroit, Michigan.

Grant No. 903: In support of paleontological research in southeastern Tasmania, involving collection of fish, amphibian, and reptile fossil material from the Lower Triassic Knocklofty Formation.

Accompanied by Thomas J. Dziewa, graduate student in the Biology Department of Wayne State Univeristy, I spent 8 weeks, from January 15 to March 10, 1971, engaged in a field collecting program in southeastern Tasmania, mainly in the environs of Hobart, the state capital. This program principally involved the search for and collection of fossil vertebrate material from the Knocklofty Formation, a stratigraphic unit deposited mainly by fresh water under continental conditions in the central, eastern, and southeastern portions of the island during early Triassic time. Exposures of the LaPerouse Formation, a lateral equivalent of the Knocklofty Formation in the extreme south of the island, were also investigated but without success. These activities represented a renewal and extension of my research from 1964 to 1967 when I was employed as a senior research fellow in the Department of Geology, University of Tasmania. The collections acquired during this recent trip form a valuable addition to those amassed previously, and the preparation and study of them promise greatly to expand and clarify our knowledge of the early Triassic biota of the Australian region.

During our stay in Tasmania the Geology Department of the University of Tasmania, located in the Sandy Bay District of Hobart (A on map), served as a base for field operations, and we were lodged at St. John Fisher College, which is adjacent to the University campus. We are greatly indebted to Drs. S. W. Carey and M. R. Banks, professor and reader, respectively, in the Geology Department, for providing us with office space and the use of research facilities, with tactical support for the field program, and with valuable consultations on problems related to our research. The kind hospitality of Fathers K. O'Sullivan and J. Smith, rector and dean, respectively, at St. John Fisher College, contributed much to our comfort and well-being while in Tasmania. We are grateful to D. Shepherd, of Shepherd's Photography Shop in Hobart, for joining us in our field work on several occasions and for contributing photographs of the principal collecting sites. Thanks are due also to the following parties: Drs. W. Bryden and L. Sutherland, director and curator of paleontology, respectively, at the Tasmanian Museum, Hobart, and Mrs. R. Smith, curator of the Port Arthur Museum (B on map), Port Arthur, for allowing us to inspect fossil specimens in their collections and to take latex peels from some of them; Drs. D. Alexander and A. Dartnell and M. Bowers, all of the Tasmanian Museum, for aiding us in our research at that Institution; and Miss S. Edwards, curator of paleontology at the Geology Department, University of Tasmania, for assisting us in our field work and for arranging the loan of fossil material to ourselves at Wayne State University.

The Knocklofty Formation and correlated units such as the LaPerouse Formation in the extreme south of the island, the Cluan Formation in the north, and the Ossa and Gould Formations in the west were deposited in a terrestrial basin that occupied much of the island during the early Triassic. The Knocklofty Formation, which has received much more extensive geological investigation than the correlated units, is a sequence of extremely varied lithology. Common types of deposits composing the formation are sandstones (often massive and usually slump-bedded), shales of various colors (black, green, red, and brown), and conglomerates of assorted types. These deposits are all very lenticular in character, and, hence, a single bed cannot be traced for any great distance. The sandstones and more extensive shale lenses seem to have been deposited under flood-plain conditions. Many of the shales, particularly the black ones, are probably pond and lake deposits. Some of the less extensive shale lenses and most of the conglomeratic deposits represent the beds of streams and small rivers channeled into already accumulated material. In addition to the highly lenticular nature of the deposits, other factors obviate possibilities for lithologic correlations between fossil localities in the formation: good exposures are relatively rare and widely separated, owing to the abundant rainfall and consequent heavy vegetation of Tasmania—the only readily accessible ones are quarries, steep mountain slopes, road cuts, and sea cliffs; and, most of the more extensive exposures reveal that the formation has been much disrupted by block faulting. The best and most complete exposures are to be seen in several brick-clay quarries, particularly those of Crisp & Gunn Pty. Ltd., on Mount Knocklofty in North Hobart (C on map). The section in these quarries shows that the formation consists of three members, an upper and a lower massive sandstone and a middle portion consisting of varied lithology. Most of the fossil localities in other areas of Tasmania occur in sequences of varied lithology and are, therefore, probably lateral equivalents of the middle member at Mount

Knocklofty. This sequence does not contain the upper and lower contacts of the formation, which, however, are to be seen in other sections. In all observed instances the lower contact is a paraconformable with the Cygnet Coal Measures, a unit ascribed to the Upper Permian through its contained palynological material. In most areas the upper contact is with a massive dolerite sill that was intruded into the sedimentary sequence in Jurassic time.

Prior to and during my previous residence in Tasmania a considerable amount of fossil vertebrate material was collected from various exposures in the formation. Some of the specimens were found as isolated occurrences in shale beds, but most were taken from a few good quarries in stream-channel clay-pebble conglomerates. The most productive of the quarries are at Old

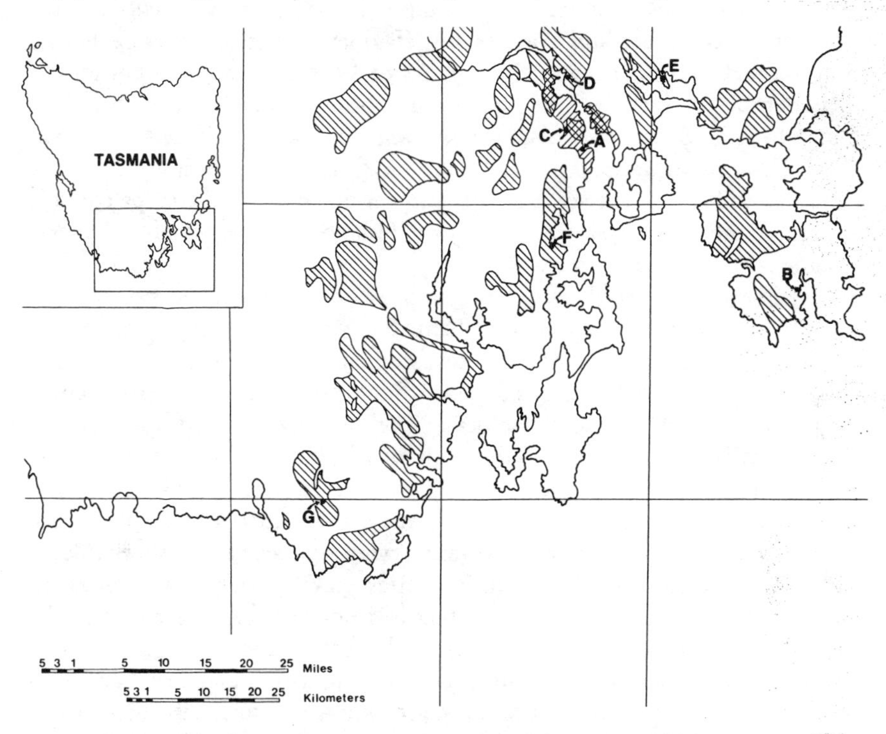

FIG. 1. A portion of southeastern Tasmania showing areas in which exposures of the Knocklofty and LaPerouse Formations outcrop (hatched from upper left to lower right), the city of Hobart (hatched from upper right to lower left) and institutions and fossil localities as follows: A, University of Tasmania; B, Port Arthur Museum; C, Crisp, & Gunn Pty. Ltd., quarries on Mount Knocklofty; D, Old Beach locality; E. Midway Point locality; F, Conningham locality; G, Mount LaPerouse.

Beach, Midway Point, and Conningham (D, E, and F on map), all of which were extensively worked from 1964 to 1967. The assemblages collected from these, although consisting principally of broken and disarticulated fragments of skeletons, are rather extensive taxonomically for a Triassic fauna. Common items are skull, jaw, shoulder girdle, and limb-bone fragments of amphibians and scale patches, spines, and teeth of fishes. The assemblages are almost identical in taxonomic content from one locality to the next and consist entirely of animals—fishes, amphibians, and rare reptiles—that were native to the fluviatile, lacustrine, and flood-plain environment of the early Triassic basin. Many of the taxa, including all the fishes, were native to the streams in which the conglomerates were deposited. Others, represented by less abundant remains in the conglomerate deposits, probably lived on the adjacent stream banks and flood plains, fragments of their skeletons having been washed into the streams. By the end of 1967 the identified portions of the assemblages included the thecodont reptile *Tasmaniosaurus triassicus*; four labyrinthodont amphibians—*Blinasaurus townrowi, Chomatobatrachus halei, Deltasaurus kimberleyensis,* and *Derwentia warreni*; a lungfish of the genus *Ceratodus*; a coelacanthid of undetermined genus; two paleoniscid species of the genus *Acrolepis*; and two subholostean species of the genera *Cleithrolepis* and *Saurichthys*.

Field work during this collecting trip was concentrated on two sea-cliff localities at Old Beach and Conningham, five weeks being spent at the first and one week at the second. Before commencing the excavations at Old Beach we had to remove a considerable amount of sandstone overburden to expose the pebble conglomerate lens. The Jennings Construction Co. of Hobart was engaged to perform this with air hammers and explosive charges. Approximately 8 square yards of conglomerate, 2 feet in thickness, were exposed by these means. This matrix proved to be extremely rich in fossil remains and, consequently, the excavation work proceeded very slowly. Some 340 fossil specimens were collected. In contrast to Old Beach, access problems at Conningham were not a factor. Matrix from the fossil-bearing pebble-conglomerate lens on the sea cliff is easily removed from large blocks of containing sandstone that were undercut by wave action and that have tumbled onto the beach. The matrix, however, is less rich in fossils than that at Old Beach and only some 40 specimens were collected during the week's activity at this locality.

The new material from Old Beach and Conningham greatly expands the collections on hand from previous years, and the analysis of it should add many details to knowledge of the morphology of most of the taxa present in this early Triassic fluviatile-flood plain fauna of Tasmania. Material augmenting the hypodigms of the four labyrinthodont amphibians and the two subholostean fishes should prove to be particularly interesting in this regard. In addition, the recent collections contain items representative of completely new taxa. These, when prepared and studied, may establish the presence in the fauna of two more labyrinthodont species, two or three more types of actinopterygian fishes, and one or two reptiles. More effort was expended during the recent excavations in collecting small items such as fish scales and spines, isolated teeth, and coprolites. Analysis of the scales, spines, and teeth may establish still other taxa, and close investigation of the coprolites may contribute toward a reconstruction of the food chain and other ecologic aspects of the fauna.

Attempts were made to locate new fossiliferous areas in the Knocklofty Formation and its correlated units during the little time available between the collecting programs at Old Beach and Conningham. One of these involved a week's prospecting on and near Mount LaPerouse in the southern part of the island (G on map). The Triassic strata here, although named the LaPerouse Formation, probably constitute an extension of the Knocklofty Formation. Although the mountain and its flanking hills and ridges contain a complete and well-exposed section of the formation and this section was inspected exhaustively, no vertebrate material was found, with the exception of some oblong objects that may be casts of lungfish burrows. The area of Mount LaPerouse is very inaccessible and can be reached overland only by a 12-mile hiking trail. As a large amount of general supplies and excavating material had to be included in the luggage, transport into the area by helicopter was arranged with the Hydro-Electric Commission of Tasmania. A good clear day was chosen for the flight, and the helicopter landed us at a sheltered camping spot at the foot of the mountain. The original arrangements called for retrieval by helicopter after 10 days, but as 6 days of prospecting proved unprofitable, the area was entirely searched, and supplies were mostly expended, it was decided in the interests of economy to walk out to the settlement of Lune River and call for a car to come down from Hobart to get us.

Following the field work, the collected material was packed and crated at the Department of Geology and arrangements were made through the University and the Tasmanian Museum to place it on loan to us at Wayne State University. It arrived and preparatory work preliminary to study of the material commenced. This will prove to be an extensive undertaking as the rock matrix surrounding the fossils is extremely hard, particularly in the case of the Old Beach material. Consequently, preparation must proceed slowly and with great care.

Once the preparation has been completed the basic investigations will proceed along three lines: (1) detailed morphologic analyses of each specimen achieved through comparisons with published reports of other fossil material in order to determine the taxonomic position of the species that it represents; (2) attempts to determine the environmental preferences and dietary habits of each taxon through considerations of its habitus features, its faunal associates, and lithologic features of the sediments that it was collected from; and (3) attempts to determine the nature and structure of the paleoecologic community (or communities) represented by the fossil assemblages, utilizing all available material, both the recently acquired collections and those available from the previous program. These basic investigations will, it is hoped, help provide solutions for problems of a broader but scientifically more interesting nature in the spheres of paleogeography, paleoecology, biostratigraphic correlation, and evolution. The possibilities for making contributions in all these are excellent, as much faunal information is already available for the early Triassic interval. Rather surprisingly, more collected fossil material from this interval is available over the world than is the case for most other comparable time spans in the Mesozoic Era. The extensive foundation for studies of the early Triassic rests on a number of taxonomically rich vertebrate faunas that have been collected from areas on all the continents (including Antarctica) and on the large islands of Madagascar, Greenland, and Spitsbergen. This abundance and wide distribution of material create potential for adding biologic information to attempts at geographic reconstructions, for determining ecologic relationships within communities, for filling gaps in the system of stratigraphic correlations, and for tracing evolutionary changes within individual lineages of animals. Much basic work involving morphologic and taxonomic comparisons between faunas remains to be done, however, before considerations of these broader topics can be initiated. This is particularly true of the Lower Triassic fishes and amphibians, which have received less attention from investigators than the reptilian groups contemporary with them.

The ultimate objective of research on the early Triassic fauna of Tasmania, then, is to contribute synthesizing information to the large topics noted above and defined in more detail as follows:

1. *Paleogeography.* Comparative work thus far accomplished on the early Triassic faunas of the world has highlighted a marked taxonomic correspondence among all of them, indicating that the present-day physical and faunal isolation of the world's large land-masses was not then in effect. Most early Triassic families and many of the genera are represented in areas widely separated by present-day geography. Land connections between all the

continents and larger islands were surely present during latest Paleozoic and/ or earliest Mesozoic time to allow overland migration of various widely spread groups of land tetrapods and fresh-water fishes. These connections were probably occasioned by contact of the edges of the land masses, a situation later altered by the action of continental drift, a phenomenon for which abundant and convincing geophysical evidence has been accumulated in recent years. It remains to determine more exactly the times and positions of these contacts. Increase in the knowledge of taxonomic relationships and stratigraphic sequences among Lower Triassic faunas would contribute information relevant to the probable length of contacts between land masses and, perhaps, something as to the nature and positions of the contacts.

2. *Paleoecology.* The ubiquitous distributions of many groups of fishes and tetrapods during the early Triassic indicate not only the presence of numerous continental connections but also the absence of climatic, ecologic, and physical barriers that would restrict the distributions of these groups. This is in sharp contrast to the over-all climatic and ecologic zonation observed in the present-day world where mountain, desert, and forest barriers prohibit extensive faunal interchange between continents. Early Triassic vertebrate faunas occur in areas that are presently polar, such as Greenland, Spitsbergen, and Antarctica; in areas that are presently dry-tropical, such as Western Australia; in areas that presently wet-tropical, such as India; and in areas presently temperate such as Tasmania. The close resemblances among these faunas strongly suggest that a much more uniform climate extended over the world at that time. It remains to determine more exactly such aspects of these faunas as food chains involved in the natural communities and the physical and climatic conditions to which these communities were adapted. Additions to knowledge of the early Triassic faunas and more detailed study of them may illuminate slight differences in environmental conditions from area to area and patterns of climatic zonation that are not apparent from information presently available.

3. *Biostratigraphic correlation.* Thorough and extensive comparative work among the fish and amphibian components of the world's Lower Triassic faunas will, undoubtedly, provide much insight into the stratigraphic-time relationships among these faunas and contribute to the construction of a more reliable and complete stratigraphic framework for the entire Lower Triassic.

4. *Evolution.* There are large gaps in our knowledge of the evolutionary histories of many of the groups of vertebrates extant over the world during the early Triassic. Comparative work among groups represented in the various faunas will serve to fill in some of these gaps.

JOHN W. COSGRIFF, JR.

Biotelemetry Research and Feasibility Experiments with IRLS[1] for Tracking Animals by Satellite

Principal Investigators: Frank C. Craighead, Jr., Atmospheric Sciences Research Center, State University of New York at Albany, and Environmental Research Institute, Moose, Wyoming; and John J. Craighead, Montana Cooperative Wildlife Research Unit, Missoula, Montana.

Grant No. 911: For continued biotelemetry research and satellite monitoring.

Over a 12-year-period, from 1960 through 1971, we and our colleagues developed, perfected, and applied in field studies a biotelemetry system for gathering ecological information on the environment and data on free-roaming wild animals. This research has been supported in part by the National Geographic Society.

The radiotracking and location system was developed first; and grizzly bears, elk, and black bears were instrumented and information on such subjects as movement, ranges, activity, behavior, migration, and feeding habits was gathered on these animals (Craighead and Craighead, 1972, 1973; F. C. Craighead, Jr., 1976).

Next, transmitters were developed and used that telemetered specific types of information such as body temperature, activity, and heart rate. With these, 24-hour body-temperature patterns of elk were obtained, as well as nycthemeral, 24-hour body-temperature patterns of hibernating black bears (Craighead and Craighead, 1973, 1974; J. Craighead et al., 1976). A motion-sensing, or activity, transducer, which causes the transmitter to pulse when moved or shaken, was used to obtain daily activity patterns of elk as well as of grizzlies. EKG, or heart-rate, transmitters have been developed and tested on humans. This has been confined to pulse-rate changes during skiing and white-water boating. There is great research application for this type of transmitter in measuring therapeutic values of outdoor activities. Small-bird transmitters, on 27 MHz, were also developed and applied in the gathering of field data. However, these transmitters have not yet been perfected to the point where they supply information at all comparable to that obtained from those we have been using on bears and elk.

[1]Interrogation, Recording, and Location System (IRLS).

Three different approaches were taken in the development of automatic recording and monitoring equipment. The purpose of this was to record continuously data from our information-type transmitters. All methods were successfully field tested but still require modification for optimum field use under extreme environmental conditions (Craighead and Craighead, 1974).

The aforementioned research led to a cooperative program in which an elk was tracked by the Nimbus 3 satellite by means of the Interrogation Recording Location System (IRLS; Craighead et al., 1971).

A major objective of the 1971 research (under grant 911) was to continue equipment design and modification of the IRLS collar used the previous year in a feasibility experiment with an elk. The purpose of a continuing program was to test an improved animal-tracking satellite system that could be used to locate various instrumented animals around the globe, to monitor information on the environment through which the animal moves or travels, and simultaneously to sample and transmit physiological data that could be correlated with the animals' movements and behavior. Such a system should provide a tremendous advance in technique for acquiring information on wildlife and ecosystems. The research was to be a continued joint endeavor between the Smithsonian Institution and the National Aeronautics and Space Administration (NASA) conducted in collaboration with the Montana Cooperative Wildlife Research Unit, the Environmental Research Institute, the State University of New York at Albany, and the National Geographic Society. Research team collaborators and field assistants included Joel Varney, Harry Reynolds III, Jack Seidensticker, Jay Sumner, and Jim Claar.

Accordingly, the IRLS collar was redesigned and modified by NASA engineers under the direction of Charles Cote and with input from the field biologists and engineers working on the first animal-tracking project.

The weight of the collar was reduced by half and preparations were made to instrument another elk on the National Elk Refuge in Jackson Hole in early April 1971. While this work was progressing we redesigned the mockup collars, lightened them to correspond with the weight of the new electronic collar, and built into them a Craighead-Varney 32-MHz ground-tracking system. This insured that elk instrumented with the mockup collars could be readily located, immobilized, and instrumented with the IRLS electronic package at the designated time.

A few days before placing the mockup collars on free-roaming elk NASA decided to drop the project. The decision was influenced by the fact that IRLS equipment would not be included on the Nimbus 5 satellite, and meant that future research could not be conducted using the modified equipment.

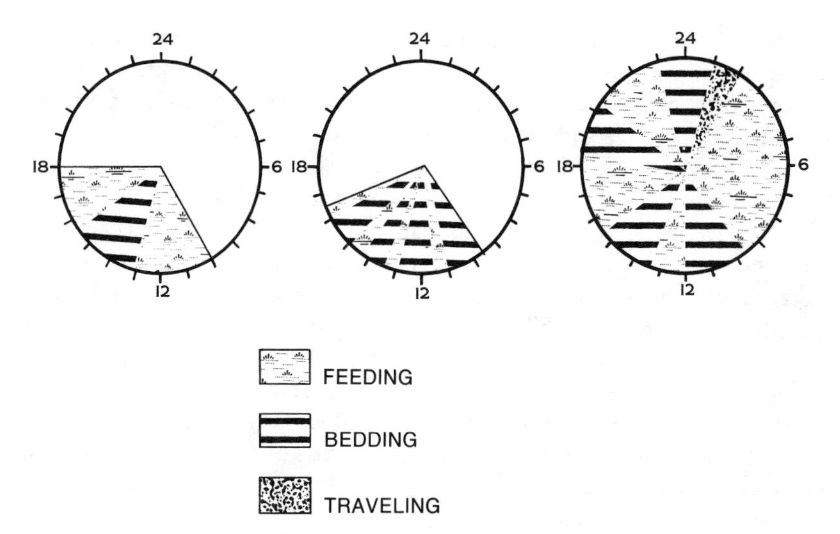

FIG. 1. Instrumented activity patterns, Elk no. 3 (female), Old Faithful, Yellowstone National Park, 1965.

	Time Feb. 10		Time Nov. 14		Time Nov. 19–20	
Activity	Hours	Percent	Hours	Percent	Hours	Percent
Feeding	5.5	69	1.8	28	14.6	61
Bedding	2.5	31	4.8	72	8.4	35
Traveling					1.0	4
Standing						
Totals	8.0	100	6.6	100	24.0	100

Prior to receiving word that this experiment would be cancelled we had acquired a horse trailer, built a corral, and made all the necessary arrangements for a busy field season of tracking a migrating elk.

We accordingly shifted the objectives of our biotelemetry work. In late October and early November we spent several weeks trapping both black bears and grizzlies in the vicinity of West Yellowstone. The aim of instrumenting one of these animals was to track it to a den for later physiological telemetry work in midwinter. Although a number of grizzlies were trapped, none suitable for the experiment was captured. One black bear was instrumented and tracked, but he removed the collar before entering a den.

Early in our radio tracking work we began to devise varied and better techniques for recording animal activity. Biotelemetry techniques previously reported have enabled us to observe specific instrumented animals from hour to hour, day to day, and from season to season. During 1965 to 1966, 19 24-hour activity patterns were recorded for elk (Craighead et al., 1973). Observation ranged from a few hours to continuous 24-hour observation periods. In the gathering of information on activity and behavior from instrumented animals the total observation time is limited only by manpower. The potential for gathering quantitative data has far exceeded the actual use made of this capability. For example, out of 564 elk instrumentation days only 167 days were utilized to observe the instrumented animals and during these days total direct observation time was only 241 hours. Nevertheless, this far exceeded the observation time possible without the use of radio. In gathering data on activity patterns, three types of transmitters were used: the conventional varied-pulsed tracking transmitter, body temperature transmitters, and the activity transmitter.

Observation periods were graphed to illustrate how activity patterns were obtained and compared by use of the conventional transmitter. Figure 1 (left) shows an 8-hour activity graph for elk no. 3 during February. The long feeding periods interspersed by extended bedding and resting periods were found typical of elk in winter. Figure 1 (center) shows quite a different activity pattern for the same elk in November. This pattern of short periods of feeding followed by short rest periods was common among the elk and did not appear to be seasonally oriented.

A 24-hour activity period is illustrated for elk no. 3 in Figure 1 (right), where the percentages of time spent in four major activities of feeding, bedding, traveling, and standing are shown. More specialized types of behavior and the time spent by elk in various types of vegetation, habitats, or microhabitats were also recorded and interpreted. In this particular 24-hour period, 61 percent of the time was devoted to feeding, and the most extensive feeding period was from 2 to 10 a.m., with a short period at noon, one in the afternoon, and one before 12 p.m. Data obtained to date indicate that the nocturnal-diurnal activity of elk varies from preconceived ideas. Activity patterns varied greatly with the individual animals and even with the same animal from season to season. In the future it will be possible to determine the variations in 24-hour activity patterns for the same elk from year to year and between different individuals.

There were times when we could not continuously observe instrumented elk for entire 24-hour periods. To overcome the deficiency we developed and used an activity transmitter (Varney, 1971). During most of one summer a motion-sensing transmitter was placed on an adult cow elk, no. 12. After experimenting with the activity transmitter we found that we could recognize certain sound patterns and that these patterns could be correlated with elk activity. A steady pulse (51–52 bpm) indicated that the elk was bedding or standing or generally inactive. Occasionally, when the elk spotted an observer, she would sneak or walk carefully with only a slight change in the steady

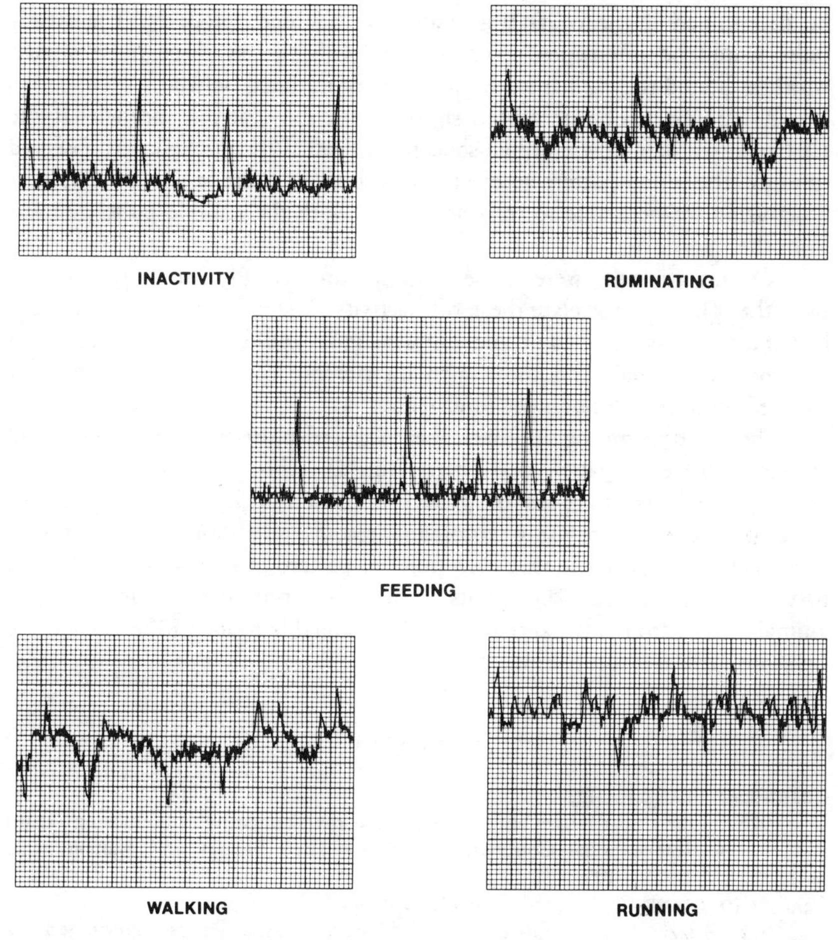

FIG. 2. Strip chart of elk activity transcribed from tape (accelerometer or activity-sensing transmitter). Inactivity = standing or lying down.

pulse. When the elk was moving rapidly from one place to another the steady signal was characterized by a multitude of rapid beats. When the elk was feeding, the steady signal would be interrupted every three or four beats. If she moved her head from side to side while grazing, the signal would fade, then increase, then fade again. Occasionally when feeding, she would jerk her head with each bite. This signal could be confused with moving or traveling except that the change in signal strength from loud to faint did not occur when she was traveling. Ruminating could sometimes be determined if the collar was resting on her neck properly. The steady pulse would be interrupted every minute with two or three pulse signals which indicated the elk has swallowed and regurgitated bolus.

A loud burst of interrupted signals for a short period meant that the elk had arisen, lain down, or had shaken her head. When the elk was observed running, the sound pattern received was a constant burst of signals. Through observation we were able to correlate activity with the audible pulse received from the transmitter.

Various attempts were made to tally automatically pulses per minute from the collar and correlate these with activity. The tape-totalizer equipment had the advantage that faint and distant signals could be recorded or taped but the faint signals and those with interference could not be adequately counted when run through the totalizer.

The most promising approach was to record pulse patterns on tape and transcribe these to paper strip charts (fig. 2). This provided recognizable visual patterns which could be greatly improved with refinements in the transmitter circuit. In using automatic recording equipment, transmitter modification is needed so that each pulse or pattern of pulses can be counted or visually represented. The results of this work indicated that recording of animal activity from a distance could be considerably refined to reveal specific behavior. This is a future aim.

REFERENCES

CRAIGHEAD, FRANK C., JR.

1976. Grizzly bear ranges and movements as determined by radiotracking. Third International Conference on Bears—Their Biology and Management, pp. 97–109.

CRAIGHEAD, FRANK C., JR., and CRAIGHEAD, JOHN J.

1972. Grizzly bear prehibernation and denning activities as determined by radiotracking. Wildlife Soc. Wildlife Monogr. no. 32, 35 pp. illus.

1973. Radiotracking of grizzly bears and elk in Yellowstone National Park, Wyoming, 1966. Nat. Geogr. Soc. Res. Rpts., 1966 Projects, pp. 33–48, illus.

1974. Radiotelemetry research on large western mammals in Yellowstone National Park, Wyoming, 1967. Nat. Geogr. Soc. Res. Rpts., 1967 Projects, pp. 35–51, illus.

CRAIGHEAD, FRANK C., JR.; CRAIGHEAD, JOHN J.; COTE, C. E.; and BUECHNER, HELMUT K.

1971. Satellite and ground radiotracking of elk. Pp. 99–111 *in* "Animal Orientation and Navigation." NASA Scientific and Technical Information Office, Washington, D.C., 606 pp.

CRAIGHEAD, JOHN J.; CRAIGHEAD, FRANK C.; ET AL.

1973. Home ranges and activity patterns of non-migratory elk of the Madison Drainage herd as determined by biotelemetry. Wildlife Soc. Wildlife Monogr. no. 33, 50 pp., illus.

CRAIGHEAD, JOHN J.; VARNEY, JOEL R.; CRAIGHEAD, FRANK C., JR.; and SUMNER, JAY S.

1976. Telemetry experiments with a hibernating black bear. Third International Conference on Bears—Their Biology and Management, pp. 357–371.

VARNEY, JOEL R.

1971. A tracking and telemetry system for wildlife research. Pp. 247–252 *in* "IEEE National Telemetering Conference Record 71C 10–NTC."

FRANK C. CRAIGHEAD, JR.
JOHN J. CRAIGHEAD

Early People and Extinct Animals at China Lake, California

Principal Investigator: Emma Lou Davis, Natural History Museum of Los Angeles County, California.[1]

Grant Nos. 861, 936: For studies of the late Pleistocene archeology and paleontology of China Lake, Mojave Desert, California.

Background

In the autumn of 1969, upon learning that very ancient artifacts had been discovered on missile impact ranges of the Naval Weapons Center at China Lake, California (fig. 1), we immediately began a project to assess the value of an organized archeological program in the area. On the basis of initial information, China Lake appeared to possess unusually rich and well-preserved records of California prehistory from 10,000 to 14,000 years B.P.—information of a kind that has been destroyed elsewhere or is at best scanty. Shortly after initiation of archeological studies, fragments of bone were also found to be thinly scattered over the same surfaces on which the artifacts occurred, and by year-end some were recognized as representing extinct taxa.

Various factors combined to suggest that the China Lake situation was perhaps of major importance to New World prehistory and offered a unique opportunity to piece together a story of early people and animals in the northern Mojave Desert—the abundance of faunal and cultural material, its relatively undisturbed condition, and the interspersed nature of occurrences among them. We felt that these data formed a body from which inferences as to paleoenvironment could be drawn; further, that the area merited inspection by experts in the fields of paleontology, archeology, geology, and palynology. To this end application was made to the National Geographic Society for support of a field conference.

[1]Grateful acknowledgment is made to the Naval Weapons Command for allowing access to restricted areas; to the National Geographic Society for the grants that made this research possible; and to the Maturango Museum for sponsorship of the project.

Pilot Project Conference

The conference was held on July 4–5, 1970, at China Lake under local sponsorship of the Maturango Museum. By the time the team of specialists arrived to look over the sites, a rather considerable inventory of cultural and faunal material was ready for their inspection.

The faunal inventory at the time comprised a Rancholabrean fauna composed of the following genera: *Anas, Aquila, Canis, Smilodon, Equus, Camelops, Bison,* and *Mammuthus*. Even at that preliminary stage it was becoming apparent that paleoecological inferences concerning physical environment and prey-predator relationships would ultimately be possible.

Some of the stone tools found in surface association with these taxa are illustrated in figure 2. There are fluted and unfluted lanceolate points; Lake Mojave Pattern points; gravers; crescents; a wide variety of scrapers; choppers; borers; planes; cores; and flakes. The high percentage of large points suggests that these were hunting tool-kits.

The following scientists participated in the conference:

DAVIS, EMMA LOU, archeologist, Natural History Museum of Los Angeles County.
DAWSON, JERRY, archeologist, Southern Methodist University.
DIXON, KEITH A., archeologist, California State University, Long Beach.
FORTSCH, DAVID E., paleontologist, Natural History Museum of Los Angeles County.
HAYNES, C. VANCE, geologist, Southern Methodist University, Dallas, Texas.
MEAD, GILES W., director, Natural History Museum of Los Angeles County.
MEHRINGER, PETER J., paleobotanist, University of Utah.
PANLAQUI, CAROL archeologist, Maturango Museum, China Lake.
ROSS, LESTER A., archeologist, Archaeological Research, Inc.
ROZAIRE, CHARLES E., archeologist, Natural History Museum of Los Angeles County.
TAYLOR, D. W., zoologist, San Diego Museum of Natural History.
UTTER, S., geologist, U.S. Geological Survey, Menlo Park, California.
WHITMORE, FRANK C., JR., geologist and paleontologist, U.S. Geological Survey, Washington, D.C.

Views of Participants

Among others, the participants made the following suggestions:

Dawson provided particularly valuable insight based upon extensive experience with Paleo-Indian sites in New Mexico and Colorado (Judge and Dawson, 1972). He had observed patterns of camping, hunting, kill, and meat-processing sites, in addition to being familiar with artifact assemblages peculiar to these activities. While the Colorado and New Mexico situations are not identical with China Lake, they are similar.

Mehringer thought that China Lake basin offered little palynological opportunity to correlate paleoecological regimes with early hunters. In his opinion such associations could be better determined at bog locations in the adjacent Sierra Nevada or Owens Valley. Mehringer was the first to recommend that back-hoe trenches be cut through the residual land forms supporting the archeological and paleontological sites. Such trenches could conceivably establish either the presence or absence of bones and tools in situ. (Note: These trenches were made but results are not yet available.)

Ross posed the question that had been our bogey from the outset: Is the proximity of artifacts to faunal remains due to cultural or to geologic activities? It is hoped that the back-hoe cuts will be informative on this subject.

Haynes thought that the best procedure would be to investigate possible sources for the materials of which the various specimens we find on surfaces are composed. How did they get there? He further recommended searches of spring areas and of arroyo wall exposures as well as use of low-level air photos.

FIG. 1. California, showing location of China Lake.

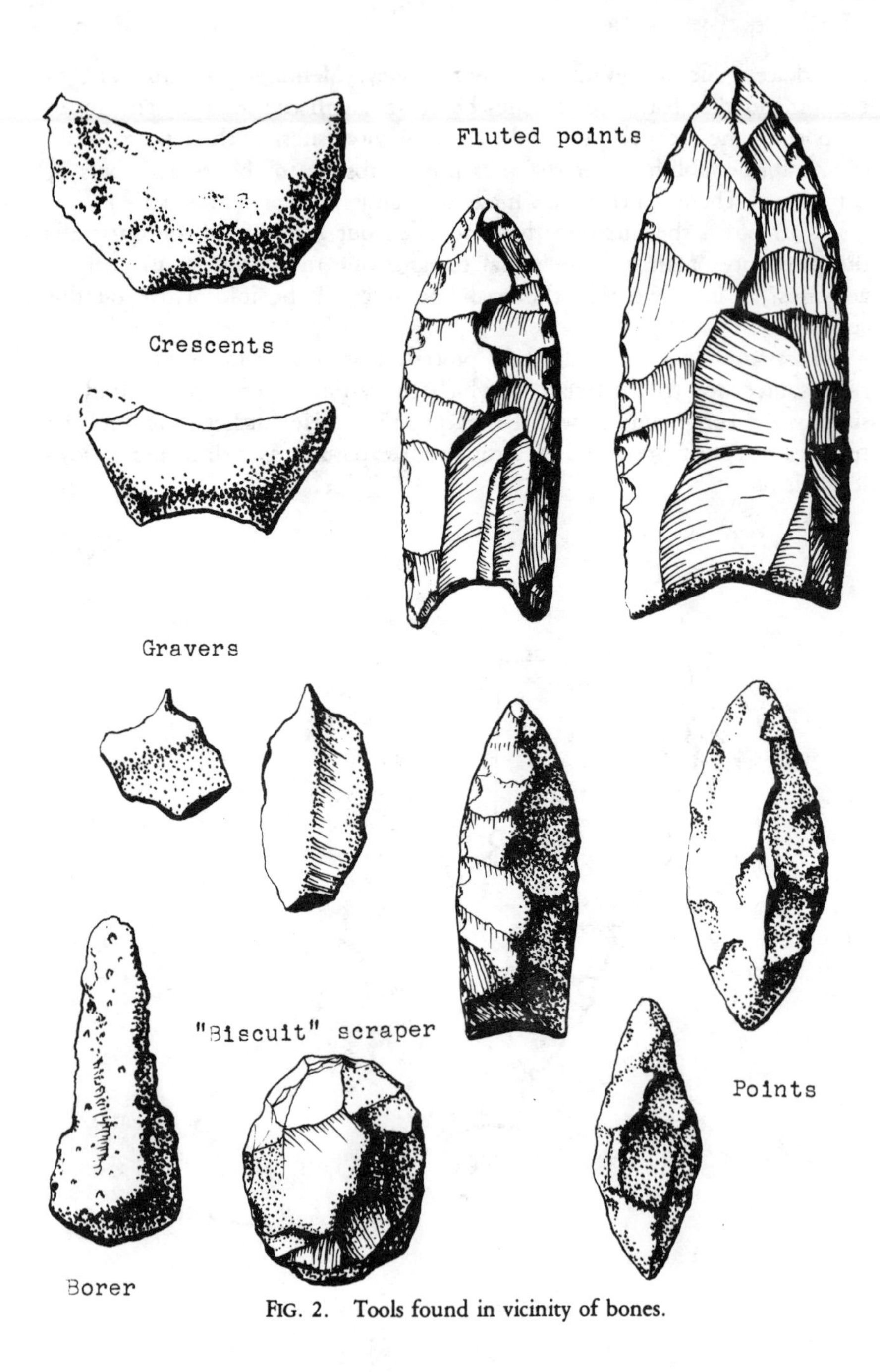

FIG. 2. Tools found in vicinity of bones.

a) Residual landforms (former lake beds sculptured by erosion)

c) Artifacts (Middle Paleo-Indian, of fluting cotradition)

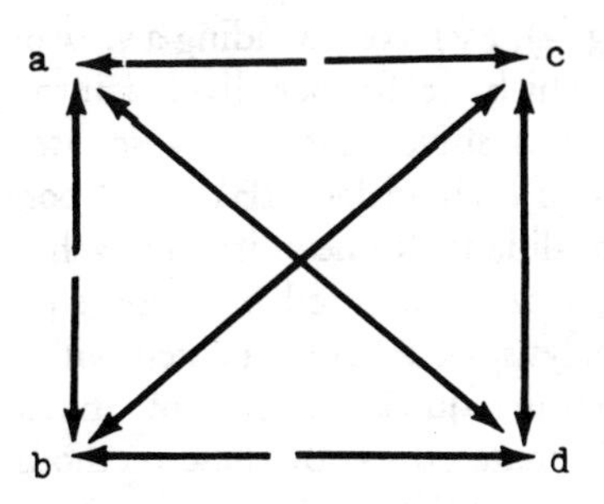

b) Artifacts (Late Paleo-Indian of Lake Mojave pattern)

d) Animal bones

FIG. 3. A 6-way relationship figure to be solved for any pair of variables at a time.

Continuation of Research

During the following year and a half we developed a steadily expanding project, with Panlaqui and Davis cooperating on the archeology and Fortsch on the paleontology. As an initial step we acquainted ourselves with access roads on the base and developed familiarity with the surprisingly diverse environments present: marsh, desert, mountain. Within this valley (which has held a fluctuating lake since Pleistocene time) animal bones and stone tools are spread over tens of square miles. As our work progressed, we saw with increasing clarity that we had to consider six relationships between four factors as shown in the chart, figure 3. A tightly controlled mapping program would be the only way to determine degrees of relatedness. Further, we had to have a permanent record of situations and positions for later reconsideration and introspective recognition. At all times this project has been an interaction of the strict mechanics of "square thinking" and the intuitive jumps and syntheses of "inner space" (Holden, 1973: 282–283).

Mapping Procedures

We selected an area approximately 1 mile square in the dismal and nearly featureless landscape, which contained as much topographic and geomorphic variety as possible. In this square mile we established a series of instrument stations (fig. 4), each commanding a view of an area approximately 1,000 feet on a side, which we further divided into quadrants. This done, we then made a rigorous survey over every square foot of the area and mapped the occurrence of each artifact, flake, and bone to ± 5-foot accuracy using plane table and alidade. Concomitantly each item was entered on a 5-by-8-inch edge-punch card, recorded on a log sheet for the station, and filed for laboratory analysis after being marked with pertinent coding data. This cross-indexing permits quick retrieval of any item and allows cross-checking of data to eliminate errors. By these methods we were able to glean a surprising quantity of data (fig. 5) from a landscape that appears entirely devoid of significant features to the casual observer. We determined the slight changes in geomorphic character contain evidences leading toward ultimate explanations of how the faunal and cultural remains arrived at their present positions. The work has been a blend of "inner space" (Holden, 1973: 282–283) understanding, and strict mechanics, alternately.

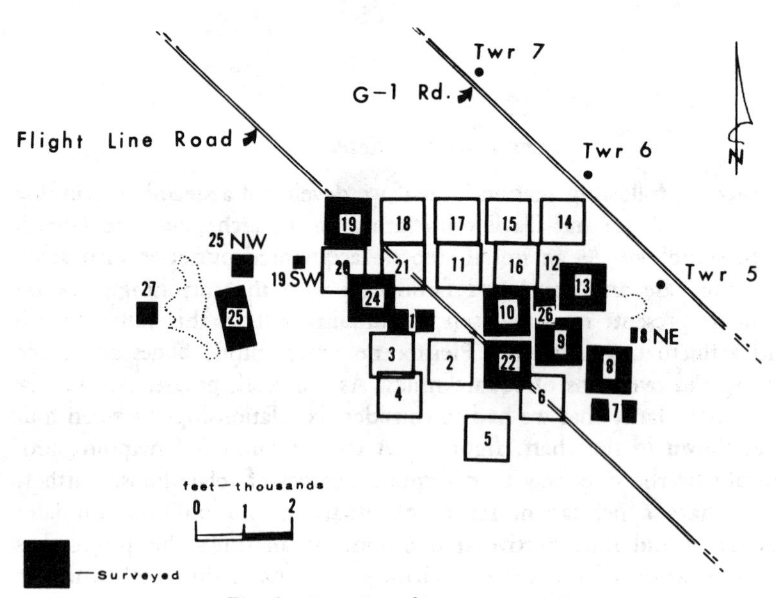

FIG. 4. Location of instrument stations.

Geology Conference

In January 1972 a weekend field consultation was attended by geologist George I. Smith (U.S. Geological Survey), David Weide (University of California Los Angeles), Kenneth Pringle (Naval Weapons Center), Alan Basset, and Theodore Downs, paleontologist, Natural History Museum of Los Angeles County. After having visited typical site areas, the geologists agreed that, at this point, our most useful research tool would be a back-hoe. We needed cuts, as deep as possible, into the clays and gravels of the old land forms that support our sites. The anatomy of the substrate would hopefully furnish us with a prior history of the area and perhaps yield both dates and pollen (essential for understanding effects of paleoclimates). Also, we wanted very much to know how the gravels on which artifacts lie relate to the latest high stand of China Lake that occurred about 10,000–11,000 years B.P. (Smith, 1968, fig. 10).

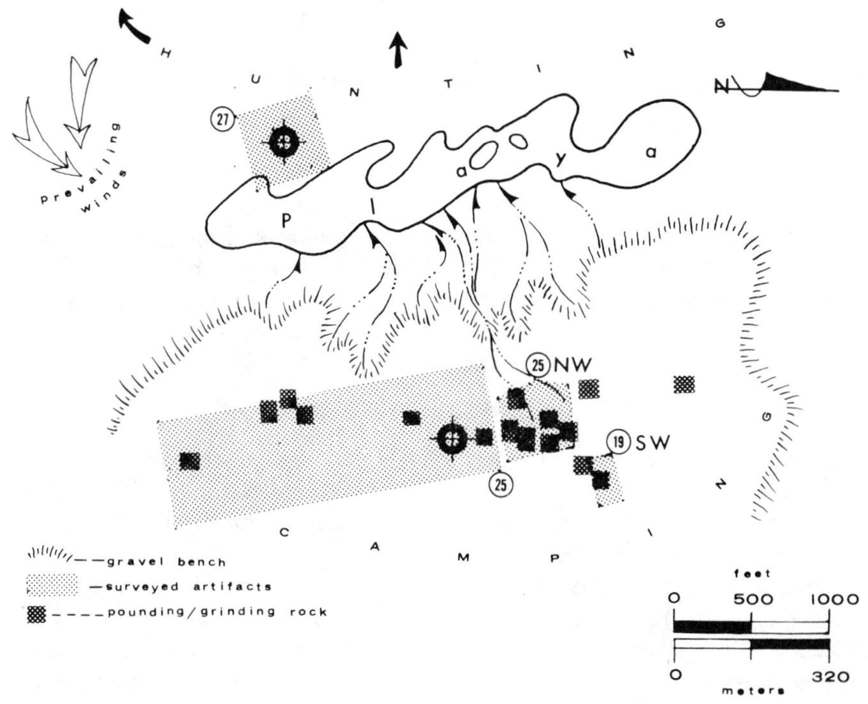

FIG. 5. Paleo-Indian land use: Pattern 1

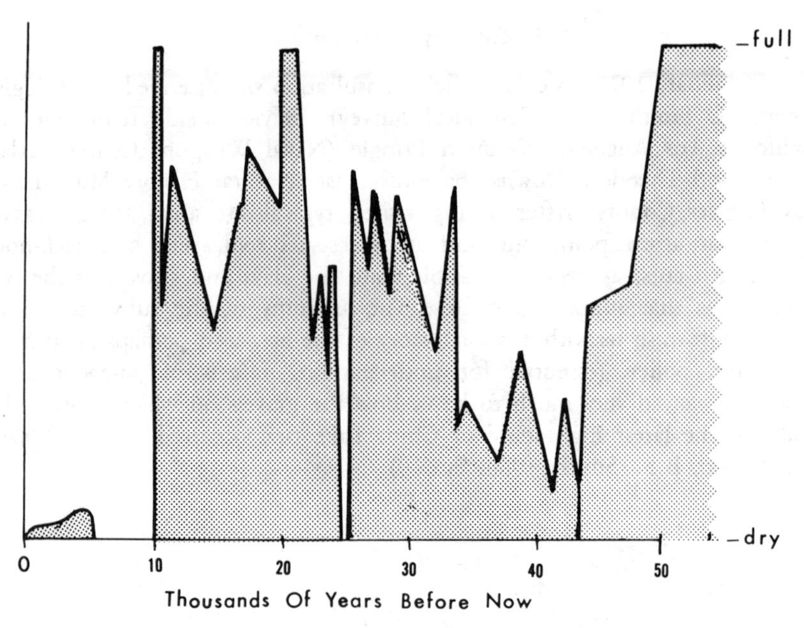

FIG. 6. Levels of Searles Lake (Smith, 1968).

Dates

A radiocarbon date was assayed on a mammoth skull mentioned below: 18,600 ± 4500 years B.P. (U.C.L.A. 1800). Six pounds of ivory shims from a tusk were used, and compensation was made for a high content of "dead" carbonates. Ivory, like all other animal remains at China Lake, had been permineralized and little organic material is left.

Transects

In addition to the extremely detailed instrument-station surveys, a different sort of exploratory scouting has been undertaken. This is being done along narrow transects, 5 to 15 miles in length, much of the distance being traversed on foot by relays of people. The purpose of these probes is to give us information about how different groups of hunter-gatherers used (or avoided) different parts of the huge valley over a long period of time. We suggest the span to be 10,000 to 12,000 years. This transect work is not yet complete but will be of great importance for understanding changes in culturally determined preference in land use as the environment changed.

Summary and Conclusions

In order to date the sites it will be necessary to date several stands of the lake when water stood considerably higher than 2,180 feet above mean sea level (fig. 6). This information can be obtained only through the straticuts mentioned above.

In those cases where residual land forms remain, we have noted that bones and artifacts appear to have different distributions. Artifacts are more common on ridges, while the bones are usually stratigraphically lower. At present we are not sure why this is so. Perhaps the bones originally underlay the stone tools and are just not weathering out. As an example, an associated partial skeleton of a mammoth (Fortsch, 1972: Specimen LACMV 7013/29140) lay in clayey silt and gravel with only the left side being shielded by burial. The right side of the animal had been exposed to wind-driven sand and had been planed off at ground surface. Further conclusions concerning paleoecology as indicated by faunal elements and expanded faunal lists are available in Fortsch (1972).

The people, however, were undoubtedly hunters of large animals by preference. The stone tools (fig. 2) resemble those that have been found with mammoth and bison kills in the high plains. At present we suggest the bones are those of animals that died (or were killed) during a moist cycle so that hard tissues were *quickly* buried and become permineralized. Artifact assemblages without bone might represent drying cycles when hunting-gathering bands were able to re-occupy the grassland bed of a retreating lake. In this case, the kills of the hunters may have lain exposed to sun and wind, which destroyed them.

Our work so far had produced these hazy pictures. Much remains to be done to clarify and expand our understanding. Meanwhile, the project encompasses much more than a site report. It has already become a synthetic study of the life styles of a least two traditions of early American cultures as they adapted to changes in climate and countryside.

REFERENCES

DAVIS, EMMA LOU

1975. The "exposed archaeology" of China Lake, California. Amer. Antiq., vol. 40, no. 1, pp. 39–53, illus.

FORTSCH, DAVID E.

1972. A Late Pleistocene vertebrate fauna from the northern Mojave Desert of California. M. S. thesis, University of Southern California, Los Angeles.

HOLDEN, CONSTANCE

1973. Altered states of consciousness: Mind researchers meet to discuss exploration and mapping of "inner space." Science, vol. 179, pp. 982–983.

JUDGE, W. JAMES, and DAWSON, JERRY
1972. Paleo-Indian settlement technology in New Mexico. Science, vol. 176, pp. 1210–1216, illus.
SMITH, GEORGE I.
1968. Late-Quaternary geologic and climatic history of Searles Lake, southeastern California. *In* "Means of Correlation of Quaternary Succession." Proc. Congr. Int. Assoc. Quaternary Res., vol. 8, no. 7. University of Utah Press.

EMMA LOU DAVIS
DAVID E. FORTSCH
CAROL PANLAQUI

Ornithological Research in Ethiopia

Principal Investigator: Michel Desfayes, Smithsonian Institution, Washington, D.C.

Grant No. 894: To study the distribution, ecology, and systematics of birds in two little-known regions of Ethiopia.

The avifauna of Ethiopia is one of the least known among the avifaunas of Africa, owing to the fact that the country has remained, except for a brief period in the 1930's, free of the colonialism that brought so many scientists to other African countries. The purpose of my expedition in March and April 1971 was to study the distribution, ecology, breeding phenology, and, in particular, altitudinal zonation of the birds.

The Simien Mountains

The Simien constitutes the highest part of the Ethiopian Plateau, which ranges mostly between 6,000 and 9,000 feet. The research area, situated between 8,000 and 12,000 feet, was composed of rather flat-topped, open areas dissected by deep valleys with very steep slopes. The whole country is intensively cultivated, even on slopes so steep that one has to watch every step lest he slide downhill. Nevertheless, no retaining walls or terraces are built as is the custom in mountainous Asian or European countries. This mode of cultivation is extremely ruinous for the land. Already in the middle of the 18th century, the explorer James Bruce commented on this disastrous situation. New land is being cleared every year by uncontrolled burning, although firewood, which is indispensable for village life, is becoming very scarce. In the Simien National Park, recently created for the conservation of the rare endemic Waalia ibex, an area of over 250 acres of primeval giant heath forest was illegally reduced to ashes two weeks before our arrival (plus another 250 acres outside the park). During our stay not one day went by without a bush fire. Land is indiscriminately burned, whether arable or not. According to botanists, this land was once probably covered with a tall juniper (*Juniperus procera*). Only a few isolated trees now remain, near village churches. On our entire trip we saw only one remnant of juniper forest, estimated at 100 acres. Nowhere in the world have I seen such mismanaged land. In the dry season the tilled fields are exposed to winds that raise enormous whirls of dust, while in the rainy season topsoil is washed away. How have the local people been able to survive through the centuries of improper land management? One answer is that in many places the extremely fertile volcanic soil reaches a surprising depth. In other areas, particularly on steep slopes, large surfaces have been abandoned after the topsoil has been washed away. Another answer is that the people are only barely surviving and certainly not improving their life. The poverty is such that a lower standard of living would be all but impossible; it is quite reasonable to assume that, several centuries ago, their ancestors were better off as they worked prime land. This deforestation has presumably had deep repercussions on animal life although no comparison is now possible.

Although an excellent botanical work had been published (Scott, 1957–58), it was not possible to determine through his paper—or from any other botanical or zoological publications on the area—whether the plant-life zonation had any effects on the avifaunal zonation or whether there was any zonation at all. Our research showed that the altitudinal distribution of birds in the Simien is relatively homogeneous throughout, in spite of the great height of the massif, reaching 15,000 feet at one point. Local avifaunal variations are little influenced by altitude, except that the bird-life is poorer above ca. 10,000 feet with a diminishing diversity of habitats.

A hundred specimens of birds of 55 species were collected in this area and notes taken on the distribution and biology of over 100 species.

The Southwestern Rainforest

Halfway during our trip the country became too rugged to permit further travel and investigation toward the east. Sure-footed mules are nonexistent in the area although both horses and donkeys are available. One of our horses fell off the trail—fortunately not on a dangerously steep slope—and crushed one of our especially made metal boxes, fortunately containing no valuable equipment. To avoid another mishap, which could have ruined irreplaceable film and expensive instruments, we decided to halt further research in the Simien and to spend the rest of the time in another part of the country, the unexplored rainforest of southwestern Ethiopia. The decision proved to be a wise and rewarding one.

The humid southwestern part of the Ethiopian Plateau located between the towns of Jimma and Gore is covered with an unbroken islandlike expanse of rainforest, apparently the largest continuous forest east of the Congo basin. It is separated from the Congo forest, however, by a thousand miles of arid country. No other ornithologist has worked in the forest: It is, for all practical purposes, impenetrable. Our investigations were therefore limited to marginal areas where cultivation is gradually replacing the primeval forest. Every effort, however, was made to study the primeval forest, which is composed of high evergreen trees with an extremely dense substage. Short trips were taken along streams and trails whenever available. The humid conditions of the region, in contrast to the generally dry Ethiopian Plateau, have resulted in well-marked subspecific differentiation of birds, of which specimens of three new subspecies were obtained.

In this region, 170 specimens of birds were collected and data on biology and ecology gathered on more than 200 species.

The Spelling of Two Toponyms

It may be apropos to call attention to the spelling of the names ***Simien*** (meaning "the north") and its summit the ***Ras Degien***, the highest in Ethiopia. The orthography of ***Simien*** has been commented upon by Scott (1957–1958, p. 79) and the transliteration of its pronunciation verified in situ by myself. ***Ras Degien*** is usually spelled "Ras Dashan" on most English maps. Yet it is pronounced "dedjen" or, as put by Scott (p. 79), "not unlike the English word "dudgeon," and that is the way we always heard it pronounced by the local people. "Ras Dashan" is the transliteration of the Italian pronunciation of "Ras Dasciàn" (the Italian language does not have the "j" sound as in "jam"). The spelling ***Ras Degien***, as proposed by Scott, is the closest to the pronunciation we heard and should be considered in future mapmaking.

REFERENCE

SCOTT, HUGH

1957–58. Biogeographical research in High Simien (northern Ethiopia), 1952–53. Proc. Linn. Soc. London, vol. 170, pp. 1–91.

MICHEL DESFAYES

Microbiology of an Isolated Alpine Lake (Lake Waiau, Hawaii)

Principal Investigator: Raymond D. Dillon, University of South Dakota, Vermillion, South Dakota.

Grant No. 879: In aid of grantee's studies of the ecology of isolated protozoan communities.

The immediate objective of this investigation was to study the microbiology of a highly select isolated alpine volcanic lake, Lake Waiau, in Hawaii (fig. 1), as an extension of the ongoing research on isolated melt-water lakes in Antarctica and elsewhere as related to the ecology and biogeography of Protozoa and their community structure. Additional objectives were to determine diatom diversity and note the interactions between populations of primary producers as affected by herbivorous zooplankton.

Lake Waiau is situated near the summit plateau of the inactive volcano Mauna Kea. It lies 13,020 feet above sea level and is undoubtedly one of the highest lakes in the United States. The body of water occupies a shallow crater, once a breached cinder cone deepened by glaciation. The surface area measures approximately 1.8 acres; maximum depth, about 10 feet. The lake is accessible by roads provided by the U.S. Geological Survey's Hawaiian Volcano Observatory, which helped to make the study at this location feasible. As we had anticipated, this tropical mid-Pacific mountain lake provided a living laboratory for our work. We concentrated on the physical and chemical characteristics of the lake and on phyto- and zooplankton analyses, collecting water, interface, and soil samples at two periods during the summer (June and August).

It is well known that Protozoa and other microorganisms occur almost everywhere from the depths of the ocean to the poles (Lackey, 1961; Murray, 1910; Penard, 1911; Dillon, 1967; and others), as well as in the atmosphere. It has been shown that the algae and protozoan content of the atmosphere frequently exceeds that of pollen grains during particular seasons (Brown et al., 1964).

The isolated work of Penard (1911) and the more recent studies of Schönborn (1966a, 1966b) indicate that the less-explored areas of the earth,

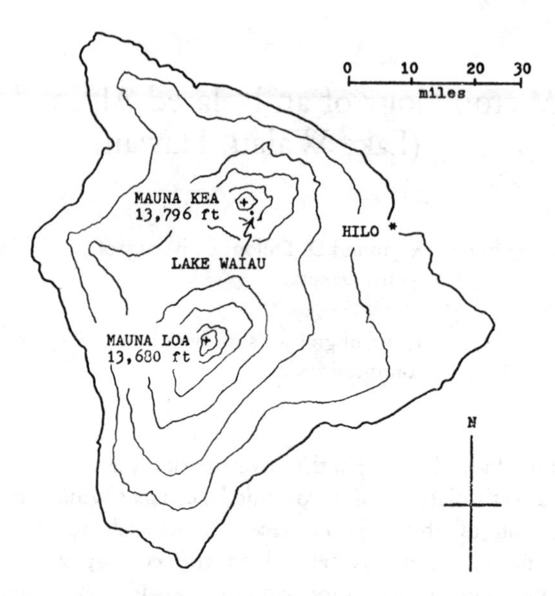

FIG. 1. Map of Hawaii showing location of Lake Waiau.

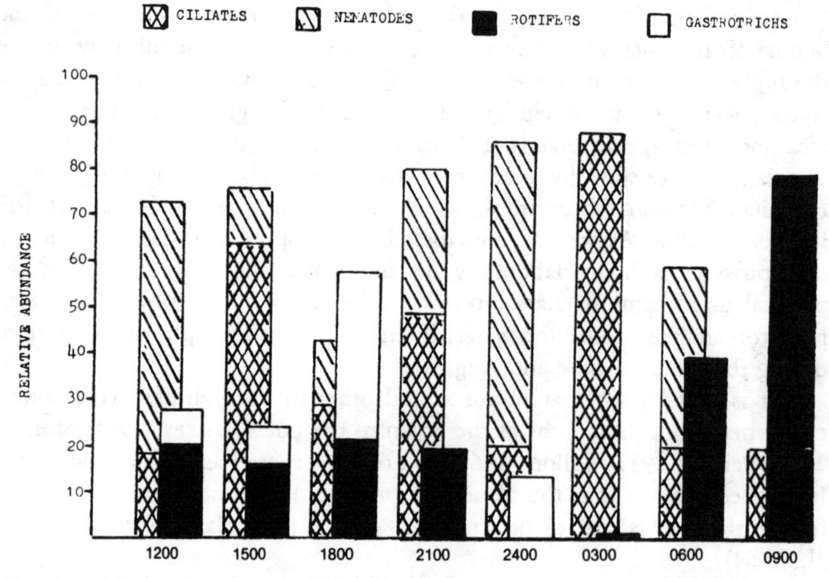

FIG. 2. Relative abundances of zooplankton in a 24-hour study for June 8–9, 1970, at bottom, Lake Waiau.

especially those where Protozoa are more restricted to specific habitats, offer a better research opportunity for exploring their ecological interactions. Hence, the selection of Lake Waiau for this study. The sediments of the lake indicate some evidence of annual layering of blue-green algae that might date back to Pleistocene time (Woodcock et al., 1966).

Specific volumes of surface-water and benthic samples were collected for planktonic and benthic microorganisms. Duplicate samples were fixed for enumeration and identification by means of a modified millipore slide method. We used a Hach DR colorimeter to study the chemical parameters of PO_4, SO_4, NO_3–N_3, NO_2–N, and NH_3–N and made separate tests for O_2, Ca^{++} temperature, and pH.

The nearly isothermal temperatures of Lake Waiau (Woodcock et al., 1966), near 6 °C., would characterize an environment similar to the summer temperatures of an Antarctic lake. The local climate is said to be cool and very dry and to support algal mats similar to those of Coast Lake and Cape Royds, Antarctica.

Population counts showed that algae doubled in number from June to August. Phytoplankton communities were dominated by the Chrysophyta genera *Fragilaria*, *Gomphonema*, *Navicula*, *Nitzchia*, and *Synedra*, by the Cyanophyta genus *Anabaena*, and by the Chlorophyta genus *Cosmarium*. The diatom *Navicula* was a more dominant phytoplankton component in late-summer waters, with *Fragilaria* decreasing in importance. The blue-green algae *Anabaena* was almost completely absent from August water samples. The phytoplankton community showed a decrease in diversity from June to August. Comparison of early to late zooplanktonic forms showed in June samples that ciliates and nematodes dominated while in the August samples rotifers and gastrotrichs dominated the zooplankton populations (fig. 2).

Two graduate students—Kenneth L. Kaswick and Larry L. Stefanick—carried out a substantial part of the collecting and analyses for this project. Indeed, this brief report is based in large part on Mr. Stefanick's detailed master's thesis (1973) at the University of South Dakota.

REFERENCES

BROWN, R. MALCOLM, JR.; LARSON, DONALD A.; and BOLD, HAROLD C.

1964. Airborne algae: Their abundance and heterogeneity. Science, vol. 143, pp. 583–585.

DILLON, RAYMOND D.

1967. The ecology of free-living and parasitic Protozoa of Antarctica. Antarctic Journ. United States, vol. 2, no. 4, pp. 104–105.

GREGORY, H., and WENTWORTH, CARL M.
1937. General features and glacial geology of Mauna Kea, Hawaii. Bull. Geol. Soc. America, vol. 48, pp. 1719–1742.
HART, E. E., and NEAL, M. C.
1940. The plant ecology of Mauna Kea, Hawaii. Ecology, vol. 21, no. 2, pp. 237–266.
LACKEY, J. B.
1961. Bottom sampling and environmental niches. Limmol. Oceanogr., vol. 6, pp. 271–279.
MACIOŁEK, J. A.
1969. Freshwater lakes in Hawaii. Verh. Int. Verein. Limnologie, vol. 17, pp. 386–391, illus.
MURRAY, JAMES
1910. On microscopic life at Cape Royds. Report on the Scientific Investigations, British Antarctic Expedition 1907–09, under the Command of Sir E. H. Shackleton, C.V.O., vol. 1 (Biology), pt. 2, pp. 17–22, illus.
PENARD, EUGÈNE
1911. Rhizopodes d'eau douce. Report on the Scientific Investigations, British Antarctic Expedition 1907–09, under the Command of Sir E. H. Shackleton, C.V.O., vol. 1 (Biology), pt. 6, pp. 203–262, illus.
PICKEN, L. E. R.
1937. The structure of some protozoan communities. Journ. Ecol., vol. 25, pp. 368–384.
SCHÖNBORN, WILFRIED
1966a. Beitrag zur Ökologie and Systematik der Testaceen Spitzbergens. Limnologica, vol. 4, pp. 463–470, illus.
1966b. Untersuchunger über die Testaceen Schwedisch-Lapplands. Ein Beitrag zur Systematik und Ökologie der beschalten Rhizopoden. Limnologica, vol. 4, pp. 517–559, illus.
SKOTTSBERG, C.
1931. Remarks on the flora of the high Hawaiian volcanoes. Acta Horti Gotlands, vol. 6 (1930), pp. 47–65.
STEFANICK, LARRY L.
1973. Summer succession of the micro organisms inhabitating Lake Waiau, Hawaii, 73 pp., illus. M.A. thesis, University of South Dakota.
WETZEL, R. G.
1964. A comparative study of the primary productivity of higher aquatic plants, periphyton, and phytoplankton in a large, shallow lake. Int. Rev. Hydrob., vol. 49, pp. 1–64.
WOODCOCK, ALFRED H.; RUBIN, MEYER; and DUCE, R. A.
1966. Deep layer of sediments in alpine lake in the tropical and mid-Pacific. Science, vol. 154, pp. 647–648. illus.

RAYMOND D. DILLON

Cretaceous Foraminifera from the Shatsky Rise, Western North Pacific Ocean

Principal Investigator: Robert G. Douglas, University of Southern California, Los Angeles, California.[1]

Grant No. 852: For a study of Jurassic and Cretaceous Foraminifera from the northwestern Pacific.

Until recently our inventory of Cretaceous fossils recovered from the deep sea was meager. Ordinary oceanographic sampling techniques of coring and dredging are unable to penetrate the thick veneer of younger Tertiary and Quaternary sediments that normally covers Cretaceous deposits. Outcroppings of pre-Tertiary strata on the seafloor are rare. Consequently, our knowledge about Cretaceous Foraminifera and other fossil organisms from the deep ocean was limited.

An extensive literature exists on Cretaceous Foraminifera based upon the study of outcrop or bore-hole samples collected on the continents. These deposits predominately represent two types of ancient environments: continental margins (shelf and perhaps upper slope) and shallow, interior seaways. Planktonic foraminiferal assemblages from continental margin environments and semi-land-locked seaways usually differ in species composition and diversity from those of oceanic areas. Likewise, benthic foraminiferal assemblages from such environments are composed of shallow-water species and are different from deep-sea assemblages. The existing literature on Cretaceous Foraminifera contains virtually no information on the nature of oceanic planktonic or benthic assemblages.

In 1968 the Deep Sea Drilling Project (DSDP) was created and developed capabilities for drilling and coring thick sections of sediments. For the first time it was possible to sample the oldest deposits beneath the sea floor. During

[1] Sincere thanks are extended to Mrs. Eva Topfl, Case Western Reserve University, who aided me in compiling the data contained in the tables and in preparing samples for isotopic analysis, and to Dr. Samuel M. Savin, in whose laboratory the oxygen and carbon isotope geochemical analyses were conducted. This article was written while I was in residence at Scripps Institution of Oceanography, La Jolla, California, and I gratefully acknowledge the use of their facilities.

DSDP Leg 6 of the R/V *Glomar Challenger*, Cretaceous sediments were cored at six sites in the western North Pacific Ocean (Fischer et al., 1971). Subsequently, Cretaceous deposits have been drilled at other localities in the Central Pacific during DSDP Legs 16 and 17 (van Andel et al., 1971; Winterer et al., 1971) (fig. 1). For the most part, the recovered cores are biogenous calcareous sediments, chalks, and limestones, which contain abundant and diverse foraminiferal faunas. A complete section of Cretaceous strata has not been recovered at any of the sites drilled to date, although a nearly complete section was obtained at site 167, on the Magellan Rise. Despite the incompleteness of our core coverage, and the fact that in some cases the core material is flawed by poor preservation, fossil material is available to study the paleoecology and paleobiogeography of Cretaceous Foraminifera in the Pacific.

With the aid of the National Geographic Society an investigation was begun in 1970 of the Cretaceous Foraminifera in the northwestern Pacific recovered during DSDP Leg 6. This investigation has since been expanded to include faunas from the central Pacific and south Atlantic Oceans and is still in progress. In the initial study, the available core material allowed the examination of two questions:

(1) What is the nature of Late Cretaceous planktonic foraminiferal assemblages from oceanic sediments and how do the assemblages differ from contemporaneous nearshore equivalents?

(2) How do Early Cretaceous Pacific benthic Foraminifera compare to contemporaneous assemblages in North America, the Atlantic Ocean, and Europe; what do the benthic assemblages suggest concerning the bathymetric and biogeographic distribution of Early Cretaceous benthic Foraminifera?

Materials

Planktonic Foraminifera of Maastrichtian age (about 65 to 70 million years B.P.) were studied from five cores taken at two drill sites, DSDP sites 47 and 48, located near the crest of the Shatsky Rise (lat. 32°W., long. 158°E.) in water depths of a little over 2,600 meters. At site 47, the Cretaceous-Tertiary boundary was encountered at 109.7-meter depth in the hole, and the hole was terminated owing to hard chert at 129.2 meters. At site 48, the Cretaceous was penetrated at about 58.5 meters and is overlain unconformably by the Miocene. The hole was also terminated because of hard chert, at 71.9 meters. The lithology at both sites is a very similar white chalk ooze with varying amounts of brown chert. Preliminary description of the planktonic assemblages is contained in Douglas (1971) and a discussion of the oxygen and carbon isotope and Mg geochemistry is contained in Douglas and Savin, 1971, 1973).

Benthonic Foraminifera of Barremian-Hauterivian age (about 110–120 million years B.P.) were studied from three cores taken at DSDP sites 49 and 50, situated on the western flank of the Shatsky Rise in depths of 4,282 and 4,487 meters, respectively. Four holes were drilled at the two sites in an attempt to sample the oldest sediments overlying the basaltic basement on the rise. Drilling difficulties developed when hard cherts prevented further penetration in all the holes; the sites were abandoned after recovering small quantities of soft, white chalk ooze and chert. Approximately 4 meters of sediment were recovered at site 49 and 2.7 meters at site 50.

Preliminary descriptions of the stratigraphy, lithology, and paleontology of the Shatsky Rise sites can be found in Fischer et al., 1971.

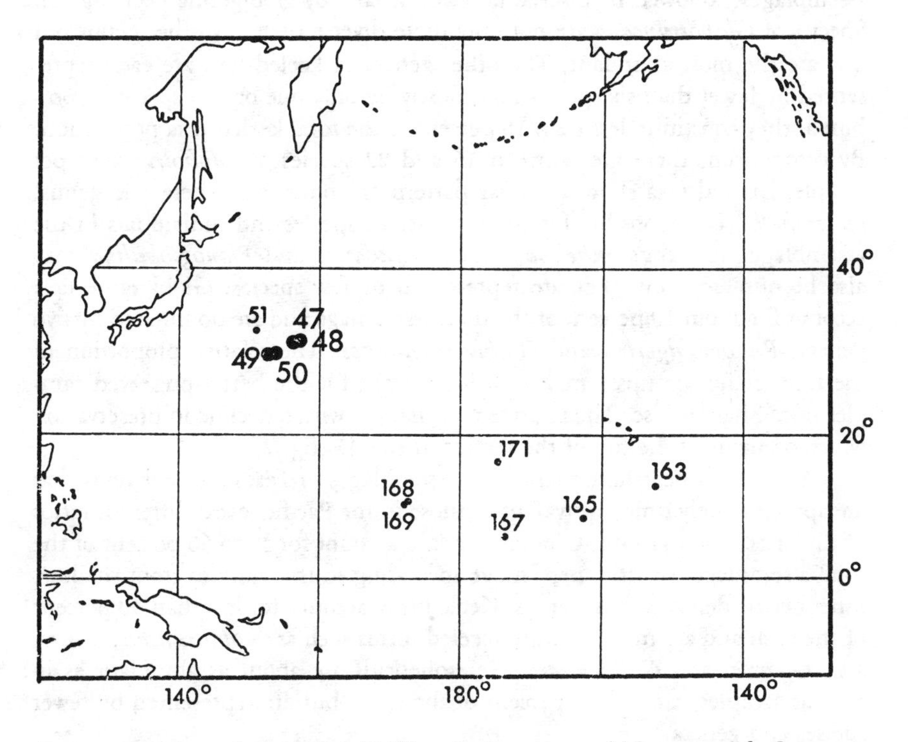

FIG. 1. Location of Deep-Sea Drilling Project sites which recovered Cretaceous Foraminifera. Sites 47 to 51 were drilled during Leg 6, Site 163 during Leg 16, and Sites 165 and 171 during Leg 17. Planktonic Foraminifera from Sites 47 and 48 and benthic Foraminifera from Sites 49 and 50 were investigated with the aid of NGS funds beginning in 1970. These faunas are discussed in the text.

Results

1. Planktonic Foraminiferal Assemblages

Late Cretaceous planktonic species can be grouped into three major morphologic categories that have broad taxonomic significance: globigerine taxa—species of *Rugoglobigerina* and *Globigerinelloides*; keeled taxa—species of *Globotruncana, Abathomphalus, Rugotruncana,* and *Globotruncanella*; biserial taxa—the Heterohelicidae, which in the Maastrichtian include species of *Heterohelix*, *Pseudoguembelina*, *Planoglobulina* (= *Ventilabrella* of some authors), *Pseudotextularia,* and *Racemiguembelina.*

In the samples examined from the Shatsky Rise, keeled taxa dominate assemblages, followed by biserial taxa and finally by globigerine taxa (fig. 2). Species of *Globotruncana* are not only more diverse than any other genus but also are the most abundant. The other genera of keeled taxa are each represented by fewer than six species and mostly by only one or two species. Combined, they constitute less than 10 percent of the total keeled taxa population. By comparison, there are between 16 and 22 species of *Globotruncana* per sample. Biserial taxa show a similar pattern of dominance where one genus, *Heterohelix*, is responsible for the majority of species and individuals in the assemblage. *Pseudoguembelina*, *Pseudotextularia*, and *Planoglobulina* may also be numerous but they are represented by few species. Globigerine taxa account for about 10 percent of the total assemblage and are dominated by two genera, *Rugoglobigerina* and *Globigerinelloides*. The relative proportion of the three major groups remains fairly constant for the better-preserved samples from Shatsky Rise. The relative mix changes with a decline in preservation which occurs near the top of the section at site 47 (fig. 2).

Analyses of nearshore planktonic assemblages in Texas and Arkansas that are approximately time-equivalent to those in the Pacific reveal different ratios of the three major groups. Globigerine taxa account for 40 to 60 percent of the total assemblage with the percentage increasing in the samples from shallow, inner neritic deposits in Arkansas. Keeled taxa account for less than 30 percent of the total and are mostly double-keeled forms such as *Globotruncana linneiana, G. arca*, and *G. fornicata*. Heterohelicids are about as abundant as in oceanic samples, around 25 percent of the total, but are represented by fewer species and genera.

The comparison suggests that the ratio of globigerine taxa to keeled taxa is related in part to the environmental differences between ancient oceanic and nearshore conditions, with the highest number and diversity of keeled taxa associated with oceanic conditions. *Rugoglobigerina* and *Globigerinelloides* and other globigerine taxa were apparently opportunistic species and better adapted to the more variable conditions of nearshore neritopelagic environments.

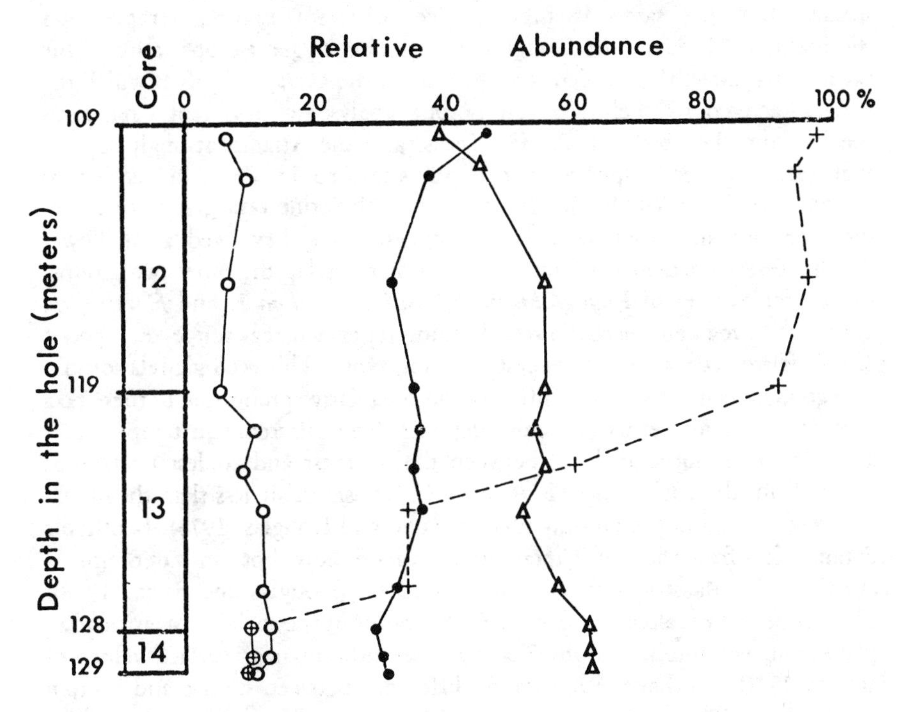

FIG. 2. Relative abundance of major groups of Maastrichtian planktonic Foraminifera and foraminiferal carbonate loss due to dissolution at DSDP Site 47. Globigerine species belong to *Rugoglobigerina* and *Globigerinelloides*. Keeled species include mainly *Globotruncana* and a few species of *Abathomphalus*, *Rugotruncana*, and *Globotruncanella*. Biserial, or heterohelicid species belong to *Heterohelix*, *Pseudoguembelina*, *Pseudotextularia*, *Racemiguembelina*, *Gublerina*, and *Planoglobulina*. The percent foraminiferal carbonate loss (L) due to dissolution of planktonic Foraminifera was estimated from the equation L = 100 $(1 - Ro/R)$ where *Ro* is the assumed original percentage of benthonic Foraminifera (0.2 percent) and R is the actual measured value. Where *R* is equal to or less than 0.2 percent, *L* was set as less than 10 percent.

Present-day planktonic Foraminifera tend to live at different depths in the water column ranging from near the surface to several hundred meters below the surface. An oxygen isotope paleotemperature analysis of different species from the same assemblage gives different isotopic temperatures (Emiliani, 1954; Savin and Douglas, 1973). The oxygen isotope ratios of the calcite tests reflect the ambient temperature at the average depth at which the species secreted its shell. Oxygen isotope analyses of different Cretaceous species from the northwest Pacific, Texas, and the Atlantic strongly suggest that Late Cretaceous species were depth stratified in a fashion similar to present-day species (table 1). The fact that globigerine taxa give warmer isotopic temperatures than keeled taxa suggests that they lived at shallower depths. Biserial taxa give a range of values that overlap the other two groups. In general, species of *Rugoglobigerina*, *Globigerinelloides,* and *Heterohelix* appear to have been the shallowest-dwelling types, whereas single-keel species of *Globotruncana* were the deepest-dwelling types. This ecologic relationship is in good agreement with the difference in the relative proportion of these taxa present in oceanic versus nearshore deposits. The difference in temperature, according to isotopic analysis, between the warmest and coldest Cretaceous species from the same sample is about 3 °C., considerably less than the 10 °C. difference found in present-day species (Savin and Douglas, 1973). Benthonic Foraminifera from the same Cretaceous samples indicate bottom-water temperatures in the Maastrichtian were around 12 °C. (Douglas and Savin, 1978). The temperatures calculated from the $0^{18}/_{16}$ ratios in the shells of Maastrichtian planktonic Foraminifera from Shatsky Rise indicate near surface values of around 23 °C., so that the minimum difference between surface and bottom temperatures 68 million years ago was 11 °C. or less than one-half that of the present-day in tropical regions. It is not surprising, therefore, that species living in the upper few hundred meters of the Maastrichtian ocean show small temperature differences as compared to Recent planktonic Foraminifera.

Although the ecologic model proposed for Cretaceous planktonic Foraminifera explains the major variation in species composition observed between oceanic and nearshore deposits, it fails to explain the considerable variation in relative species composition observed in some oceanic cores, and especially the peculiar assemblages composed almost solely of *Globotruncana*.

Studies of Recent planktonic Foraminifera show that an important phenomenon that alters species assemblages is the dissolution of calcium carbonate. Thin-walled, highly porous shells are selectively destroyed, relative to thick-walled, slightly less porous shells (Berger, 1967). This process begins as shells settle in the water column and continues after burial. Selective dissolution appears to be the primary agent in the destruction of Foraminifera

TABLE 1. OXYGEN ISOTOPE AND TEMPERATURE VALUES OF LATE MAASTRICHTIAN PLANKTONIC FORAMINIFERA (Values averaged for analyses from Deep Sea Drilling Project Sites 47 and 48.)

	Average δO^{18}	Average Dev.	Inferred T°C
Biserial taxa			
Pseudoguembelina costulata	− 1.36	.06	21.8
Heterohelix striata	− 1.04	.05	20.2
Pseudotextularia elegans	− 1.09	.06	20.3
Planorbulina multicamerata	− 0.59	.06	18.4
Globigerine taxa			
Rugoglobigerina rugosa	− 1.17	.05	20.8
Globotruncana fornicata	− 1.06	.07	20.2
Keeled taxa			
G. arca	− 0.95	.04	20.0
G. elevata	− 0.80	.10	19.4
G. stuartiformis	− 0.79	.07	19.3

ISOTOPIC TEMPERATURE RANKING OF MAASTRICHTIAN PLANKTONIC FORAMINIFERA

(Average ranking based on analyses from DSDP Sites 47, 48, 171, samples from Texas and Arkansas and Lamont-Doherty core RC-5-12; data from Douglas and Savin, 1978.)

		Depth Habitat
Globigerinelloides multispinata	↓ Decreasing Temperature	Shallow ↓
Pseudoguembelina costulata		
Rugoglobigerina rugosa		
Heterohelix striata		
Pseudotextularia elegans		
Globotruncana fornicata		
G. arca		
G. elevata		
G. stuartiformis		
Planoglobulina multicamerata		Deep

in deep-sea sediments and not only leads to the direct removal of shells but also contributes to breakage and fragmentation of shells (Berger, 1971).

Examination of the Cretaceous Foraminifera from the Shatsky Rise reveals: (1) clear evidence of dissolution of planktonic species, (2) that the effects are selective among species, (3) that selective solution has altered the original makeup of certain fossil assemblages, and (4) there is a predictable sequence to the relative susceptibility of different Cretaceous species to solution. The order of increasing resistance to dissolution among the major groups is as follows: globigerine taxa—biserial taxa—keeled taxa. There are exceptions, as certain species and even morphotypes within a species may be more resistant to dissolution than are similar-appearing fossils. The precise position any taxon holds in a solution ranking seems to depend upon a number of complex factors concerning its shell, including size, thickness of the wall, porosity of the shell, type of wall structure, degree and type of surface ornamentation, and shell chemistry (especially the amount of Mg in the shell). Other factors being equal, the chances of a shell being preserved are proportionally decreased the longer a shell is exposed on the seafloor before being buried, and the greater the thickness of sediment under which a shell is ultimately buried. Three stages can be recognized in the progressive dissolution of Cretaceous Foraminifera (table 2):

Stage 1: The first stages are a chalky appearance and the destruction of the initial chambers on the spiral side. Small holes appear in the first 4 or 5 chambers and grow in size until the entire spiral surface is destroyed.

Stage 2: Holes appear in other parts of the shell, and the weakened shell tends to fragment. Usually the last one or two chambers are separated from the rest of the shell.

Stage 3: In the final stage, the walls of the shell have been destroyed, and only a "skeleton" composed of the keel or marginal rim and the inner septa remain.

The changes in the relative proportion of the major groups in the upper part of cores 12 and 13 at site 47 (fig. 2) can be attributed in part to the effects of selective preservation. Only the microfossils in core 14 can be described as well preserved and have probably undergone minor loss due to dissolution. The enrichment of keeled species and thick-walled biserial taxa, such as is observed in core 12 at site 47, is due to the destruction of more readily dissolvable species, especially globigerine species. Assemblages which contain species in the final stage of preservation (stage 3) have suffered greater than 90 percent (destruction) of the original assemblage. It is clear that the selective preservation of Cretaceous planktonic Foraminifera is much more important than had previously been recognized in biasing fossil assemblages.

2. Early Cretaceous Benthonic Assemblages

During leg 6 of the Deep Sea Drilling Project, the first Early Cretaceous benthonic Foraminifera found in the Pacific Ocean were recovered from the basal beds on the Shatsky Rise. Initially the faunas were believed to be both Early Cretaceous and Late Jurassic in age, but subsequent study of the assemblages has shown them to be entirely Cretaceous (Hauterivian-Barremian) in age (Douglas and Moullade, 1972). Also, it is now clear that the sediments from which the Foraminifera were recovered have suffered at least a moderate amount of carbonate loss due to dissolution. Thus, the absence of planktonic Foraminifera and possibly of certain benthonic genera and the concentration of nodosariid taxa in the assemblages are due, in part, to selective preservation. Based on the taxa present in the assemblages from Sites 49 and 50, a comparison was made with contemporaneous benthic Foraminifera in North America (Canada and California), Trinidad, Europe, and the recently described assemblages from the Atlantic Ocean (Maync, 1973; Luterbacher, 1972). The major findings of this comparison can be summarized as follows:

1. Assemblages from the Shatsky Rise are most similar to the benthic faunas of northern Europe, next to the deep-sea faunas in the Central Pacific and North Atlantic, and least similar to those of Trinidad and California. There are very few taxa in common with the Early Cretaceous assemblages found in Arctic Canada.

2. There are no endemic taxa in either the Pacific or Atlantic deep-sea samples. Instead, deep-sea assemblages are composed primarily of widely distributed "cosmopolitan" genera. Of the 90 species identified from the Shatsky Rise, at least 80 were originally described from northern Europe. The degree of faunal resemblance at the species level is nearly as high with the assemblages in California and Trinidad.

3. The differences in general between deep-sea assemblages and those from localities in California, Trinidad, and Europe appear to be mainly due to the absence of bathymetrically restricted genera—such as miliolids and epistominellids (*Brotzenia*)—that are common in shallow epicontinental deposits and in the lower taxonomic diversity of deep-sea assemblages. The latter, in large part, may be due to sampling, as the 3-inch diameter cores of the Deep Sea Drilling Project limit the amount of material available for study.

4. The high degree of faunal affinity at the species level between assemblages from the Shatsky Rise, where the present water depth is greater than 4,400 meters, and the assemblages from northern Europe, that were deposited in shallow, epicontinental deposits or probably no more than a

TABLE 2. PRESERVATION OF MAASTRICHTIAN PLANKTONIC FORAMINIFERA IN THE NORTHWEST PACIFIC
(Modified from Douglas, 1971; n = specimens counted; all values given in percent.)

DSDP SITE 47		PRESERVATION STAGE					
		1		2		3	
			Pct. holes				
Sample	Total count	Chalky appearance to test	Initial chambers	Adult chambers	Pct. test broken	Rims only	Pct.[a] foram carbonate loss
47.2-12.1, top	(n = 378)						97
Keel	46.00%	++	49	11	34	+	
Globigerine	7.00%	++	7	4	19		
Heterohelicid	40.00%	++	39	—	59		
Benthonic	6.00%	++	+	—	12		
47.2-12-2, 7-9	(n = 445)						95
Keel	38.00	++	50	8	31	+	
Globigerine	10.00	++	7	2	33	+	
Heterohelicid		++	56				
Benthonic	4.00		+	5	28		
47.2-12-4, 145-150	(n = 419)						97
Keel	54.00	++	50	2	48		
Globigerine	7.00	++	10	7	17		
Heterohelicid	31.00	++	44	20	33		
Benthonic	6.00		—	11	29		
47.2-12, core catcher	(n = 404)						92
Keel	54.00	++	51	18	29		
Globigerine	6.00	++	4	—	22		
Heterohelicid	++	44	—	56			
Benthonic	2.50		+	—	33		
47.2-13-1, 145-150	(n = 510)						50
Keel	52.00	++	8	6	20		
Globigerine	11.00	++	2	1	12		
Heterohelicid	37.00	++	61	—	20		
Benthonic	0.40		—	—	—		

47.2-13-3, 6-8	(n = 597)					60
Keel	55.00	+	2	7	15	
Globigerine	9.00		—	—	7	
Heterohelicid	35.00		48	1	41	
Benthonic	0.50		—	—	—	
47.2-13-4, top	(n = 372)					34
Keel	52.00	+	4	4	11	
Globigerine	12.00		—	6	15	
Heterohelicid	36.00		67	3	20	
Benthonic	0.30		—	—	—	
47.2-13-5, 145-150	(n = 542)					34
Keel	57.00	+	6	8	14	
Globigerine	12.00		2	9	14	
Heterohelicid	31.00		61	2	22	
Benthonic	0.30		—	—	+	
47.2-13, core catcher	(n = 380)					<10
Keel	61.00	+	5	10	10	
Globigerine	13.00		2	5	7	
Heterohelicid	26.00		55	3	26	
Benthonic	0.2		—	+	—	
47.2-14.4, 145-150	(n = 548)					<10
Keel	61.00		2	6	18	
Globigerine	11.00		—	3	5	
Heterohelicid	28.00		55	5	33	
Benthonic	0.10		—	—	—	
47.2-14, core catcher	(n = 393)					<10
Keel	62.00		5	9	15	
Globigerine	7.00		—	—	7	
Heterohelicid	31.00		60	2	20	
Benthonic	0.20		—	—	—	

[a] Calculated from the equation L = 100(1-Ro/R) where Ro is the assumed original component of benthonic Foraminifera and R is the measured percentage. Ro was assumed as 0.2%. When the measured benthonic component was ≤ 0.2%, L was arbitrarily set as < 10%.

few hundred meters in depth, requires one of two possible explanations:

(a) If we assume that the western flank of the Shatsky Rise has undergone no bathymetric change since the Cretaceous, then it would require that Cretaceous benthonic species have very broad bathymetric ranges. Species must have extended over at least 4,000 meters of depth—which no modern benthic species can match. However, this explanation fails to explain why deep-sea assemblages from the Atlantic Ocean, which are geographically much closer to northern Europe, are more similar to Pacific deep-sea assemblages and those from deeper water deposits in France and Trinidad. The bathymetric range of Early Cretaceous benthic species appears to have been greater than for either Late Cretaceous or Tertiary Foraminifera, but shallow-water and deep-water assemblages are distinctly different—even in the Hauterivian-Barremian.

(b) However, if we assume that the Shatsky Rise has subsided several thousand meters since the Early Cretaceous, the faunal similarity with northern Europe can be easily accounted for. This explanation suggests that in the Early Cretaceous the Shatsky Rise had a bathymetry similar to the epicontinental deposits of northern Europe and that the faunal resemblance is a reflection of similar benthic environments. The faunal differences between the Shatsky Rise and coeval deep-sea assemblages from the central Pacific and North Atlantic would be due to differences in paleodepth between these localities in the Early Cretaceous.

Other lines of evidence support this argument. Sclater, Anderson, and Bell (1971) have shown that oceanic crust moves into progressively deeper water with increasing age. Using their age-seafloor depth curve and the back-tracking paleodepth technique of Berger and von Rad (1972), we can reconstruct the depth of the Shatsky Rise for any moment in geologic time since its origin. By this method, the depth of the western flank would have been around 800 meters in the Hauterivian-Barremian. This is in good agreement with estimates of the paleodepth of epicontinental deposits in Europe.

The paleobathymetry of the benthonic assemblages and geophysical evidence suggest that Shatsky Rise has subsided over 3,400 meters in the past 115 million years.

5. Early Cretaceous benthic species had remarkably broad geographic distributions in low and middle latitudes. Many of the same species can be found in the western Pacific, California, Trinidad, Europe, and Russia. There is no evidence of the provinciality that characterizes Indo-Pacific and Atlantic-Mediterranean faunas in the Late Cretaceous and Tertiary. Apparently east-west migration was unrestricted in the circumequatorial Tethyan sea. There is, however, evidence of north-south faunal boundaries. Assemblages from

the western Pacific differ from species and generic assemblages found in Arctic Canada and western Siberia. Unfortunately, there are no Southern Hemisphere localities for comparison.

Summary

The initial study of Cretaceous Foraminifera from deep-sea cores in the western North Pacific was aimed primarily at examining the paleoecology of Maastrichtian planktonic species and Hauterivian-Barremian benthic species.

Oxygen isotope analyses of different species of Maastrichtian Foraminifera from the same assemblage yield different isotopic temperatures. The data indicate that species lived at different depths—as do present-day planktonic species. In the Cretaceous, as in the modern ocean, globigerine species appear to have lived near the surface whereas species with globorotaliid shapes and keeled margins lived at greater depths, probably down to several hundred meters. As a result, globigerine taxa such as *Rugoglobigerina* and *Globigerinelloides* dominate fossil assemblages from shallow, continental margin and interior seaway deposits. In oceanic deposits, where depth was not a restricting factor, both globigerine and keeled taxa are common and abundant. However, selective dissolution tends to remove globigerine taxa preferentrially in relation to keeled taxa. The greater susceptibility of globigerine species to dissolution seems to be related to the fact that on the average species of *Archaeoglobigerina, Globigerinelloides,* and *Rugoglobigerina* have thinner walls and a higher test porosity (i.e., number of pores per unit area) than do species of *Globotruncana, Abathomphalus, Rugotruncana*, or *Globotruncanella*. However, there are notable exceptions to the rule. A preliminary analysis of shell geochemistry suggests susceptibility is related to the amount of Mg contained in the shell. It is worth noting that there is a link between a species ecology and its relative susceptibility to dissolution. Shallow-dwelling species are in general the most easily dissolved; deeper-dwelling species are the most resistant to dissolution. Selective preservation tends to impose a systematic bias on fossil assemblages. The effects of dissolution are not random as might be supposed.

The recognition that Cretaceous planktonic species were depth stratified should improve our understanding of the biogeography and biostratigraphy of this major group of fossil plankton. It seems likely that depth stratification has played an important role in the evolutionary development of the group.

Early Cretaceous benthic assemblages in the western Pacific were composed of cosmopolitan genera and species and so far no endemic deep-sea taxa have been identified. The assemblages from the Shatsky Rise are most like species assemblages found in shallow, epicontinental deposits in northern Europe rather than other deep-sea assemblages. The resemblance probably reflects the similar bathymetric environments of these distant localities and suggests that water depths over the Shatsky Rise in the Hauterivian-Barremian was less than 1,000 meters. Shatsky Rise has subsided over 3,400 meters in the past 110–115 million years. The fact that many Early Cretaceous species have wide geographic distributions and narrow stratigraphic ranges makes them attractive potential tools for age dating and correlation in deep-sea deposits.

REFERENCES

BERGER, WOLFGANG H.

1967. Foraminiferal ooze: Solution at depths. Science, vol. 156, pp. 383–385.

1971. Sedimentation of planktonic Foraminifera. Marine Geol., vol. 2, pp. 325–358, charts.

BERGER, WOLFGANG H., and VON RAD, ULRICH

1972. Cretaceous and Cenozoic sediments from the Atlantic Ocean. Initial Reports of the Deep Sea Drilling Project, vol. 14, pp. 787–954, illus. National Science Foundation.

DOUGLAS, ROBERT G.

1971. Cretaceous Foraminifera from the northwestern Pacific Ocean: Leg 6, Deep Sea Drilling Project. Initial Reports of the Deep Sea Drilling Project, vol. 6. pp. 1027–1053, illus. National Science Foundation.

1973. Planktonic foraminiferal biostratigraphy in the central North Pacific Ocean. Initial Reports of the Deep Sea Drilling Project, vol. 17, pp. 673–694, illus. National Science Foundation.

DOUGLAS, ROBERT G., and MOULLADE, MICHEL

1972. Age of the basal sediments on the Shatsky Rise, western North Pacific Ocean. Bull. Geol. Soc. Amer., vol. 83, pp. 1163–1184, illus.

DOUGLAS, ROBERT G., and SAVIN, SAMUEL M.

1971. Isotopic analyses of planktonic Foraminifera from the Cenozoic of the Northwest Pacific: Leg 6. Initial Reports of the Deep Sea Drilling Project, vol. 6, pp. 1123–1129. National Science Foundation.

1973. Oxygen and carbon isotope analyses of Cretaceous and Tertiary Foraminifera from the central North Pacific. Initial Reports of the Deep Sea Drilling Project, vol. 17, pp. 591–605, illus. National Science Foundation.

1978. Depth distribution in Tertiary and Cretaceous planktonic Foraminifera based on oxygen isotope analyses. Marine Micropaleont., vol. 3, no. 2 (in press).

EMILIANI, CESARE

1954. Depth habitats of some species of pelagic Foraminifera as indicated by oxygen isotope ratios. Amer. Journ. Sci., vol. 252, no. 2, pp. 149–158.

FISCHER, ALFRED G.; HEEZEN, BRUCE C.; BOYCE, ROBERT E.; BUKRY, DAVID; DOUGLAS, ROBERT G.; GARRISON, ROBERT E.; KLING, STANLEY A.; KRASHENINNIKOV, VALERI; LISITZIN, ALEXANDRA P.; and PIMM, ANTHONY C.

1971. Initial Reports of the Deep Sea Drilling Project, vol. 6, 1,329 pp., illus. National Science Foundation. (Whole volume.)

LUTERBACHER, HANSPETER

1972. Foraminifera from the Lower Cretaceous and Upper Jurassic of the Northwestern Atlantic. Initial Reports of the Deep Sea Drilling Project, vol. 11, pp. 561–593, illus. National Science Foundation.

MAYNC, WOLF

1973. Lower Cretaceous foraminiferal fauna from Gorringe Bank, eastern North Atlantic. Initial Reports of the Deep Sea Drilling Project, vol. 13, pt. 2, pp. 1075–1111, illus. National Science Foundation.

SAVIN, SAMUEL M., and DOUGLAS, ROBERT G.

1973. Stable isotope and magnesium geochemistry of Recent Foraminifera from the South Pacific. Bull. Geol. Soc. Amer., vol. 84, pp. 2327–2342.

SCLATER, JOHN G.; ANDERSON, ROGER N.; and BELL, M. LEE

1971. Elevation of ridges and evolution of the Central Eastern Pacific. Journ. Geophys. Res., vol. 76, pp. 7888–7915, charts and maps.

VAN ANDEL, TJEERD; HEATH, G. ROSS; BENNETT, RICHARD H.; CHARLESTON, SANTIAGO; CRONAN, DAVID S.; RODOLFO, KELVIN S.; YEATS, ROBERT S.; BUKRY, J. DAVID; DINKELMAN, MENNO G.; and KANEPS, ANSIS G.

1973. Initial Reports of the Deep Sea Drilling Project, vol. 16, 949 pp., illus. National Science Foundation. (Whole volume.)

WINTERER, EDWARD L.; RIEDEL, WILLIAM R.; BRÖNNIMANN, PAUL; GEALY, ELIZABETH L.; HEATH, G. ROSS; KROENKE, LOREN; MARTINI, ERLEND; MOBERLY, RALPH, JR.; RESIG, JOHANNA; and WORMSLEY, THOMAS

1971. Initial Reports of the Deep Sea Drilling Project, vol. 7, 1,757 pp. illus. National Science Foundation. (Whole volume.)

ROBERT G. DOUGLAS

A Field Study of the Thick-tailed Bushbaby *Galago crassicaudatus* (Primates: Lorisidae) in South Africa

Principal Investigators: Gerald A. Doyle and Simon K. Bearder, University of Witwatersrand, Johannesburg, South Africa.

Grant No. 851: In support of a study of aspects of the ecology and behavior of the thick-tailed bushbaby.

In recent years considerable interest has been shown in the social behavior of primates. An increasing number of field studies illustrate a great diversity of basically different social systems and many variations on each theme. Studies of diurnal monkeys, apes, and some lemurs of Madagascar naturally preceded those concerned with the generally smaller nocturnal species, but the development of relatively simple methods of observing animals at night has altered this bias. A number of field studies of nocturnal lemurs and lorisids (bushbabies and lorises) have now been undertaken, among which those of J. J. Petter and R. D. Martin working in Madagascar and P. Charles-Dominique in Gaboon deserve particular mention.

Our own interest in nocturnal prosimian primates began in 1964 with a laboratory investigation of social behavior in the lesser bushbaby (*Galago senegalensis*). This species breeds freely in captivity. When they are housed in large enclosures and illuminated with red light it is possible to observe their behavior in detail from behind one-way mirrors, but the freedom of the subjects to come or go, or to associate with particular companions, is largely determined by the restraints of captivity. A field study of this species was therefore instigated in 1968 with the aid of a grant from the National Geographic Society (see Doyle and Bearder, 1976) and followed up in 1970 by a study of ecology and behavior in the thick-tailed bushbaby (*Galago crassicaudatus*), the only other southern African representative of the family Lorisidae, which forms the subject of this report.

Studies of social behavior in relation to ecology have indicated that social functioning is but one of a number of behavioral systems adapted to meet the varied demands of the environment. A particular social system may not only result from inheritance of a common behavioral repertoire set by the genotype but may also reflect a molding of behavior in the developing individual as it conforms to constraints within the social milieu into which it is born. In either case the behavior observed will often appear to be species-typical, but, where a species has been studied in a number of habitat types, it has been demonstrated that social functioning may vary from one to the next with respect to the availability of particular resources (food, sleeping places, cover). Contemporaneous etho-ecological studies of related prosimians can therefore provide a natural background for the interpretation of social behavior in species generally considered to have remained most similar to the earliest primates. Furthermore, interspecific comparisons of behavior can help to clarify their taxonomic affinities and to indicate possible evolutionary trends.

Study Areas and Methods

The single most important factor in the study of behavior in a nocturnal species, in the absence of radiotracking, is to find a locality where the vegetation is sufficiently open to allow prolonged observation. Dense forests are the preferred habitats of *G. crassicaudatus*, but the range of the species extends along tracts of riverine vegetation into timber plantations, and even into open woodland, where the animals can be followed more easily. A small population of bushbabies was discovered in an isolated patch of riverine forest on the farm of Mr. and Mrs. P. G. McNeil in the northeastern Transvaal. Regular sightings were made of an adult female, her two consecutive sets of infants (two males and three females), and a large adult male with which they associated during a period of 15 months from the beginning of April 1970. A total of 411 hours was spent watching one or another of these individuals, all of which were captured and marked distinctively during the course of the study.

For comparative purposes observations were also made on the same subspecies (*G. c. umbrosus*) in a region adjoining the main study site; on a second subspecies (*G. c. lönnbergi*) on the farm of Mr. and Mrs. J. Wylie near Umtali, Rhodesia; and on a third (*G. c. garnetti*) in the dense temperate and dune forests of Eshowe and Mtunzini in Zululand, falling under the control of Ranger R. E. Webster of the Natal Parks Board. Data from these areas are drawn from a total of 252 hours of direct observation on animals that could seldom be recognized individually.

In a resonably open environment bushbabies can be followed at any time of night, irrespective of the weather conditions or the state of the moon, by means of red light from a head-band torch. A red celluloid filter is simply mounted in front of a hunter's lamp powered by a 6-volt motorcycle accumulator battery in preference to dry cells. This will provide a strong beam of light for up to 20 hours before it need be recharged. Red light has the dual advantage that it neither disturbs the animals nor ruins the night vision of the observer, but a white light can be usefully employed when the need arises. The brilliant reflections from the bushbabies' eyes, their frequent vocalizations, and the noise of their movements facilitate their observation for several hours at a time, while under ideal conditions it is possible to remain in contact with a single animal throughout the night. It is often most instructive to follow a bushbaby back to its sleeping place at dawn and again when it leaves that sleeping place on the following evening.

Results

The results of this study form the basis of a doctoral thesis submitted to the University of the Witwatersrand, Johannesburg. Particular attention was paid to a comparison with the lesser bushbaby, which, it has been noted, is the only other lorisid species that ranges far beyond the tropical forest zone of central Africa and that is found together with *G. crassicaudatus* in some areas. Some etho-ecological characteristics of only the latter species are considered briefly below.

The southern races of *G. crassicaudatus* are the largest of the living Lorisidae, attaining a maximum weight of 1,800 grams. The subspecific classification remains in a state of some confusion, but 11 races are at present recognized, extending from just north of the Equator (southern Somalia) through Kenya, Uganda, and other countries of east and southern Africa to a point south of Durban in Natal. To the west the species is reported to be widespread in Malawi, central and eastern Rhodesia, and western Zambia but sparse in western Rhodesia. The animals are apparently found also in eastern and southern regions of Zaire, extending westward to the coast of Angola south of Luanda. They are absent from Botswana and South-West Africa apart from the Caprivi Strip.

G. crassicaudatus is found at various altitudes and is tolerant of marked seasonal and diurnal variations in temperature. Estimates of population densities indicate that these bushbabies are most abundant in high-rainfall, humid forest areas where there are many trees bearing fleshy fruits. This species, unlike its central African relatives, does not confine its activities to a particular zone of the forest and shows little preference for one type of support, but its movements vary to suit the nature of the vegetation. *G. crassicaudatus* requires dense cover for sleeping purposes and is extremely wary before descending onto the ground, but observed differences in the pattern of movements in a variety of habitats indicate that the height or density of the vegetation is not the most important factor that controls the distribution of the species. In eastern Rhodesia bushbabies were frequently seen to cover distances of up to 100 meters along the ground or to forage there for periods of 15 minutes at a time.

G. crassicaudatus is strictly nocturnal. The animals leave cover after sunset and return before sunrise at times dependent upon the level of light intensity beneath the trees. They usually remain completely hidden during the day and are extremely unwilling to move. Their nocturnal activity follows a broadly bimodal pattern, with periods of rest tending to increase toward midnight. Initial "toilet" activities are usually followed by a rapid and direct progression to a familiar food tree (or trees), and this sequence is reversed shortly before dawn. Long spells spent in a single tree are often followed by sudden movement through several trees, which can be related to the use of, and movement between, well-used food trees or resting places. Certain behaviors show quantitative variations from one season to the next. For example, more time is spent foraging during winter than in summer when bouts of grooming, play, rest, and sleep increase to a maximum.

Fruits and gum represent the staple diet of *G. crassicaudatus* in the main study area, but seeds, nectar, and insects also are consumed. Moisture may occasionally be licked from leaves, but otherwise these bushbabies have not been seen to drink. Gum is extremely important to them in winter when soft fruits are unavailable. Particular gum licks appear to be well known to the animals, which regularly move directly to these spots from a considerable distance. Gum is licked from wounds in the bark of *Acacia* trees in particular, but the bark can be chewed away slightly to expose more gum for licking. A number of characteristic gum-licking postures may be assumed, which enable bushbabies to reach gum in the most inaccessible places.

Continuous exploration ensures that small new sources of food are not missed, but there are indications that large sources are smelled from a distance (trees in fruit or flower). The animals, thereafter, return to a food tree for as long as it remains productive. Predation on birds and other small vertebrates has often been reported for *G. crassicaudatus*, but all evidence points to the fact that it is not a universal characteristic of the species. It appears to be a local habit that, once learned, may spread within one population while being absent from another nearby.

Bushbabies (subfamily Galaginae) are universally recognized for their leaping abilities aided by the elongated hindlimbs. *G. crassicaudatus* individuals are capable of jumping up to 2 meters between trees without losing height, or they may leap downward through 5 meters, covering a horizontal distance of 3 meters, but the over-all pattern of their locomotion differs from that of other galagines and is in many ways similar to that of the slow-moving lorises (subfamily Lorisinae). Despite morphological specializations that suit an active leaping mode of progression, this species is behaviorally adapted to a slower quadrupedal gait. The slow movement of the lorises has been interpreted by Charles-Dominique as being a strategy of "preventative defence." Undoubtedly the quiet and stealthy movements often employed by *G. crassicaudatus* enable them also to avoid detection by potential predators, but nevertheless they are still capable of rapid escape. The apparent compromise that is seen here may be considered as being a result of a relatively recent secondary, behavioral adaptation toward life in a "dense forest" environment, which has not been matched by skeletal changes. It is assumed that the ancestral form was better adapted to more open conditions and that similarities between the locomotion of *G. crassicaudatus* and, for example, the potto (*Perodicticus potto*) merely reflect convergent adaptation.

G. crassicaudatus makes use of a number of sleeping places during the day, providing concealment and direct protection from predators and extremes of temperature. Nest-building was infrequent in the main study area, but leafy nests were found during the breeding season when young infants most require a suitable support. The offspring may be afforded additional protection from predators at this time by their mother's habit of moving them from one sleeping place to another.

All births occur within a single period of approximately three weeks at the start of the rainy season (November), when food and dense cover is readily available. Twins are most common, but triplets and a singleton have also been recorded. The infants are generally weaned before the onset of the dry winter months. Mating is restricted to a short period in midwinter when, judged from vocalizations, it is accompanied by a general increase in the level of excitability within a population.

The majority of primates are gregarious, with cohesive groups containing more than one adult. Such groups are not found among the nocturnal prosimians. A relatively solitary or dispersed social system is common to all species so far studied. The spatial distribution of adults is largely maintained by indirect communication (olfaction, vocalizations), but this does not exclude direct social contact between particular individuals on a regular basis.

G.c. umbrosus sleeps either alone or in small groups of up to six animals, the composition of which may vary from one day to the next. Such sleeping habits are typical of nocturnal prosimians. At night the members of a sleeping group generally go their separate ways and may or may not come together again the following morning. An examination of social dynamics and the mother/offspring relationship within the isolated population serves to illustrate the nature of associations between individual *G. crassicaudatus*, which differ somewhat from the normal pattern.

In this species small groups are regularly seen foraging together at night. It is the female and her offspring of one generation that move as a cohesive unit, while mature animals usually move alone. Infants are confined to a nest or similar retreat for most of their first three weeks of life, but thereafter, even when they are too small to follow the mother, she will carry them with her at night. In contrast to small-bodied bushbabies that "park" their infants for long periods in order to continue their activities unencumbered, "infant parking" by *G. crassicaudatus* is infrequent. Either the infants are carried one at a time in the mother's mouth (in the characteristic manner of smaller bushbabies) or they cling to the fur of her back, or both. A close association between a mother and her young persists until they are at least subadult (± 300 days). Adult bushbabies may occasionally join a maternal group and move with it for varying periods without any signs of serious hostility, and even larger nocturnal groupings can be formed through attraction to a particular food source.

In the main study population the single adult male moved over a wider range than the female and offspring, which utilized an annual home range of 7 hectares. The maternal group spent most time in a central "core area" containing many sleeping sites, food trees, and resting places, yet covering only 4 percent of the total range. The male made use of the same "fixed points," covering at least 80 percent of the range of the female and young, but he frequented a different core area. *G. crassicaudatus*, like many other primate species, shows little in the way of active territorial defence but individuals remain attached to a single range for long periods, while much of their behavior maintains cohesion between familiar individuals, dispersal of maturing offspring, and separation between rivals.

It has been noted that prosimian primates generally make more extensive use of the olfactory channel of communication than their simian relatives. *G. crassicaudatus* performs six marking or rubbing actions: urine washing of the hands and feet; rhythmic micturition directly onto a support; foot rubbing; chest rubbing; anogenital rubbing; and head or mouth rubbing. The significance of many of these actions is hard to demonstrate, but the situations in which they are performed suggest that they aid spacing and contact within a dispersed population.

Scent marks may persist through time but give litle indication of the exact whereabouts of their authors. This result is achieved through numerous vocalizations, one of which is particularly well adapted for long range vocal advertising, apparently carrying information concerning the identity of the caller. Several calls are made in alarm situations and in the avoidance or maintenance of direct contact. In these respects the vocalizations of *G. crassicaudatus* are better developed for use in a "group" context than those of the closely related and more solitary *G. senegalensis*. In addition, the prolonged association between the female and her young ensures that they groom one another and play together on a regular basis, and this tendency persists into adulthood. Such behaviors represent strong cohesive forces. Social tension during encounters is therefore mild and fighting is rare.

G. crassicaudatus in South Africa is protected by law, and capture of these animals as pets or for use as food is minimal. Their role in biomedical research is also limited at present, but they can and should be bred in captivity when the need arises. Undoubtedly the most damaging influence on bushbaby populations is the destruction of their habitat through fire or development schemes. Fortunately a number of government-protected forest reserves still remain where bushbabies thrive, and owing to their secretive nocturnal habits they frequently avoid direct, and usually detrimental, contact with man.

REFERENCES

BEARDER, SIMON K., and DOYLE, GERALD A.

1974. Ecology of bushbabies, *Galago senegalensis* and *Galago crassicaudatus,* with some notes on their behaviour in the field. Pp. 109–130 *in* "Prosimian Biology," 938 pp., illus., R. D. Martin, G. A. Doyle, and A. C. Walker, eds. Gerald Duckworth & Co., London, and University of Pittsburgh Press.

CHARLES-DOMINIQUE, PIERRE

1971. Eco-éthologie des presimiens du Gabon. Biol. Gabonica, vol. 7, pp. 121–128.

CHARLES-DOMINIQUE, PIERRE, and MARTIN, ROBERT D.

1970. Evolution of lorises and lemurs. Nature, vol. 227, pp. 257–260.

DOYLE, GERALD A., and BEARDER, SIMON K.

1976. Field studies of the lesser bushbaby, 1968–1969. Nat. Geogr. Soc. Res. Rpts., 1968 Projects, pp. 69–74.

EISENBERG, JOHN F.; MUCHENHIRN, N. A.; and RUDRAN, R.

1972. The relation between ecology and social structure in primates. Science, vol. 176, pp. 863–874.

GERALD A. DOYLE
SIMON K. BEARDER

The Shape of Geographos and Other Asteroids

Principal Investigators: J. L. Dunlap and Tom Gehrels, Lunar and Planetary Laboratory, Tucson, Arizona.

Grant Nos. 885, 924: To study the shapes of asteroids by comparing the lightcurves of laboratory models to telescopically observed lightcurves of asteroids.

Tens of thousands of asteroids compose the intermediate-sized objects in our solar system. The diameters of nearly 2,000 catalogued asteroids range from 1,000 kilometers to about 10 kilometers. The origin of these objects and their relationship to meteorites and comets have stimulated lively debate, especially because it is becoming feasible to explore the solar system by spacecraft in order to seek clues to its origin and history. What events from the distant past are recorded in the shape, composition, and motion of the asteroids? Are they primordial accretions from the condensed solar nebula? Are they collision fragments from a few large original bodies? Or are they a mixture of both? Studies of the lightcurves of asteroids is one method of obtaining information needed to answer these questions.

The periodic fluctuations in the brightness of an asteroid was first noticed in the case of (443) Eros in 1900. Using visual and photographic techniques, astronomers constructed lightcurves of Eros with a period of 5^h 16^m and an amplitude up to 1.5 magnitudes. This was interpreted as due to the rotation of Eros, and it stimulated theoretical investigation on the problem of whether the light variation was due to an irregular shape or to a distribution of spots over the surface. Van den Bos and Finsen (1931) observed Eros visually in 1931 and reported seeing a nonspherical image rotating with a period of 5^h 16^m. Roach and Stoddard (1938) assumed Eros to have the shape of a 3-axis ellipsoid and calculated its dimensions to be 35 by 16 by 7 kilometers.

In the 1950's, Kuiper initiated a survey of asteroid lightcurves using more precise photoelectric techniques. This work was continued at the Lunar and Planetary Laboratory. Photometric lightcurves have now been obtained for over 50 asteroids. However, little is known about the detailed shape of most of these objects. Only in the past few years have indirect techniques been developed to obtain reliable estimates of even their diameters.

Asteroid (1620) Geographos came within 9.3 million kilometers of Earth

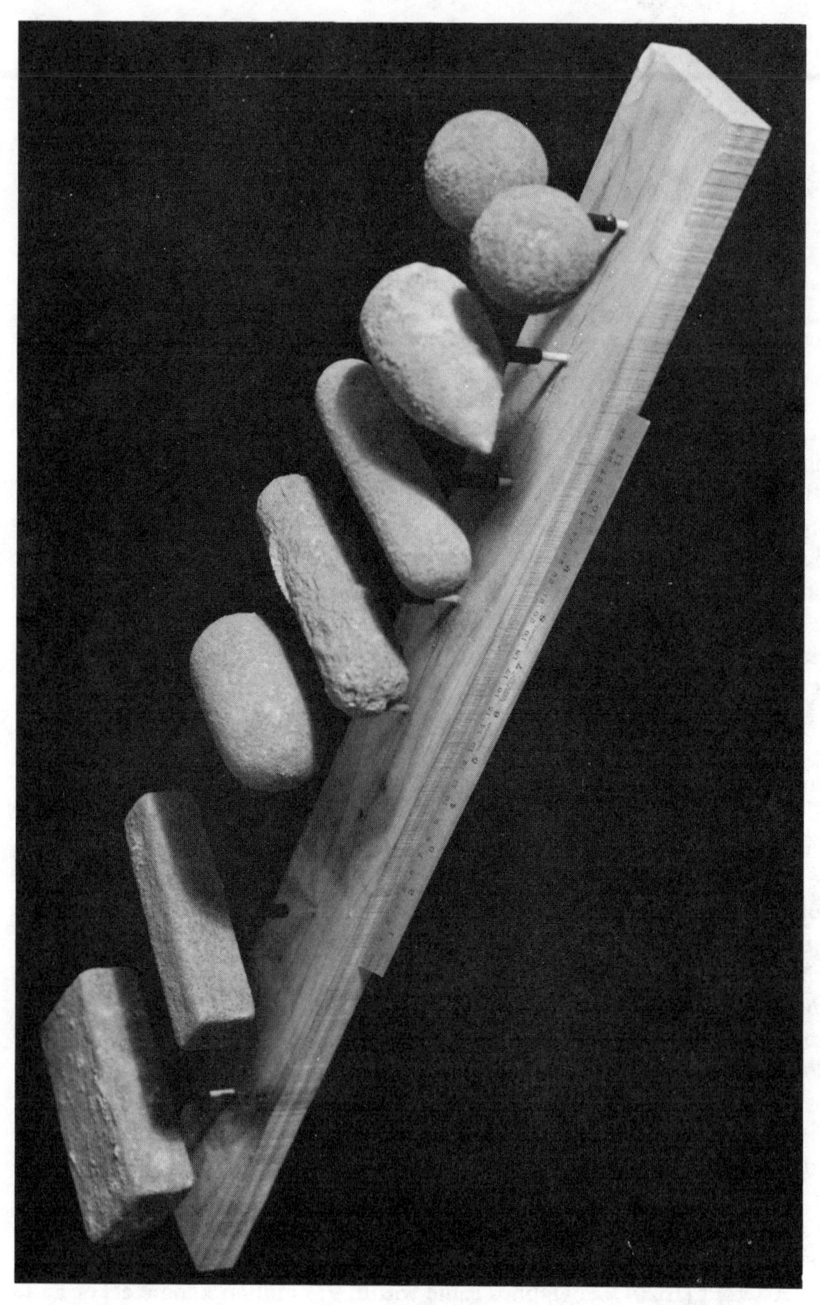

FIG. 1. A sample of some early models.

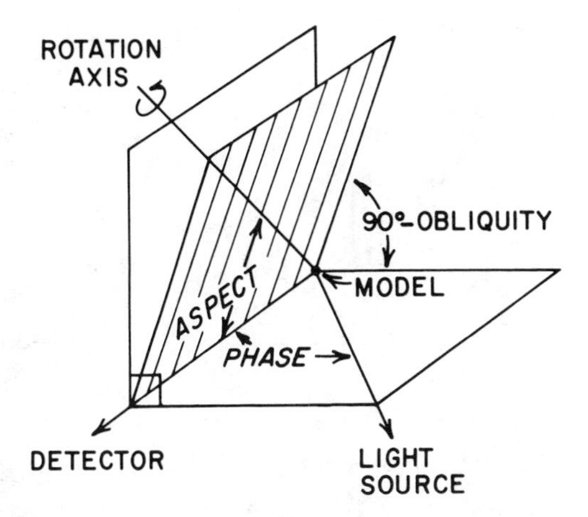

FIG. 2. The geometry of the laboratory observations.

in 1969. Lightcurves obtained over an 8-month interval showed an amplitude of up to 2.0 magnitudes. If all this variation were caused by the shape, Geographos might be six times longer than wide! However, there was 0.1 magnitude difference between maxima and an even larger difference between minima of the lightcurve. This suggested a possible reflectivity effect that could reduce the length-to-width ratio to about 4. It was decided to conduct a laboratory investigation of the lightcurves of models to systematically study the effect of shape on the lightcurves and perhaps to find a particular shape that would reproduce the observed lightcurves of Geographos.

Production of model lightcurves: Figure 1 illustrates some of the first models that were observed. Each model was made with a Styrofoam center covered with a thin layer of Plasticene and finally dusted with powdered rock. The model was turned about its shortest axis by a stepping motor, and the integrations of the photoelectrically observed brightness were usually made every 3° (or 5°) over 240° (or 360°) of rotation using the same photometer we used at the telescope (Coyne and Gehrels, 1967).

Figure 2 defines the geometry of the observations. The model's rotation axis can be oriented in space around two perpendicular directions. One is the line of sight, a rotation about which causes a change in ***asterocentric obliquity.***[1] The other direction is perpendicular to the line of sight at the model's center,

---

[1] Obliquity refers to the dihedral angle between the plane determined by the line of sight and the axis of rotation, and the plane perpendicular to the scattering plane and containing the line of sight. (See fig. 2.)

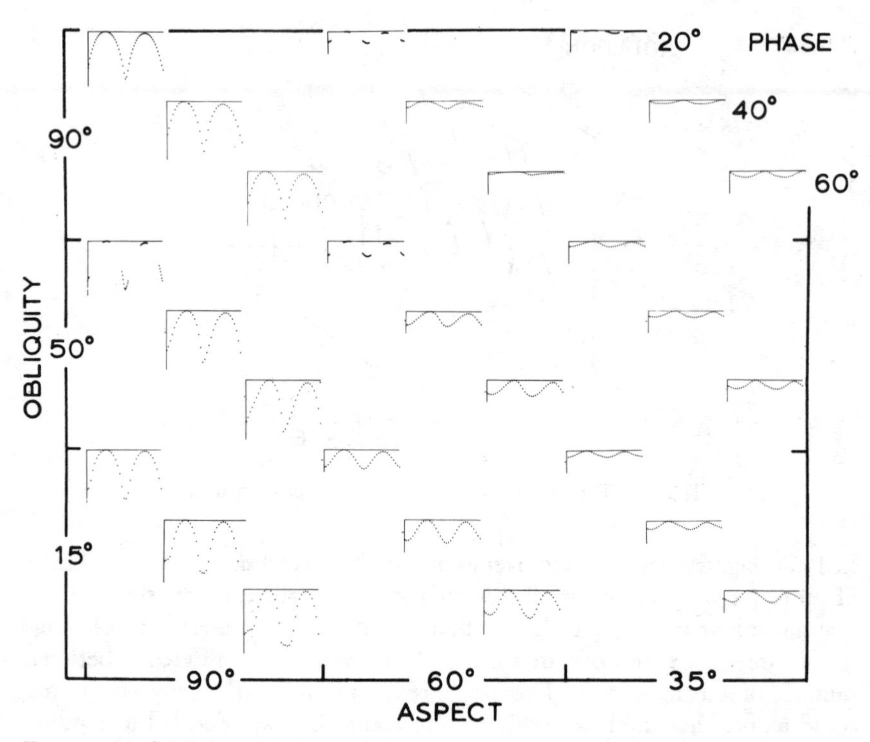

FIG. 3. Model lightcurves in a 3-by-3-by-3 matrix. The model was a cylinder with hemispherical ends having one end darkened and an over-all length-to-width ratio of about 4. The lightcurve at 90° obliquity, 90° aspect, and 20° phase (top left) has an amplitude of 2.12 magnitudes.

about which a rotation causes a change in *aspect* (the angle between the rotation axis and the line of sight.) The light source can be moved horizontally to change the *phase*. For each of the models, up to 27 lightcurves were produced by varying the aspect (90°, 60°, 35°), the obliquity (90°, 50°, 15°) and the phase (20°, 40°, 60°). The probable error of angle measurements is estimated at ± 1°. Figure 3 illustrates lightcurves obtained from a smooth-surfaced, long cylindrical model with rounded ends. One end and part of one side were artificially darkened with graphite powder to produce the apparent reflectivity difference between primary and secondary features seen in the lightcurves observed for Geographos (shown in figure 4). The curves of figure 3 generally illustrate the effects of changing aspect, phase, and obliquity. Several characteristics of the lightcurves can be identified that are used later in making comparisons of models:

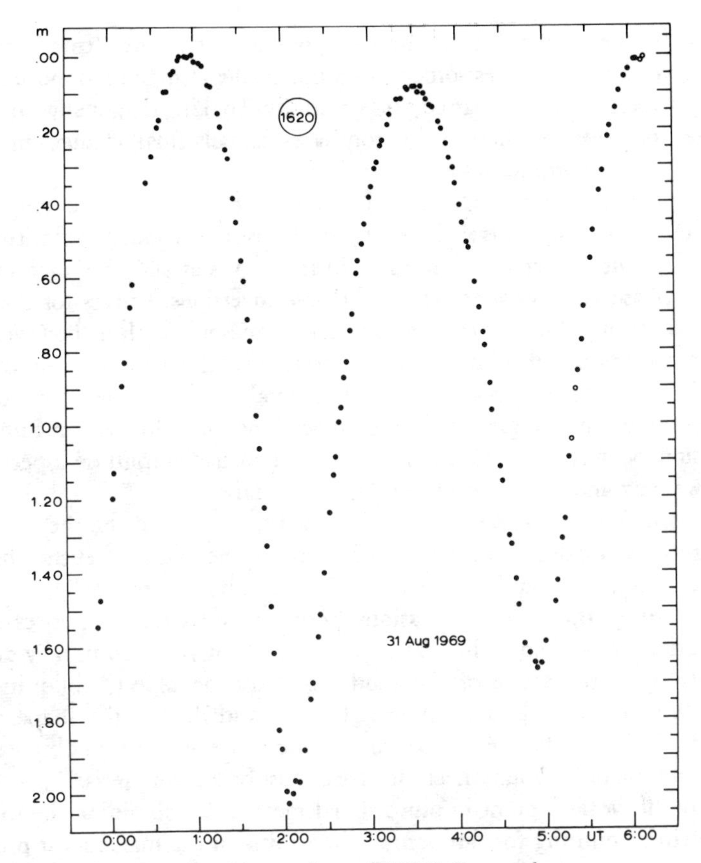

FIG. 4. Observations of (1620) Geographos.

(1) Amplitude: the height of the curve from minimum to maximum.
(2) Shape of minima: sharp, flat, and/or asymmetric.
(3) Width of minima at half amplitude.
(4) Time shifts of maxima or minima relative to the observation at 90° obliquity, 20° phase.
(5) Lightcurve inversion: maxima become minima and vice versa (time shift is 90°).
(6) Primary and secondary maxima and minima.

Looking horizontally from left to right in figure 3, one sees the change produced by decreasing the aspect; most noticeable are the decreases in amplitude and the time shifts (leading to two lightcurve inversions and two partial inversions at the top of the figure). The inversions are understood roughly as occurring when the illuminated part of the "true" maxima has a smaller area (as seen by the detector) than the illuminated part of the "true" minima. Looking vertically, one sees sometimes a noticeable change in amplitude with obliquity and sometimes changes in asymmetry. Looking diagonally (in groups of three), one sees the changes due to phase—usually small changes in amplitude with some asymmetries and time shifts.

Amplitude-aspect relations: Figure 5 is the set of nine amplitude-aspect curves for lightcurves from figure 3 (using secondary amplitudes to avoid reflectivity effects). The minima in the curves at 90° obliquity and 40° and 60° phase are associated with lightcurve inversions. Curves for the other models are similar but not exactly the same as these. It is clear, however, that there is no unique amplitude-aspect function for this or any of the models studied. Therefore, it is not possible, in general, to determine a rotation axis precisely by using a single amplitude-aspect function. This was an important conclusion because several authors have tried to use amplitude-aspect functions; we now understand where this approach fails.

Comparison of models: Table 1 is a brief summary of the results of comparing five models. To see how differences in the shape affect the observed light variation, each model was compared with a reference; finally, the lightcurves made at the same orientations were examined for differences in the characteristics described earlier. The changes in light variation usually depend not only upon the shape of the model but also on aspect, obliquity, and phase. We cannot look at a single lightcurve and deduce the shape of the asteroid. Therefore, before comparison can be made with actual observations, the orientation of the rotation axis in space must be known precisely ($\sim \pm 1°$). Probably the weakest point in our original method for obtaining the rotation axis was in accounting for differential time shifts in the maxima (or minima) that depend on aspect, obliquity, and phase. An analysis of time-shifts of model 1 in table 1 showed that they were equal to $\delta/2$ where δ (see figure 6) is the angle at the asteroid north pole between the subearth point (EP) and the subsolar point (SP). With this correction to our analysis, the rotation axis of Geographos was obtained at $\lambda_0 = 200° \pm 8°$, $\beta_0 = 60° \pm 4°$, ecliptic longitude and latitude, respectively.

Comparison with telescopic observations: Some additional models were built and observed, and a computer program was written to compare the lightcurve amplitudes of these models with those of Geographos for trial values of the rotation axis and to solve for the rotation axis giving the best amplitude agreement. The solution was the same as that given above. Figure 7 illustrates the comparison of two of the models to the observations of Geographos on August 31, 1969. No attempt was made to reproduce the deeper minimum because earlier work suggested that it could be caused by reflectivity

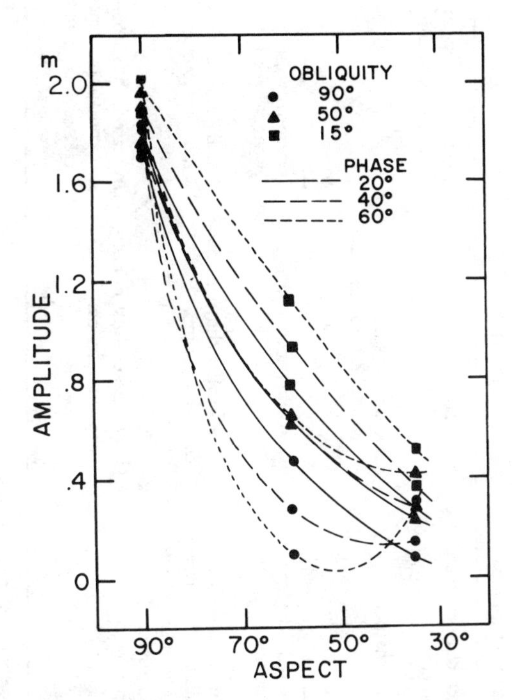

FIG. 5. Amplitude-aspect curves obtained from the secondary amplitudes of figure 3.

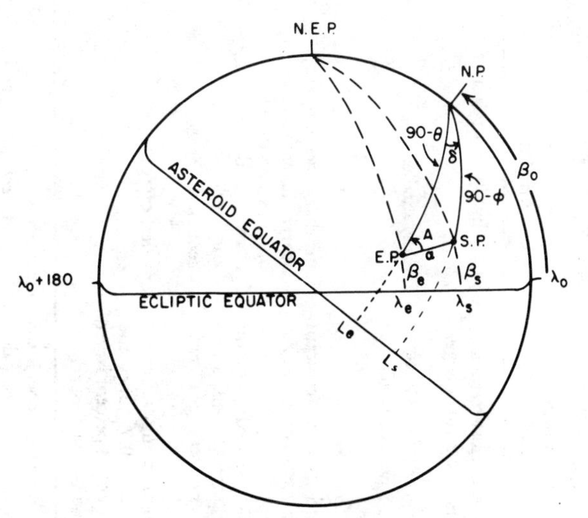

FIG. 6. Asterocentric coordinate system.

TABLE 1.—COMPARISONS OF MODELS

Model compared with reference[a]	Observed changes in light variation relative to the reference model[b]			
	Amplitude	Shape of minima	Time shifts	Other
1. Same shape; cross-sectional area ratio 2.3 times larger	Larger by up to a factor of 2	Narrower, sharper, more asymmetry	Some larger shifts in maxima	Lightcurve inversion is possible at smaller phase angle
2. Two tangent spheres of equal radii, 5 percent larger area ratio	Usually smaller	Narrower, sharper	Some smaller shifts in maxima, more in minima	
3. Both ends pointed (conical); ~5 percent larger area ratio	Somewhat larger; amplitude-aspect curves have less or opposite curvature	Complicated changes with less asymmetry	No significant change	Occasionally the minima are wedge-shaped
4. One end pointed (conical); some brighter spots; 5 percent smaller area ratio	Primary and secondary amplitudes larger, except at 90° aspect	Wider minima with one resembling the reference and the other those of model 3 (above)	Some smaller shifts in maxima and minima	Primary and secondary minima are frequently interchanged
5. Elongation along a second body axis 0.7 times the major axis; 3 percent larger area ratio at 90° aspect	Smaller, except at 90° aspect	Somewhat wider	Usually larger shifts in maxima and minima	Increase in brightness of the maxima as aspect decreases (up to 0.32 magnitude at 35° aspect)

[a]The reference model is a cylinder with hemispherical ends and a cross-sectional area A_{max}/A_{min} of 1.9.
[b]These changes usually depend on the aspect, phase, and obliquity and therefore do not characterize all the lightcurves.

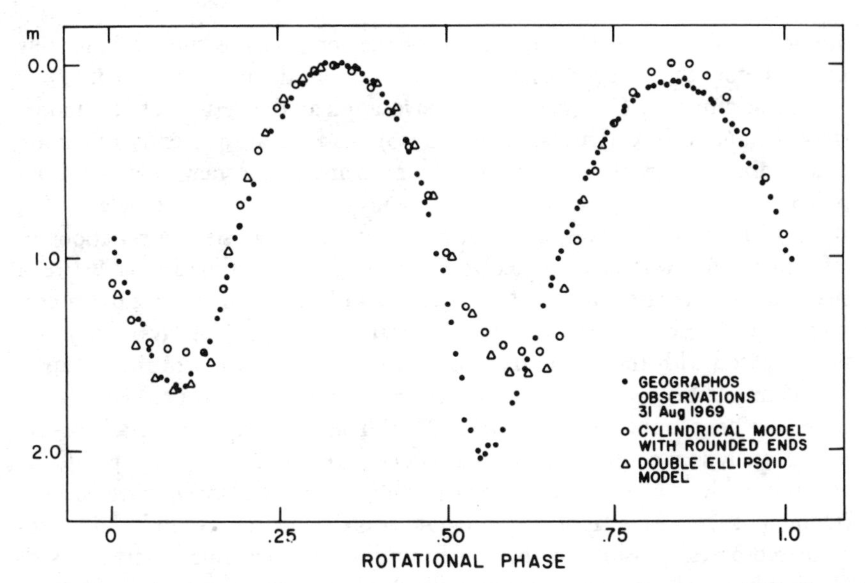

FIG. 7. Comparison of model to telescope observations.

variations. Both models have a cross-sectional area ratio of 3.2 to 1. The somewhat better fit of the double ellipsoid through the minimum suggests that the sides of Geographos are probably not as smooth as those of the cylindrical model. Using these models as a comparison, we computed the dimensions of Geographos as 1.5 kilometers wide and 4.0 kilometers long.

Surface roughness: The extreme smoothness ($\lesssim 0.004$) of all the model lightcurves is not usually seen in asteroid lightcurves, although asteroids with large light variations appear to be smoother than average. Two models with rougher surfaces (about 5 and 20 percent deviations from an average dimension) were also observed. The roughest model produced an anomaly: a smooth tertiary hump seen in certain orientations near the minimum of light. We also made a few lightcurves using a very irregularly shaped and somewhat porous rock, and they showed several small features with some indication of deviations from smoothness. More work needs to be done in modeling the surface texture, which is apparently the major source of small features in the lightcurves.

Conclusions: There is no unique amplitude-aspect function for any of the models studied, and the amplitude-aspect method should not be used for precise determinations of rotation axes. The differences in the amplitude-aspect function as well as in other characteristics of the lightcurves are partially due to the shape, but the orientation of the rotation axis must be precisely known before the shape of an asteroid may be confidently determined.

In addition to Geographos, we have applied the results of the model work to (1685) Toro (Dunlap et al., 1973), and we are presently obtaining precise observations of (433) Eros for a similar analysis. A new pulse-counting polarimeter is providing us with simultaneous observations of the polarization along with the lightcurves; this will enable us to detect sizable variations in reflectivity that will help to resolve the problem of distinguishing between shape and reflectivity effects. Other asteroids with large lightcurve amplitudes, such as (624) Hektor, (39) Laetitia, (15) Eunomia, and (44) Nysa, may also be compared with the model data to obtain some indication of their shapes.

Parts of this report have been presented to an international conference and have been published (Dunlap, 1971). The mathematical details of the model analysis are contained in a master-of-science thesis (Dunlap, 1972), and the analysis of Geographos was published in the *Astronomical Journal* (Dunlap, 1974). This laboratory program was the first of its kind and makes further progress possible in the understanding of telescopic observations of Geographos and other asteroids as well. We thank the National Geographic Society for the opportunity to explore a new field.

REFERENCES

COYNE, G. V., and GEHRELS, TOM

1967. Wavelength dependence of polarization, X: Interstellar polarization. Astron. Journ., vol. 72, pp. 887–898.

DUNLAP, J. L.

1971. Laboratory work on the shapes of asteroids. Pp. 147–154 *in* "Physical Studies of Minor Planets," NASA SP.-267, T. Gehrels, ed. National Aeronautics and Space Administration, Washington, D.C.

1972. Laboratory work on the shape of asteroids. M.S. thesis, University of Arizona, Tucson.

1974. Minor planets and related objects, XV: Asteroid (1620) Geographos. Astron. Journ., vol. 79, pp. 324–332.

DUNLAP, J. L.: GEHRELS, TOM; and HOWES, M. L.

1973. Minor planets and related objects, IX: Photometry and polarimetry of (1685) Toro. Astron. Journ., vol. 78, pp. 491–501.

ROACH, F. E., and STODDARD, L. G.

1938. A photoelectric lightcurve of Eros. Astrophys. Journ., vol. 88, pp. 305–312.

VAN DEN BOS, W. H., and FINSEN, W. S.

1931. Physical observations of Eros. Astron. Nachr., vol. 241, pp. 329–334.

J. L. DUNLAP
TOM GEHRELS

Exploration by Sonar and Coring of the Helice Site, Greece

Principal Investigators: Harold E. Edgerton, Massachusetts Institute of Technology, Cambridge, Massachusets, and Peter Throckmorton, New-castle, Maine.

Grant No. 845, 979: In aid of continuing search for the ancient city of Helice, Bay of Corinth.

This report describes an effort to take cores in the sediment at a supposed site for the ancient city of Helice. The area of interest is near the Selinous River east of Aigion, Greece, in the Bay of Corinth.

A brief background of the project is included in our account in the 1966 volume of these *Reports* (Edgerton, 1973). Previous expeditions using sonar gave a hint that subbottom structures were hidden under the heavy clay and sand sediments that pour down from the Selinous River (Marinatos, 1970; Throckmorton et al., 1970). There is some evidence also (Marinatos, 1960) that the river has changed its course to the east since 325 B.C. It is far from clear whether the site is under land or under sea. The objective of our present expedition was to perform research on the underwater area in an attempt to resolve that question.

We presented to the National Geographic Society a preliminary report of the June-July 1971 effort with a 2-inch-diameter corer of the gravity type (Edgerton and Throckmorton, 1971).

Figure 1 charts the area investigated at lat. 38°17.3′ N., long. 22°8.7′ E. (from U. S. Hydrographic Chart 3963). The beach at a village named Volimitka has two cement structures at the water's edge that can be used as survey points. The site of the coring effort is at 58° from these piers and at a distance of about 900 meters. Compass bearings from other landmarks are also given.

A 5KC sonar record, on a track designated as 5A on figure 1 is shown as figure 2. Note that the cores were made at the thin spot in the sediments over the area where a strong sonar echo was detected.

In all, 23 cores were made under several conditions (Edgerton and

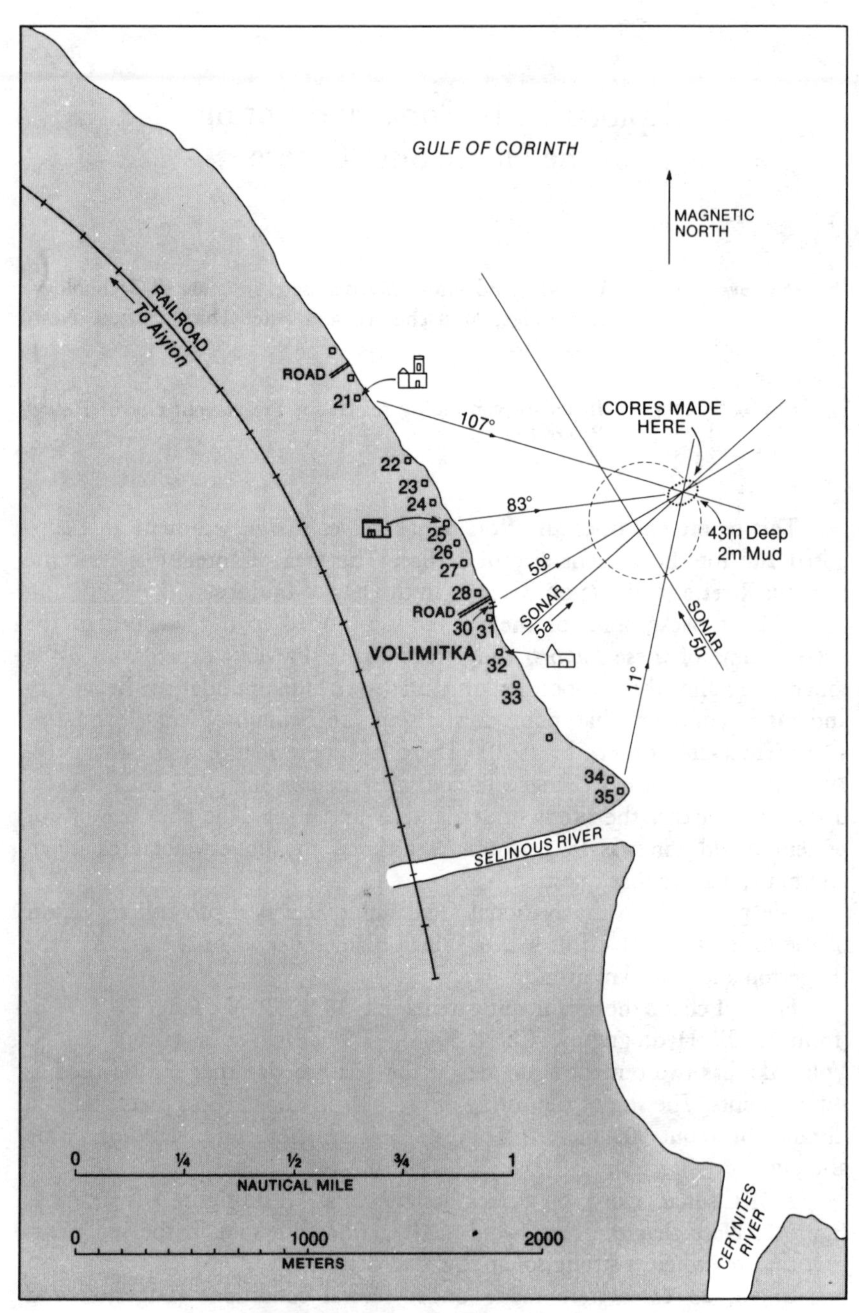

FIG. 1. Chart of area where cores were made in Bay of Corinth, showing compass bearings to area explored with corer.

Throckmorton, 1971). The longest core was about 2 meters, one of which (no. 22) was brought to Cambridge, Massachusetts, for study.

Figure 3 shows the corer on the deck. It has concentric lead weights below the fins on the tail. Figure 4 shows a core being ejected on the deck. Figure 5 shows the shells (30 grams) from the bottom 20 centimeters of the core (2 millimeters long) that were used for the carbon-14 data measurement. A screen with holes of 0.05 inch (1.2 millimeters) mesh was used to separate the clay from the shells and gravel.

A report by Radiocarbon, Ltd., gives a date of 1310 ± 110 years B.P., or about A.D. 640. This apparently shows that the marine animals were deposited after the time of the disappearance of Helice. If the sedimentation rate is uniform, then at this place the rate is (2000 millimeters/1310 years) = 1.4 millimeters year.

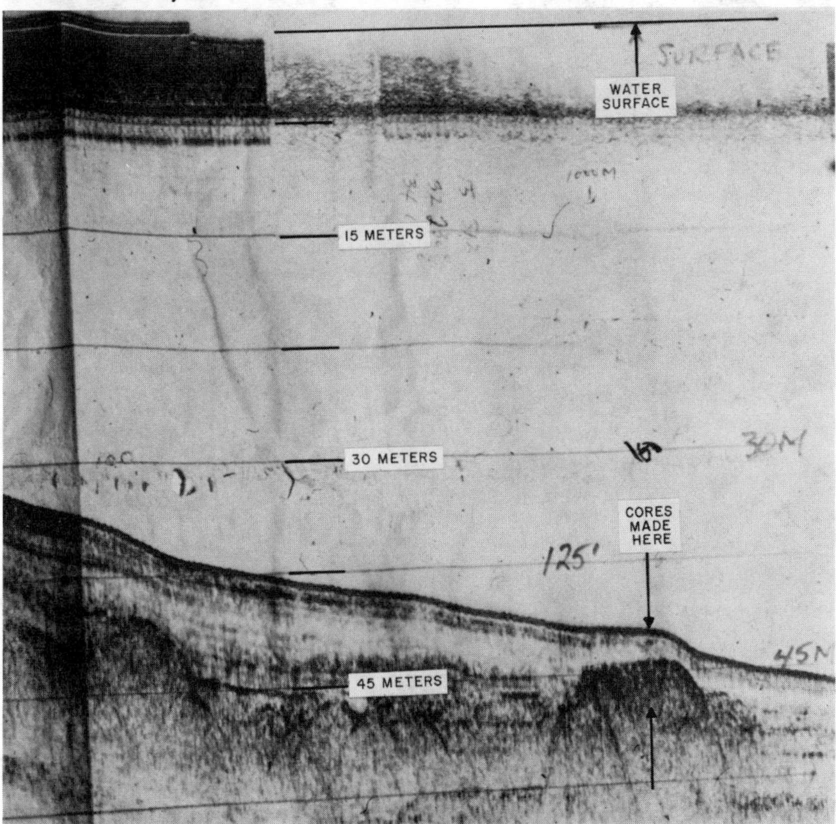

FIG. 2. Sonar record (5KC) of area where cores were made.

FIG. 3. Core shown as it is being taken out of the corer.

FIG. 4. Photograph of top end of the corer on the deck of *Stormie Seas*.

FIG. 5. Sand and gravel particles (top) and shells and other organic materials strained out of the bottom 20 centimeters of the 5-centimeter core.

Discussion

It was very disappointing to us that the *bottom* of the core always fell out and was not observed. Thus, some 10 centimeters of the choicest material did not come to the deck.

It is important to note on the sonar record that the sediment is *thinner* over the subbottom target. Apparently some of the sediment is moved horizontally owing to currents or settling during earthquakes.

Our results give no indication of human activity.

Improved methods of coring are certainly in order for further investigations of the abnormalities disclosed by the sonar.

REFERENCES

EDGERTON, HAROLD E.

1973. Search for Helice with sonar. Nat. Geogr. Soc. Res. Rpts., 1966 Projects, pp. 75–77.

EDGERTON, HAROLD E., and THROCKMORTON, PETER

1971. Preliminary reports on Helice coring project to the National Geographic Society. Ms. dated August 13, 1971.

MARINATOS, SPYRIDON N.

1960. Helice: A submerged town of Classical Greece. Archaeology, vol. 13, no. 3, pp. 186–193, illus. (See pp. 186, 191.)

1970. Investigations in Helike. Acta Acad. Athens, vol. 41, pp. 511–518, illus.

THROCKMORTON, PETER; EDGERTON, HAROLD E.; and FEYLING, FRED

1970. Helice site survey with sonar. Ms. report submitted to the National Geographic Society. Dated May 22, 1970.

HAROLD E. EDGERTON
PETER THROCKMORTON

Biosystematic and Evolutionary Study of the *Capsicum pubescens* Complex

Principal Investigator: W. Hardy Eshbaugh, Miami University, Oxford, Ohio.

Grant Nos. 901, 1025: In support of studies of the variation and evolution of the domesticated chili pepper *Capsicum pubescens*.

Chili peppers have been known to western (European) civilization since Columbus first landed in the New World. The archeological record, however, indicates that the American Indian was using peppers at a much earlier date, for pepper remains have been recovered from sites at Tamaulipas and Tehuacán in Mexico dating from 7000 B.C., while South American remains from Ancón and Huaca Prieta, Peru, date from at least 2000 B.C. (Pickersgill, 1969a, 1969b). In some archeological remains the fruit is larger than that of known wild species and a persistent peduncle is present. The record shows also that subtle change from the use of wild species of peppers to truly domesticated species, as evidenced by the increasing size of the seeds, which finally falls into a range characteristic of only domesticated chili peppers. Although three domesticated species have been reported from these remains, *Capsicum pubescens* has not yet been positively identified from any sites.

The taxonomy of the genus *Capsicum* indicates a relatively confused understanding of species within the genus. Some authors have recognized as many as 61 species (Dunal) while others have reduced all the taxa to just one or two species (Bailey). Within the past 20 years most investigators have generally agreed that there are approximately 30 wild species of *Capsicum*. The treatments of Heiser and Pickersgill (1969) and D'Arcy and Eshbaugh (1974), as well as several others, are in general agreement that there are at least 4 well-defined species of domesticated chili peppers (see list, p. 144). Other investigations by Emboden (1961), Eshbaugh (1970, 1975), Pickersgill (1971), and Heiser et al. (1971) have pointed out the relationships of these domesticated species to their probable ancestral species. These studies conclude that several different wild species gave rise to the different cultivated species, as shown in the tabulation; none of these investigations, however, concerned itself with the domestication of *C. pubescens*.

CULTIVATED SPECIES	WILD PROGENITOR SPECIES	PLACE OF ORIGIN
Capsicum annuum var. *annuum*	*Capsicum annuum* var. *aviculare*	Mexico/Central America
Capsicum chinense	*Capsicum frutescens*	Lowland Amazon Basin
Capsicum baccatum var. *pendulum*	*Capsicum baccatum* var. *baccatum*	Lowland tropical Bolivia, 500–1,500 meters
Capsicum pubescens	*Capsicum eximium*/ *Capsicum cardenasii*	Highland Bolivia, 1,500–3,000 meters

Capsicum pubescens was first described by Ruiz and Pavón in the *Flora Peruviana* . . . in 1799. Nonetheless, the species has remained relatively unknown outside South America and until 25 years ago was barely mentioned in the literature. Both Heiser and Smith (1948) and Rick (1950) have provided us with some basic data about *C. pubescens*, but their information was based on relatively limited samples of this species.

Itinerary

In 1970 and 1971, aided by grants from the National Geographic Society, the American Philosophical Society, the Society of the Sigma Xi, and the Ohio Academy of Sciences, I began a series of investigations aimed at gaining some understanding of the variation and evolution of the domestic chili pepper *Capsicum pubescens*. The initial phase of these investigations involved two extensive collecting trips throughout the South American range of the species.

The first of these expeditions began in December 1970 and continued through March 1971. *Capsicum pubescens* is basically a mid-elevational species and marketed primarily at the higher elevation markets. Collections of fruits and seeds were made from village to village along the Andes with side trips into valleys both east and west of the Andes into the zone where they are normally cultivated. The Ecuadorian collections were made in the Indian markets from Ibarra in the north to Ambato in the south with various side trips into the lowlands at Santo Domingo de los Colorados in the west and Baños and Puyo in the east. In Peru, collections were made from Huánuco in the north to Yunguyo on Lake Titicaca. Trips into the lowlands included the Cuzco and San Ramón areas. An extensive week-long trip was taken along the coast of Peru from Chimbote in the north to Nazca in the south. Although *C. pubescens* was available from these coastal markets it was not common except in Lima. One week was spent collecting along the Amazon

FIG. 1. Market, Cliza, Bolivia. *Capsicum baccatum* var. *pendulum* (foreground) and *C. pubescens* (background) are being sold by vendor.

FIG. 2. Author bartering for *Capsicum pubescens* in a market in La Paz, Bolivia. Note the "ulupica," *C. cardenasii*, in the plastic bag.

to see if *C. pubescens* had been moved into that region. This trip centered around Iquitos and 80 kilometers downriver. Several important side trips to known locations of unusual pepper species at Quince Mil, Pampas, Salcabamba, and Tingo María had to be omitted, since the rainy season had begun in these areas and made roads all but impassable. Although Bolivia potentially represented the most difficult phase of the expedition, assistance from Dr. Martin Cardenas, the Director of Agriculture, and the British Agricultural Mission allowed me to make a number of highly successful collecting trips throughout the country. These included trips from La Paz to the Yungas, La Paz to Luribay, Cochabamba to Santa Cruz, Sucre to Villa Serrano and Monteagudo, and Tarija to Padcaya and Entre Ríos. During the entire 3 1/2-month expedition my wife Barbara served as my research assistanct carefully recording various data and processing and maintaining the seed collections (Eshbaugh, 1971).

The second 6-week expedition to Colombia and northern Ecuador began in July 1972. Initially Bogotá was used as a base of operations. The first collecting trip to the northeast to Tunja and Chiquinquira yielded very little material of *C. pubescens*. A much longer, 4-week trip proved very successful and took us from Bogotá to Honda, Manizales, and Medellín. At La Ceja,

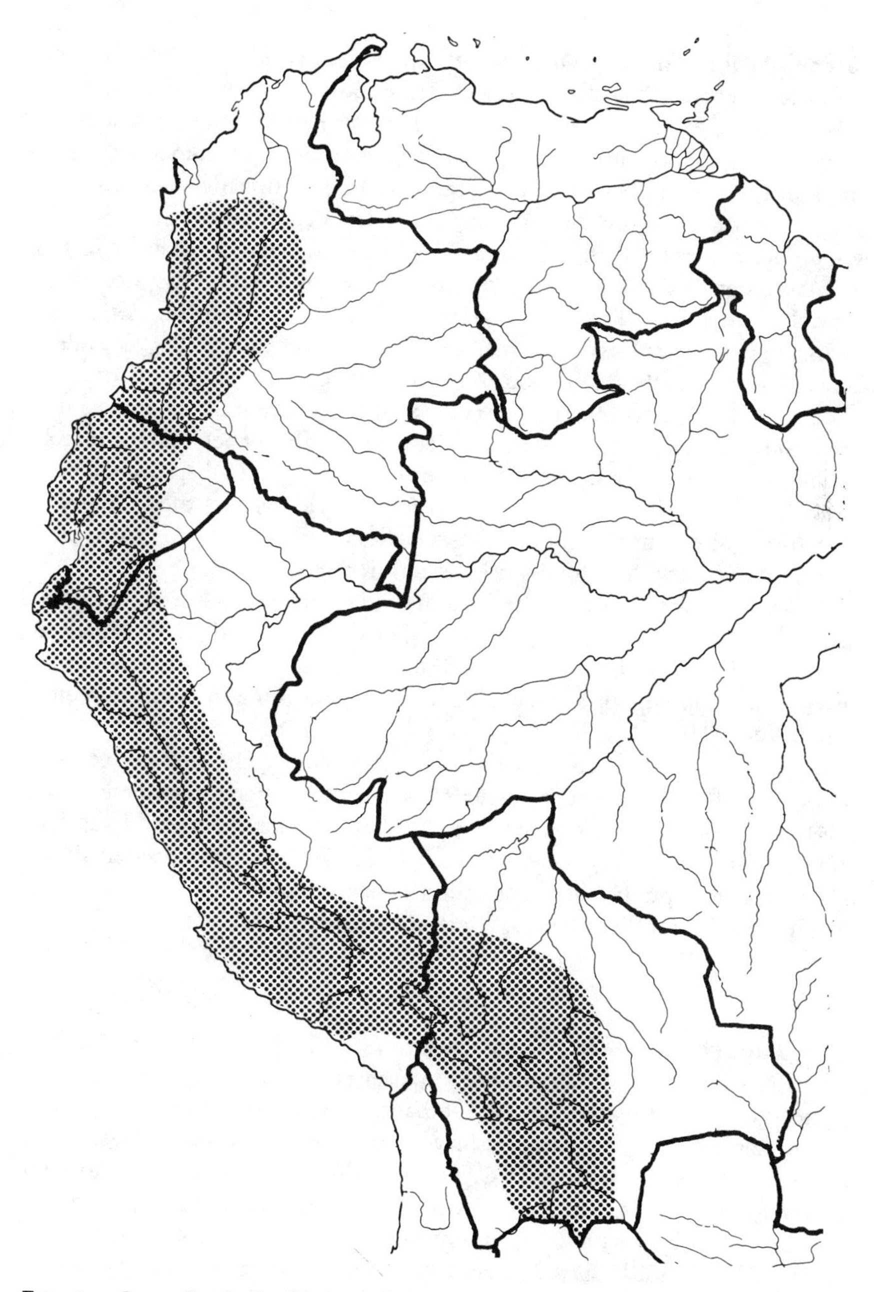

FIG. 3. Generalized distribution of *Capsicum pubescens* in South America. The map indicates both the area of cultivation and marketing.

outside of Medellín, *C. pubescens* was widely cultivated as a shrub around the various homes. From Medellín to Pereira and Cali, *C. pubescens* was not grown but was generally available in the markets. Perhaps the richest area for *C. pubescens* in Colombia was in mid-elevational villages from Popayán to Pasto and across the border into Tulcán, Ecuador. Especially successful side trips were made into the Sandona and Sibundoy Valleys where *C. pubescens* was found as a plant being grown among the coffee and bananas or in the Indian gardens. We made the trip to Bogotá by crossing the Cordillera Central to the Cordillera Oriental from Popayán to Garzón. *Capsicum pubescens* was much less abundant in the southern part of the Cordillera Oriental and virtually absent from Neiva to Girardot. An additional trip was made into the Amazon Basin. A week was spent working 80 kilometers up-river from Letecia to the Colombian-Peruvian border, where extensive collections were made among the Ticuna and Yagua Indian villages and home sites. Dr. Thomas W. Hart served as my research assistant on the Colombian expedition. Sr. Manuel Bellón, who was fluent in English, German, and Spanish, traveled with us for 4 weeks as an interpreter.

The two expeditions resulted in the collection of 734 seed lots (Colombia, 124; Ecuador, 84; Peru, 297; Bolivia, 229) and 105 herbarium specimens. This material has been used to arrive at the data in discussion that follows and is on deposit at Miami University in the Willard Sherman Turell Herbarium (MU).

Two additional collecting trips were made during the summer of 1975 and spring of 1976 to Mexico, Guatemala, and Honduras, sponsored by the National Science Foundation and the Willard Sherman Turrell Herbarium Fund (Miami University). Data obtained from these have not been analyzed in detail in this publication, but collection data indicate that *C. pubescens* is widespread in southern Mexico (Chiapas) and Guatemala.

Introduction

Capsicum pubescens, widely known as "rocoto" in the Andes and "chile manzana" or "chamburoto" in Central America, is the dominant pepper species used by the highland Indians. It can be seen in most highland Indian markets in an intriguing display of fruit shapes and colors (figs. 1 and 2). Earlier workers reported that *C. pubescens* occurred from Mexico to Peru at elevations between 1,820 and 3,030 meters. My collecting trips indicate that the rocoto is distributed from southern Mexico to the southern edge of Bolivia. Although it is not a highland species in the strict sense, *C. pubescens* is grown at elevations higher than any other domesticated pepper.

In South America, rocoto is grown both east and west of the Andes

FIG. 4. *Left,* specimen of *Capsicum pubescens*, showing the typical flower position and pendant fruit (E964, Chacalla, Bolivia, from a heterozygous fruit, which yielded both orange-yellow and red fruits). *Right,* fruit of *Capsicum pubescens* (long. sec.), showing brown/black reticulate-patterned seeds. Note the neck at the top of the fruit and the thickened flesh (E230—Mairana, Bolivia).

between 1,500 and 3,000 meters (fig. 3). It is characteristic of drier sandy soil types. Before the era of agrarian reform it was grown as a cash crop by many haciendas, and it is still grown as a field crop around Arequipa and San Ramón, Peru, but today it is grown primarily locally by the individual farmer and sold to various cooperatives and processing companies. This makes it increasingly difficult to be certain where collections in the marketplace actually come from. Many vendors sell rocoto that has been transported many miles from its original place of growth. Nonetheless, material purchased in the smaller more remote markets is undoubtedly locally grown. All evidence available indicates that *C. pubescens* was introduced into Central America in this century and that it has been locally important only since the 1940's.

Results

As described by D'Arcy and Eshbaugh (1974), *Capsicum pubescens* (fig. 4) is a large shrubby herbaceous plant that can grow to at least 3 meters in height. Although usually grown as an annual it often becomes a long-lived perennial and in this condition may develop a woody habit and a trunk 7-15 centimeters in diameter. Both Heiser and Smith (1948) and Rick (1950) suggest that with the exception of the fruit *C. pubescens* has few morphologically distinct or highly variable characters. However, I found the rocoto to be highly variable throughout its range in South America. *Capsicum pubescens* can be described as having glabrous to densely pubescent leaves, ovate in shape, and often quite rugose. The leaf margins may be smooth to ciliate. The stems are usually characterized by being purple at the nodes, but in some individuals this pigment is absent. The stem may show solid purple coloring between the nodes, be purple striate, or completely lack purple pigmentation. The flower coloring and patterning are highly variable throughout the species range in South America. Some flowers have deep-purple corolla lobes, while others grade into a rose color, and still others almost lack any hint of purple pigmentation. There is also a significant size difference in the corolla diameter from plant to plant. The corolla shape varies from being rotate to slightly semicampanulate. However, it is in the characteristics of the fruit that the greatest variability is seen. The fruit types found in *C. pubescens* vary both in shape and color. A range of fruit shapes from turban-shaped, to spherical, to elongate exists within the species. The fruit may have a pronounced neck present or absent. Some fruits are dimpled where the style existed when in flower while others lack the dimple effect. The range in fruit colors includes red, orange-red, orange, peach, yellow-orange, and lemon-yellow (figs. 5–7). Rick (1950) reported finding brown-fruited *C. pubescens* from Cuzco, Peru, but in one week's time in Cuzco I never saw this type of fruit. Rick (1950) also noted that there was supposed to be a form of rocoto that was green at maturity. I was sold a number of these so-called bronzed rocotos, but in every case they proved to be immature fruits that had not had sufficient time to develop pigmentation. The fruit of the rocoto has much thicker flesh than the other domesticated species. Its higher moisture content makes this species particularly susceptible to rotting, and it does not store or dehydrate very well. Therefore, it is usually sold fresh in the markets while several of the other peppers are bought either fresh or dried. The seeds of *C. pubescens* are unlike those of any other domesticated species. They are very rough and the seed coat usually has a fine reticulate pattern. The seeds are dark brown to black (fig. 4). Since *C. pubescens* seeds are distinct they should be fairly easy to identify from archeological remains and should be carefully looked for, particularly in Bolivia, as more sites are excavated.

The detailed analysis of character variation throughout the geographic range of *C. pubescens* is still in progress, and preliminary results indicate some significant patterns of variation. The greatest amount of variation is found in fruit characters. This is to be expected, since the fruit has under-

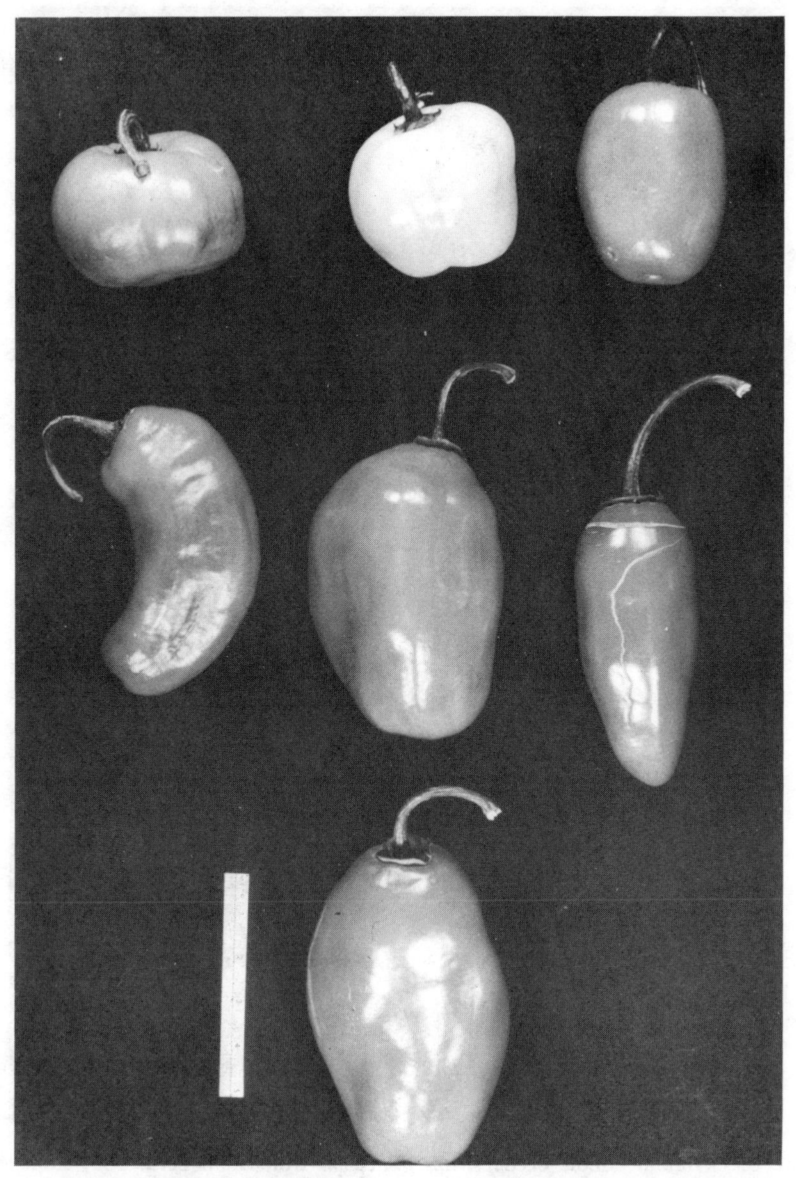

FIG. 5. Random sample of *Capsicum pubescens* fruits from Ecuador and Colombia. *Top,* from left: SA53, La Ceja, Colombia, red; E1044, Pasto, Colombia, orange; E1053, Ipiales, Colombia, red. *Middle:* E1066, E1069, E1070, Tulcán, Ecuador (said to be from southern Colombia), all red. *Bottom*: E1071, Tulcán, Ecuador, red.

FIG. 6. Random sample of *Capsicum pubescens* fruits from Peru. *Top,* from left: E688, Cuzco, lemon-yellow; E689, Cuzco, red; E695, Pisac, red. *Middle*: E697, Pisac, red; E706, Pachar, red; E717, Calca, red. *Bottom*: E722, Ollantaitambo, heterozygous collection, this fruit orange; E731, Izcuchaca (Anta), orange; E741, Urcos, yellow-orange.

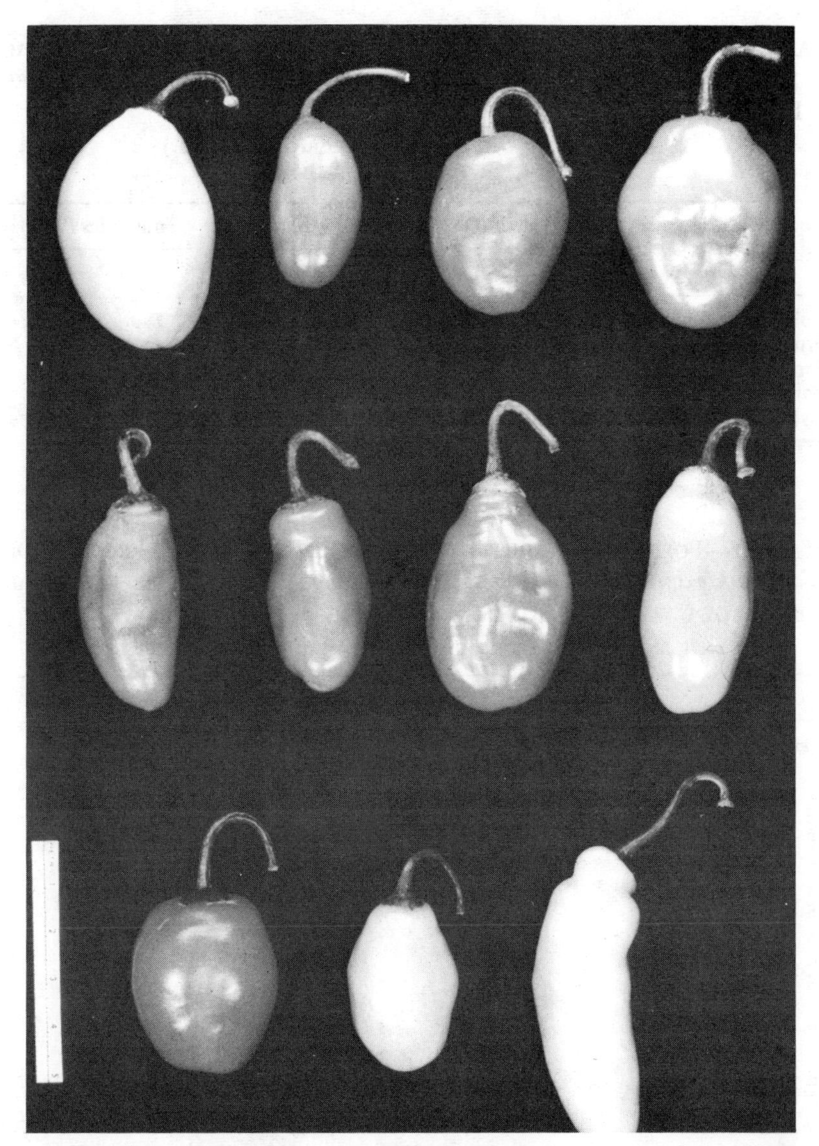

FIG. 7. Random sample of *Capsicum pubescens* from Bolivia. *Top,* from left: E666 (La Paz, said to be from the Yungas), orange; E772, Joaquin, red; E784, Cochabamba, red; E785, Cochabamba, heterozygous collection, this fruit red. *Middle*: E791, Quillacolo, red; E828, Comarapa, red; E842, Tiumayo, red; E887, Sucre, orange. *Bottom*: E948, Chulumani, red; E959, Kalakalani, orange; E963, Chacalla, orange.

TABLE 1—*Capsicum pubescens*, ANALYSIS OF VARIATION IN FRUIT CHARACTERS WITHIN FOUR COUNTRIES AS COMPARED TO THE KNOWN HYBRID E925.

($\overline{X}$ = Mean; S.D. = one standard deviation.)

Country	Fruit length (L)		Fruit width (W)		Fruit index (W/L)	
	$\overline{X}$	S.D.	$\overline{X}$	S.D.	$\overline{X}$	S.D.
Colombia	45.21	18.49	33.79	4.74	.751	.208
Ecuador	56.86	21.71	31.79	5.87	.537	.245
Peru	44.60	9.21	36.80	4.89	.849	.198
Bolivia	38.19	8.84	25.42	6.96	.706	.149
Hybrid	19.63	3.74	16.50	2.56	.850	.096

TABLE 2—POLLEN STAINABILITY (VIABILITY) IN THE HYBRID PROGENY OF A *Capsicum eximium* × *C. pubescens* CROSS (E925) COMPARED TO THE STAINABILITY OF *C. eximium* AND *C. pubescens.*

(Note that some hybrids with high pollen stainability do not set fruit.)

Species	Pollen Stainability (%)	Fruit Set
C. eximium	93-98	
E 925- 1	85	
E 925- 2	87	
E 925- 3	85	
E 925- 4	87	
E 925- 6	71	
E 925- 7	70	No fruit
E 925- 8	90	
E 925- 9	78	No fruit
E 925-10	75	
E 925-11	---	
E 925-12	54	No fruit
E 925-13	82	
E 925-14	97	No fruit
E 925-15	96	
E 925-16	91	
C. pubescens	87-95	

gone intense artificial selection by man over a prolonged period of time. With respect to qualitative character of fruit color, the greatest degree of variation occurs in Bolivia and Peru, whereas the peppers in Colombia and Ecuador are most often red or, rarely, orange. When analyzed on the basis

FIG. 8. *Capsicum eximium,* "ulupica," for sale in Tarija, Bolivia.

of several quantitative characters such as fruit length and width the most highly variable fruits occur in Colombia and Ecuador, whereas those in Peru and Bolivia are far less variable (see table 1). The most interesting aspect of such an analysis, however, is that fruit size in Bolivia, based on length and width (see table 1), is significantly smaller than that of fruits from any other geographic region. The flower pattern and coloration is impossible to quantify but far fewer patterns and a much narrower range of coloration occur with Bolivian *C. pubescens* than elsewhere. None of the other characters analyzed seemed to be distributed on a specific geographic basis.

As an integral part of this investigation, other species of *Capsicum* were collected from throughout South America in the hope that any one of these taxa might represent a closely related species or even an ancestral form of *C. pubescens*. Earlier work by Eshbaugh (1964) and Ballard et al. (1970) suggests that both *C. cardenasii* and *C. eximium,* on the basis of breeding behavior and chemical similarities, are closely related to *C. pubescens.* Another, yet unnamed species, from the Ayacucho, Peru, area appears to be very close to *C. pubescens* on morphological grounds but has never been successfully crossed with this species.

Capsicum cardenasii, first described by Heiser and Smith in 1958, is a very localized species found on hillsides in the valleys of the department of La Paz, Bolivia, where it is characteristic of very dry to desert conditions. This species can be distinguished from all other peppers except the endemic *C. scolnikianum* from northern Peru by the presence of a campanulate corolla. The flower is purple on the outer third and white along the basal two-thirds of the corolla lobe. The flower lacks any patterning in the form of spots on the corolla.

Capsicum eximium, first described by Hunziker in 1950, is a more widely distributed species than *C. cardenasii*. It ranges from the departments of Cochabamba, Chuquisaca, Tarija, and Santa Cruz in Bolivia to the provinces of Jujuy, Salta, and Tucumán in Argentina. This species is also characteristic of dry semidesert areas but is more often found in small ravines along dried up watercourses. The best diagnostic character for distinguishing *C. eximium* is the rotate corolla, which is patterned with yellow to ochre spots on each corolla lobe. The rest of the corolla lobe color ranges from a deep purple to magenta to pure white.

Both *C. cardenasii* and *C. eximium* are known as "ulupica" throughout Bolivia and northern Argentina. The fruit of the two species is spherical, ranging in diameter between 8 and 12 millimeters (fig. 8). The habit of the two species is almost identical and is distinct from that of other pepper species. They are often described as viny shrubs. However, *C. eximium* may become a large tree 3–4 meters tall with a single trunk 8–16 centimeters in diameter. Both species are often associated with disturbed sites, and *C. eximium* has been seen as an invader and colonizer of cornfields near Pojo (Carrasco/Cochabamba), Bolivia. Both species occupy elevations between 1,500 and 2,800 meters, thus overlapping with the altitudinal range of *C. pubescens*. *Capsicum cardenasii* and *C. eximium* are apparently marginally allopatric species, and as more is learned about their distribution I expect they will be shown to be truly sympatric at least on the eastern edge of the range of *C. cardenasii.*

A study of breeding behavior among these species has revealed some interesting data. Both *C. cardenasii,* which is self-incompatible, and *C. eximium,* which is self-compatible, can be crossed to each other with ease. It makes little difference which of the two species serves as the maternal parent. The hybrids produced from this cross are vigorous and have a pollen stainability of 85–97 percent. This is true for F_1, F_2, and backcross progeny. In fact the level of fertility is so high that under this criterion alone they could be considered to be a single biological species. This is in agreement

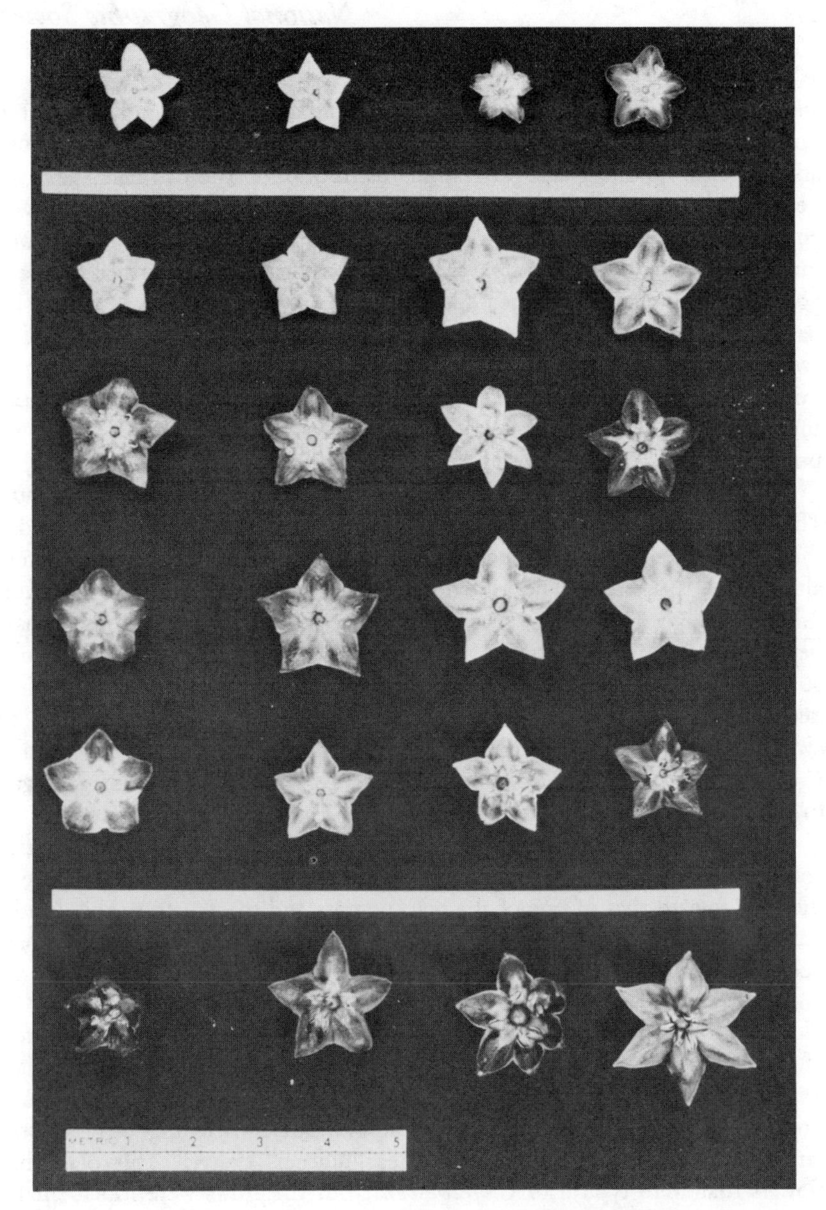

FIG. 9. *Capsicum eximium* × *Capsicum pubescens* (E925) hybrid compared with parental types. *Top,* four different samples of *C. eximium*; two samples on left are white with yellow markings, two on right are magenta with yellow markings. *Middle,* the four rows grade from typical *C. eximium* (white form, upper left) to typical *C. pubescens* (purple form, lower right); first 10 flowers in this section have corolla markings typical of *C. eximium*. *Bottom*, four flowers typical of the variation of *C. pubescens* in Bolivia.

with the numerical taxonomic findings of Eshbaugh (1964) and the chemotaxonomic findings of Ballard et al. (1970). Much more needs to be known about the morphology and geographic distribution of the two taxa, however, before they are reduced to a single species. In the Luribay Valley in Bolivia I encountered a population of *C. cardenasii* containing individuals that were intermediate between *C. eximium* and *C. cardenasii*. A number of plants possessed semi-campanulate corollas. In some cases the corolla possessed the pattern typical of *C. eximium*, while in others it was more typical of *C. cardenasii*. *Capsicum cardenasii* was growing throughout the area but *C. eximium* was not seen. Had time permitted, however, I believe *C. eximium* could have been found. These field plants were similar to the F_1 and F_2 hybrid plants that have been produced in the laboratory.

Capsicum eximium and *C. cardenasii* can be crossed with *C pubescens*. The cross is fairly easy to make when *C. cardenasii* or *C. eximium* is used as the maternal parent. It is much more difficult to make the reciprocal cross, although it is possible. The pollen stainability of the hybrids obtained from this cross ranges from 55–87 percent. Several F_2 and backcross progeny have been obtained in these studies and they also show a pollen stainability over 50 percent. The F_1 first generation hybrids obtained to date are intermediate between the domesticated *C. pubescens* and wild *C. cardenasii* and *C. eximium*. The intermediate nature of the hybrid is much more easily seen in *C. pubescens* × *C. eximium* crosses. The F_2 generation hybrids segregate to the two parental types in a ratio of three *C. pubescens* type plants to one *C. cardenasii* or *C. eximium* type of plant. The most striking morphological feature of both F_1 and F_2 progeny is the immediate reduction of the size of the fruit toward that of one of the wild parents and the return to the deciduous fruit condition. Although the crosses between these three species have been made and repeated in the laboratory and greenhouse many times, this does not prove that the same events take place in the wild.

Two plants seen during the course of my collecting trips were therefore of particular interest, since they appeared to be of hybrid origin. One plant was a weedy shrub growing next to a sawmill in the suburb of Calacata, Cochabamba, Bolivia. According to the sawmill owner, the original seed came from the Japanese plantations near Warnes, Bolivia. This plant had flowers that were typical of *C. pubescens*, but the fruits were much smaller than those of typical *C. pubescens*. The second plant was growing in the courtyard of a home in Tarata, Bolivia. It was a tree some 10–15 centimeters in diameter and approximately 3.5 meters tall. The seed from which it was grown was said to have been collected locally from a wild plant. The flowers were typical of *C. pubescens*, but once again this plant had fruit typical of

FIG. 10. Hybrid fruits (E925), *Capsicum eximium* × *C. pubescens.* Each of the eight groups of paired fruits came from a different individual grown from seed collected from the original hybrid plant.

that seen in laboratory-produced hybrids. Seed of these two plants was collected for further study in the experimental field at Miami University.

The laboratory and field studies of these seed collections reveal the true hybrid nature of the parent plants from Bolivia. The seedlings segregate into a number of different plant types ranging from that typical of pure *C. pubescens* to that of true *C. eximium*. The flower color and patterning (fig. 9) show flower types ranging from pure white with yellow spots to deep purple without spots. These hybrids again segregate into a ratio of approximately three *C. pubescens* types to one *C. eximium* type with respect to flower coloring and patterning. However, fruit size in the hybrids seems to be stabilized at 15–23 millimeters, far less than that of the smallest known *C. pubescens* fruits (fig. 10). All the hybrid fruits are deciduous, which is typical of wild *C. eximium*. The hybrid fruit size is still much larger than that of wild *C. eximium* (8–12 millimeters), but it is clearly skewed toward the wild type of plant. Some of the hybrid plants fail to set fruit or do so only on a limited basis. An analysis of the progeny for pollen stainability reveals that although there is a low stainability in some individuals, others possess a stainability as high or higher than is typical for *C. pubescens* and *C. eximium* as species (see table 2).

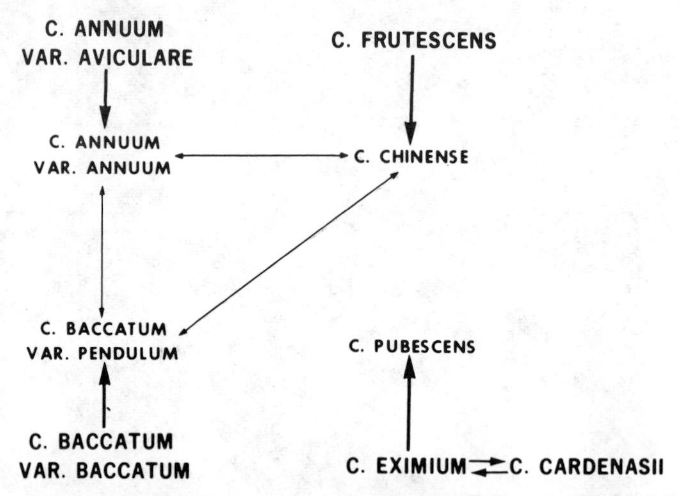

FIG. 11. Diagrammatic representation of the relationships between the domesticated species of chili peppers. The heavy thick lines indicate very strong compatibility with fertile hybrid progeny in the F_1, F_2, and backcross generations. The thin lines between the groups indicate that the production of hybrid progeny is possible but at very low levels of fertility. Note that the *Capsicum pubescens* complex is isolated from the other domesticated chili peppers.

Discussion

The domesticated chili pepper *C. pubescens* is a wide-ranging species in Andean South America and the Central American highlands. It is unreported from archeological remains at sites where other chili-pepper species have been discovered. Under domestication this species has developed large pendant fruits, which are not deciduous. All organ systems of the domesticated species show a general gigantism characterized by an increased leaf size, flower size, and number of floral parts. While most wild peppers are outcrossers, *C. pubescens* has become essentially a self-breeding species. This pattern has been seen among the other domesticated *Capsicum* species (Eshbaugh, 1970). Within South America, the largest fruit types of *C. pubescens* come from the northern range of the species while the smaller fruits, which approach a hypothetical ancestral condition, are seen in those collections from the southern range of the species in Peru and Bolivia. Seed collections from Colombia, Ecuador, and Peru give rise to homozygous lines, while those from Bolivia are quite heterozygous. The only species known to hybridize with *C. pubescens* are the "ulupicas," *C. cardenasii* and *C. eximium* from Bolivia and northern Argentina. *Capsicum pubescens* has not been reported from Argentina although it should be expected there. The weedy tendency of *C. eximium* will undoubtedly lead some botanists to conclude that this species is a weedy derivative or escape from cultivation; but even though *C. eximium* commonly invades cornfields and grows in association with *Zea mays*, its over-all distribution and ecology argue against its being an escape from cultivation. As noted earlier, *C. eximium* is characteristic of undisturbed hillsides and ravines adjacent to dried-up watercourses. In much of its range, *C. eximium* occupies sites that are clearly undisturbed and characteristic for the wild, nonweedy type. *Capsicum cardenasii* also occurs on undisturbed dry hillside locations.

When all the evidence from morphology, chemotaxonomy, and breeding behavior is considered, we are led to conclude that *Capsicum cardenasii* and *C. eximium* are two very closely related wild taxa that are the closest living relatives of *C. pubescens*. These two taxa may well represent the ancestral species complex that gave rise to *C. pubescens*, and at the very least they are representative of the ancestral wild stock from which the early domesticant was evolved. The relationship of these three species is reminiscent of that seen for the other domesticated pepper species (fig. 11). Finally, the geographic distribution of the wild "ulupicas" strongly suggests that *C. pubescens* was domesticated somewhere in the mid-elevation zone of central Bolivia.

REFERENCES

BALLARD, R. E.; MCCLURE, J. W.; ESHBAUGH, W. HARDY; and WILSON, K. G.
1970. A chemosystematic study of selected taxa of *Capsicum.* Amer. Journ. Bot., vol. 5, pp. 225–233.

D'ARCY, WILLIAM G., and ESHBAUGH, W. HARDY
1974. New World peppers (*Capsicum*—Solanaceae) north of Colombia: A résumé. Baileya, vol. 19, pp. 94–105.

EMBODEN, WILLIAM A., JR.
1961. A preliminary study of the crossing relationships of *Capsicum baccatum.* Butler Univ. Bot. Stud., vol. 14, pp. 1–5.

ESHBAUGH, W. HARDY
1964. A numerical taxonomic and cytogenetic study of certain species of the genus *Capsicum.* Ph.D. dissertation, Indiana University.
1970. A biosystematic and evolutionary study of *Capsicum baccatum* (Solanaceae). Brittonia, vol. 22, pp. 31–43.
1971. A biosystematic and evolutionary study of *Capsicum pubescens* Ruiz & Pav. Year Book Amer. Philos. Soc., 1971, pp. 315–316.
1975. Genetic and biochemical systematic studies of chili peppers (*Capsicum*—Solanaceae). Bull. Torrey Bot. Club, vol. 102, pp. 396–403.

HEISER, CHARLES B., JR.; ESHBAUGH, W. H.; and PICKERSGILL, BARBARA
1971. The domestication of *Capsicum*—A reply to Davenport. Professional Geogr., vol. 23, pp. 169–170.

HEISER, CHARLES B., JR., and PICKERSGILL, BARBARA
1969. Names of the cultivated *Capsicum* species (Solanaceae). Taxon, vol. 18, pp. 277–283.

HEISER, CHARLES B., JR., and SMITH, P. G.
1948. Observations on another species of cultivated pepper, *Capsicum pubescens* R. & P. Proc. Amer. Soc. Hort. Sci., vol. 52, pp. 331–335.
1958. New species of *Capsicum* from South America. Brittonia, vol. 10, pp. 194–201.

HUNZIKER, ARMANDO T.
1950. Estudios sobre Solanaceae: Sinopsis de las especies silvestres de *Capsicum* de Argentina y Paraguay. Darwiniana, vol. 9, pp. 225–247.

PICKERSGILL, BARBARA
1969a. The archeological record of chili peppers (*Capsicum* spp.) and the sequence of domestication in Peru. Amer. Antiq., vol. 34, pp. 54–61.
1969b. The domestication of chili peppers. Pp. 443–450 *in* "The Domestication and Exploitation of Plants and Animals," Peter J. Ucko and G. W. Dimbleby, eds. Duckworth, London.
1971. Relationships between weedy and cultivated forms in some species of chili peppers (genus *Capsicum*). Evolution, vol. 25, pp. 683–691.

RICK, CHARLES M.
1950. *Capsicum pubescens,* a little-known pungent pepper from Latin America. Missouri Bot. Gard. Bull., vol. 38, pp. 36–42.

W. HARDY ESHBAUGH

Baseline Study of Delaware Bay

Principal Investigator: William S. Gaither, University of Delaware, Newark, Delaware.

Grant No. 917: For planning work in connection with a baseline study of the Delaware Bay and in support of the production of a series of reports on the study.

This grant as originally applied for was to cover the cost of designing a comprehensive baseline study of the marine environment of Delaware Bay; however, as the baseline planning was already well advanced when the grant was received, it was mutually agreed that the funds should be used to produce a comprehensive report series on Delaware Bay. Dr. Dennis F. Polis, who had coordinated the planning, was chosen as series editor.

Owing to a fortuitous circumstance, it was possible to use the funds granted by the Society as matching money to a Sea Grant made to the Delaware River Basin Commission. This allowed additional help to be employed in the compiling of the Delaware Bay Report Series.

To date 10 volumes have been produced, and a revolving fund has been set up to provide for the publication of future volumes of the series. As it stands the series includes three general volumes: an inventory and evaluation of information, baseline study plans, and a comprehensive bibliography; two volumes dealing with the social sciences: one on history, land ownership, and laws, and one on the economic and social aspects of Delaware's coastal zone; and five volumes of scientific information: geochemistry, physical and chemical oceanography, two biological keys, and a volume on the Bay's oyster community. Thus the series represents the first attempt at a comprehensive description of this important geographical region of the Central Atlantic seaboard. The 10 volumes are cited in detail below. All were published in 1973 by the University of Delaware College of Marine Studies, Newark, Delaware.

Volume 1. Series summary: Inventory and evaluation of information on Delaware Bay; 213 pp., illus.

2. History, land ownership, and laws, including a survey of maps prior to 1840, by natural and historic resource associates, 294 pp., maps.

3. Trace metal geochemistry of estuarine sediments: Clay mineral distribution in the Delaware Bay and estuary, by Richard N. Strom; Trace metal environments near shell banks in Delaware Bay, by Frederick

Bopp, 3d, and Robert B. Biggs; Trace metal baseline studies on the Murderkill and St. Jones Rivers, Delaware Coastal Plain, by Frederick Bopp, 3d, Frederick K. Lepple, and Robert B. Biggs; 96 pp., illus.

4. Physical oceanography, by Dennis F. Polis and Stuart L. Kupferman; Chemical oceanography, by Karl-Heinz Szekielda; 170 pp., illus.
5. Guide to the macroscopic estuarial and marine invertebrates of the Delaware Bay region, by Les Watling and Don Maurer, 178 pp., illus.
6. The biology of the oyster community and its associated fauna in Delaware Bay, by Don Maurer and Les Watling, 97 pp., illus.
7. Pictorial guide to fish larvae of Delaware Bay, with information and bibliographies useful for the study of fish larvae, by Lewis N. Scotton, Robert E. Smith, Nancy S. Smith, Kent S. Price, and Donald P. de Sylva; 206 pp., illus.
8. Economic and social aspects of Delaware's coastal zone, by Joel M. Goodman, 184 pp., illus.
9. Baseline study plans, by Dennis F. Polis, 118 pp., illus.
10. Comprehensive bibliography on Delaware Bay, by Mark Plunguian, Robert E. Fothergill, Anne H. Longenbach, and Evelyn Cook, 170 pp.

WILLIAM S. GAITHER

The Thunderbird Paleo-Indian Site and the Middle Shenandoah Valley Research Program, 1971–1974

Principal Investigator: William M. Gardner, Catholic University of America, Washington, D.C.[1]

Grant No. 906: For an archeological study of Paleo-Indian quarry and living sites in the Shenandoah Valley, Virginia.

Since work under this grant (made in 1970) was initiated, extensive excavations at the Thunderbird and numerous other sites have been undertaken, and at the time of this writing (December 1974) it is difficult, if not impossible, to pinpoint what specifically resulted from the Society's funding. It was therefore decided to present a general summary and overview of what we have discovered about the prehistory and paleoecology of the Middle Shenandoah Valley since our program began.

Background

The Thunderbird archeological site is located on the South Fork of the Shenandoah River some 6 miles southwest of Front Royal, Virginia. It is a stratified site with an occupational continuum that covers the Paleo-Indian to Early Archaic periods, or from approximately 12,000 to 9,000 years ago. It is at present the only known stratified archeological site of such antiquity in North America documenting the changes that took place in the cultural systems of the ancestral North American Indians following the final retreat of the Wisconsin glaciation and the transition from Big Game Hunting to a General Foraging adaptation.

The Thunderbird site forms the core of the Flint Run Paleo-Indian complex, which in turn is the central focus of the Catholic University's Department of Anthropology Middle Shenandoah River Valley research

[1]Acknowledgment is extended to John D. Flynn. Jr., owner of Thunderbird Ranch, for allowing our excavations to continue and for providing the funds and land for the development of the Thunderbird Museum and Archeological Park; Dr. John Foss, pedologist, and Dr. Antonio Segovia, geologist, both of the University of Maryland, for their invaluable contributions; and Dr. Meyer Rubin, head, U. S. Geological Survey Radiocarbon Laboratory, who kindly ran our C-14 dates.

program. Begun in 1971 as an investigation of a single Late Pleistocene-Early Holocene archeological site, the program has expanded to include a multidisciplinary attack on an array of prehistoric, paleoenvironmental, pedological, and geomorphological problems at all time levels. The ultimate goal is to establish, through an integrated team approach, a model for such research, a detailed regional natural and cultural history, and an explication of some of the various processes that have shaped and molded the environment and prehistoric society.

In addition to the initial funds for the 1971 exploratory excavations provided by the National Geographic Society, investigations in 1972 and 1973 were supported by the National Science Foundation (grant GS-33954). The Thunderbird Museum and Archeological Park, a private tourist-oriented research institution that developed out of the ongoing program, supported excavations in 1974 and will continue to underwrite the work. The Catholic University Summer School programs also provided some support throughout this time.

The presence of artifacts dating to Paleo-Indian times, a period that archeologists date as beginning around 12,000 years ago, was first reported to me in 1970 by members of the Northern Shenandoah chapter of the Archeological Society of Virginia. These amateur archeologists realized the importance of their finds and, with the exception of occasional surface collecting, did not touch the sites involved. North American archeology owes a considerable debt to these part-time archeologists not only for reporting the sites to professional investigators but also for not subjecting them to the vandalism that collectors often wreak on sites of this antiquity.

Although it was known from the initial series of field reconnaissances that the Thunderbird was but one of the Paleo-Indian sites within the total complex, the data indicated it was the most important and largest. Therefore work was initiated at the site. The first impression was that the Thunderbird, like all other known Paleo-Indian sites in the East, was surficial and plow-disturbed. As a result, the first step in the investigation was to use a technique not previously applied to such sites. This was a controlled surface collection of all visible cultural material within the framework of a measured and mapped horizontal grid system. This technique had been applied successfully elsewhere and has yielded results wholly unobtainable with random collecting. The rationale for using this technique was that while it was highly doubtful that much cultural material lay below plow depth (generally between 0.8 and 1.0 foot), cultural activity is patterned, and even 200 years of plowing would not have completely obliterated the evidence of the patterned distribution.

Accordingly this procedure was initiated. We divided an area of about 2,000 by 200 feet into 10-foot units and from these collected artifacts and mapped and analyzed them. One of the results was that, although there was a scattering of artifacts throughout the entire gridded area, there were specific locations where high densities of cultural material congregated. Such areas of intense human activity have been labeled "hot spots" in excavations at other Paleo-Indian sites. Using these data we dug one initial excavation unit in the center of one of these hot spots. As science, and a little bit of luck, would have it, we came down directly on soil stains that were all that remained of posts that had been driven into the ground over 10,000 years ago when the Paleo-Indians erected a structure on the spot. The stains, or postmolds, formed an oval pattern some 10 by 24 feet in size. Expanded excavations in this area and analysis of the recovered artifacts showed that burned areas, pits, and clusterings of certain classes of artifacts were the keys to defining the location of Paleo-Indian residential units at the site. It was subsequently discovered also that such structural areas were restricted to a specific contour interval and that the hot spots, which correlate with residential units, were located adjacent to extinct spring stream courses. These streams, which at one time flowed out of the limestone terraces to the west of the site and emptied into the ancestral South Fork, are now visible only through the study of aerial photographs, appearing as white scars on the surface of the ground.

As part of the surface collection, our pedologist, Dr. John Foss of the University of Maryland's Agronomy Department, began a soils map of the floodplain. One of his aims was to determine if there were soil anomalies that could be detected and that might aid us in our determination of activity area distribution. For a number of reasons, particularly agriculturally related chemical input, this failed. An important byproduct of the soils investigation, however, was that from a depth of 3 feet below the present surface Dr. Foss's bucket augur brought up artifacts at a spot some 70 feet east of where we were excavating. Although we would have ultimately tested this area, this discovery completely altered our research design, and within a few weeks it was realized that we were excavating on the first stratified and undisturbed Paleo-Indian site known in eastern North America.

Since the initial support by the National Georgraphic Society our research has gone a long way. Through the combined efforts of geology, geomorphology, pedology, paleoecology, and archeology, we have generated a series of models that offer considerable insight into the natural and cultural history of the Middle Shenandoah Valley. In the Flint Run area, in which the Thunderbird site is located, we have access to approximately 3,000 acres in which there is a continuous cultural record covering the past 12,000 years and yielding as well geological, pedological, and paleoecological data carrying us back into remote antiquity.

It is difficult to do justice to what we have discovered in a short article of this nature. I will, however, summarize some of these points in the paragraphs that follow. A number of master's theses and doctoral dissertations on many aspects of this research will be produced at Catholic University over the next several years. There will also be a continuous spate of articles. Anyone who is interested is urged to keep abreast of these. A preliminary report on this work containing the data base for much of what is said below is available (Gardner, 1974).

Environmental Setting

The Thunderbird site and Flint Run Paleo-Indian complex is located in the Ridge and Valley Provinces of eastern North America. Situated between the Blue Ridge and Massanutten Mountains, it is located in the South Fork Valley, which is but one arm of the Great Valley (known also as the Valley of Virginia and the Shenandoah Valley). Lithologically the area is composed of the quartzites of Massanutten, the metamorphosed volcanic rocks of the Blue Ridge, and the shales and limestones of the Valley floor. The shales and limestones have proved important factors in our Paleo-Indian studies. For reasons that can be attributed to climatic change and water-table lowering, Paleo-Indian occupation is, with minor exceptions, restricted to the limestone zone of the Flint Run area. Conversely, the bulk of later prehistoric occupation is confined to the shale zone where spring streams, issuing out of the shale uplands and flowing laterally across the floodplain, are still extant. Such streams have proved to be of major significance in this area in prehistoric man-land relationships.

Of overriding cultural import, if of minor geological significance, is the presence of a high-grade (from the stone knapper's point of view) form of cryptocrystalline quartz known as jasper (or yellow chert) along the east side of the South Fork where the metavolcanics of the Blue Ridge overthrust the limestones of the Valley floor. This particular stone, from which Flint Run derives its name, was, throughout the Paleo-Indian and Early Archaic periods, the preferred raw material for these early inhabitants. In fact, we have come to realize that this is one of the major reasons for their choosing the Thunderbird and like locations as spots for continuous cyclical returns over the 3,000 years that they pursued this particular life style. It has become obvious also that anywhere Paleo-Indian sites occur in any number one of the focal points in the choice of settlement areas was the presence of what the Indians considered, and experimentation has shown to be, highly desired and practical forms of chert.

The South Fork follows a meandering course dictated by the underlying bedrock. It has long been entrenched in this pattern. Successively during the millennia it has, however, changed back and forth between being a braided stream and one that was cutting a new channel. The result of this behavior is that it has been sliding eastward for a long time and has left behind it a series of steplike terraces. Most of these are readily visible, but at least two recent terraces (within the past 15,000 years) lie buried on the west side of the river. It was on one of these now-buried terraces that the Paleo-Indians camped, leaving behind the remains found at what we now know as the Thunderbird site. The entire terrace was not buried, as is evident from the results of our surface collection, but enough of it was covered to a depth of 3.5 feet to protect a 3,000-year cultural continuum.

Our various analytical procedures have led us to the conclusion that, while the dip and strike and faults and layering of the bedrock control the South Fork's meandering pattern, the braiding and down-cutting have been controlled by climatic change. Most of this climatic change can be tied directly into the waxings and wanings of the continental glaciers of the Pleistocene, but we have been able also to correlate cultural patterns and river behavior with Holocene climatic events. This is extremely important from a cultural ecological point of view, because we can closely relate human behavior with environmental fluctuation and see the interrelations with man's adaptive strategies.

Another topographic element within the shale zone of the Flint Run area, which has proved to be of considerable importance for settlement patterns during the Paleo-Indian occupation, is the alluvial fans that formed along the junction of the present floodplain and the bordering uplands or earlier Pleistocene terraces. Twelve thousand years ago these fans projected out as elevated aprons onto a floodplain that lies 11 feet below the present one. In this broad floodplain backwater swamps formed. Similar swamps form seasonally today (excavations have shown that such swamps have formed periodically during the last several thousand years). Observation has shown that these swamps serve as natural attractions for a diversity of game. The archeological evidence indicates that this was true in the past and the fans served as the locus for game butchering and processing stations for whatever was killed in the swamps (to date we have recovered no faunal material; a date on the upper part of one of these now-buried swamps of 9310 ± 300 BP 1950 W3005 correlates with a date of 9250 ± 300 BP 1950 W3006 in the upper levels of the immediately adjacent Fifty site, a stratified Paleo-Indian to Early Archaic butchering site approximately 1 mile upriver from the Thunderbird site).

Through the study of pollen, phytoliths, vegetation recovered from the above-mentioned bog, and various geological and pedological analyses it has been possible to work out the various climatic events and reconstruct general environmental conditions. Also used in this reconstruction are pollen profiles, taken from a bog in the immediate vicinity on Massanutten Mountain, and various published profiles for the Appalachian area and eastward. Victor A. Carbone, a graduate student at Catholic University, is doing the compilation and detailed analysis of these data. For the present, and for purposes of this paper, we can outline the following stages:

15,000–10,000 B.P. During the early part of this period climatic conditions in the Shenandoah Valley were wetter and cooler. The higher elevations in the mountains were probably snow covered for most of the year. The valley floor and the lower elevations of the mountains were covered with extensive areas of grassland dotted with clumps of spruce and other northern conifers. Along the banks of the river and in floodplain swamps were patches of hydrophytic forests, including sycamores, willows, and other deciduous trees and nonarboreal plants. The dominant game consisted of the typical Late Pleistocene fauna such as mammoth, mastodon, musk-ox, horse, camel, and probably deer, elk, and moose. Cultural dependence on hunting was possible over vast areas. As the glaciers began to retreat and conditions in the valley became increasingly warmer and less moist, there was a trend toward a reduction in the extent of the grasslands. In the uplands, coniferous species became increasingly abundant. The gregarious megafauna underwent continuous reduction. By the end of this period closed boreal forest conditions existed in the uplands; mixed hydrophytic associations spread as gallery forests along the floodplains; and the herd animals became extinct. Favorable territory for predators on game was restricted to a limited number of eco-niches, most prominently those on the floodplains.

10,000–8,000 B.P. Coniferous species in the form of a closed boreal forest rapidly became dominant and soon began to give way to a mixed deciduous-coniferous forest with a northern hardwoods cast. Changes in fauna were probably marked by a reduction in moose population and a slow increase in deer and elk. With increasing deciduous elements, wild plant foods would have become more varied and abundant. Changes in the riverine environment would have been in the direction of increasing numbers and diversity of species. Throughout this period the climate underwent several fluctations between cooler and moister and warmer and drier. The over-all trend, however, was in the direction of a continual warming. Seasonal variation in biota became increasingly important.

After 8,000 B.P. This is the last period of immediate concern and it is marked by the Atlantic, or climatic, optimum. Conditions approach those of modern times with the reestablishment of the deciduous forest. Oaks particularly reach a maximum, with the chestnut maximum appearing later. The changes in both arboreal and nonarboreal species resulted in a wide range of nuts, fruits, seeds, and berries. Such floral conditions facilitated a radiation in mammalian population.

Although admittedly brief and generalized, the scheme presented above does summarize the salient points; particularly that the changes following the retreat of the glaciers and the transition from the Late Pleistocene to the Holocene involved both climatic and biotic alterations. It was, as we shall point out, these changes to which cultural patterns adjusted.

Cultural Background

The cultural phases at the Thunderbird site take us from Clovis or early Paleo-Indian at the lowest levels to almost terminal Early Archaic. In the past the Paleo-Indian and the Archaic have been seen as two separate stages in the history of the North American Indians. Links have been suggested between them, but other workers have seen the two as having different ancestral traditions, and even coexisting in different environmental niches: Paleo-Indian in grassland dominated areas, Archaic in woodland zones. The data from the Thunderbird suggest that this is a false dichotomy and that there is a continuous development from Paleo-Indian through Early Archaic, with only slight modifications in the techno-industrial inventory. The major changes come only with the Middle Archaic, when there is the wholesale appearance of new technological items and a break with many traditions of the past. Even here, research in the Middle Shenandoah Valley indicates there is continuity throughout the remainder of prehistory. There is, however, a hiatus in the archeological record, due mainly to settlement shifts, with the abandonment of the limestone area and intensive exploitation of the shale region. In the Flint Run area this involved movement of only a little over a mile. Recent work at the Rudacil site in the Flint Run floodplain is providing the link between cultural phases of the Middle and Later Archaic periods and the Early Archaic.

The chronological phases given below are based primarily on projectile-point styles and their correlation with similar styles elsewhere. These are, in essence, archeological fossil indices. Radiocarbon dates from the Flint Run complex are so noted. The remainder of the dates are extrapolated from dates obtained elsewhere. The chronology runs only to the Woodland period, which is separated on the diagnostic index of pottery or ceramics. All the sequences are subject to revision, and we are on the surest ground only up to the Late Archaic phases.

Cultural Phase	Temporal Placement
Paleo-Indian Period	12,000–10,000 B.P.
Fluted Point Phases	
Clovis	12,000–11,000
Mid-Paleo	11,000–10,500
Dalton-Hardaway	10,500–10,000
Notched-point Phases (Early Archaic)	10,000–8,000 B.P.
Palmer	*9,940 ±
Kirk	**9,300 ±
Kirk A	
Warren	9,000
Archaic Period	
(Middle Archaic Phases)	8,000–5,000 B.P.
LeCroy	8,000 B.P.
Stanley	7,000
Morrow Mountain	6,000
Guilford	5,000
(Late Archaic Phases)	5,000–3,000 B.P.
Halifax	4,500
Savannah River	4,000
Perkiomen	3,500
Woodland Period	3,000–2500 B.P.

*From the Thunderbird site.

**From the Fifty site.

The form as presented above differs somewhat from conventional schemes. The major point of departure is the inclusion of Early Archaic within the Paleo-Indian period. This is done because the major break in cultural continuity and change in the Flint Run cultural systems does not come until the Middle Archaic phases. I feel that since ours is the most complete cultural and paleo-ecological record to date and that previous divisions were based on erroneous data such a departure is justified.

Within the Paleo-Indian period the major differences between the Fluted-point and Notched-point phases is the loss of fluting and the addition of notching in the latter. In addition, projectile points in the Palmer, Kirk, and Kirk A subphases have the added attribute of lateral serrations. Kirk A points are side-notched; the earlier two are corner-notched. Warren subphase points are side-notched but lack lateral serrations.

All the points in the Fluted- and Notched-point phases have either basal and lateral grinding (Clovis and Mid-Paleo) or basal grinding (Dalton-Hardaway, Palmer, Kirk, Kirk A, and Warren). Within the Fluted-point phases there is an over-all dimunition in size, with Clovis being the largest. Mid-Paleo points differ from Clovis points in being considerably smaller and thinner, with more marked basal indentation and greater length of fluting. The stylistic changes evident in these points at the Thunderbird site closely resemble similar changes between Clovis and Folsom points in the Plains. The addition of notching during the Notched-point phases suggests to me the introduction of the spear-thrower or atlatl. I see previous points as being used as attachments to thrusting spears. Such an assumption is based on a number of lines of indirect evidence, primarily the widespread appearance of notching almost simultaneously at 10,000 B.P. I cannot see a simple stylistic innovation being so nearly universally accepted unless it was accompanied by a technological change that made projectile-point usage more efficient. With minor exceptions the basic tool kit remains the same through all phases and subphases of the Paleo-Indian period. As far as the archeological data indicate there is little substantive change in the cultural system. Some important changes are noted particularly in population growth and settlement pattern. Notched-point phase artifacts occur in the same places as Fluted-point phases, in addition to occurring in geographical locations not previously occupied.

The major changes in settlement pattern and population distribution occur during the Archaic period at ca. 8,000 B.P. Formerly occupied areas are totally abandoned and populations begin exploiting vast areas that were minimally touched before. A whole battery of new tools appears in the inventory. The almost completely exclusive use of cryptocrystalline stones such as jasper becomes a thing of the past, and a wide range of lithic raw material is utilized. Such a simple shift facilitated changes in demographic distribution because the prehistoric populations were no longer confined to lithologically restricted locations.

Correlation with Climatic Change

The Fluted-point phase correlates with the period of the Late Pleistocene and the presence of grasslands and herd animals in the Shenandoah Valley.

Although man in association with now-extinct fauna has not been recorded in the East, I feel it is only a matter of time until this occurs. What it requires is for Eastern United States archeologists in conjunction with scientists from other disciplines to analyze all available data and predict where such factors as favorable past microenvironments, game, man, and preservation factors would be in conjunction. The association of fluted points with extinct fauna in the West, and the presence of such fauna, the proper environment, and similar points in the East, lead to the logical inference that Fluted-point phase populations were primarily hunters, principally of big game.

The climatic shifts during the 10,000–8,000 B.P. time ranges are coeval with the Notched-point phase. While, as I have noted, there are few major adaptive shifts, certain adjustive changes appear to correlate with the changed biota. For instance, it has often been noted that the spearthrower would make a more effective weapon when hunting and stalking solitary or small group mammals in a wooded environment. The change in thick-skinned cold-adapted herd animals to the typical mammals of the Holocene Eastern Woodlands may also correlate here. The beginning of the movement into new niches ties in very closely with the changed ecological setting. The North American Indian is viewed during this period as shifting from big-game hunting to simply intensive hunting with increasing diversification in the direction of more general foraging.

General foraging really reached its peak during the final climatic stage I have outlined and continued until the historic period. Agriculture late in the Woodland period supplements this general foraging adaptation, but such a way of life was never really abandoned until European disruption became complete.

The major settlement-pattern shifts occur during the transition from the Paleo-Indian to the Archaic period and the establishment of basically modern biotic conditions. Whereas during the Paleo-Indian period population movement was controlled by the ranges of the herd animals, inevitable exhaustion and necessary refurbishment of the tool kit, and the distribution of required and/or desired raw material. Rounds during the Archaic period became more cyclical and scheduled in conjunction with the availability of seasonally variable resources. In an area such as the Middle Shenandoah Valley where seasonal variation is marked and there is considerable horizontal and vertical zonation, these cyclical shifts are readily traced.

Summary

The initial season of the Middle Shenandoah Valley research program resulted in the delineation of areas of intense activity at the site; the correlation of these areas with extinct streams; the recovery of a postmold outline marking the floor plan of the earliest structure thus far reported for North America; the discovery of the unique stratification at the Thunderbird site; the isolation of temporally distinct but functionally similar living floors; and a springboard from which a single site excavation could be developed into a broad, all-encompassing, regional natural and cultural-history research program.

REFERENCE

GARDNER, WILLIAM M., ED.
1974. The Flint Run Paleo-Indian complex: A preliminary report 1971–73 seasons. Occas. Pap. no. 1, Archeological Laboratory, Department of Anthropology, Catholic University of America, 146 pp., illus. Washington, D.C. (Contributions by William M. Gardner, Antonio V. Segovia, John E. Ross, Victor A. Carbone, J. Ivor Gross, Deborah W. Harrison, William P. Boyer, Kurt W. Carr, Joan M. Walker, Rosalie Fanale.)

WILLIAM M. GARDNER

Analysis of Soils, Construction, and Geologic Materials from the Ai (et Tell) Excavations, Israel

Principal Investigator: George R. Glenn, Rutgers University, State University of New Jersey, New Brunswick, New Jersey.

Grant No. 890[1]: To make an analysis of the soils, construction, and geologic materials in connection with the Ai (Khirbat et Tell) archeological excavation, Israel.

The effective utilization of available water was a perennial problem that beset early farmers in the Nile and Euphrates Valleys. Only by early written sources do we know what was done about it, for later work has almost totally obscured whatever dikes and drainage canals were built. Firsthand evidence of methods of irrigation is found only in written sources.[2] Indeed, the cradle of hydraulic engineering was on the shores of these rivers.

Particularly pertinent to the specific geographic study reported herein is the writing on the Moabite Stone, probably the oldest alphabetic inscription in the world, which dates from the 9th century B.C. Near its conclusion are words translated as: "Mesha built two conduits, and since there were no cisterns in the city, Kasha, Moab, he ordered the inhabitants to place a cistern in each house."[3] This might very well have been an instruction given by the ruler of a village located in the hill country of Judah, particularly on the eastern slope of the watershed where from ancient times there has been practically no precipitation between April and November. The general problem was one of conservation but, different from the river valleys mentioned

---

[1]In addition to the grant from the National Geographic Society, the research here reported upon was supported by the Bureau of Engineering Research, Rutgers University, and the American Schools of Oriental Research, Jerusalem: "1970 Joint Archeological Expedition to 'Ai," Dr. J. A. Callaway, director.

[2]Hodges, Henry. *Technology in the Ancient World,* pp. 58, 60. Alfred A. Knopf, New York, 1970.

[3]Committee on History and Heritage of American Civil Engineering. Amer. Soc. Civil Eng. Hist. Publ. no. 1, pp. 17, 18, 1970.

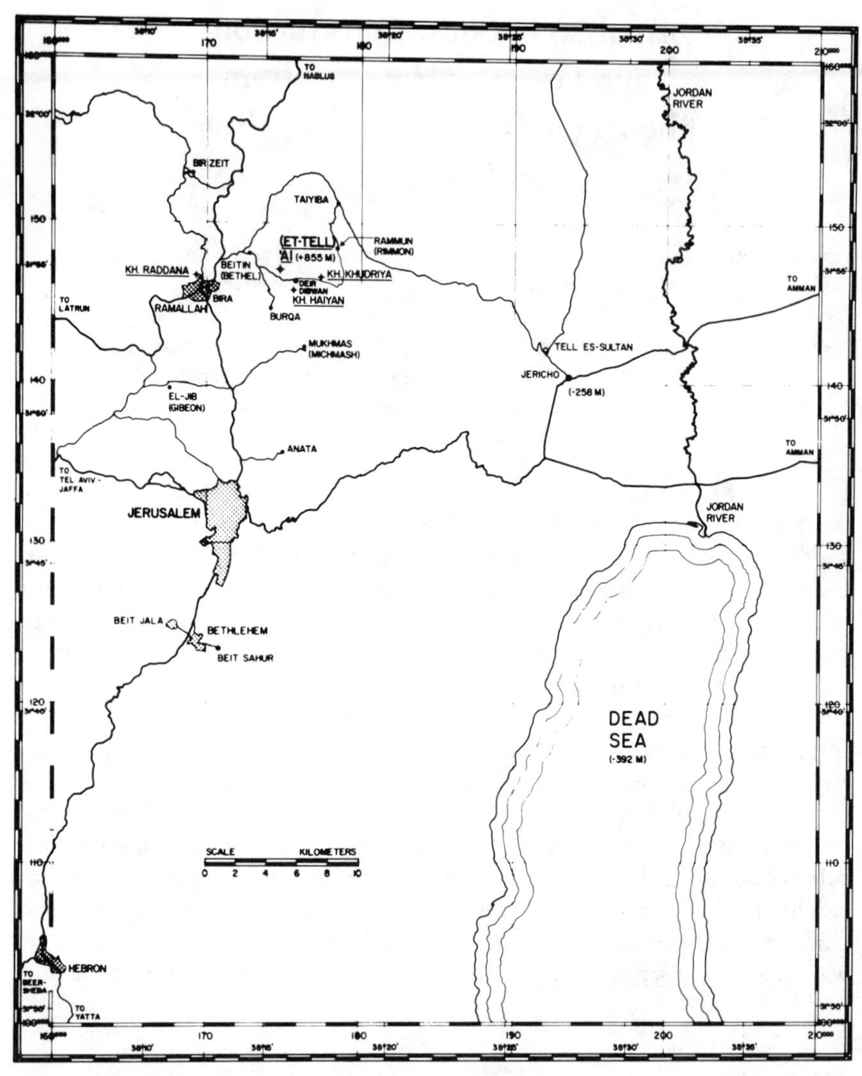

FIG. 1. General map showing Ai (et Tell) and vicinity.

above, the only source of water on some sites was rainfall. Rapid runoff into the valleys that led down to the Dead Sea necessitated some means of its interception. Roof drainage was no doubt caught and stored in pottery vessels. The multitude of fragments of water-storage pots attests to this mammoth effort to conserve water for everyday use. The cistern, however, was the major

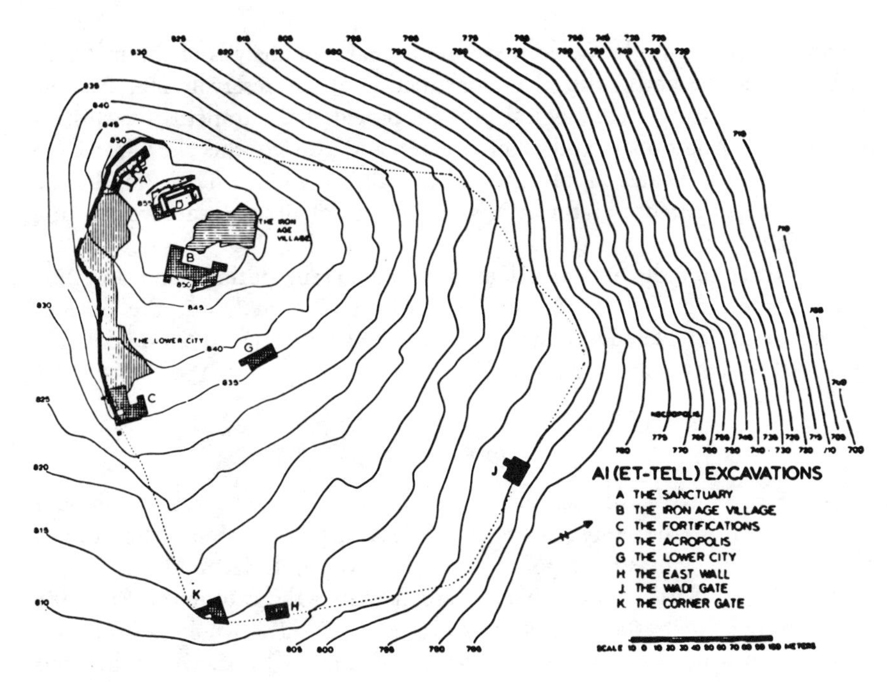

FIG. 2. Topography of archeological site at Ai.

household storage receptacle, as indicated in the inscription. In the absence of a steady flow of water from springs or frequent rainfall as a regular source of supply, it was necessary to provide even larger storage volume for the long dry periods. It was just such a situation that stimulated the construction of the water reservoir described in this paper.

Dating from the early part of the 3d millennium before Christ, the reservoir at Ai (et Tell) is believed to be the oldest of its kind discovered to date in the Middle East. The ingenuity of the design, as evidenced by the constructed project, still standing, acclaims it as the work of men who must have thought much as the engineer does today. Although surrounded by three fortified walls, the village was destroyed after about 700 years of use. Fortunately for us, this unfortuante event meant that the reservoir was buried progressively beneath an accumulation of water-borne and windblown soils. From this series of events this outstanding example of the best engineering thought of the day was preserved for us. And it befell a Biblical archeologist to uncover portions of it while searching for the answer to the problem of the location of the ancient Canaanite city of Ai. Recognizing the need for engineering expertise he called upon me to make an analysis of the materials and possible methods utilized in construction at the reservoir site. Possible indications of early technological prowess provided the impetus for this investigation. Additional studies of a later addition to the site, Iron Age housing and its water-supply system, are also analyzed. These results are reported first, because of the relative simplicity of design employed by the ancients.

I carried on the investigations reported herein during June and July 1970, while "on site" at Ai (et Tell), which is located near the modern Jordanian city of Deir Dibwan (Israeli-occupied territory), about 16 kilometers north of Jerusalem, as shown in figure 1.

Historical Setting

The most extensive mention of Ai on record is in the Biblical account of the march of the Hebrews under the leadership of Joshua. They passed through Moab, crossed the Jordan near its mouth, and conquered Jericho "at the edge of the sword." The record describes the capture of Ai in the hill country as well as other cities in the Shephelah.[4] The whole facies of this account, with its raidings, destroyings, and burnings by the fierce invaders from the desert, reminds us forcibly of the contemporary record (circa 1200 B.C.) of the Tell el-Amarna letters, which tells of the doings of the Khabiru and the Suti all over Palestine from north to south.[5]

The occasion for the construction (3d millennium B.C.) of such a formidable city, containing one of the earliest Canaanite sanctuaries (cf. Megiddo, Jericho), is uncertain.[6] However, from its location near an ancient Egyptian trade route one might associate its origin as commercial. It was certainly a stronghold of defense, being completely encircled by three walls.[7]

---

[4]Kittel, Rud., ed. *Biblia Hebraica*, pp. 328–331. Privileg. Wurtt. Bibelanstalt, Stuttgart, 1950.

[5]Hall, H. R. *The Ancient History of the Near East,* pp. 410–411. Methuen & Co., London, 1950.

[6]Finegan, Jack. *Light from the Ancient Past,* p. 124. Princeton University Press, 1946.

[7]Callaway, J. A. *The 1968–1969 'Ai (et Tell) Excavations.* Bull. Amer. Schools Oriental Res., no. 198, p. 9–31, illus., 1970. Technological findings from the present study are to be found on page 46 of Callaway's article on Ai in the *Encyclopedia of Archeological Excavations in the Holy Land,* pp. 36–52 (New York: Prentice-Hall, 1975).

FIG. 3. View looking down steep southwest slope to spring in wadi.

FIG. 4. Truncation of limestone layers, viewed from south with the *tell* at the summit.

Physical Setting

Regional geologic study indicates that Israel is mostly Marine Cretaceous, Jurassic, and Triassic. Basaltic lavas touch east and central Jordan and extend eastward. The geomorphology of the vicinity of Ai (et Tell) is mountainous and the lithology is karst. The landscape is rough and rocky.

The mountain body, known as the Judean Hills, is dissected by wadi cuts, which belong to the marine Cenomanian-Turonian, up to 800 meters thick. The Jerusalem anticline is some 10 kilometers west of the site, and so the runoff in the area is generally to the east. The principal strata at the site, which subdivide thicker chalky layers, are hard limestone. Tectonic forces that have been active in the past are folding, uplifting, and faulting. Residual soil on slopes of the site is only inches above bedrock in most instances.

FIG. 5. George R. Glenn surveying cisterns in Iron Age house near base stone of building column.

Site Investigation Plan

The area inside the fortified walls contained 0.11 square kilometer. Figure 2 shows an area designated as site B, which is part of the Iron Age village, situated near the summit of the *tell* and covering about 0.01 square kilometer. It contained a housing compound, consisting of south and north dwelling units having a cistern and cavern water-storage system, all of which were analyzed. Additional studies were devoted to the intact Bronze Age reservoir, which was situated at the southeast corner of the site, shown in figure 2 as site K. Detailed elevation, plan, and slope measurements were taken of surface bedrock and, where needed, of underlying strata as well. Flow measurements were made of water from a spring, viewed in figure 3 outside the walls and deep in the wadi north-northwest of the *tell*. Detailed sampling both on and off the site was made of soil and geologic materials, and on site construction materials, in order to correlate the construction phases and to appraise the level of technological innovations by the occupants of the site.

Laboratory studies included particle-size analyses made by the use of conventional combined hydrometer-sieve techniques. These were supplemented by compositional studies, by X-ray diffraction and infrared spectroscopy, of constructed and natural materials.

Results and Discussion

GEOLOGICAL ALTERATIONS:

The severity of truncation by water erosion of the uplifted bedrock may be noted in figure 4, which shows a view of the *tell* from the south. The same strata were cut by the wadi on the north slope of the *tell* to a depth of 100 meters. The rock strata generally slope downward in an east-southeast direction at a ratio of 1 (vertical) to approximately 4 (horizontal). The regularity of the alternating hard and soft layers that actually underlay the site is shown in bold relief. Slope of the resulting ground surface inside the fortress walls ranged up to 25 percent.

Additional surface alteration by the ancient occupants themselves consisted of the removal of hard stone layers, which were subsequently used as construction materials. This removal was done in such a way that the resulting surfaces would be suitable for erection of buildings or as depressions for containment and diversion of water, etc., as will be noted in detail in later discussion.

FIG. 6. View of Iron Age house walls and columns.

CONSTRUCTED PROJECTS:

Iron Age housing compound (*ca. 1200 to 1000 B.C.*). The examined construction (B, fig. 2) was part of a compound consisting of two housing or dwelling units, divided by an east-west wall with no openings for its entire length. Construction was on the bare bedrock surface, which was depressed below existing terrain by removal of one or two upper layers; these removed materials were subsequently used as building stones and mortar as well as for packed-earth floor-leveling material. General fracturing of bedrock in the area permitted easy removal of the thinner harder layers, which were subsequently broken into convenient sizes for wall construction. After being leveled for specific room areas, spaces between the adjacent room areas were excavated in a stair-step fashion, and the process repeated.

Owing to the precipitation patterns on the area, which analysts indicate have remained more or less the same since very early times, provision had been made for storage of water for the 9 months or so each year without rainfall. This need was particularly urgent for the *tell* occupants because there was no natural water source on the site. The builders carved cisterns from the

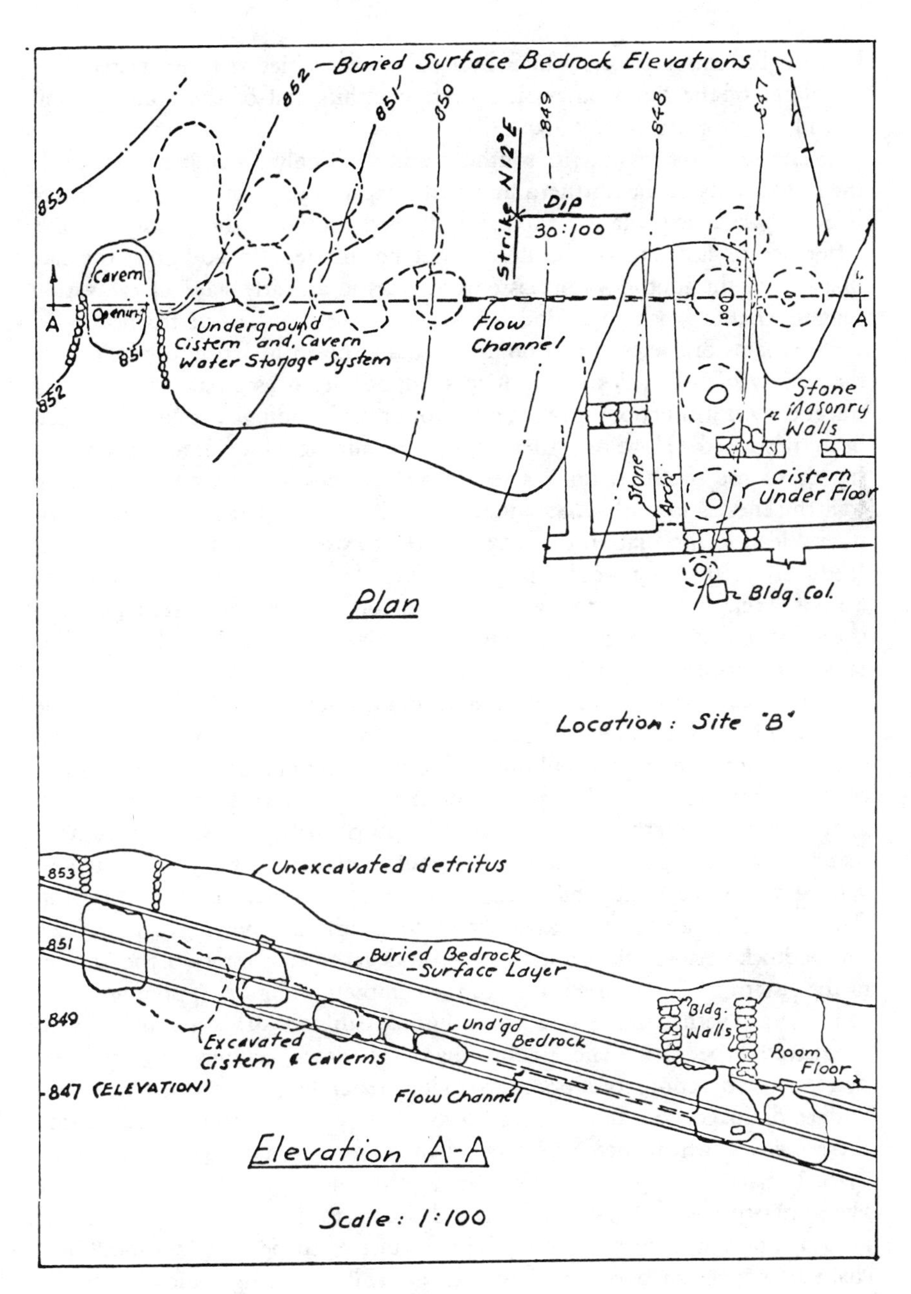

FIG. 7. Iron Age water-storage system.

bedrock for this purpose. These bottle-shaped cavities were excavated into the floors of the rooms along the western uphill wall of the housing compound, as shown in figures 5 and 6.

The three cisterns in the southern unit held only 3 cubic meters, while the five cisterns in the northern unit had a capacity of 38 cubic meters. There is no apparent explanation for the difference although the possibility of a difference in function of the unit might be inferred. In addition, the fact that one of the southern unit cisterns appears in an early stage of excavation suggests that expansion was under way at the time of its last destruction.

Remains of the construction are partially shown in figure 6 to illustrate the variety of wall thicknesses. It was impossible to ascertain whether wall thickness was a function of overhead floor or roof loadings because these had been destroyed. However, there were the additional columns (shown in fig. 6) of the southern unit. The shortened spans accompanying increased wall thicknesses in both units adjacent to the western perimeter of the compound lead to speculation that a second floor existed. The higher terrain immediately to the west would have been ideal for a terrace leading into such a floor level. Almost certainly, the reason for the westerly cistern locations is the convenient surface drainage pattern from the west and south slopes just outside the western wall.

Additional water storage is located uphill from the northern unit of the compound. As indicated in figure 7, it has a capacity of 38 cubic meters, almost equal to the total of all downhill cisterns combined. The storage space consists of one cistern and a series of underground caverns, interconnected in a meandering pattern from an uphill entrance to the lowest point some 5 meters from the northern unit. A complete underground horizontal and vertical survey was made and related to the surface construction, as shown in figure 7. As indicated, the caverns were found to have been excavated from soft bedrock between the same two hard-rock layers that intersect the bottom of the cistern in the northern unit of the compound. Figure 8, photographed inside the caverns, shows that the columnar support structure consisted of unexcavated bedrock. The smooth harder bedrock ceilings provided the necessary slab action to support overlying materials (unexcavated to date). Surface drainage from uphill areas flowed by way of the cavern entrance into these cavities, which measured more than 10 meters in extent. Cylindrically shaped channels may be observed in figure 9 in the eastern walls at the lowest cavern levels. These led directly downhill to the northern unit cistern, as also shown in figure 7. From their distinctive shape and location, these channels appear to have been formed originally by design and not as the result of a natural erosion process. These channels apparently converged into

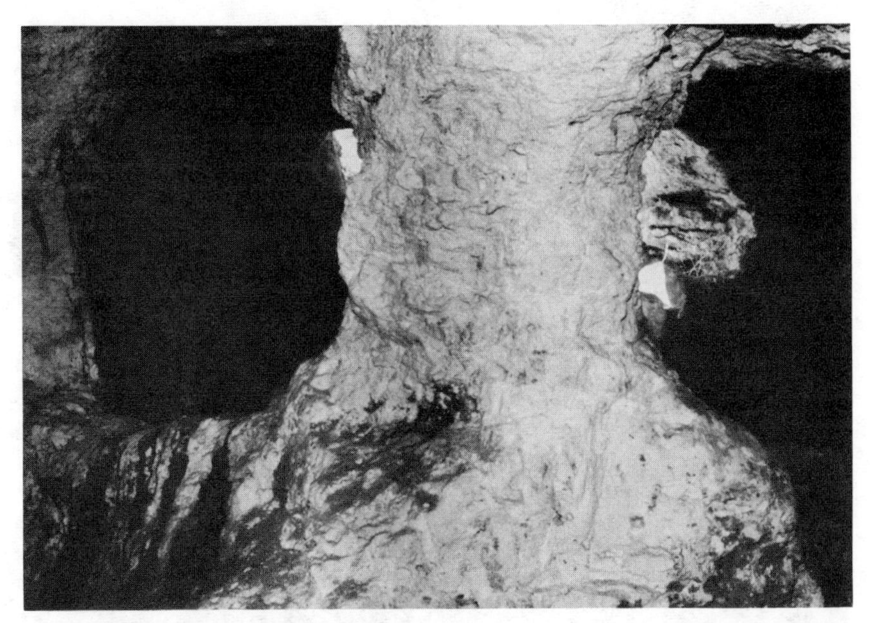

FIG. 8. View of inside caverns showing columnar support structure.

FIG. 9. Cylincrically shaped channels in east wall of lowest cavern.

FIG. 10. Rectangularly shaped channel outlet in cistern of Iron Age house downhill from caverns.

a single rectangular opening in the cistern, the dark area in the background of figure 10.

The rate of flow of seepage water originally may have been quite small. In later times, as the flow rate increased because of channel erosion, control of flow rate to prevent overflow of the downhill cisterns was needed. At the present time there are no definite indications of means of blockage, either in the caverns or in the cisterns. One may say, however, that replenishment of the northern cisterns occurred by gravity flow from the caverns more or less automatically until some system of control was needed. As shown in figure 7, there were two other large cisterns that were interconnected to the receiving cistern and the tops of which are still buried beneath accumulated dust, earth, and rubble. Figure 11 shows a cistern lid still in place with fragments of broken pottery and rock projecting through the cracks by the lid. Figure 12 shows a top view of the opening in the receiving cistern through which I had access. Shown in the bedrock floor above the cistern is a series of shallow liquid retainers, carved in a stair-step fashion down into the opening. These retainers were in the path of water flow for a second means of filling the cisterns, probably from roof drainage; evidently they served to intercept water, in a sequential fashion, and collected sediment, which subsequently would have been removed periodically to prevent its entrance into the cisterns.

A variety of methods of wall construction may be observed at the compound. One wall had been preserved at its original height and was noted to contain a beam seat measuring 30 centimeters across and some 1.6 meters above the floor. Stones having a rectangular cross-section, more or less, were used mostly for the more precise construction, such as openings and arches. Figure 13 shows coursing with interlocking of stones such as is commonly encountered in present-day masonry construction. The first course was laid of stones end to end. The second was offset by approximately a half block's length to give greater stability to the wall. Walls were apparently commenced at the location of the desired door openings and extended in both directions from the jambs. In order to provide stability against lateral buckling, i.e., perpendicular to the wall's length, the wall was constructed in two parallel rows of leader stones per course with the thickness of wall approximately equal to one block's length. Interlocking of the two rows was achieved by turning alternate stones at 90° to its predecessor. Figure 14 shows a door jamb indicating such a technique in the wall.

Scraps of rocks left over from preparation of block-shaped building stones were often used to construct wall sections between door openings. In some, less evidence of coursing may be noted in the background of the preceding figure. Note the irregular pattern shown in figure 15 in a wall containing an arch about a meter in height as the only entrance into a long narrow room, probably housing domestic animals. It was clearly evident that workmanship and materials employed in areas in which people were housed were superior to those used in other areas.

Analyses of building materials employed in the Iron Age house wall and cistern construction indicate that they were totally of local origin and apparently used in their natural state after removal from stratified layers followed by minor shaping. Building joints contained a mud-type mortar that

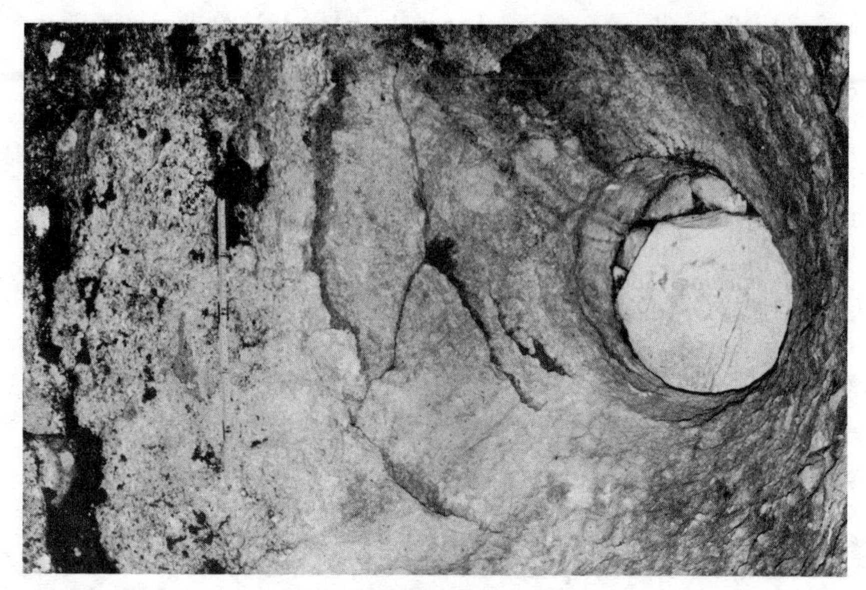

FIG. 11. Inside view of Iron Age house cistern with lid in place.

FIG. 12. Top view of cistern, opening through floor, with adjacent water-sediment retainers.

had largely washed out and been replaced by other residue washed and blown in through the centuries. Sealant if used in the cisterns had long ago lost any unique character and was indistinguishable from fine sediment that had washed into crevices in the rock. Irregularly eroded solution channels, commonly found in limestone rock exposed to penetrating surface waters, had formed in cisterns not covered by residue.

The covered cisterns were so well preserved, however, that their retention capability has not been affected significantly to the present day. This was evidenced by standing water in one uncovered in the last season of excavation.

The combined capacity of stored water in the Iron Age housing compound would provide a minimum of 1 gallon each per day for as many as 80 persons during the dry seasons. Although off the site, additional water was probably available in ancient times from a spring in the wadi (see fig. 3). Flow was 47 liters per hour during July 1970; however, it was likely greater in earlier days, as evidenced by other openings above the present flowing spring shown in figure 16. Natural caves in an eroded limestone cavity may have been enlarged in an adjacent hill to provide additional sources of water. Stalactites met stalagmites between roof and floor and formed solid columns, 15 to 20 centimeters in diameter. These were formed by vertical seepage of solute containing dissolved limestone.

Ingenuity on the part of the ancients during the Iron Age is clearly demonstrated in the construction, just cited. Building skills enabled the erection and maintenance of homesteads of which their occupants could be duly proud and within which reasonable comfort and adequacy were assured.

Water-storage reservoir—Early Bronze (*ca. 2700–2400 B.C.*). The detailed analysis of an almost intact reservoir (K, fig. 2) was even more illustrative of the technological prowess of the ancients. As suggested earlier, the greatest challenge the ancients faced was the conservation of water in sufficient quantity to provide for minimal needs and to enable them to support other activities requiring water. In meeting and overcoming this challenge, they developed a technique certain to be admired by modern engineers. Inasmuch as the water-storage capacity provided by the reservoir was sufficient to sustain adequately a population at site capacity during a given dry season, domestic animals as well as plants and trees could easily be maintained.

The reservoir had been constructed some 45 meters lower in elevation and 260 meters in an east-southeast direction from the Iron Age village described previously. The dike enclosure was horseshoe in shape, with open end uphill. It measured more than 3 meters in height at its highest point, as

FIG. 13. Coursing and interlocking of stones in Iron Age house wall.

FIG. 14. Door jamb of Iron Age house wall.

FIG. 15. Archway in Iron Age house wall.

FIG. 16. Flowing spring in wadi (see also fig. 3).

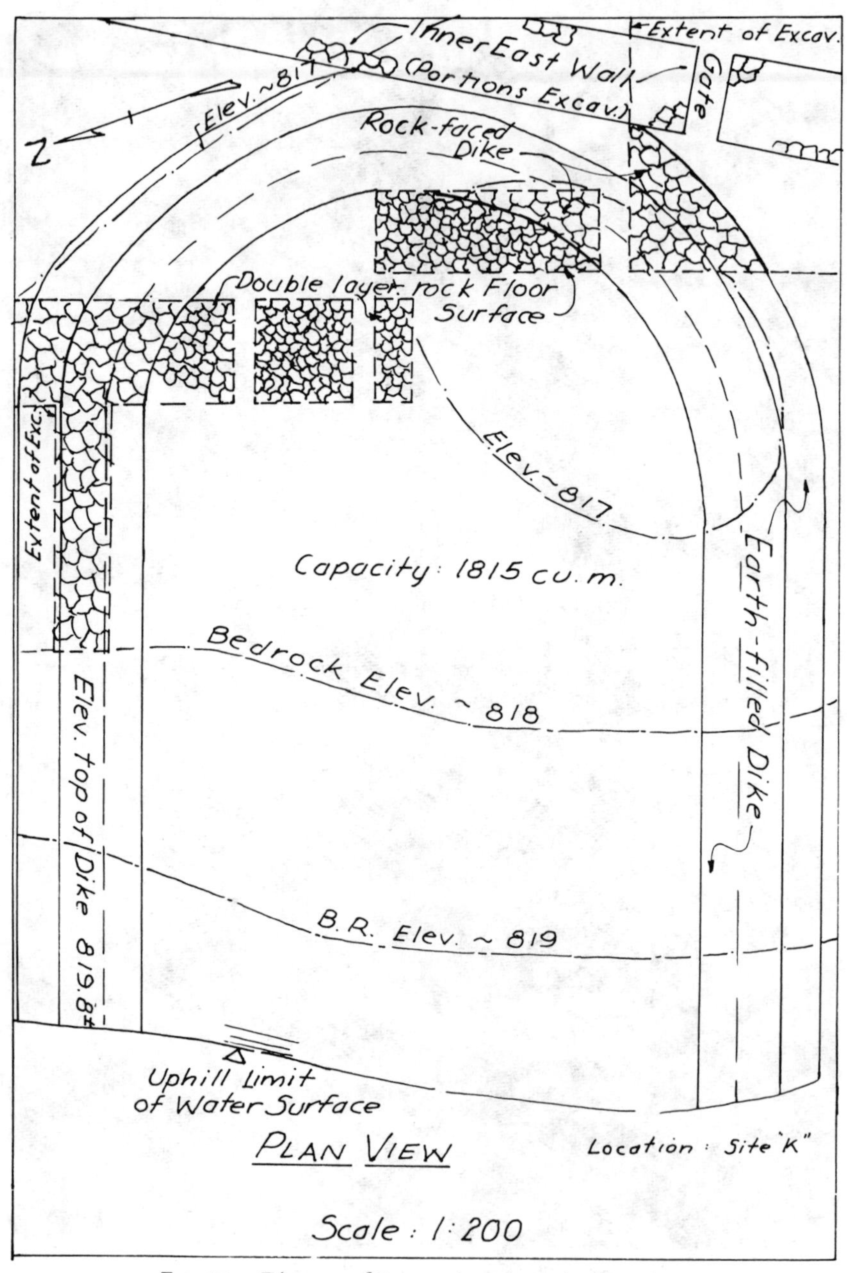

FIG. 17. Diagram of Bronze Age reservoir: Plan view.

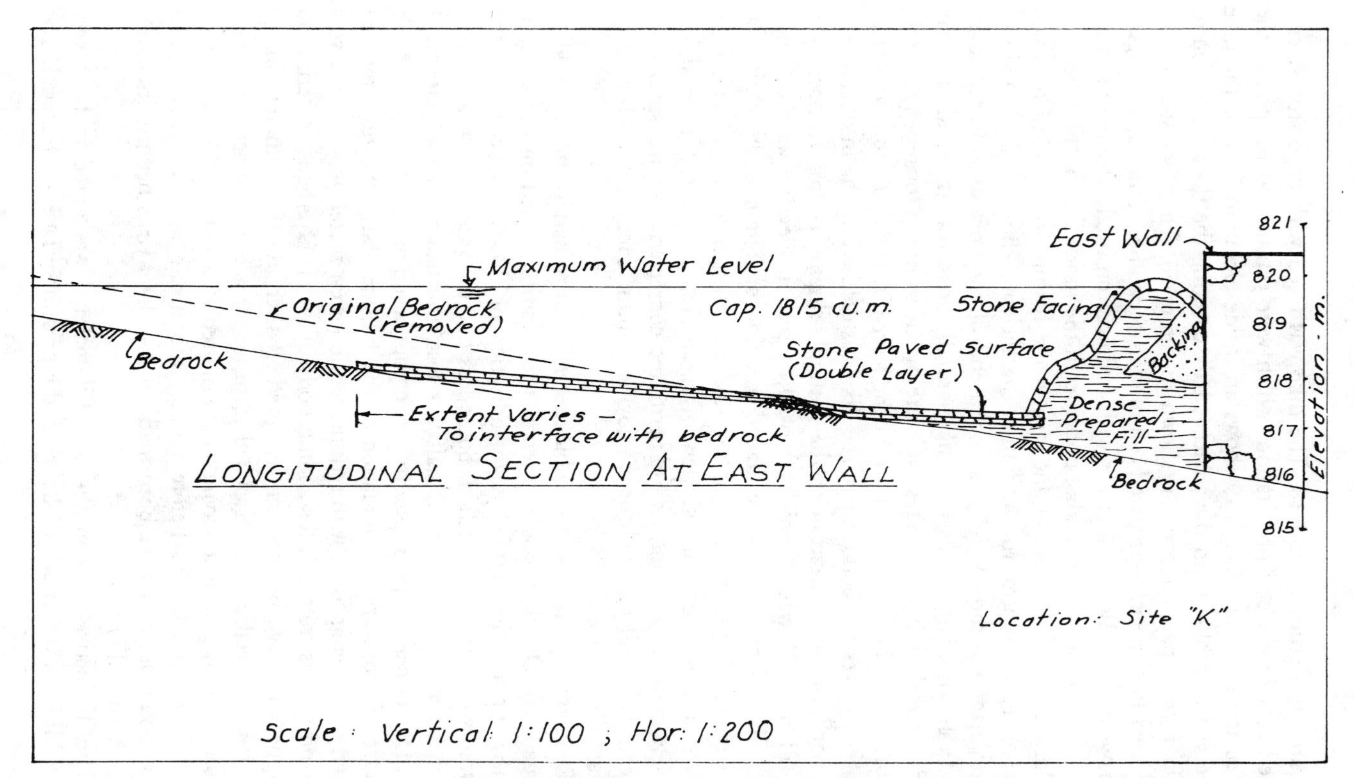

FIG. 18. Diagram of Bronze Age reservoir: Longitudinal section.

illustrated in figures 17 and 18. The dike was faced with large stones, embedded in a special soil preparation, which were constructed integral to the floor of the reservoir. Figure 19 shows an inside elevation view of the dike with caved-in rubble from the adjacent balk covering the floor. A section of the floor, with part removed, is shown in figure 20. The floor stones were embedded in a specially prepared soil mortar in two horizontal layers. Figure 21 shows that the floor's interface with bedrock consisted of only one layer. Note also that the floor extended underneath the inside face of the dike.

Inspection of the natural and man-made features of the area occupied by the reservoir confirms the wisdom of the ancients' choice. The natural surface drainage ran directly into the open end of the horseshoe-shaped reservoir. As shown by figure 2, waters that naturally drained to the southeast were also directed downhill to the reservoir site by the southern fortress wall. From measurements of excavated sections of the reservoir, the dike, and borings to bedrock, the western boundary of the dike was defined by the intersection of its upper horizontal surface with the naturally sloping bedrock surface. The dike fill material was partially removed; a section view shows the darker special fill material; the wedge-shaped insertion of lighter backing material used near the upper backside of the dike is shown in figure 22 and is illustrated also in the sectional view of figure 18. This latter material was relatively more porous, and its use permitted conservation of the special impermeable dike fill material for employment immediately behind the inside rock face of the dike.

Reservoir capacity is 1,800 cubic meters (approximately one-half million U.S. gallons). During a year of average precipitation, based on the assumption that present-day rainfall is an indication of that 5,000 years ago, the reservoir would easily have filled. Some loss due to evaporation would occur in such an arid atmosphere. If half was lost, the balance would provide 4 liters of water per day per capita for a site population of 1,000.

Over the centuries, denudation of the hillside above the reservoir had resulted in its being filled with sediment, the lowest meter of which is a very fine sandy silt as from a still-standing body of water. Overlying materials do not appear to have been water-deposited. Rather, they contain remains of living space as well as the occasional intrusion of a burial trench. It would, therefore, appear that the reservoir had been used for a 400- to 500-year period, as mentioned previously, before falling into disuse as a well-maintained facility. Some use may have been made of it in later years because its water-retention capability seems intact.

The distinctive color of the dike fill material was noted to be a very dark reddish brown, much darker than the present surface soil material. The

FIG. 19. Inside elevation view of dike face.

FIG. 20. View of reservoir floor with layers removed (looking down at 45° to horizontal).

possibility was considered that imported additives of a special nature might have been used. However, exhaustive separation and analytical testing showed the special color and physical properties to have resulted from a concentration of selected portions of certain soil deposits, probably from the site itself or its immediate vicinity. Confinement of the selected material in the dike for extended time may have resulted in some darkening, due particularly to worm activity.

The density of the darker in-place dike fill material was as high as obtainable from present-day compaction procedures applied to similar soil materials, namely, 1.9 grams per cubic centimeter. The materials used in the actual construction and those occurring in the natural environment from weathering of the bedrock, worm action, etc., were sampled and analyzed. The resulting qualitative analysis is shown in figure 23. Except for more acidity in surface soils due to organic matter present, the other soil constituents were the same as those of the constructed materials. Results of quantitative analyses of particle sizes present in selected natural and constructed materials are shown in the form of a series of particle size distribution curves in figure 24. The larger quantity of clay-sized particles in core and sealant materials is shown by textural classification in figure 25.

Studies of figures 23, 24, and 25 show at a glance the distinct difference between the natural or raw materials and the constructed or fill and mortar materials. Figure 23 indicates that silica distributes into the soil as the rock masses break up as a result of weathering. Its source is the limestone beds bearing flint. Clay formation may also be noted as the compositional difference between buried and surface soils. The clay is micaceous (10 Å. layers) in character but include some 7 Å. and 14 Å. constituents as well. These have particle sizes less than 0.002 millimeter and are, therefore, classified as "clay" under the U.S. Bureau of Soils system. The "clay" and the finer "silt" sized particles are the constituents that give the special properties to the sealant used in the reservoir dike and floor, as illustrated by figures 24 and 25.

Figure 24 compares the particle-size distribution of the natural raw materials to those of these materials after modification for use in the construction of the sections of the dike and the reservoir floor. The gradation indicated by the shape of the upper distribution curve of the fill materials used in the south section of the dike possessed superior sealing capability to those used in the north section. The "refinement" procedures, employed in preparing the "sealant" for the dike and floor of the reservoir, in most instances, tripled the amount of 2μ-sized material.

Analyses showed that the soil particles were graded in size from large to small so as to provide necessary resistance to water penetration of the dike

FIG. 21. Reservoir floor partially removed adjacent to inside face of dike, showing floor layer extending underneath dike.

FIG. 22. Inside of dike—view of darker fill material at right in contrast to lighter backing material at left.

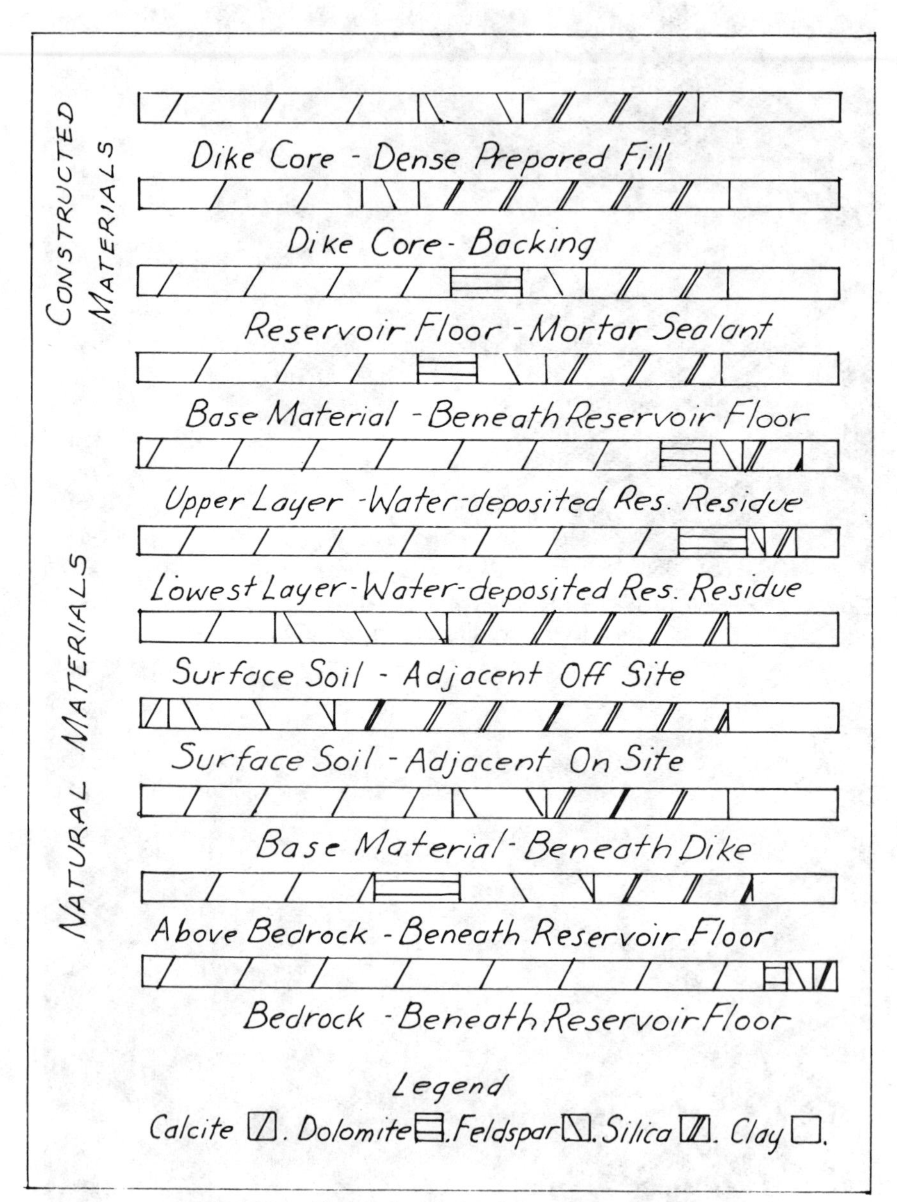

FIG. 23. Chemical analysis of reservoir materials.

and floor. Increase of uniformity coefficient, shown in figure 24, also indicated this desirable characteristic. Figure 25 shows the larger amount of fine-grained or clay-sized materials used in the dike and floor construction.

Further study of figure 23 provides insight as to the specific location from which the raw materials were obtained. The occurrence of dolomite in the reservoir floor mortar as well as in the buried soil and bedrock under the floor indicates the likelihood that the in-place material had been refined from this deeper-level dolomitic limestone as opposed to bringing in surface soil material not containing this constituent. On the other hand, the absence of dolomite in the dike fill material would indicate that raw material for the dike was from other nearby surface soil, formed by weathering of overlying calcitic limestone layers.

Conclusions and Discussion

In addition to providing adequate structural stability in their construction, one must conclude that the ancients devised a means for effectively preventing passage of water through otherwise unsuitable soil materials. The logical basis for the construction technique employed may easily be inferred from the findings.

The ancient technologists no doubt had had experience with dikes made from rocky, more porous soil from which water was lost at a fast rate. This experience may have been coupled with the finding of inadequate structural strength and durability from an earth dam built without rock on front, top, and back surfaces. In addition, observation of the fractures and dissolution channels in the bedrock and resultant passage of water would have been a part of their experience. Ideally, excavation to unfractured bedrock would have been the best solution, but the area of such continuous solid surfaces is limited. Instead of trying to seal the fine fracture cracks, they obviously chose to remove the fractured nonporous rock materials. Convenient rock sizes and shapes were chosen for the reservoir floor and dike. For the floor these were placed in a bed of special soil mortar and wedged tightly together, both horizontally and vertically, with the mortar in between (see fig. 20). By the use of two layers, each abutting joint in one layer was offset so that a rock surface in the other layer overlapped it. In this way the construction would present pathway for water passage of the smallest cross-sectional area and of the most circuitous length, in addition to providing structural stability. Because of the need for horizontal structural stability, the dike facing, on the other hand consisted of only a single layer of larger stones, 20–30 centimeters in thickness (about double the thickness of stone used for the floor). These

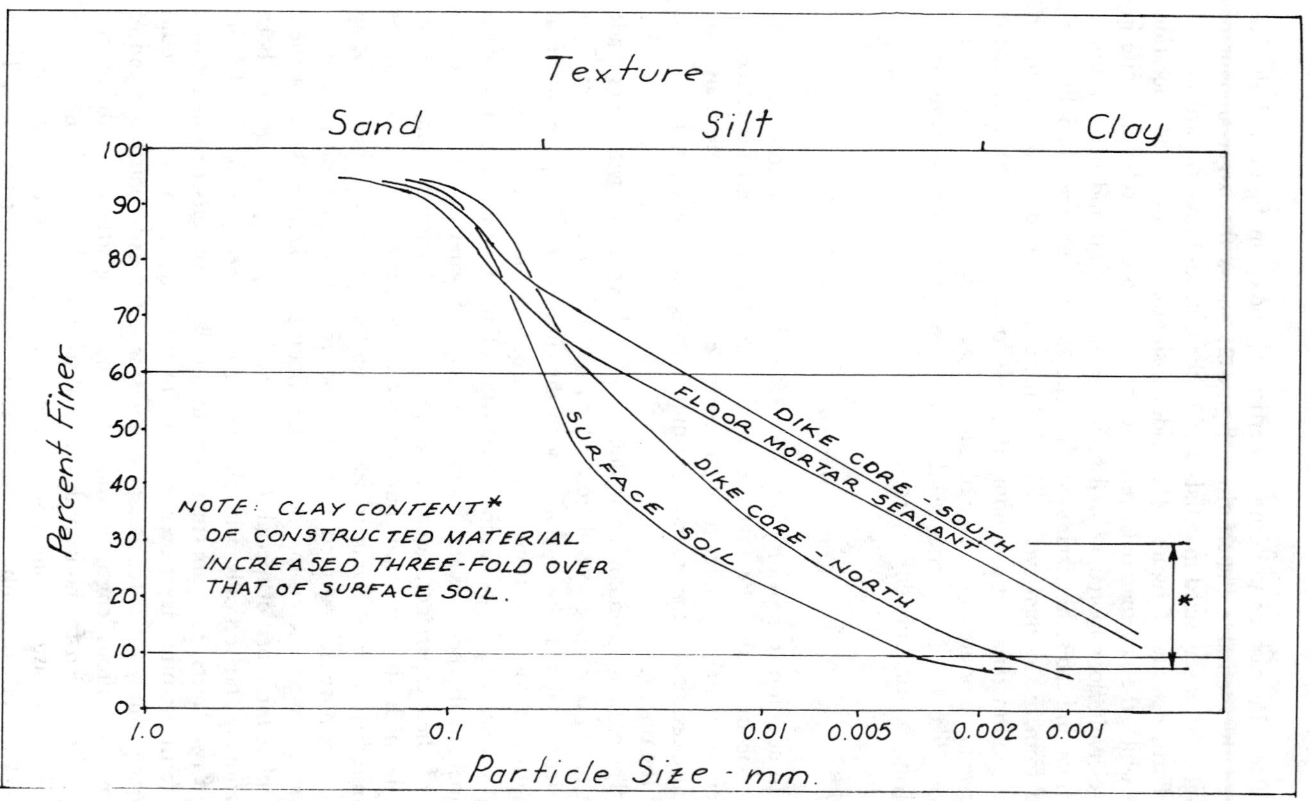

FIG. 24. Particle-size distribution of reservoir materials.

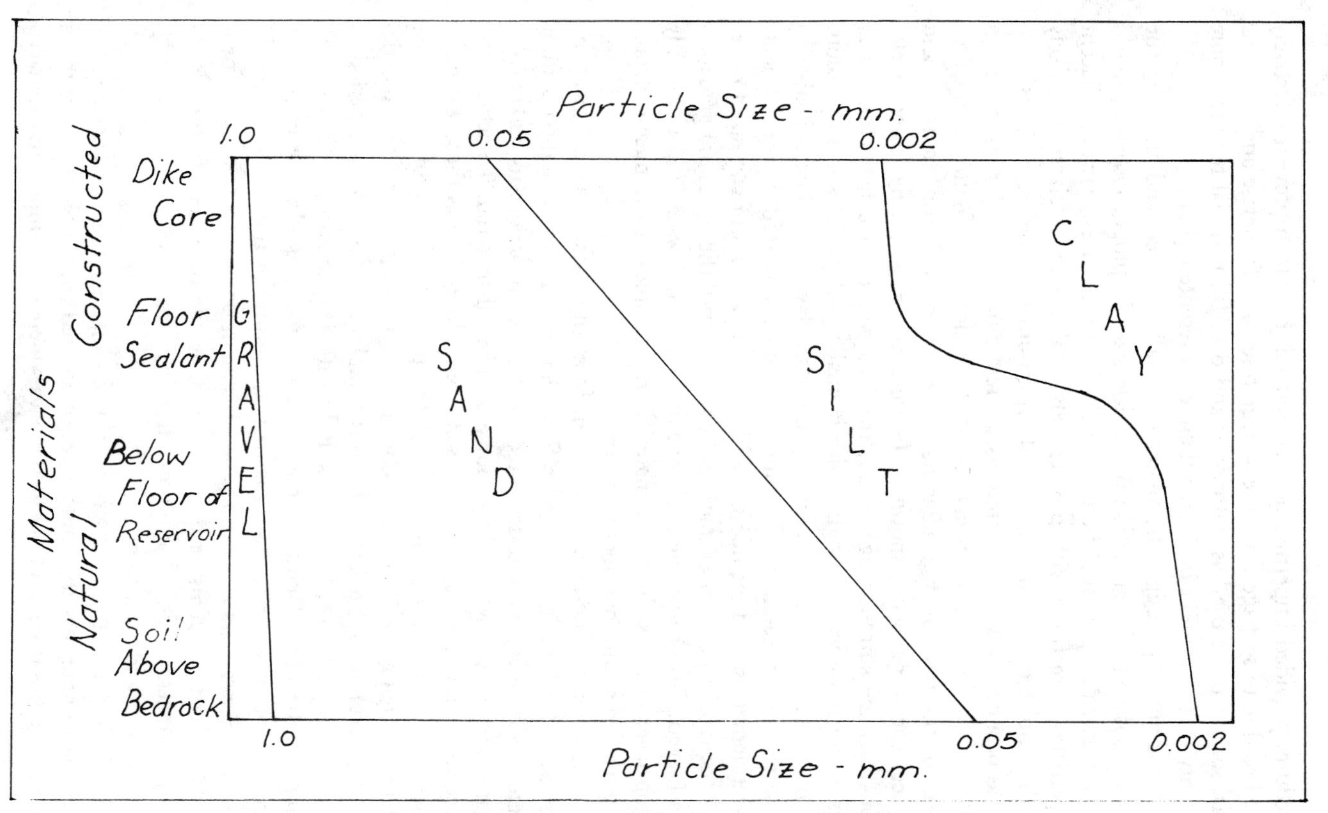

FIG. 25. Relative texture of reservoir materials.

procedures provided impermeable rock and soil mortar to prevent effectively water loss due to seepage from the storage reservoir. To devise and place the special sealant to be used as soil mortar and dike fill material required more ingenuity than is evident in the development presented so far.

Apparently by design the material actually selected and used by the ancients consisted of a gradation of particle sizes in proportions that would provide very small potential flow channels. The interstices between adjacent soil particles were filled with progressively smaller particle sizes. It is likely that this choice of material was based on certain previous experiences, possibly associated with other attempts at retaining water, for example, in small ponds or in making pottery vessels. As indicated by figure 17, the area chosen for the reservoir was adjacent to the fortress walls on the south and east near the corner gate, shown in figure 2 as site K. Being lower in elevation than the surrounding terrain, the area would have been flooded at times from surface water bringing with it smaller soil particles in suspension. This finer material accumulation in the surface layer was then available to serve as the bed of sealant material for the floor with little further refinement. This refinement would include the addition of quantities of clay-sized material or the removal of coarser material by sorting until the optimum gradation was achieved. Disturbing the sediment in an excess of water and using only the top layer of the sedimented material are examples of the means of providing needed additional finer particles.

In addition to fine-grained sediment from the surface, the soil near the site possessed a high percentage of fine-grained particles brought up from underneath the bedrock and deposited there by worm action; its darker color also indicates that it was a likely source of dike fill material. To achieve the desired distribution of particle sizes, some procedures such as those described previously may also have been necessary. The possibility exists, of course, that in some low-lying area, inside or outside the site walls, this finer material may have accumulated naturally to considerable depth over a long period of time. If so, it may have been available in sufficient quantity and quality to accomplish the desired ends without further processing. In any event, the choice the ancients made suited the desired end-use of the materials, and of course the necessary transportation and placement procedures were developed. Probably placed in a moistened state, the soil would have been further densified by compaction, dehydration and from the weight of the material itself and rock layers and/or facing.

In closing this discussion of the obvious ingenuity of the ancients it is interesting to note that they must have considered the problem of maximum weakness in a given system to be at the place where one component interfaced with another. The best example is that of the floor and dike surfaces in contact with water impounded inside the reservoir. Another example occurred at the point of discontinuity of the paved floor surface; in each instance a somewhat different aspect presents itself. At the floor's juncture with the dike, the floor was continued some distance underneath the dike, giving structural continuity (reducing the probability of the opening of a crack between the two masses) and extending the potential water flow path of minimum cross-section to that provided by the double floor thickness (see fig. 21). At the location where the floor reached its uphill limit, at the intersection of the horizontal surface with the bedrock surface, the ancients extended the upper floor surface layer for some distance on top of the bedrock layer with the sealant between the two (see fig. 18). In this way water was not likely to penetrate underneath the construction. If such procedures had not been followed, the internal sealing properties of the reservoir would have been lost, owing to the erosive action by water flow. The final result, of course, would have been the breakup of the structures after being undermined. Instead, the reservoir walls and floor served for many decades, as evidenced by the fine sediment from uphill deposited to a depth exceeding 1 meter during its use. The present integrity of the reservoir, still intact after about 5,000 years, is the final proof of the validity of techniques employed in its construction.

George R. Glenn

Behavior of Free-ranging Chimpanzees, Tanzania, 1969–1971

Principal Investigator: Jane Goodall, Gombe Stream Research Centre, Kigoma, Tanzania.

Grant Nos. 841, 968: For continued support of a long-term study of chimpanzees in the wild, conducted at Gombe National Park, Tanzania.

It is unfortunate that 1969 was marred by the tragic death of Ruth Davis, who fell over a precipice while following chimpanzees in the mountains. She was one of our most dedicated and hard-working students and her death was a great loss. Ruth was buried at the Gombe National Park in accordance with the wishes of her parents.

One outcome of the tragedy was a new National Park rule that no student should leave the central research valley (Kakombe) alone. Thus we initiated the training of Tanzanian field assistants to accompany students while making observations. During 1970 the significance of the use of such trained personnel gradually became apparent. We realized that we could benefit the research by the use of carefully trained field assistants of this type, since they could add considerably to our knowledge of chimpanzee and baboon behavior and would, moreover, provide long-term continuity in a research center where most researchers are constantly coming and going.

General Records

A total of nine research assistants collected information for the long-term record on individually known chimpanzees during the 2-year period. L. Baldwin, A. Shouldice, C. Clark, and A. Pusey worked on the mother-infant study, in pairs. H. Bauer and R. Wrangham worked on relationships between older siblings, which had become independent of their mothers. N. Washington and D. Bygott collected information on spacing within groups and behavior of adult males, and G. Teleki collected data on chimpanzee predatory behavior.

Reproductive Behavior

From mid-1969 until the end of 1970 Patrick McGinnis collected data on sexual behavior in chimpanzees. In the early part of 1969 he fulfilled residence requirements at Cambridge University where he is working for a Ph.D. degree in ethology. McGinnis is concentrating on consort behavior in the chimpanzee when a male "forces" a female to follow him off into the forests, often actually attacking her if she tries to escape. One male (Leakey) was unusual in that he attempted several times to take two females off at the same time—with the result that he invariably lost both. This 2-year period also saw the coming to sexual maturity of the adolescent female Fifi (daughter of Flo). Fifi did not show the fearful behavior typical of some young females when they first become sexually attractive to the adult males. Rather, she actively solicited copulation.

Grooming Behavior of the Adult Male Chimpanzee

Dr. Michael Simpson joined our team in January 1969 as senior scientist. He worked (with Science Research Council funds) for 18 months on a study of grooming behavior in the males. He was particularly interested in partner preference and in correlations between frequency of grooming or being groomed and social status in agonistic contexts.

Research in the South of the Park

In order properly to understand the nature of a chimpanzee "community" it is necessary to habituate a neighboring community. There is exchange of females between communities, and there are interesting interactions among communities. But none of these behaviors can be fully understood until a second community has been habituated.

During 1969, therefore, Carole Gale, who had worked for some time at the Centre as a research assistant, moved to live in the south of the Park. She attempted to survey the chimpanzee population immediately adjacent to our study community. She managed to identify some individuals, particularly a female with her infant who was resident near Miss Gale's hut, but her task was difficult. Just as the chimpanzees had fled from myself in the early days of my study at Gombe, so the southern population ran from a human observer.

Miss Gale left toward the end of 1969 because of ill health. After a short break in the observations, her place was taken by Lori Baldwin, who continued the process of habituation. Miss Baldwin was able to work in the south only, for three or four months, after which there was a break in the work there before the arrival of Mr. and Mrs. Sean Sheehan toward the end of 1970.

FIG. 1. The alpha male Mike, begging for part of a baboon kill from lower-ranking adult male Leakey. Photo by G. Teleki.

Baboon Research

During the 1969/70 period one study on baboon behavior was concluded, one complete study was made, and a third was initiated.

Early in 1969 Timothy Ransom, who pioneered the baboon research at Gombe, left after a 2-year field study of general social behavior. He returned to the University of California, Berkeley, to write up his results for a doctoral dissertation.

Leanne Taylor (now Nash) arrived in October 1969 and worked for a full year on mother-infant behavior in Beach Troop—the troop studied by Ransom. Her research also was for a doctoral dissertation at Berkeley.

Nicholas Owens joined the research team at Gombe at the end of 1969 and worked on play behavior and socialization in another troop (Camp Troop) throughout 1970. This was for a doctoral dissertation at Cambridge University.

Of major interest was the fact that, during the year, Beach Troop divided. Causes of this division were not clear cut but were related in part to extreme tension among the adult males and in part to severe fighting among the females. A small group finally moved right away from the main troop

FIG. 2. Male embracing infant, illustrating male tolerance.

and eventually established its own range to the north of the parent troop. Some baboons vacillated back and forth between the two during the early months of the split before finally deciding in which one to remain.

Red Colobus Behavior

In January 1969 Timothy Clutton-Brock initiated an ecological study of the feeding and ranging patterns of a troop of red colobus monkeys (*Colobus badius*). This study, which ended in 1970, was for a doctoral dissertation at Cambridge University.

Vegetation Survey in the Kahama Valley

Dr. Simpson and Tim Clutton-Brock undertook a short survey of vegetation types and densities at different altitudes. Transects, 100 yards square, were made during the course of the red-colobus study, and these greatly facilitated the vegetation survey.

Administration

Mr. and Mrs. N. Pickford, who were employed as administrators, left during 1969. Subsequently we took on Gerald Rilling as administrator and part-time research assistant on data analysis.

Some Points of Interest

Dominance. Our long-term research is gradually yielding some interesting results concerning the gaining or losing of status in individual chimpanzees. The mature male Mike became alpha in 1964 and maintained this position until the end of 1970. Initially Mike was aggressive, frequently attacking females and performing charging displays with high frequency. As the years went by, however, Mike became less aggressive: by 1968 he was a very tolerant male indeed. By 1969 another male, Humphrey, had become the most aggressive male; he was also one of the largest. During 1969 and 1970 females and adolescent males became increasingly submissive to Humphrey. However, both males and females continued to show deference to Mike, including Humphrey himself.

During 1970 two young adult males, Figan and Evered, both began to challenge Mike, displaying near him and, when he responded with displays of his own, ignoring those displays. Figan, indeed, would sit with his back to Mike, even when the latter displayed so vigorously that Figan was hit by the ends of swaying branches. Nevertheless, neither of these young males actually attacked Mike, and both continued to show a good deal of submission to Humphrey.

In 1969 the old male Goliath apparently suffered a bad illness. He was not observed for some months at the feeding station, and when he appeared he seemed emaciated. Previously he had continued to enjoy a high rank, but after this absence he was attacked by many of the adult males, and his status dropped very low. Gradually his health improved, but he became increasingly solitary, often seeming to avoid large groups of chimpanzees.

A final comment on dominance involves the young male Figan mentioned above. Figan, from adolescence onward, always seemed highly motivated to better his social status. He would quickly take advantage of illness or injury in a superior and, at such times, would challenge the other with repeated displays. During 1969 Figan began to travel frequently with his elder brother Faben (crippled in the 1966 polio epidemic). In cooperation with Faben, Figan, in 1970, was able to attack a young male, one year older than himself, who had previously been able to dominate Figan on almost all occasions. During this attack, observed by D. Bygott, Figan and Faben slowly drove the other male, Evered, out along a branch. Together they leaped on him and, as they grappled, fell some 30 feet to the ground below. During the fight the old mother Flo barked and displayed on the ground below, and Figan's infant brother, Flint, displayed through the lower branches of the tree. After the fight Evered, who was badly wounded, showed extreme submission during interactions with Figan.

It is also of interest that Figan, on one occassion, tried to copulate with a female in oestrus who was consorting with Mike. Mike attacked Figan, and the pair fell to the ground. Of note was the fact that Mike screamed loudly (as did Figan) and ran to seek reassurance from another male.

Predation. A good deal of predation was observed during the 2-year period. The principal prey animal was the baboon. All kills were made fairly close to the feeding area, and it was suspected that the frequency with which chimpanzees and baboons came together in competition for bananas may have influenced the predatory behavior of the chimpanzees. Geza Teleki was able to collect valuable information on hunting techniques, and on the eating and distribution of meat. These data were analyzed by him for a master's dissertation.

Mother-offspring. The key observations concerned the Flo family. Early in 1969 the last-born infant of the old female Flo died during an epidemic of a flulike diesease. This had a profound effect on the behavior of the previous offspring, Flint.

At the time of Flame's birth, Flint had only just been weaned. He had not stopped riding on his mother's back and he was still sharing her nest at night. After Flame's birth, while Flint stopped riding on Flo for a few months, he subsequently reverted to this dependent form of travel. Moreover, unlike other juveniles, he did not start to make an independent night nest after the birth of his sibling, but shared the communal nest with Flo and Flame. During the 6 months of Flame's life Flint remained "depressed" and highly dependent on Flo. His relationship with Flo became increasingly aggressive; when she did not respond positively to his demands (for grooming, food sharing, and so on) Flint threw violent tantrums during which he often hit or bit his mother. Often Flo retaliated in kind.

After Flame's death, however, the relationship between Flint and his mother improved. Flint appeared less depressed, but he continued to ride

FIG. 3. The female baboon Myrna, who was responsible, in part, for the splitting of Beach troop. Here she is seen with her two infants. She, with one adult male who frequently accompanied her, together with a number of females with whom she had "maternity bonds," formed the nucleus of the troop that shifted its range to the north. Photo by L. Nash.

frequently on Flo's back and to share her night nest. This dependency on his mother continued throughout 1970.

Flo and her elder offspring, Faben, Figan, and Fifi, also maintained close ties during this period. Fifi traveled very frequently with her mother except when she herself was in oestrus and traveling with adult males. During Flame's short life Fifi, as well as Flint, showed great fascination for the new infant, carrying her and playing with her. Flo was particularly tolerant of Fifi's attentions, and sometimes Fifi "minded the baby" for periods of over 30 minutes.

On one occasion Faben was attacked by another young male. Flo, hearing his screams, rushed to assist him. In so doing Flame was dropped to the ground; the 4-month infant was retrieved by Flint since Flo did not return to her until she had assisted Faben in chasing away his aggressor.

In January 1969 the young female Miff gave birth to her first infant, Moeza. In 1965 Miff, as a young adolescent, had "adopted" her infant brother, Merlin, after the death of their mother. Miff had continued to travel and sleep with Merlin until his death at the end of the following year. It is perhaps significant that Miff was a particularly efficient primiparous mother: possibly her experiences with Merlin had helped to prepare her for maternal behavior.

Intercommunity contact. Ruth Davis and Carole Gale both made observations of interest. On two occasions when a group of chimpanzees that included Mike was being followed, calling from individuals of neighboring communities was heard. On both occasions Mike became very silent, stared intently toward the calling, and eventually moved away from the "strangers."

Normally interactions between habituated chimpanzees and their neighbors are almost impossible to observe, since the unhabituated chimpanzees run off upon sighting the human follower. On two occasions, however, Ruth Davis observed male chimpanzees of the habituated community feeding or traveling with groups of "strangers" including adult males.

During 1970 it appeared that the main study community was beginning to divide into two; five adult males and two adult females visited the feeding area less and less frequently during the year and were observed traveling to the south. It is interesting that the three males observed to mix with strangers from the south were part of this sub-group.

Gilka. During 1968 Gilka, a juvenile female, was first observed with a swelling of her nose. In 1969 the condition became gradually worse, and by 1970 she had a grotesquely distorted face, with a huge bulbous nose and swellings appearing on her brows.

After consultations with various experts, it was decided to try to perform a biopsy. For several months prior to the planned operation, Gilka was given a tablet of valium daily (when possible). The dosage was gradually increased over time. The pill, inserted into a banana, was always given in a cage (originally built for the protection of my son). On the day scheduled for the operation the cage door was closed after Gilka had received her banana. Drs. Anthony and Sue Harthoorn administered anesthetic and Prof. Douglas Roy performed the biopsy. Dr. Bradley Nelson also attended.

Gilka recovered safely from the operation and continued to tolerate observers following her through the mountains. The biopsy was successful. Professors Roy and Cameron were able to grow a culture and the condition was diagnosed as the fungus infection *Rhinophycomycosis entomophthorea*. Her condition was improved by massive doses of potassium iodide administered in bananas.

REFERENCES

(See also previously published volumes of these Reports.)

VAN LAWICK-GOODALL, JANE

1968. The behaviour of free-living chimpanzees in the Gombe Stream Reserve. Animal Behav. Monogr., vol. 1, pt. 3, pp. 161–311, illus.

1970. Tool-using in primates and other vertebrates. Pp. 195–249 *in* "Advances in the Study of Behavior," vol. 3, 262 pp., illus., Daniel S. Lehrman, Robert A. Hinde, and Evelyn Shaw, eds. Academic Press, New York and London.

1971. Some aspects of mother-infant relationships in a group of wild chimpanzees. Pp. 115–128 *in* "The Origins of Human Social Relations," 297 pp., illus., H. R. Schaffer, ed. Academic Press, New York and London.

JANE GOODALL

Collections, Observations, and Illustrations of the Flora of Tierra del Fuego

Principal Investigator: Rae Natalie Prosser Goodall, Estancia Harberton, Ushuaia, Tierra del Fuego, Argentina.[1]

Grant No. 907: In support of plant exploration to provide collections, observations, and illustrations of the flora of Tierra del Fuego, Argentina.

Tierra del Fuego extends its intricate islands and channels farther south than any other regularly inhabited land area. Its botany was considered well known as early as 1845 (Hooker, 1847); indeed, since the first botanical collection there about 280 years ago, at least 130 persons have made some sort of collections from the area. Many of these were botanists on early expeditions of ships rounding the Horn, which touched only the outer edges of the larger islands. Many others were botanists with only a short time at their disposal, who followed the main highway and collected near the main towns. Until the present there has been no resident who could make collections and observations at various times of the year in a larger range of habitats.

Since coming to Tierra del Fuego in 1963, I have collected and illustrated the flora, at first in a very small way, hampered by lack of transportation and funds and by two small children. The plants collected were sent to a number of institutions, including Leicester, England; the U.S. National Arboretum, Washington, D.C.; the Instituto Nacional de Tecnología Agropecuarie, Mueseo de La Plata, and the Instituto de Botánica Darwinion in Argentina; Universities of Michigan and California; Miami University, and several others. With the encouragement of Drs. Lincoln Constance and David Moore, the collections increased and I began making observations that will be helpful in the treatment of the *Flora of Tierra del Fuego* in preparation by Dr. Moore and myself. Identifications were sent by various experts, and a herbarium was built up at Harberton.

[1]Dr. David M. Moore, Botany Department, University of Reading, England, acted as an associate investigator; he was the main recipient of the collections and identified most of the plants.

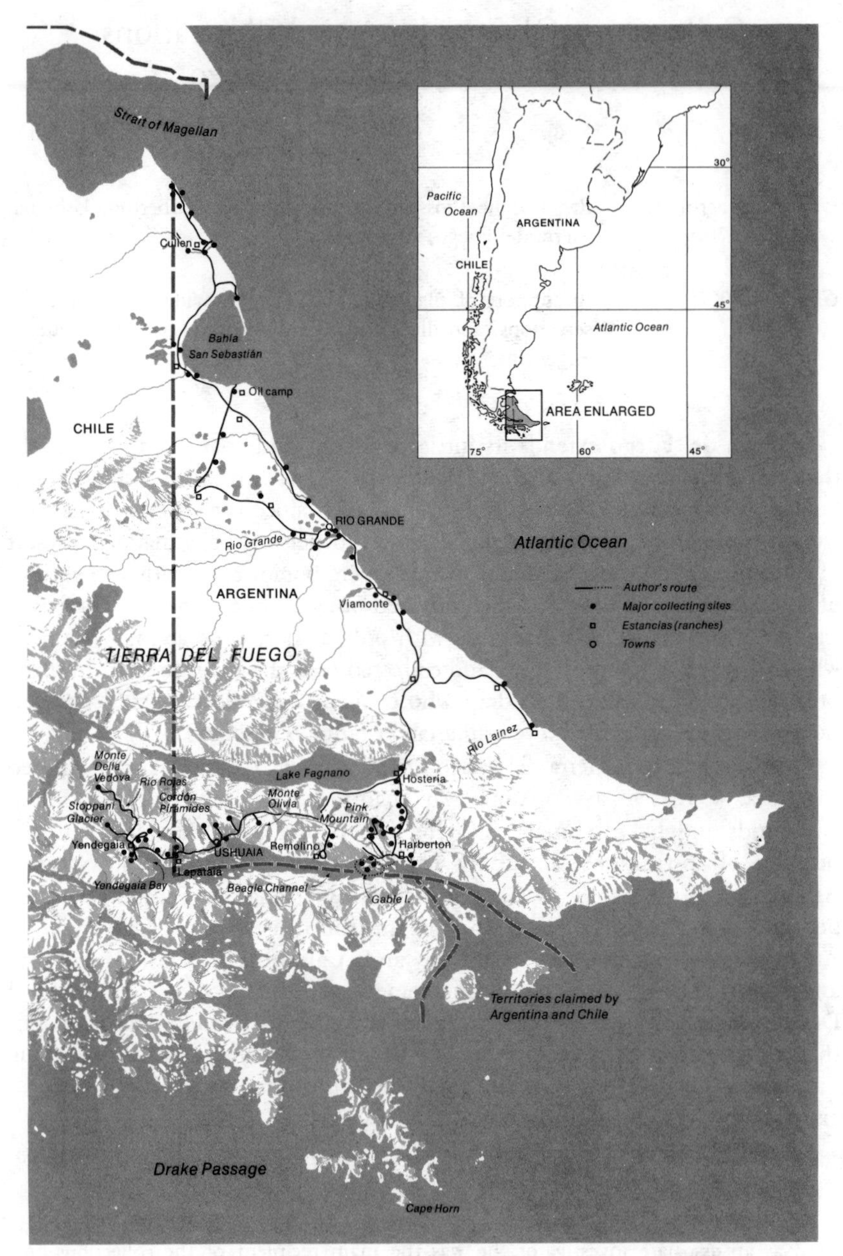

FIG. 1. Route and major collecting sites, many of them away from the few roads available, that were visited by the author in Tierra del Fuego.

The receipt of a National Geographic Society research grant in November 1970 enabled the work to proceed much more quickly. I was able to obtain herbarium cabinets, mounting paper, camping equipment, and other supplies, and, most important, an assistant, Jane Wood, was engaged for three months.

The emphasis, as usual, was on collecting localities that were little known (see fig. 1), especially in mountain areas, since very little work had been done on mountains. Herbarium specimens with as many as eight duplicates were prepared. When possible, we made bud collections so that Dr. Moore could try for chromosome counts—practically no chromosome counts were known for this area. Notes were made on habitats, associations, flowering times, etc. When there was time, I prepared pen-and-ink illustrations of the plants (see fig. 2), especially of the rarest ones. A collection of cultivated plants was made for the U.S. National Arboretum, and bird and fossil records were made for experts in those fields.

Areas Collected

From November 12 to 16 (1970) I collected in the area from Estancia Viamonte to Estancia Cullen with some friends, using a vehicle lent by Estancia Viamonte. This resulted in material for several new chromosome counts. In December, near Ushuaia, I found the island's third record of *Amsinckia hispida*. In the mountains behind Ushuaia we collected four rare mountain plants—*Tetrachondra patagonica* subsp. *fuegiana, Ourisia fuegiana*, *Saxifragodes albowiana*, and *Abrotanella linearifolia*—and three new chromosome counts. On the way home we found *Lunaria annua* and *Glechoma hederacea*, both weeds previously unrecorded for Tierra del Fuego.

At Lapataia we recorded for the first time *Ruppia filifolius*, a new native for Tierra del Fuego. At Estancia Viamonte in January we extended the records of *Potamogeton* and *Myosurus* quite a bit farther south. Another new native, *Zannichellia palustris*, was found near the Río Grande.

On January 2–3, 1971, I went on a family trip to the Río Lainez, making the first botanical observations on that area in almost a century.

From January 5 to 8, Jane Wood, the children, and I went to Estancia Cullen. There we found a new *Sisyrinchium*, collected some rare seeds, and made the second collections of *Nardophyllum bryoides, Satureja darwinii,* and *Chiliophyllum fuegianum*, plants that have not been found since 1898. They turned out to be fairly common. All are very unnoticeable except at the blooming stage. We also made the second record for *Littorella australis*, which I had found for the first time the year before. There were several other

FIG. 2. *Nassauvia magellanica* J. F. Gmelin, a Compositae collected on Mount Wood, February 1971. Common in open, damp places above the tree line in Tierra del Fuego, it is one of the typical and perhaps the showiest of the mountain flowers; its snaky-looking stems form low mats among the rocks. Drawing by the author.

rare plants and a few new weeds. Later, at Estancia Viamonte, we found *Spergularia marina*, another new native for Fuegia.

After a spell at Harberton for pressing, processing, and illustrating plants, we hiked over the mountains to the north with some visiting geologists. The main find was a new hybrid between *Caltha appendiculata* and *C. dionaeifolia* (Moore and Goodall, 1973). Many evergreen forest plants were found unexpectedly in this area.

On February 12–14 we went with the geologists to the mountains behind Estancia Remolino, where we again found many of the rare mountain plants.

From February 22 to 25 we went with the Harberton workmen to Gable Island, traveling completely around it and nearby Waru Island. Back at Harberton we again worked at pressing, processing, and labeling the collections. On March 7, at Harberton, we found two new naturalized plants, *Digitalis purpurea* and a thistle.

On a trip to Pink Mountain (March 10–12) we found *Koenigia islandica* for the first time in Argentine Fuegia. In March I also climbed Monte Olivia and Los Mentirosos, without finding any new plants but always collecting representative samples of the vegetation.

From March 23 to April 1 we hiked to Yendegaia Bay in Chile, visited the Stoppani Glacier, and rode up the valley of the Río Rojas to Monte Dalla Vedova; although we would like to have gone farther, our host, Leo Serka, who furnished the horses, was obliged to return. We then climbed the Montes Piramides, where we found several rare plants. The visit to Estancia Yendegaia provided us with a number of new weeds (*Juncus bufonius, Triofolium aureum, Linum catharticum, Prunella vulgaris,* and *Crepis capillaris*). Later at Ushuaia I found three more naturalized plants (*Medicago sativa, Cardaria draba,* and *Avena sterilis*), new for the Territory.

Summary

In less than six months we were able to collect over 1,400 numbers with numerous duplicates; we climbed in six different mountainous regions, spending some time in each, as well as visiting the plains and some Beagle Channel islands. We did an enormous amount of pressing, sorting, gluing, and labeling in order to put the collections in order and send them off to the universities. The plants are represented in works by Cabrera (1971), Correa (1969), and Moore (1974).

On receiving a new herbarium cabinet and genus folders, it was possible to get the world's southernmost herbarium out of its wooden cupboard and cardboard boxes. This work went on during the winter and spring.

About 25 new drawings were completed and many smaller sketches and studies made.

As a result of our bud collections, Dr. David Moore was able to make about 12 chromosome counts, six of them previously unknown. Four new native species and one new hybrid were found, and nine species were collected for the second time in Tierra del Fuego. At least 13 and perhaps more (all the results have not yet been finished) naturalized species new to Tierra del Fuego were collected (Moore and Goodall, 1978).

REFERENCES

CABRERA, ANGEL L.

1971. Compositae. *In* Correa, ed., pt. 7.

CORREA, MAEVIA N., ed.

1969, 1971. Flora Patagonica. Colección Científica de INTA, vol. 8, pt. 2, 219 pp.; pt. 3 (in press); pt. 7, 451 pp. Instituto Nacional de Tecnología Agropecuaria, Buenos Aires.

GOODALL, RAE NATALIE P.

1975. Tierra del Fuego, ed. 2, 253 pp. Ediciones Shanamaiim, Buenos Aires.

HOOKER, JOSEPH DALTON

1847. The botany of the Antarctic voyage of H. M. discovery ships *Erebus* and *Terror*. . . ., pt. 1: Flora Antarctica, 574 pp. London.

MOORE, DAVID M.

1974. Catalogo de las plantas vasculares nativas de Tierra del Fuego. Ans. Inst. Patagonia (Punta Arenas, Chile), vol. 5, nos. 1–2, pp. 105–121.

MOORE, DAVID M., AND GOODALL, RAE NATALIE P.

1973. Interspecific hybridization in Feugian *Caltha* L. Bol. Soc. Argentina Bot., vol. 15, no. 1, pp. 72–76.

1974. Further additions to the native vascular flora of Tierra del Fuego. Not. Notiser, vol. 127, pp. 38–43, illus.

19 . La flora adventicia de Tierra del Fuego. Ans. Inst. Patagonia. (In press.)

RAE NATALIE PROSSER GOODALL

Biology of the Kaibab Squirrel

Principal Investigator: Joseph G. Hall, San Francisco State University, San Francisco, California.

Grant Nos. 870, 972: In support of a study of the Kaibab squirrel *(Sciurus kaibabensis).*

This report summarizes the results of a field study of the Kaibab squirrel in Grand Canyon National Park during the summer of 1970, the summer and fall of 1971, and the early spring and summer of 1972. During the 1970 season Jack A. Cranford, graduate student in biology at San Francisco State, was employed as my field assistant. In addition, many naturalists, rangers, and biologists in the National Park Service as well as the members of my own family contributed very significantly to this investigation. The Grand Canyon Natural History Association also made important financial contributions through its research fund.

For many years the Kaibab squirrel, handsome in its gray and maroon coat and showy white tail (fig. 1), has been an attraction to naturalists and summer travelers visiting the Kaibab Plateau of northern Arizona. Here in the 220,000 acres of ponderosa pine is the only place the animal occurs, although 8 races of the closely related Abert squirrel *(Sciurus aberti)* are found in similar habitats throughout the Southwest.

Because of its rarity and the concern over marked fluctuations in its numbers, the National Park Service began a study of the squirrel's ecology and habitat requirements in 1960. The goal has been to learn enough about its life history to allow biologists to manage the environment for the perpetuation of this interesting mammal. The Arizona Department of Game and Fish and the U. S. Forest Service have since initiated their own studies of this squirrel, and the three agencies cooperate closely in their research efforts.

In order to assess any management program it is necessary to know the density of animals in a given area. The specific goals of the study reported on here were to obtain information on size of home range and on activity patterns and to work on a census method.

Materials and Methods

Although only about one-tenth of the squirrel's range falls inside the boundary of Grand Canyon National Park, our studies were limited to the park on the assumption that whatever findings were made here would probably apply in the remainder of the range. Then, too, the forest within the park probably represents a more natural habitat than that outside, since harvesting timber is not permitted in national parks. Even with this restriction the squirrel habitat in the park is so far-flung and in many cases so difficult of access that we divided the work into an extensive phase, mainly concerned with an annual tally of sign of squirrel occupancy, and an intensive phase in which our objective was to become intimately acquainted with the habits of a few squirrels on a small area.

In making the annual tally of sign an observer would count the number of needle clusters in circular tenth-acre plots spaced systematically along the fireroads in what was judged to be potential squirrel habitat. These needle clusters are cut by the squirrels in winter and early spring when they depend heavily on the phloem of subterminal twigs (Rasmussen, Brown, and Jones, 1975). Where squirrels are relatively abundant there are many such clusters, especially under favored "feeding trees." This procedure provides an index to relative density from place to place in a given year and, with certain qualifications, from year to year in a given area.

The intensive phase consisted primarily of choosing an area, usually 50 acres or less, in which squirrels were reasonably abundant, and observing with binoculars and notebook. Owing to the very shy nature of these squirrels, it was important for the observer to remain as unobtrusive as possible to avoid interfering with their normal behavior. This precaution, of course, posed its own special problems; for example, how could one census an area or plot home ranges if he had to keep a respectable distance from the animals, all of which look almost identical in the first place? This problem was attacked by live-trapping and marking squirrels and releasing them for further observation. Picric acid, sprayed on the white tail according to several patterns, gave a yellow field mark that lasted about 2 weeks and permitted identification at 100 yards or more. We succeeded also in attaching telemetry transmitters to some of the animals. These, worn as collars, weighed only 20 grams (less than 3 percent of the weight of the lightest animal) and had no apparent effect on behavior.

By using a directional receiver we could thus locate a squirrel even when it was in a nest or in hiding, as they often are, in the crown of a tree. Unfortunately the average life of a transmitter was less than 2 weeks.

FIG. 1. "Linea," an adult female Kaibab squirrel whose home range and activity pattern were studied on the north rim of Grand Canyon National Park.

A third method of marking, attaching a colored plastic collar around the neck, provided a more permanent mark than picric acid and was used in 1972 when the telemetry transmitters were not functioning properly.

The home-range maps were made by plotting the various sightings of identifiable animals on a master map of the intensive study area. At the end of a field season a line was drawn around the peripheral sightings for each individual and the area of the resulting irregular polygon measured by planimeter. Distances in the field were measured by pacing, azimuths by Suunto compass.

Results and Discussion

Distribution and Population Trends 1970-72. As mentioned above, the results of the annual tallies of needle clusters or clippings can be used to compare squirrel densities between various localities at a given time (distribution) as well as to compare densities from year to year at a given locality. Although neither type of comparison has been precisely checked against a known population, there are reasons to believe that the inferences about distribution are more reliable than those about year-to-year population trends. This could be restated by saying that, in reference to table 1, the vertical comparisons are probably more valid than the horizontal ones.

The reasoning behind this opinion is based on the observation that when a good cone crop is produced (a regional phenomenon) the squirrels will feed heavily on pine seeds for a period of as long as 8 months. For

TABLE 1.—NEEDLE CLUSTER TALLIES

Area	Plot acreage	Number of clusters 1970	1971	1972
E-4	1.2	124	45	5
E-4A	1.0	217	207	2
E-5	1.2	145	85	2
E-6	1.6	305	155	4
E-7	0.8	33	25	10
Cape Royal	1.0	82	43	5
Tiyo Point	1.2	495	186	126
Point Sublime	0.8	223	53	18
Swamp Point	1.2	82	302	27
Total	10.0	1,706	1,101	199
Clusters per acre		170.6	110.1	19.9

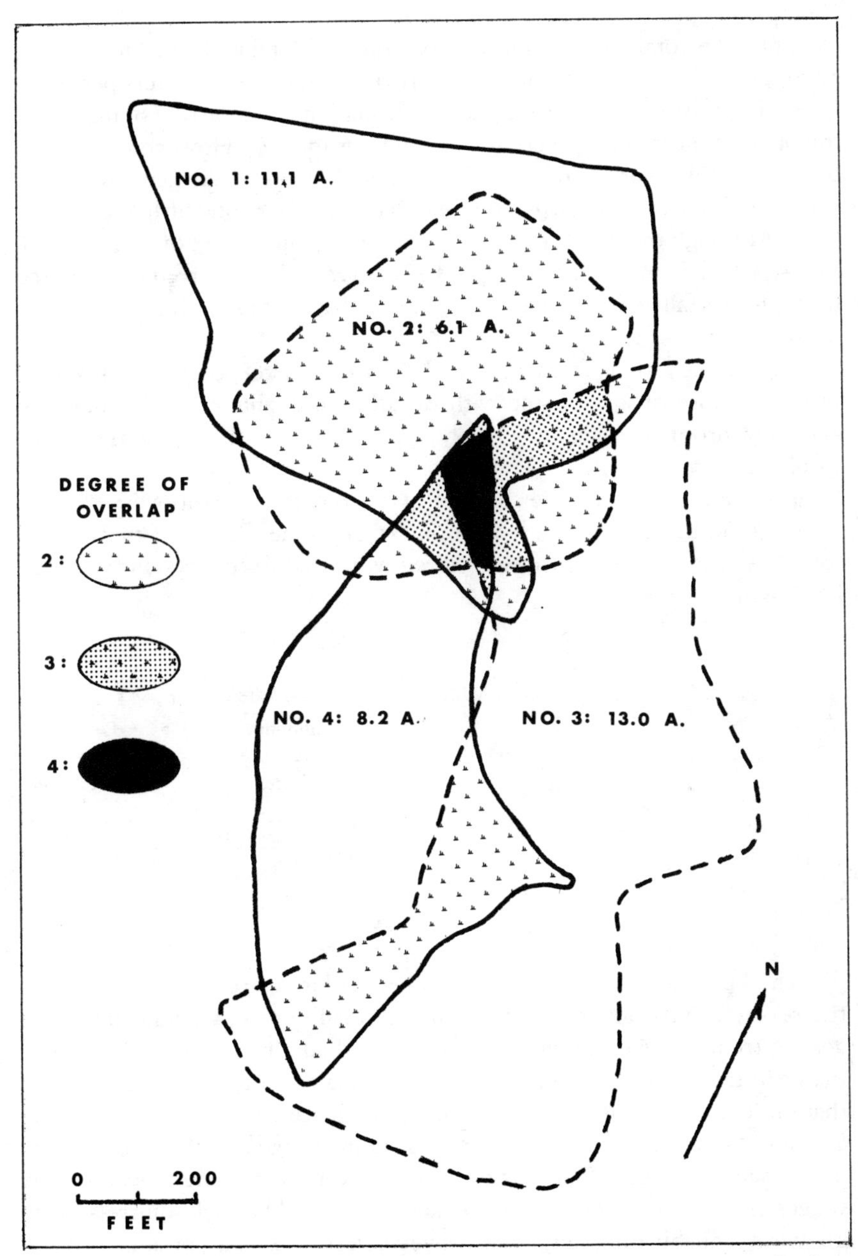

FIG. 2. Approximate summer home ranges and degree of spatial overlap for four Kaibab squirrels on the Bright Angel Point study area, 1970.

example, the total cluster density from the 1971 tally (110.1 clusters per acre) was noticeably lower than in the previous year (170.6 clusters per acre). I feel that this drop does reflect a real decline in the squirrel population in the park, as there simply were fewer sightings in 1971. However, we would be misled if we were to take the 1972 tally of 19.9 clusters per acre at face value and infer that the population had fallen to about one-fifth of the 1971 level. Although there did indeed seem to be a drop in the population level, the excellent crop of pine seeds in 1971 served as a preferred food source through that fall and winter and accounts for part of the decline in cutting of needle clusters.

In summary, then, from 1970 to 1971 the squirrel population dropped, probably more or less in step with the decline in abundance of clippings, and then dropped again in 1972 but not nearly so sharply as the tallies would suggest.

Home Range. During the summer of 1970 eight squirrels were thought to reside on the 35-acre study area on Bright Angel Point. Of these eight, four were individually marked (three with radio collars) and tracked intensively.

TABLE 2.—SUMMER HOME RANGES 1970

Squirrel	Sex	Wt. in grams	Minimum home range in acres	Percent of home range not shared
1	♂	660	11	45
2	♀	610	6	8
3	♂	680	13	73
4	♂	660	8	63

The findings are summarized in table 2 and in figure 2. Bearing in mind the severe limitations imposed by such a small sample, we find some suggestive trends. For example, the lone female had a home range little more than half the size of the average of the three males. In addition, it is possible that there is a relationship between size of animal and size of its home range, as the 610-gram female had the smallest home range and the largest male, no. 3, had the largest. There is even more overlap in home ranges than is suggested by these records, since about four additional squirrels were known to inhabit the study area. Nevertheless, the data pertaining to the four marked individuals suggest a third possible relationship between size of the individual and degree of overlap with its neighbors. The largest squirrel showed least and the smallest squirrel showed most overlap. Obviously many more individuals would have to be followed for a longer period to document the existence of these possibilities.

That these estimates of home range size are, in fact, minimum was strongly indicated during the 1971-72 season when, thanks to the discovery of a naturally marked female on the study area, we were able to follow the movements of one individual over a much longer period than was possible in 1970. We were fortunate to be able to plot "Linea's" movements during all seasons except for winter. Her home range was estimated to be 29 acres, at a minimum. This is over twice the size of the largest and three times the size of the average home-range estimate for the summer of 1970. This clearly indicates that the *apparent size* of an animal's home range will increase for an initial period. When the size of the home range "levels off," it can be presumed to approximate the "true" home range in size. In Colorado, Farentinos (personal communication) found 8.6 acres to be the average size of summer home range for three male Abert squirrels. This agrees reasonably well with the 10.6-acre average estimate for our three males in 1970. Keith (1965) estimated summer home range for Abert squirrels near Flagstaff, Arizona, to be about 18 acres. His largest summer home range was 24 acres, which is somewhat less than Linea's.

Estimates of "true" home range are very laborious to obtain and are crude at best. Comparisons between different individuals, even on a given area during a given period, should be made with caution.

Activity Patterns. This phase of the squirrel's natural history was studied from two different approaches, both involving dawn-to-dusk "vigils." In 1970 we kept track of all squirrel activity at one particular site known to be within the home ranges of several squirrels. In 1972 we monitored the activity of a single individual, following it from place to place as it went about its business or rested. The two approaches were complementary and indicated that there are two major peaks of activity, the first and most intense beginning at sunrise and ending in midmorning, the second occurring in late afternoon and ending shortly before sunset. Midday is spent in resting with occasional minor spurts of activity. About half the waking hours are spent foraging on the ground; resting while on the ground is a rare event. Of its waking hours spent in trees, about half are spent resting, half in feeding. A squirrel may cover as much as 2½ miles during a day's wanderings.

Census Techniques. As mentioned, we have been using the annual tallies of squirrel clippings as an index to abundance of the animals. So far only relative densities can be inferred from these tallies. If one knew what *absolute* densities of squirrels were indicated by a given density of needle clippings, this method could be used as a census. In 1970, having made an estimate of eight squirrels on the 35-acre study area, we tallied the number of feeding trees on the area. The result, 227 trees, allowed us to arrive at a ratio of approximately 28 feeding trees per squirrel. Theoretically this ratio would permit one to census the squirrels on an area (provided the seed crop were poor) by dividing density of feeding trees by 28. In point of fact, the utility of this ratio is far from proved owing to the great variability in number of clippings per feeding tree. What is needed is a total tally of clippings on a small isolated area inhabited by a known population of squirrels. There are several sites within the park that are topographically suitable for such an undertaking.

Summary

Studies of the natural history of the Kaibab squirrel were carried out in Grand Canyon National Park during the 1970-1972 period, mainly in the summers.

The trend in population during this interval, as indicated by density of feeding detritus, has been slightly downward.

Home ranges were found to vary from 6 to 13 acres per animal in the summer of 1970 to 29 acres for one individual in 1972. Difficulties in assessing true home ranges are considered.

The activity pattern typically consists of a major peak in early morning, a midday rest period and a late afternoon peak. Squirrels rest mostly in trees but may cover over two miles on the ground in one day.

A tentative ratio of feeding trees to squirrels was calculated and could theoretically serve as a census tool. Needed refinements of this technique are mentioned.

REFERENCES

KEITH, JAMES O.

1965. The Abert squirrel and its dependence on ponderosa pine. Ecology, vol. 46, pp. 150-163.

RASMUSSEN, DAVID I.; BROWN, D. E.; and JONES, D.

1975. Use of ponderosa pine by tassel-eared squirrels and a key to determine evidence of their use from that of red squirrels and porcupines. Wildlife Digest, Arizona Game and Fish Dept., Abstract 10, pp. 1-12.

JOSEPH G. HALL

Observations of Blue-water Plankton

Principal Investigator: William M. Hamner, Australian Institute of Marine Science, Cape Pallarenda, Townsville, Queensland, Australia.

Grant No. 913: For observations of living, undisturbed, blue-water plankton.

In 1970 the National Geographic Society agreed to support a Blue-water Plankton Project in Bimini to investigate live, undisturbed planktonic animals in the open ocean, using SCUBA techniques. We then felt beleaguered by those who believed that a direct approach to biological oceanography was either impossible, because "... plankton are too little to see ..." or foolish, because "... plankton don't do anything but float." Today we no longer encounter these criticisms. We have resolved technical problems associated with diver investigation of plankton and have demonstrated that the work is productive. It remains now to evaluate the importance of the approach. In order to address these questions in more detail this report is organized into sections dealing with the technical aspects of blue-water diving, the productivity of the research, and the apparent importance of this approach.

Technical Aspects

Florida Current. The National Geographic Society provided funds for equipment to work in the Florida Current from the Lerner Marine Laboratory on Bimini in the Bahamas. Because of the strong northward set of the Gulf Stream we used powerful but small (21-foot) boats, often running far offshore. Wind drift was a perennial problem and as divers were set adrift at sea for the duration of their dive, the need to develop, test, and implement strict safety procedures was essential to eliminate accidents under such unusual circumstances. Procedures were developed to protect divers from being lost at sea, distressed by sharks, or disoriented under water. These safety procedures have been described in detail elsewhere (Hamner, 1974); so other divers need not spend many months simply learning what not to do. Additionally, contributed material on "No-Bottom Reference Diving," is included in the new N.O.A.A. Technical Divers Manual. The safety procedures developed at Bimini are indeed safe. By 1973 approximately 1,000 hours of blue-water diving time had been logged. Dives at sea were aborted because of storms, engine failure, sharks, fire, sea sickness, bad air, and cold, but there were no accidents. We are hopeful that we will have none.

Photographic problems not completely resolved during the Bimini project required extension of the project through the summer of 1971, so that diving in the waters of the Gulf of California, the coastal California Pacific water mass, the open ocean of the Sargasso Sea, and California lakes, could provide the experience needed to complete our photographic record.

In the Bahamas two of my students, Dr. Stanley Dunn (Florida Atlantic University), and I spent several months in a related technical exercise. Impressed while diving by the importance, dominance, and power of large billfishes, dolphins, and sharks, we wished to study these animals more closely, but they simply swam away. We then designed and built an enclosed, towed wet-submarine (described in Hamner and Dunn, 1972) to keep pace with and observe blue-fin tuna. In 40 days we had broken all prior underwater speed records (± 4 knots) for in-water research vehicles. Eventually we reached speeds of 15 knots, which, because of limitations in visibility and pilot response-time, may be as fast as anyone will care to go under water. This exercise may well be the most important technical innovation resulting from the project. The U. S. Bureau of Commercial Fisheries recently spent many millions of dollars in Hawaii in an abortive 10-year attempt to observe tuna under water.

Sargasso Sea. In 1972 Lawrence Madin returned from a Woods Hole Oceanographic cruise to Bermuda, during which he organized and supervised 12 blue-water dives in the Sargasso Sea, thus demonstrating that blue-water diving can be accomplished at sea from a small boat lowered from the large ship without disturbing in any way normal operations of that ship. As a consequence, one can now go to sea on practically any ship and investigate blue-water animals without interfering with normal ship routine or incurring extra cost.

Gulf of California and California Lakes. Variations on our normal diving procedures were tried during the summer of 1971, and we found that many craft, as varied as Zodiacs and sailing outrigger canoes, are often suitable as diving boats at sea and in a variety of different waters. The efficacy of our diving safety procedures was reevaluated. These diving procedures are now incorporated into the research diving program for the University of

California, Davis Campus. Exercises designed to expose divers to problems of blue-water diving are reviewed in pool session and later usually executed in neighboring lakes.

Productivity of the Research

Those papers already published, in press, or in manuscript form are listed at the end of this report. In addition to research on planktonic organisms, work on other organisms was undertaken by members of the group, and reference to their projects is also included. Although several investigations begun in Bimini are not yet completed, the final list of publications acknowledging obligation to the Society will exceed 20.

Our most valuable contributions, I believe, were in the area of classical invertebrate zoology. Many animal phyla are planktonic, and more than several higher taxa are exclusively so. For example, the Hydromedusae and Scyphomedusae, and the Ctenophora, Chaetognatha, Salpida, Appendicularia, Heteropoda, and Pteropoda, are entirely planktonic; previously most of these different types of animals had never before been alive in their own habitat. Observations of these groups have resulted in basic contributions to the natural history of many phyla, classes, or orders of animals which, although perhaps unfamiliar to most laymen, are of critical importance in the ecology of the open sea. Observations on many new trophic interactions suggest that marine food-webs are considerably more complicated than we had envisioned.

Lastly, we contributed to knowledge of the physiology, systematics, and morphology of many groups because we collected animals carefully at sea by hand and they are thus collected undamaged and often live well in the laboratory, whereas those collected in abrasive nets are crushed and often die.

Apparent Importance of This Approach

Although it is perhaps too early to evaluate the full significance of a direct observational approach to biological oceanography, it is possible to indicate what can be done in the future.

Increase quantitative observational skills. One must develop statistically reliable methods for evaluating quantitative observational data. Terrestrial field biologists have resolved this perennial problem, but in blue water it is difficult, although not impossible, to obtain numerical data because many of the animals are small and hard to count. It is also difficult to evaluate spatial relationships at sea, because, unlike a terrestrial environment, in the open sea there are no fixed reference points. We hope to resolve these problems by combining photographic and visual techniques within an introduced grid system.

Develop mathematical and engineering skills to study plankton distribution in relation to ocean currents. It is usually not possible for a diver to sense subtle changes in the oceanic environment because the diver is weightless or neutrally buoyant, cannot hear over the noise of the regulator, cannot feel, because he wears gloves, cannot taste, and cannot see well. Even though important discontinuities exist between neighboring water masses, and even though the diver may be aware of these "fronts" because he often can see plankton piled-up along the edge, the diver cannot adequately experience this physical-chemical system because he has no sensory equipment to understand, intuitively, a 3-dimensional world of water. For these reasons we have turned our recent attention to the disciplines of fluid mechanics and ocean engineering, and have begun to develop diver-operated devices to measure and evaluate subtle differences in water speed, chemistry, density, and productivity.

Expand interest in fast-swimming oceanic fishes. Our program on high-speed under-water research vehicles will soon be reinstituted.

Our work on the natural history of plankton will continue for many years because we have only begun to exploit this rich area of investigation and the several important, additional areas of related activity noted above. It is possible that the potential importance of this direct observational approach to biological oceanography is even greater than we had hoped.

REFERENCES

ALLDREDGE, ALICE L.

1972. Abandoned larvacean houses: A unique food source in the pelagic environment. Science, vol. 177, pp. 885-887.

ALLDREDGE, ALICE L., and JONES, B. M.

1973. *Hastigerina pelagica:* Foraminiferal habitat for planktonic dinoflagellates. Mar. Biol., vol. 22, pp. 131-135.

GILMER, RONALD W.

1972. Free-floating mucus webs: A novel feeding adaptation for the open ocean. Science, vol. 176, pp. 1239-1240.

1974. On some aspects on feeding in the thecosomatous pteropod molluscs. Journ. Exp. Mar. Biol. Ecol., vol. 15, pp. 127-144.

HAMNER, WILLIAM M.
1974. Blue-water plankton: Ghosts of the Gulf Stream. Nat. Geogr. Mag., vol. 146, pp. 530-535.
1975. Underwater observations of blue-water plankton: Logistics, techniques and safety procedures for divers at sea. Limnol. Oceanogr., vol. 20, pp. 1045-1046.

HAMNER, WILLIAM M., and DUNN, STANLEY E.
1972. Direct observations on free-swimming bluefin tuna: A feasibility study. Florida Atlantic Univ. Dept. Ocean Engineering Techn. Rpt. no. 2. Boca Raton, Florida.

HAMNER, WILLIAM M.; MADIN, LAWRENCE P.; ALLDREDGE, ALICE L.; GILMER, RONALD W.; and HAMNER, PEGGY P.
1975. Underwater observations of gelatinous zooplankton: Sampling problems, feeding biology and behaviour. Limnol. Oceanogr., vol. 20, pp. 907-917.

HARBISON, G. R.; BIGGS, D. C.; and MADIN, LAWRENCE P.
——. Association of hyperiid amphipods with gelatinous zooplankton: II, Associations with medusae, siphonophores and ctenophores. (MS.)

MADIN, LAWRENCE P.
1974a. Field observations on the feeding behaviour of salps (Tunicata: Thaliacea). Mar. Biol., vol. 25, pp. 143-147.
1974b. Field studies on the biology of salps (Tunicata: Thalacea). Ph.D. dissertation, University of California, Davis.

MADIN, LAWRENCE P., and HARBISON, G. R.
——. Associations of hyperiid amphipods with gelatinous zooplankton: I, Associations with salps. (MS.)

SWANBERG, N.
1973. The feeding behaviour of *Beroe ovata.* Mar. Biol., vol. 24, pp. 69-76.

WILLIAM M. HAMNER

Excavations at Shahr-i Qūmis, Iran, 1971

Principal Investigators: John F. Hansman, School of Oriental and African Studies, University of London, and David Stronach, British Institute of Persian Studies, Tehran.

Grant No. 855[1]*:* For archeological excavation of the Parthian site at Shahr-i Qūmis, Iran.

The Background of Qūmis

One of the more important cities of antiquity in Iran was Hecatompylos, an early capital of the Parthian dynasty. The Parthians ruled in Iran and over much of the adjoining country from the late third century B.C. to the early third century A.D. However, we first learn of Hecatompylos from classical sources in the year 330 B.C., when Alexander the Great pursued Darius III of Persia through Media into Parthia. Three days after coming upon the body of the murdered Darius, the invading army rested in the "wealthy city" which was later to be called Hecatompylos. At this point Alexander announced to his assembled soldiery that he would continue his campaign of world conquest in the East.

Following the division of the empire after Alexander's death, firm government was only restored to Parthia by Seleucus Nicator between 311 and 302 B.C. Appian credits Seleucus with the foundation of Hecatompylos. It is more likely, however, that Seleucus merely gave this name to the existing Iranian city which Alexander visited.

In about 238 B.C. Arsaces, chief of the nomadic Parni tribe, after an earlier revolt in Parthia, seized control of the province, and in 209 B.C. Hecatompylos, and much of the district of Comisene in which the city was located, were reoccupied by the Seleucids. Yet on the conclusion of peace the city was returned to the control of the Parni-Parthians and it became

[1] The grant from the National Geographic Society (made in 1970) comprised the major support of the excavations. Help was received also from the British Museum, the Ashmolean Museum at Oxford, the Corpus Inscriptionum Iranicarum, and the British Institute of Persian Studies.

their capital for nearly 200 years. At the end of the first century B.C. Isidore of Charax records eight villages in Comisene but "no city." By this date the Parthian capital had been moved west with the expanding Parthian empire to Ctesiphone in Mesopotamia (modern Iraq).

During the past hundred years a number of locations have been proposed as the site of Hecatompylos. These ranged from the Gorgan valley in northeastern Iran to Shahrud, Damghan, and other points on or near the ancient Silk Route leading along the base of the Elburz Mountains in north-central Iran. However, none of the sites claimed (up to 1966) as that of Hecatompylos, was described as possessing cultural remains of the extent appropriate for the former capital of Parthia.

In autumn 1966 the writer undertook to locate the unknown site of Hecatompylos from a consideration of the distances cited by classical writers. Although the measure of the Greek *stade* may vary, Strabo, quoting the earlier Apollodorus, gives both the distance from Rhagae (modern Ray) to the Caspian Gates (fig. 1) and that from the Caspian Gates to Hecatompylos. The Caspian Gates are to be associated with a natural gap in a spur of the Elburz Mountains east of Ray through which passes the Silk Road leading to Khurasan in eastern Iran. This distance, when applied to the present Khurasan road, leads to a point near the village of Qusheh. A figure in Roman miles given by Pliny for the same journey also measures reasonably close to Qusheh. Investigation of these distances on the ground led the writer to Qusheh and to the nearby archeological site of Shahr-i Qūmis.

The harsh effects of wind and water erosion are visible on all sides at Shahr-i Qūmis. Strong winds, constantly eating at the loose topsoil, have helped to lay bare a thick carpet of pottery over the whole site. This cultural debris extends for a distance of 4.8 kilometers from northwest to southeast with a maximum width of 2.1 kilometers across a semiarid plain. A total of 25 ruined structures of mud brick are scattered over this extensive deposit (fig. 2).

The name Hecatompylos, "city of a hundred gates," is, as we have seen, the Greek appellation given by Greek conquerors to an established Persian city. There is, therefore, every possibility that the present name of our site, Qūmis, is derived from a hypothetical Old Persian form **Komisha* through an attested intermediate form *Komish,* which represents the original Iranian name for Hecatompylos.

Three mounds were examined by the writers during a 2-week season at Shahr-i Qūmis in 1967 (see fig. 2). Of these, Sites IV and VII were cleared only in part. The recovery of large quantities of bones, especially at Site IV, suggested that both buildings may have served a funeral purpose.

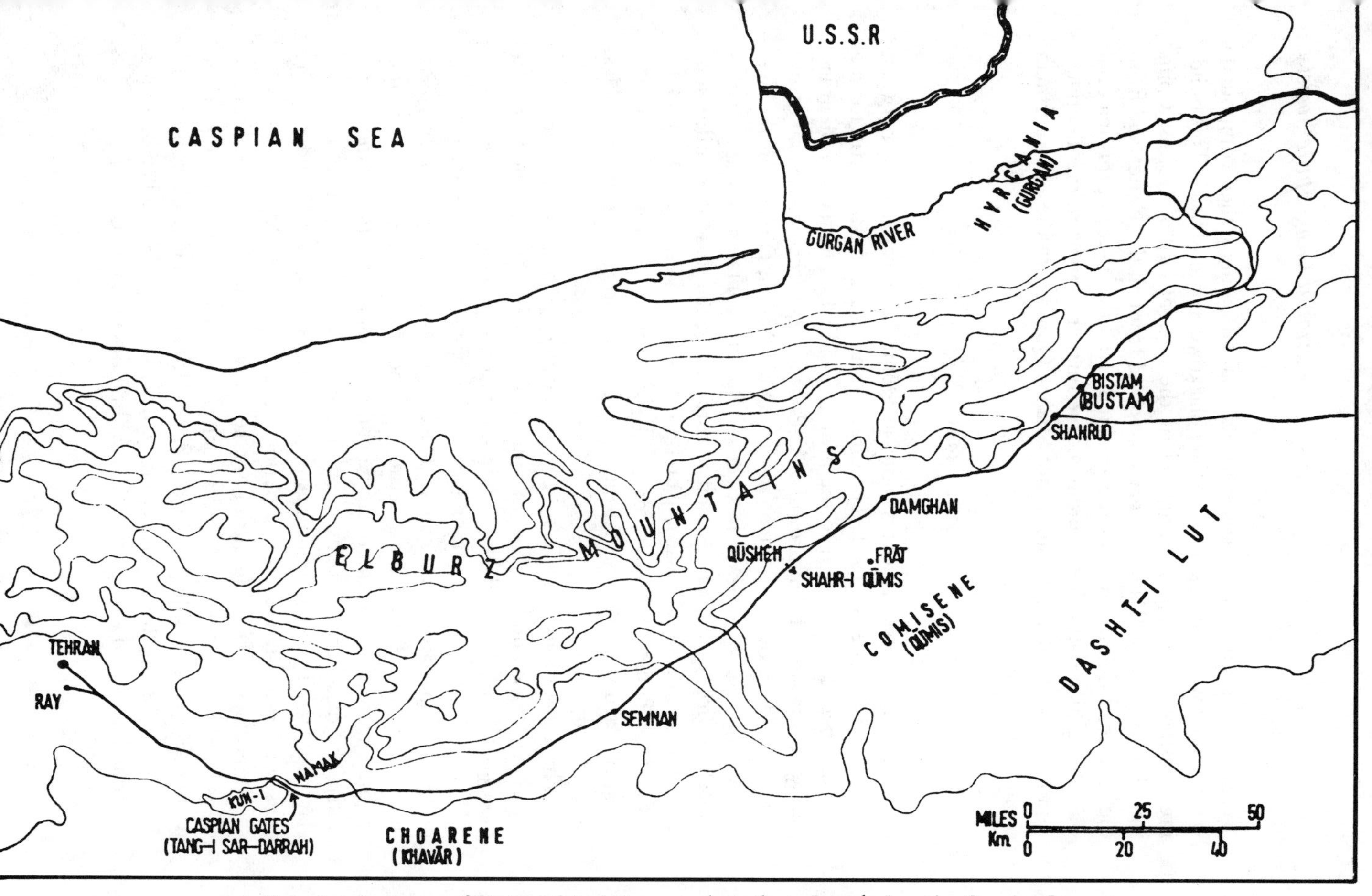

FIG. 1. Location of Shahr-i Qūmis in central northern Iran, below the Caspian Sea.

Site VI, a much larger structure with an adjoining walled compound, was fortified with a series of six rectangular towers of mud brick. This building possibly had been a stronghold of the ancient city of Qūmis. Coins found within Site VII and pottery recovered from all three sites and from the surface of Qūmis, over a wide area, indicated that much of this material was of Parthian date. These findings gave further support to the identification of the archeological complex of Shahr-i Qūmis with the early Parthian capital Hecatompylos.

Excavations, 1971

The second season's excavations at Qūmis were carried out between August and October in 1971. The directors are again most grateful for the close cooperation extended to the project by His Excellency Mr. Mehrdad Pahlbod, Minister of Culture; Mr. A. Pourmand, Director General of the Iranian Archaeological Service; and by Dr. T. Naimi, Director of the Service. On the excavations Mr. B. Badek, field representative of the Archaeological Service, gave every assistance throughout the season. In addition to the directors, those who participated on the excavations were Dr. A. D. H. Bivar, Miss Emily Alexander, Mr. R. Biscione, Miss Charlotte Marten, Mr. Jeoffery Payne, Mr. Michael Rolf, Mrs. Marian Sturz, and Mr. and Mrs. Stuart Swiny.

The excavations of 1971 were designed to explore a wider selection of the remaining mounds at Shahr-i Qūmis. To this end we resumed work at mounds IV and VII and began new excavations at two other sites, V and XIII (fig. 2). Each of these mounds proved to consist of a single architectural unit built of mud brick throughout. The four buildings are essentially square in original plan. They are also cruciform, however, in the sense that rectangular projections extend from the middle point of each face of their outer walls. The discovery of rounded and pointed vaults composed of moulded clay struts in all of these buildings provides valuable new knowledge of the construction techniques of this period.

Important finds made during the season were the 16 clay seal impressions from Site V (see fig. 8) and a quantity of fine and highly characteristic pottery from this building and from Site VII. The following notes provide a description of the four mounds investigated. The three similar buildings identified as Sites IV, VII, and XIII will be discussed first.

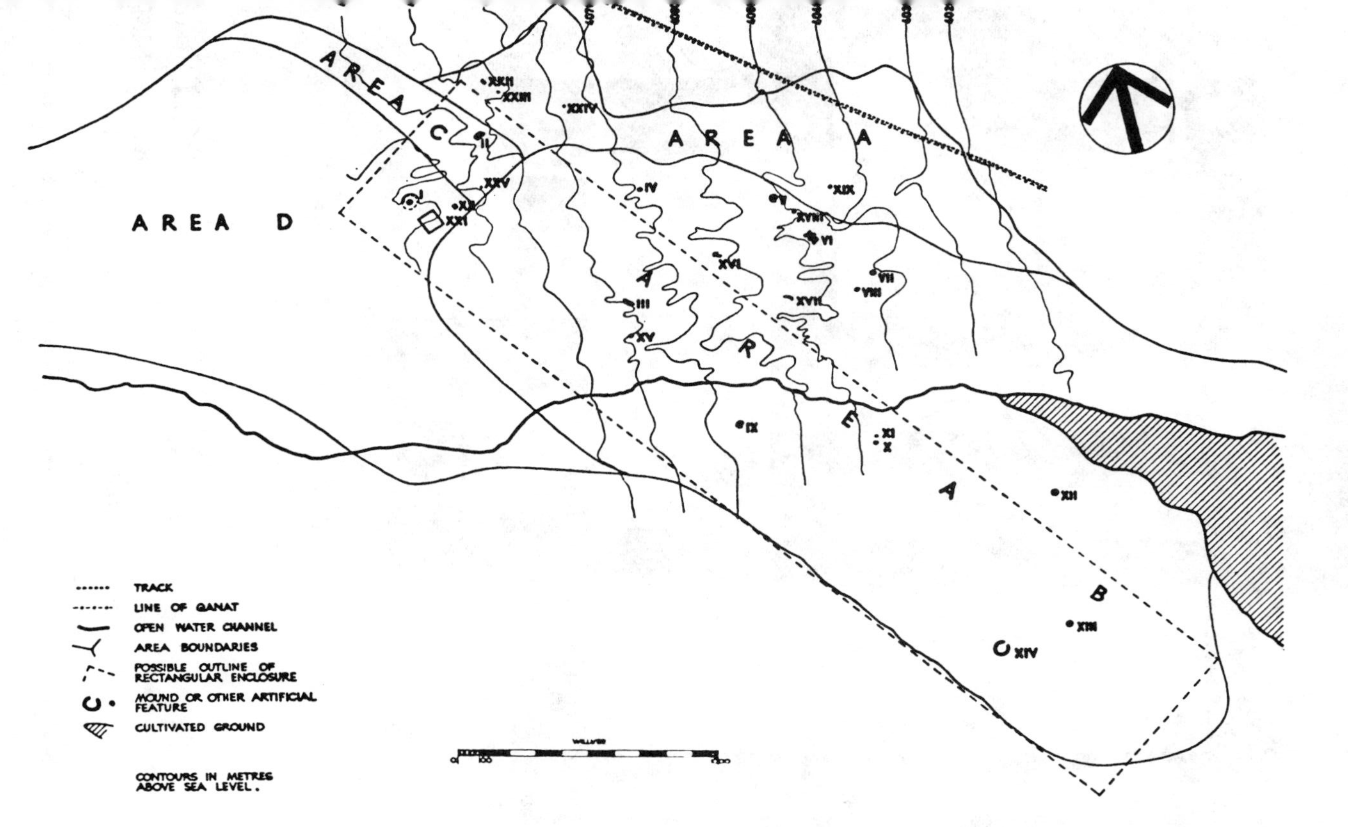

FIG. 2. Plan showing Sites IV, V, VII, and XIII excavated in 1971. Area A contains primarily Iron Age and Achaemenian deposits; B, primarily Hellenistic and Parthian deposits; C, primarily Sasanian deposits; and D, primarily Islamic deposits.

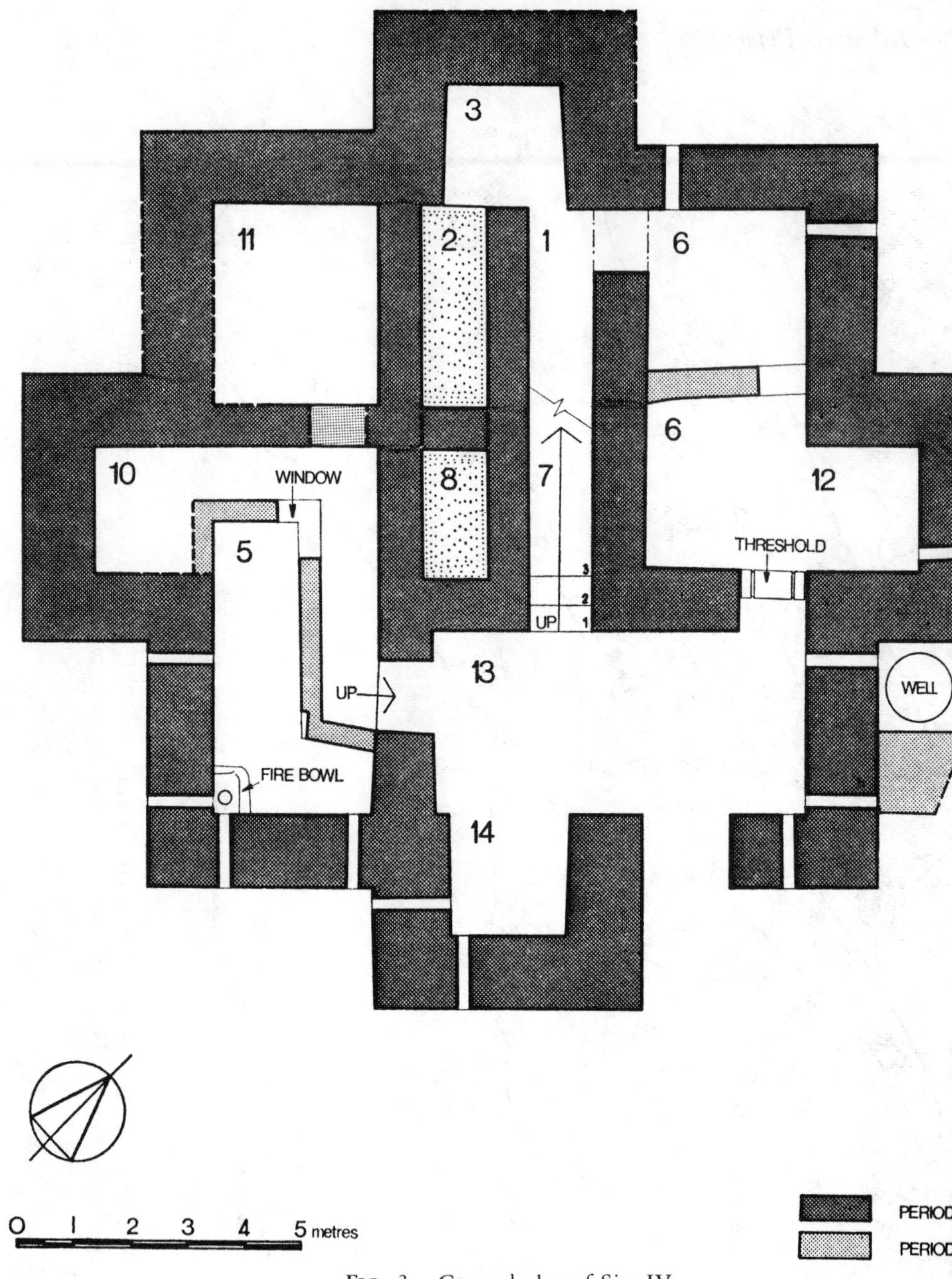

FIG. 3. Ground plan of Site IV.

Site IV

The interior plan of Site IV consists of four main rooms with extended alcoves, grouped around a central staircase (fig. 3). Perhaps the most interesting architectural feature is Room 1, the undercroft of the first flight of the staircase, which is composed of a series of 10 successive stepped vaults or arches (fig. 4). Each of these vaults consists of two opposed sets of three moulded clay units. The vaults are pointed, slightly curved, and covered with a fine plaster of mud and chaff.

At the southwest corner of Room 5 a small altar of plastered mud brick supported a shallow fire bowl. The walls behind and above this bowl show signs of burning. A secondary wall separates the altar and an adjacent area from the rest of the room. The only communication between the two parts of the room appears to have been via a form of window set within the partition at a height of about one meter.

Directly southeast of alcove 12 work continued on the excavation of a well shaft (see fig. 3) first located in 1967. The shaft has now been cleared to a depth of 23 meters. The deposit here was mostly sterile earth. However, at 5 meters were found several broken lumps of clay bearing the impressions of stylized leaves on their one smooth side. Moreover at 20 and again at 23 meters isolated deposits containing the fragments of vessels and numerous bones of sheep and goats were also recovered.

Site IV appears to have been filled in purposely with a packing of clay. This fill had been greatly disturbed in antiquity, but it did still contain a number of human skulls and many equid and other animal bones which, apparently, had been placed there at the time of the original blocking. An outer casing of packed clay, now much eroded, also surrounded the primary walls of the site.

Site VII

The plan of this building is closely similar to that at Site IV. Again we have four rooms in the ground floor arranged around what once had been a central stairway (fig. 5). The undercroft of the upper flight of this stair survives in part. Like that at Site IV it consists of a series of stepped vaults formed from moulded clay units. The vaulting of Room 5, which is more or less intact throughout the southwest half of the room, is also composed of these moulded units. Here, however, the builders necessarily used three,

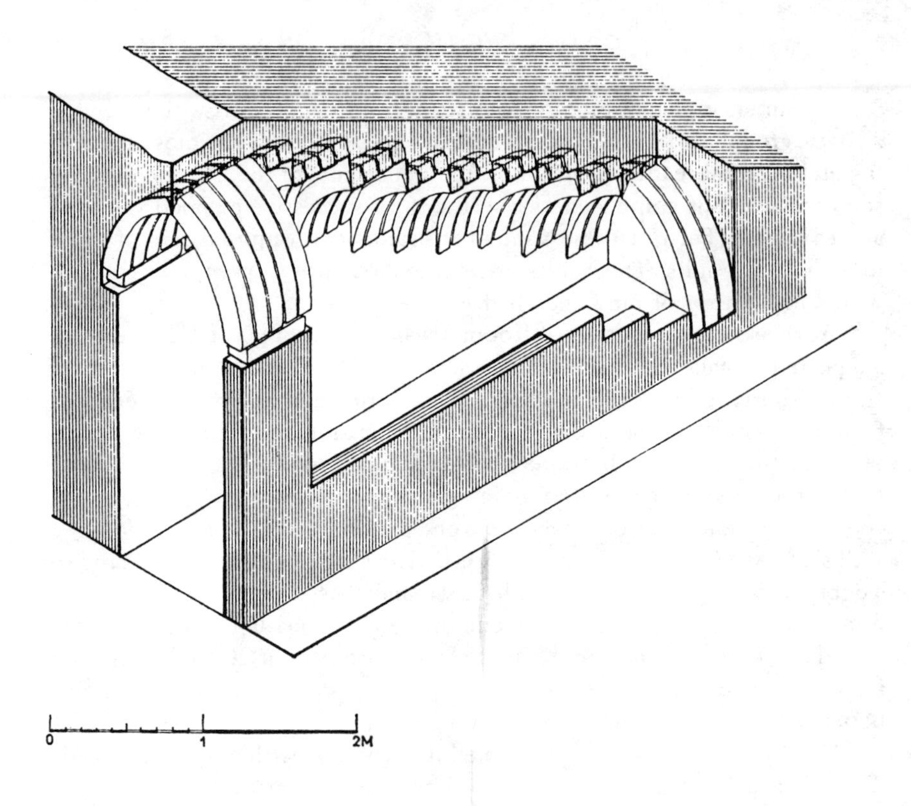

FIG. 4. Isometric view of Room 1 at Site IV.

rather than two, curved units to span the 2.30-meter width of the room. This has produced a barrel vault which is possibly one of the earliest examples of this form of vaulting known. Similarly to Site IV the present building had been filled in with a blocking of packed clay and mud brick. Already in the trial explorations of 1967 a quantity of human skulls and animal bones was recovered from this fill, in most of the rooms, at an average height of 2 meters above floor level. Further remains were recovered during the 1971 excavations. These, from both seasons, include 18 human skulls and parts of one human skeleton, 10 skulls and numerous other bones of several different species of equids, some cattle remains, and the skulls of two dogs, several sheep or goats, two suckling pigs. The frontal regions of the skulls of three goitered gazelles were recovered from as many rooms of the site. A hoard of four finely made pottery vessels came from the floor level of alcove 17 located at the eastern side of the building. These consist of two pouring jars, a rounded pilgrim's flask, and a two-spouted amphora. As with Site IV, the original structure of Site VII had been surrounded with a thick outer skin of packed clay.

Still within the thickness of the base of the outer wall on the south side, three human skeletons were exposed. These were placed in cavities ranged in a line parallel with the wall. The wall was then built up over the burials to form a continuous construction. There is no disturbance of the wall above the deposits to indicate that they were placed there after this considerable addition had been completed. The skeletons were lying in a flexed position, two faced southward while one looked northward.

Site XIII

Again at Site XIII we have an essentially square plan with extended projections on each side (fig. 6). Very little of the ground floor is as yet excavated. However, the main rooms appear to be located to the east and south of the stairway rather than grouped around it as at Sites IV and VII. Room 3, the central chamber on the ground floor, had been roofed with a slightly pointed vault of moulded clay units. In the east wall of this room a rounded-arched doorway led to the base of a ramp (Room 6). The ramp doubled back toward the west in the adjoining Room 5 and from there reached the upper level of Site XIII.

A secondary wall 90 centimeters thick, which is perhaps best described as a rough square with rounded corners, surrounds the whole of Site XIII. A series of small connecting rooms lie between this outer shell and the original building on the exposed upper floor. Rooms 9 and 11 contain the bases of pottery storage jars some of which are fixed in low platforms of packed clay and mud brick. The fill of Site XIII is much disturbed, but as with Sites IV and VII parts of it appear to have been placed there to seal the building. Two human skulls and a number of animal bones, including many equid remains, were recovered from this deposit. Outside the limits of the curved extension just described are the remains of a protective outer wall of packed clay, which in places encases the whole building up to 3.50 meters.

What are we to make of Sites IV, VII, and XIII? Excavations show that all three structures were filled in purposely with mud brick and/or packed clay, and further, that the outer walls of each building were encased in thick skins of clay. Presumably these secondary features were employed to protect the fabric of the structures from decay. It has already been noted that Sites IV and VII show a closely similar plan and that all three sites, in a sense, were cruciform in original conception. Moreover, human skulls and a variety of animal remains have been found deposited within the fill of each building. The apparent lack of primary burials at Sites IV and VII, however, does not now support their identification as tombs. On the other hand, the finding of an altar containing a fire bowl at Site IV does suggest that these structures of similar plan may have been used for some kind of religious activity. Although the available evidence would make it difficult for a more precise explanation of these sites to be given at this time, it may be helpful to consider briefly the possibly relevant Parthian background.

The little that is known of early Parthian religious practice comes almost entirely from scattered references in classical sources. These, taken collectively, do suggest that the Parthians continued to maintain traditional forms of Zoroastrian worship which were known in Iran during the preceding Achaemenian period. If this is indeed the case, then it is equally conceivable that each of our three buildings located at widely separate points within the cultural area at Qūmis served a Zoroastrian function. This suggestion requires justification.

The well at Site IV, for example, could indicate a need for the pure water necessary at all Zoroastrian temples for cleansing, for purification, and for libations. The essentially sterile nature of the fill of the well certainly suggests that this shaft was closed deliberately, presumably in one operation. It is conceivable that the shaft was filled in at the same date as the building of which it forms a part. The isolated find of a jar with a deposit of sheep and goat bones, recovered at 20 meters, and a stone bowl also found with a deposit of similar bones at 22 meters, suggests further that these vessels may have been placed purposely within the well during its closing. Moreover, the lumps of clay, also from the well, found at a depth of 5 meters in 1967, and which contain seal impressions in the form of stylized leaves, could be similarly associated. If this were the case, it would seem legitimate to propose that the two vessels might originally have served a religious or ritualistic use within the building before its closure. A similar employment may be conjectured for the two pouring vessels, the pilgrim flask, and the 2-handled, double-spouted amphora deposited at floor level of Room 17 at Site VII. Thus the need for water or other liquids required in religious rites may explain the preservation of vessels at both sites.

The positioning of an altar against corner walls in Room 5 of Site IV does not, on the other hand, accord with what we would expect for a Zoroastrian sacred fire. This is because Zoroastrian priests, at the present time at least, would normally expect to be able to circumambulate a fire altar.

The secondary wall which restricts the view of the altar at Site IV would agree in part with the requirements of a Zoroastrian sacred fire which is also shielded from general view. Yet, while Zoroastrian priests would be expected to have comparatively unimpaired access to such a fire, the altar at Site IV is reached only by climbing through a meter-high window set within the secondary wall there.

If a possible association of Site IV with Zoroastrian practice is to be considered, therefore, it may be more appropriate to suggest that this building and the other two sites presently under discussion served individual *Yazatas* (beings to be worshiped). Very little is now known of Zoroastrian rituals relating to the worship of the *Yazatas,* as these ceremonies were gradually abandoned with later concentration on veneration of the more important sacred fire. It seems conceivable, then, that Sites IV, VII, and XIII may relate to a type of Zoroastrian devotion or other religious practice of the Parthian period that was no longer observed.

Whatever the function of our three buildings, the fact that all were carefully preserved by the Parthians certainly indicates that they continued to be held sacrosanct in some way even after their closure. The depositing of equid and other animal remains and of human skulls within these structures is reminiscent of similar remains which have been found in Scythian burials in South Russia. Equally, the three articulated human skeletons placed within the foundation of the outer skin of wall at Site VII presents a parallel with Scythian practice, in that articulated human skeletons are also found distributed around the main structure of some of their burial mounds. In the case of Site IV at Qūmis, however, the deposition of bones is associated with the closure of a building which presumably is not a tomb. Quite apart from any rituals practiced in funeral contexts, the Parthian leadership, which is considered to be of Scythian stock by some classical authors, also sacrificed equids in the cause of a variety of religious rites. Philostratus, in reference to the first century A.D., attests that a Persian (Parthian) king sacrificed a white horse of the best Nisaean breed to the Sun. Tacitus relates how the Parthian king Tiridates (in A.D. 35) sacrificed a horse to propitiate the river god at the Euphrates. According to Strabo (late first century B.C.), inhabitants of the Persian province of Carmania (modern Kerman), sacrificed donkeys to Ares. The Greek Ares, the god of war, was traditionally identified with the Zoroastrian deity Verethragna. If, therefore, any religious ritual was performed in connection with the sealing of a disused place of worship by the Parthians, then the occurrence in this association of sacrifice involving horses would, perhaps, in no way be unusual.

So far as the deposition of human heads at Qūmis is concerned, on the other hand, the problems raised in a Zoroastrian context are more difficult. For the modern Zoroastrian, the introduction of dead human matter into a religious shrine would not ordinarily be considered possible. However, the Early Islamic historian Tabari quotes an episode in which a Sasanian king (Ardashir I) sent the heads of defeated enemies to the Anahit fire-temple; apparently that they should be exposed or exhibited there. In the case of the Parthians at Qūmis, the occurrence of human skulls at Sites IV, VII, and XIII may therefore be explained on the same lines, i.e., that they are the heads of defeated enemies or captives, deposited or sacrificed in connection with the closing of these three buildings.

The question of the age of Sites IV, VII, and XIII will now be considered: two of these, Sites IV and VII, have hitherto been held as Parthian on the evidence of architectural features and of archeological finds made during the 1967 season; this evidence will be briefly recounted and further considered in light of the present excavations.

Unfortunately, owing to the lack of datable finds in Site IV, and since parallels to the vessels found in the well there in 1971 are not known to the writers, we must continue to turn to Site VII, which is closely identical in plan, for evidence of the date of Site IV.

During the Qūmis excavations in 1967 seven coins, in mint condition and all of the same Parthian king, were recovered from beneath a part of the mud-brick fill in Room 2 at Site VII. This king has been identified as Sinatruces (ca. 77-70 B.C.) by Wroth and as Orodes I (ca. 89-79/8 B.C.) by Sellwood. Since both kings ruled in the last third of the first century B.C., however, we may in either case assume that the coins relate to this general period. By association, then, it would seem possible to propose that the filling in of Site VII was undertaken while these coins were still current. A further confirmation of this relative date is supplied by an ostracon (an inscribed potsherd) recovered from the fill of Room 11 at Site VII. This shows a Parthian inscription and can be dated epigraphically to about the first century B.C. The coins and ostracon, therefore, suggest that Site VII was sealed at some point during the late first century B.C. and that the building was in use before that date. The Parthians, as we have seen, were in control of Iran for over 400 years from the late third century B.C. On the evidence of its plan being almost identical to that of Site VII, it is further proposed that Site IV dates from the same general period as that building.

Site XIII yielded no coins or other readily datable material. Although a beak-spouted vessel recovered during excavations there would usually be

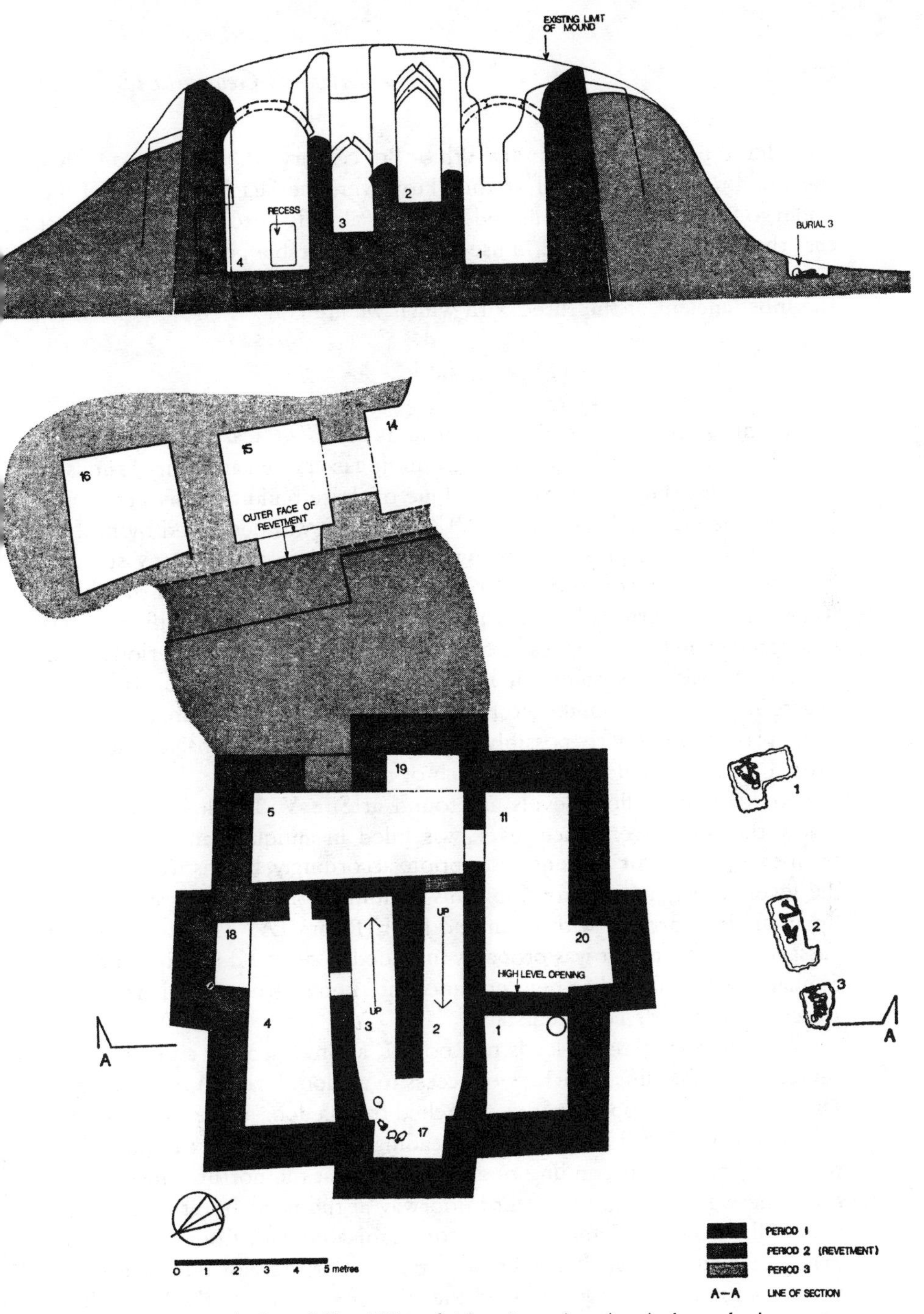

FIG. 5. Ground plan of Site VII and (above) section A—A through site.

considered pre-Achaemenian (ca. 9th or 8th century B.C.), it is unlikely that the building itself is as old as this. However, the fact that Site XIII did undergo the major alterations and additions already described does suggest that the structure remained in use over a considerable period of time. This point taken together with the beak-spouted jar may indicate that the site is the most ancient of the three with which we are concerned.

Site V

From the point of its plan and of finds of *bullae* (seal impressions) and pottery, perhaps the most interesting building excavated at Shahr-i Qūmis in 1971 was also the largest, Site V. Alone of those buildings this site, which lies 200 meters northeast of Site VI (see fig. 2), was destroyed by fire. Indeed, the evidence presented below indicates that parts of Site V suffered damage from at least two major conflagrations. Because many of the rooms were sealed by burnt debris, a large quantity of pottery and of other objects recovered from them can be associated with the building's final period of use.

Site V was constructed of mud bricks and in original plan formed a square measuring 23 meters to the side (fig. 7). As with the previous three sites, projections—here possibly to be identified as defensive salients—extend from the middle point of each of these sides.

At least three floor levels are found at Site V. The lowest of these, below the present entrance level, was filled in antiquity and has not yet been excavated. Our present description, accordingly, begins with the middle level. The visitor approaching this building from the east gained entry by an angled corridor with a ramped floor (Room 1A). The layout of this passage suggests that it was probably intended to serve a defensive purpose. Similar types of angled or bent entrances are known from Parthian fortified structures in South Turkmenistan.

The entrance passage leads to Room 1, a long chamber situated at the center of the building, which gives access to all floor levels. A ramp (Rooms 18 and 26) to the upper floor was reached from a door at the southwestern end of the west wall and a corridor leading to a series of six ground floor rooms, from a corresponding opening located at the northwestern end of the same wall (see fig. 7). A third doorway at the northeastern end of the east wall, which was later blocked, communicated with Room 16. The remains of a stepped vault descends to the east at the east end of this last room, and must once have formed the roof of a passage to the lower floor. This access was later filled in, presumably at the same time as the lower floor level was closed.

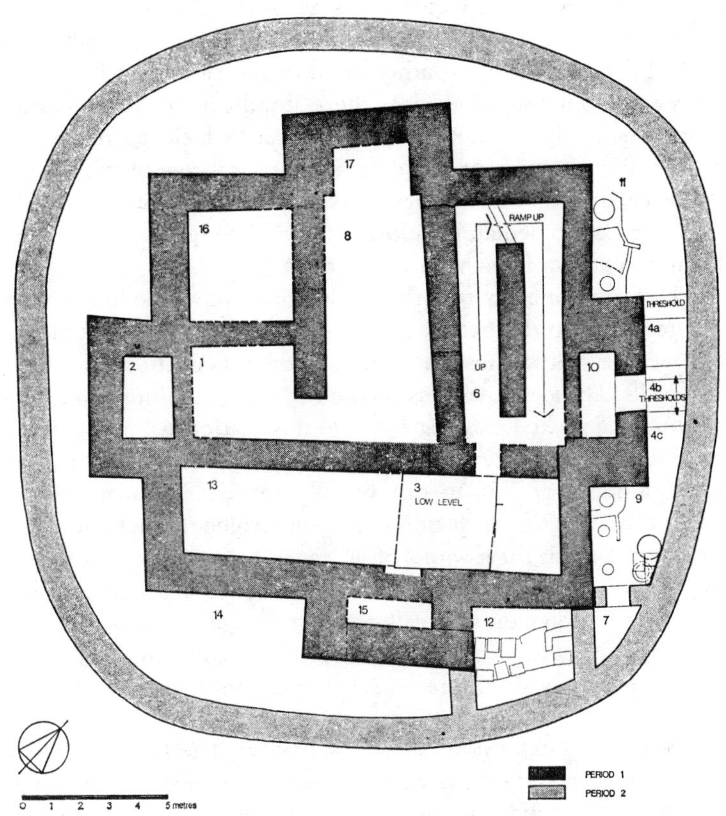

FIG. 6. Ground plan of Site XIII.

At some date during the lifetime of the building a second skin of mud brick, which averages 70 centimeters in thickness, was added to the east wall of Room 1 along its full length. A second skin of similar thickness was also added to the southern wall of the upper length of the entrance passage (Room 1A). The mud-and-chaff plaster of the original walls in these two areas are to be seen where higher sections of the later walls are no longer preserved. In order to maintain entry into the doorway leading to Room 16, after these alterations, an arched recess was constructed in the new wall at this point. The line of moulded-clay struts which formed the vault of Room 1 rests on this second skin of the east wall. It is therefore evident that the vault of Room 1 was reconstructed after the addition of this skin. A further reconstruction in Room 1 was the raising of the floor 45 centimeters to bring it level with the top of a mud-brick bench (not shown on fig. 7) which had originally existed at the southern end of the eastern wall.

Between Room 1 and Room 22 there stood a doorway with a rounded arch, composed of the usual moulded-clay struts, which was made narrower after the raising of the floor. To do this, a vertical row of mud bricks was inserted at each side of the door, and a wooden lintel laid across the two uppermost bricks immediately below the arch. The space between the lintel and the arch was also filled with mud bricks.

Possibly contemporary with the reconstructions within Site V were substantial alterations to the exterior of the building. To investigate these, test trenches were put down near the center of the salients in the southern and northern walls. These excavations showed that the building originally stood on a platform of packed clay. At its edge this platform slopes gently down about 1.5 meters to the level of the present plain. The platform was later overlaid to a depth of 2.50 meters by an extensive secondary fill of small stones and clay. The top of this fill had been leveled off and covered with a smooth layer of earth for a width of at least 2.50 meters on all sides of the building. It thus formed the foundation for a series of more-or-less evenly spaced projecting fragments of wall which are ranged around all sides of the site. At the southeastern side these secondary walls are best preserved. Here, where the fill is also more extensive than on the other sides, the plan includes parts of at least three rooms (3, 4, and 6).

Room 6 of this extension has two doorways. The northern jamb is all that is left of the presumed external doorways located at the eastern limit of the extension. A second entranceway in the north wall leads into an area, devoid of structural remains, which may have served as a small courtyard. A bench of mud brick is set against the western wall of Room 11. The position of this room suggests that it is likely to have served as an entrance porch to the outer enclosure mentioned above. Room 4, which is entered through a doorway located at the western limit of this enclosure, possesses a narrow window or arrowslot which is directly centered on the axis of the outer (eastern) door of Room 11. It is therefore possible that Room 4 served as a guardroom for this entrance. Fragments of fallen clay struts found in Room 4 indicate that it was originally roofed by a vault, but whether rounded or pointed is not clear.

Also of interest in Room 4 are the two engaged, pointed arches built against the west wall. These are composed of symmetrical pairs of struts three courses deep. A single course of mud bricks is laid directly on top the struts. While such bricks may have been introduced to provide a bond, the arches themselves were presumably inserted in order to narrow the main span of the vault over Room 4.

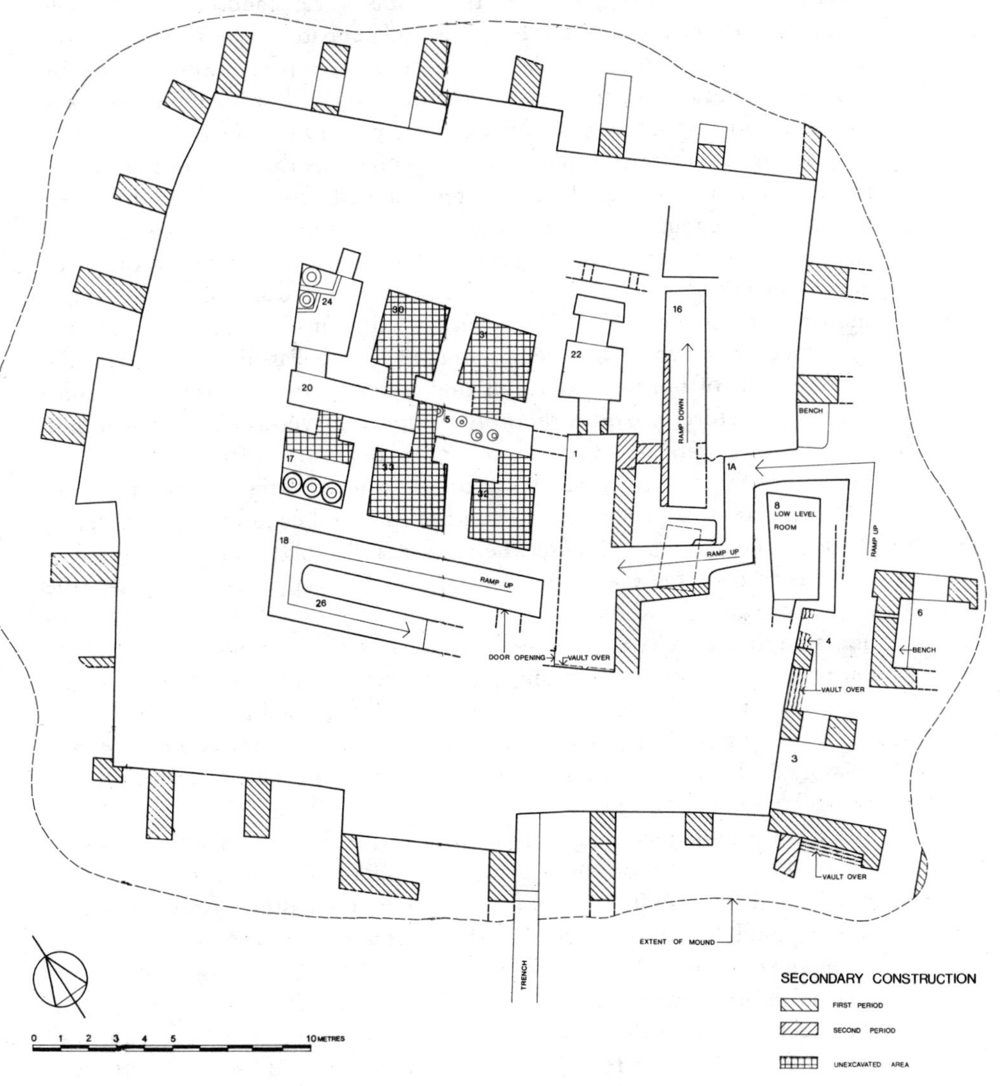

FIG. 7. Ground plan of Site V.

It is not as yet known how long after its reconstruction Site V suffered the first of its major fires. The excavations have shown all the rooms so far cleared on the western side of the building (Rooms 17, 18, 22, and 24) to be filled with burnt debris. The pottery recovered from these rooms is closely homogeneous. This suggests that the rooms were abandoned on a single occasion, presumably after a fire. It is equally apparent that Room 1 and the angled entrance corridor (Room 1A) in the eastern part of Site V were also abandoned because of fire, for a great quantity of burnt rubble was excavated in both of these areas. However, the pottery taken from the western complex is of a distinctly different family of wares than that of the eastern rooms. No horned-handled or animated-handled vessels, for example, were found in the ceramic deposits from Room 1 or in the entrance area. Yet examples of this ware have been recovered from all the western rooms. The horned-handle is known in the Achaemenian period in Iran. An example similar to those from Site V, was recovered from the well at Site IV, the construction of which has been assigned to the Parthians. This and the parallel finds of horned-handles in the western rooms at Site V at Shahr-i Qūmis, therefore, provides the only evidence as yet available which indicates that the ware survived into the Parthian period in Iran. Equally, however, since this family of wares was totally absent from the mass of pottery recovered in the eastern part of Site V, horned-handles had apparently already gone out of general use when this final area of the building was burnt.

It is to be noted that in the last stage of the occupation of Room 1, the doorway leading to Room 16 had been crudely blocked with mud brick. At the same time a badly constructed second skin of mud brick was built along the west face of Room 16 behind this doorway (see fig. 7). That these additions were made after a fire in that area is confirmed by the recovery of burnt mud-brick fragments from within the blocking of the door. Again, possibly at this later period, the door leading from Room 1 north to Room 22 was completely blocked and plastered over. As Room 22 was found filled with burnt rubble including several vessels with animated handles, this final modification to its door was evidently undertaken subsequently to the initial fire at Site V. It is in any case clear that the eastern part of this complex continued to be occupied after the areas to the west and north of Room 1 were abandoned. The single exception to this finding, on the other hand, appears to be the corridor designated Rooms 5 and 20, located in the northwest section. While the walls of this corridor show signs of burning, very little burnt debris was found in the fill there. It would seem that after the fire which closed the northwest complex, Room 20 was cleared for further use. The excavations show that five unbaked vessels, set in the floor of this room, were placed there after the level of the floor had been raised approximately 50 centimeters above that of the six rooms to which it once led. It is most unlikely that a series of large-mouth storage jars would have been allowed to obstruct a passageway leading to these rooms while the latter were still in use. At this later stage the function of Room 20, therefore, would seem to have changed from a corridor to a storage area—presumably for occupants who remained in the eastern part of the building.

During its final period of occupation Site V appears to have been

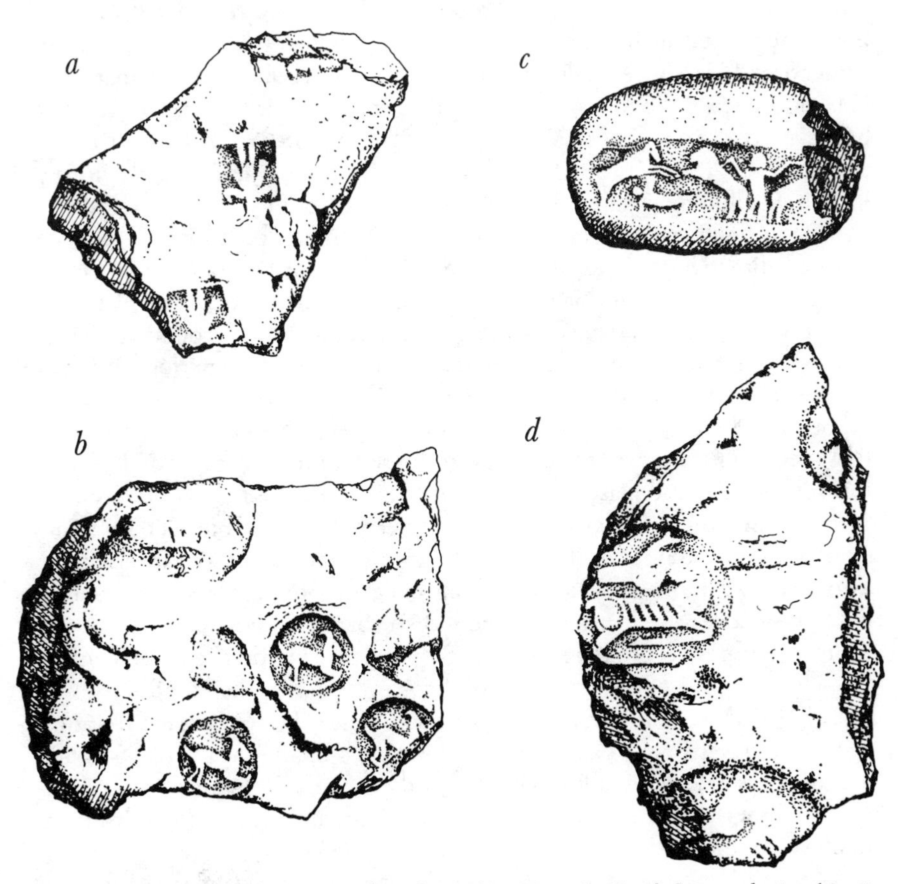

FIG. 8. Clay seals of Parthian date from Site V: *a,* Stylized flower; *b,* "rocking" gazelle; *c,* two human figures, one standing and one fallen between two horses raised on their hind legs; *d,* sitting, hoofed animal, perhaps a deer.

reduced to humble uses. Indeed, the finding of a large quantity of burnt chaff deposited on the floor of Room 1 suggests the adaption of this area of the building for storage or possibly as a stable.

Much of the fill of Room 1 consists of collapsed struts of moulded clay from the roofing vault and of other debris, all badly burnt. It is clear, therefore, that the final abandonment of Site V had resulted from a second fire of considerable intensity.

Large deposits of human skulls and equid remains were recovered at a high level within the fill of the corridor identified as Room 20 and also in the fill of the ramp (Room 18). This suggests that after Site V ceased to be inhabited, it was further used as a repository for bones. Associated with the bones deposited in Room 18 is a jar of poppy seeds which are perfectly preserved. It is conceivable that all these finds are intended to mark the final closure of the building as, it has been proposed, are similar deposits of bones recovered at Sites IV, VII, and XIII. At Site V, however, we are, perhaps, also dealing with a more specifically funeral use of a previously inhabited building. The evidence for this can be briefly stated.

On the uppermost floor at Site V the doorways of Rooms 21 and 25 (located directly above Rooms 31 and 30 on the main floor) were blocked at some stage with mud brick. In both rooms the blocking was plastered over on the inside and this plaster continued unbroken around the walls and over the floor. It is obvious, therefore, that in this final period, access to Rooms 21 and 25 was not gained by the original doors. However, because of the poor state of preservation of all but the southern walls of both rooms, the later points of entry are not now to be seen. Moreover, parts of several low receptacles, also plastered over, were built upon the floors of the rooms. Animal and human bones were found scattered over both floors. This evidence lends some plausibility to the view that the rooms were used finally as ossuaries for the deposition of bones and that the receptacles formerly held these excavated remains. Their disturbance is possibly due to the rooms having been broken into after their closure but before deterioration.

The available evidence would perhaps not support the identification of Site V, fortified as it is, as a town garrison post. The six massive bastions, walled courtyard, and extensive storage rooms of the very large building identified as Site VI and located 750 yards to the southwest of Site V are, on the other hand, certainly more suited for the needs of a substantial military contingent.

At Site V on the main floor level we have essentially an entrance complex, the central Room 1, and seven much smaller rooms. Two of these chambers, Rooms 22 and 24, contained fragments of numerous small and medium-sized pottery vessels, a quantity of clay jar stoppers and many clay sealings—some with stamped impressions (fig. 8). The impressions are of special historical interest, for very few seals have survived from the Parthian period. Depicted are a variety of subjects, including flowers, animals, and human figures. Figure 8a shows a stylized flower, perhaps honeysuckle, a favorite motif used in contemporary Hellenistic architectural decoration. On the principle of the nursery rocking horse, figure 8b may be best described as a rocking gazelle. The cylinder seal impression of figure 8c shows a man holding in his left hand a line connected to a horse. With his right hand he appears to be stabbing another animal, perhaps another horse. Both animals seem to be menacing a second human figure lying prostrate below. Finally figure 8d shows a hoofed animal, possibly a deer, looking very thin, and resting with its legs folded underneath.

The association of these sealings with the jars and jar stoppers suggests that both rooms in which they were found may have served as wine stores. This would be in keeping with the archeological finds recovered from a number of rooms at the Parthian stronghold of Old Nisa (in present Soviet Turkmenistan) where sherds of similar vessels were found in association with plain and stamped clay sealings. The rooms at Nisa have been identified as wine stores from a series of inscribed potsherds (ostraca) also found there.

A third chamber on the middle level at Site V at Qūmis, Room 17, contained the bases of three very large storage vessels each set into a low platform at the southern wall. No residue other than fallen debris was deposited within these jars and it is probable that they were used for the storage of water. Taken as a whole, then, it appears that the smaller ground floor rooms already excavated at Site V were used for storage. Living quarters would no doubt have been located on the now badly preserved upper story. However, the fortified nature of this building suggests that there must also have been a small guard contingent stationed there. This force may originally have occupied the lowest floor and, after the blocking of this level, the western extension of the building where we have already postulated the existence of an entrance porch (Room 11) and guardroom (Room 4).

Shahr-i Qūmis had previously been identified with the early Parthian capital known to classical historians as Hecatompylos. Since the Parthian elite would require a substantial fortified residence at their chief city of the period, and as Qūmis contains no other ruins on the scale of Site V, other than Site VI, proposed as a garrison post, it would seem probable that Site V may be one of the local residences of this elite.

It is perhaps of interest to note as a closing point that over 2,000 ostraca were recovered during excavations of the wine storage rooms at Nisa mentioned above. The language of these documents, executed in a form of the Aramaic script and by means of an ideographic writing system, is in fact the Parthian dialect. They provide a great deal of information on the delivery, storage, and distribution of wine and of other commodities; on the structure of Parthian estates; and on the process of tax collecting. They also give important new evidence on the descent of some of the earlier Parthian kings. It has been proposed that at least two of the ground-floor chambers in Site V at Qūmis served as wine stores. Others of the five remaining unexcavated rooms in that part of the complex may have been used for a similar purpose. The recovery of ostraca in one or more of these blocked chambers is therefore a reasonable possibility. Since this part of the site was sealed with burnt rubble at the time of the first conflagration in the building, it is to be expected that other informative artifacts could be found here. There is also a case for undertaking the excavation of the blocked lower level of Site V to confirm that this represents an earlier stratigraphic layer.

REFERENCES

HANSMAN, JOHN F.

1968. The problems of Qūmis. Journ. Roy. Asiatic Soc., 1968, pt. 1, pp. 111-139.

HANSMAN, JOHN F., and STRONACH, DAVID

1970. Excavations at Qūmis. Journ. Roy. Asiatic Soc., 1970, pt. 1, pp. 29-62.

1970. The Sasanian repository at Qūmis. Journ. Roy. Asiatic Soc., 1970, pt. 2, pp. 142-155.

1974. Excavations at Shahr-i Qūmis, 1971. Journ. Roy. Asiatic Soc., 1974, pt. 1, pp. 8-22.

JOHN F. HANSMAN

DAVID STRONACH

Stratigraphy, Age, and Environmental Interpretation of the Olduvai Beds, Tanzania

Principal Investigator: Richard L. Hay, University of California, Berkeley, California.

Grant Nos. 838, 1075: In support of geologic studies in Olduvai Gorge, Tanzania, complementary to the over-all explorations of Drs. Mary D. and Louis S. B. Leakey.

Grant No. 905: In support of writing a monograph on the geology of Olduvai Gorge, complementary to the archeological studies of the Leakeys.

Work supported by these grants was part of an on-going geological investigation of Olduvai Gorge: the stratigraphy, age, and environmental interpretation of the Olduvai Beds, which contain a remarkable record of human evolution and cultural development over the past 2 million years. Work in the summers of 1970 and 1972, supported by grants 838 and 1075, was devoted principally to the stratigraphy and environmental interpretation of Bed II, the most complex of the Olduvai Beds. Bed II was subdivided on a fine scale, greatly improving the accuracy of age assignments for the many (at least 63) known archeologic sites in Bed II. This dating was imperative to establish the contemporaneity of Acheulian and Developed Oldowan sites and to determine the paleogeographic locations of these different cultural assemblages. This work showed that Acheulian sites tend to lie at least 1 kilometer from the lake margin, whereas most Developed Oldowan sites were situated nearer to the lake shore. This should aid in archeologic interpretations of the two cultures or "tool kits."

Grant 905 made possible the writing of a preliminary draft on the geology of Beds I and II. A published paper (Hay, 1973) resulted from this draft, which was later revised and embodied in my monograph *Geology of the Olduvai Gorge* (1976).

REFERENCES

HAY, RICHARD L.
1973. Lithofacies and environments of Bed I, Olduvai Gorge, Tanzania. Journ. Quaternary Res., vol. 3, pp. 541-560.
1976. Geology of the Olduvai Gorge, 203 pp., illus. University of California Press, Berkeley, Los Angeles, London.

RICHARD L. HAY

Archeological Investigations at the Murray Springs Clovis Site, Arizona, 1970

Principal Investigator: C. Vance Haynes, University of Arizona, Tucson, Arizona.

Grant No. 853: For continuation of archeological investigations at the mammoth-kill site near Murray Springs, Arizona.

Excavations were concentrated in two areas of the site (fig. 1) during this field season of June 1970. In area 8 an average of 2.5 meters of overburden was removed mechanically from a 90-square-meter area around the ancient spring conduit discovered the previous season. The black mat (units F2 and F3) was removed with the same careful control and hand methods as employed in the past, and the sand in the spring conducts was removed in the same manner.

Within this area of excavation only one artifact, a bifacial thinning flake, was found on the Clovis occupation surface, approximately 4 meters north of the conduits and among a concentration of horse teeth. The material is similar to the cherts found in previous excavations and is probably of Clovis origin. Several disarticulated bones and teeth of bison and horse were found scattered on the same surface.

Under the supervision of archeologist Gerald Kelso and paleontologist Jeffery Saunders excavation of the spring sands revealed not one but three overlapping conduits, each containing a remarkable concentration of bones and teeth of extinct Pleistocene mammals, including horse, camel, bison, mammoth, and a large cat. Many teeth were in articular position but without any jawbone remaining, which indicates differential solution of bone by apparently acid water. Inasmuch as the concentration was so great that only a small portion of the conduits could be properly excavated and mapped during June, Saunders continued excavation and removal of specimens on several occasions during the remainder of the summer.

The sand-filled conduits of the springs have penetrated the sandy clay stratum of unit D, and in this unit eight small cobbles (7 to 13 centimeters) were found adjacent to the north side of the conduits. Four of these were spaced approximately 1 meter apart in an east-west line, and two occurred at random on each side of the alignment. All the cobbles were found within unit D, but three were in contact with the black mat (unit F2).

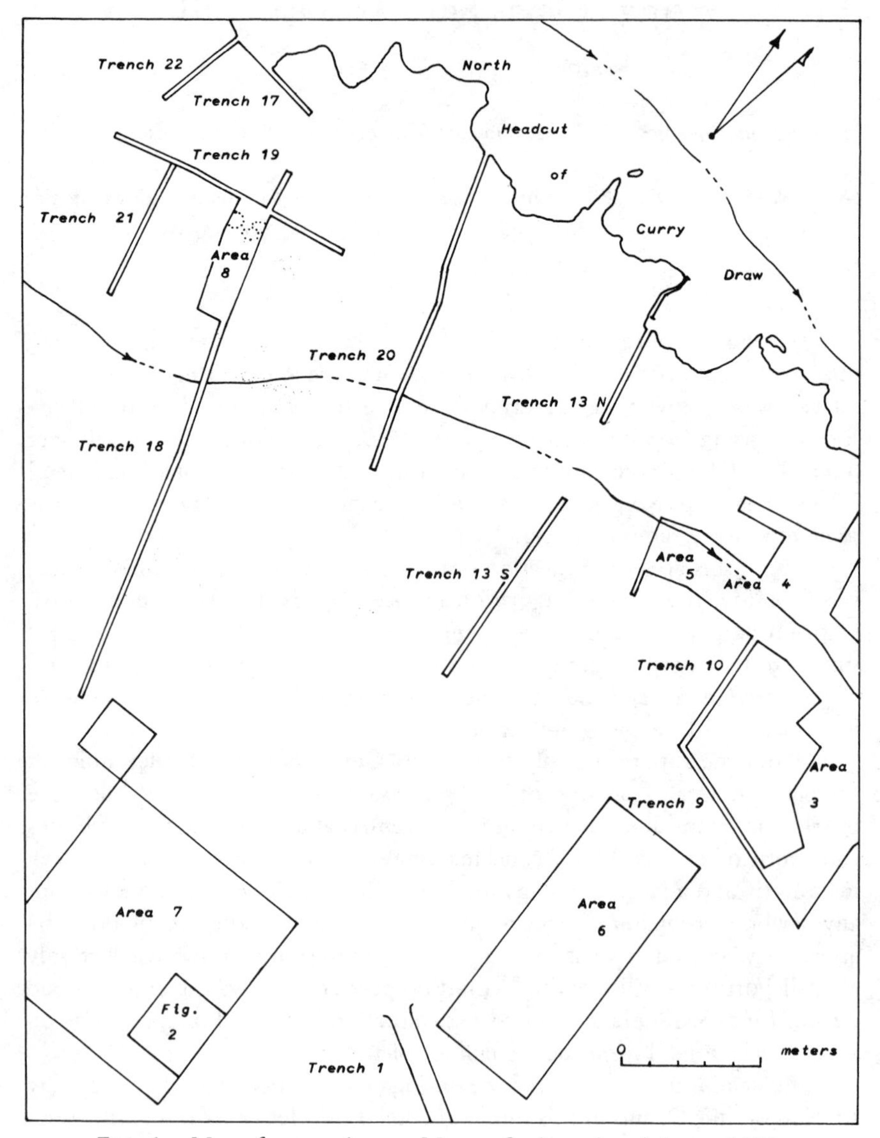

FIG. 1. Map of excavations at Murray Springs site, Arizona, 1970.

These occurrences are anomalous, but their significance is uncertain at this time. They could derive from the activities of Clovis people around the ancient springs, but in spite of extensive excavations we found practically no other evidence of man's activity there other than the single flake mentioned earlier.

Because of the paucity of Clovis artifacts, it is probable that these springs had become inactive by the time Clovis people appeared there. It is possible then that the anomalous stones are the result of an earlier human occupation, and in this regard a fractured cobble found on the unit E/D contact in trench 1 in 1966 is of interest. One end of this stream-rounded cobble is fractured by percussion, which removed three or four chips to leave a sharp but irregular edge. Taken by itself it is not possible to tell whether it is a man-made tool, but it was found in very fine-grained pond sediments that are between 22,000 and 23,000 radiocarbon years old.

The probability of natural origin for the stones will have to be further evaluated by additional trenching about the spring conduits to ascertain the nearest ancient outcrop of unit Z, which contains cobble gravels.

Under the supervision of Larry D. Agenbroad excavations were continued in area 7 (fig. 1), the surface site that we had raked and screened the previous year. This year a colluvial, silty rubble layer overlying unit E was excavated over an area of 132 square meters (fig. 2) and found to contain Clovis artifacts and waste flakes, most of which occurred in three distinct concentrations indicating activity sites. Two Clovis point bases, a scraper, utilized flake, and nearly 500 flakes were recovered from within the surface layer, which is a mixture of loose, pale-brown, sandy silt and firm irregular masses of light-gray calcareous clay.

The gray clay forms an irregular layer resting upon the eroded surface of the unit E marl and is pockmarked with innumerable holes of various sizes up to 4 centimeters in diameter and commonly with hemispherical bottoms. Insect pupae were observed in some of these pockets, and mammal burrows and root molds are numerous. Intermixed with fragments of the gray clay and filling voids is the loose gray silt, which is clearly slope wash in origin. The gray clay is probably derived from pedogenic reworking of unit E marl and may be an upland facies of the unit F1 channel sand in the kill area.

The presence of a concentration of several hundred Clovis waste flakes in an area of less than 1 square meter within the gray clay clearly demonstrates that the concentration has not dispersed laterally to any significant degree during the 11,000 years since the flint knapping was done, but it is entirely possible that there has been some disorientation of the flakes by the action of insects. The colluvial silt layer has probably been turned over many times by the action of plant roots and burrowing animals, but the lack of dispersal of flakes beyond that to be expected by the knapper himself is surprising and indicates that the gray clay has not been reworked by slope washings.

Artifacts are dispersed in both the gray clay and the brown silt, but the tight flake concentrations are confined mainly to the gray clay. Artifacts of the San Pedro stage of the Cochise Culture occur on the surface and in the loose silt, but differences in lithology and flaking technique make most of them clearly distinguishable from the Clovis material. A concentration of small subrounded cobbles found in the silt is probably the remains of a hearth of this late stage.

The Clovis artifacts from area 7 suggest a hunting camp site where broken projectile points were discarded and replaced, where bifacial thinning was performed, and where some sort of scraping activity took place.

In addition to the archeological and paleontological developments the 1970 field work produced some important geological results. With the expert assistance of Jonathan Gell an accurate paleotopographic map of the Clovis occupation surface (base of the unit F2 black mat) was plotted on a scale of 1:750 with 20-centimeter contour intervals. This has brought out significant features of the relief in the form of shallow troughs and depressions and has more clearly defined the drainages that existed at the time of the Clovis occupation.

As a result of contouring the surface at the base of F2 the presence of a buried channel was suspected behind the south wall of the north headcut at the site. Subsequently backhoe test trenches revealed a complex stratigraphy within the black mat including a small channel deposit. Because of this cut-and-fill sequence the stratigraphic thickness of the black mat was increased to over 2 meters as compared to its normal range of between 4 and 30 centimeters. This discovery explains the 2,500-year time period of black mat deposition suggested earlier by radiocarbon dating. Radiocarbon and pollen analysis of close-interval samples within this stratigraphy at the northward extension of trench 13 will provide a precise chronology for the paleoecological conditions under which the black mat was deposited between 8,500 and 11,000 years ago.

One more field season is required to complete scientific excavation of the camp area and clear up remaining questions about the age, depth, and direction of flow of the "fossil" springs in area 8.

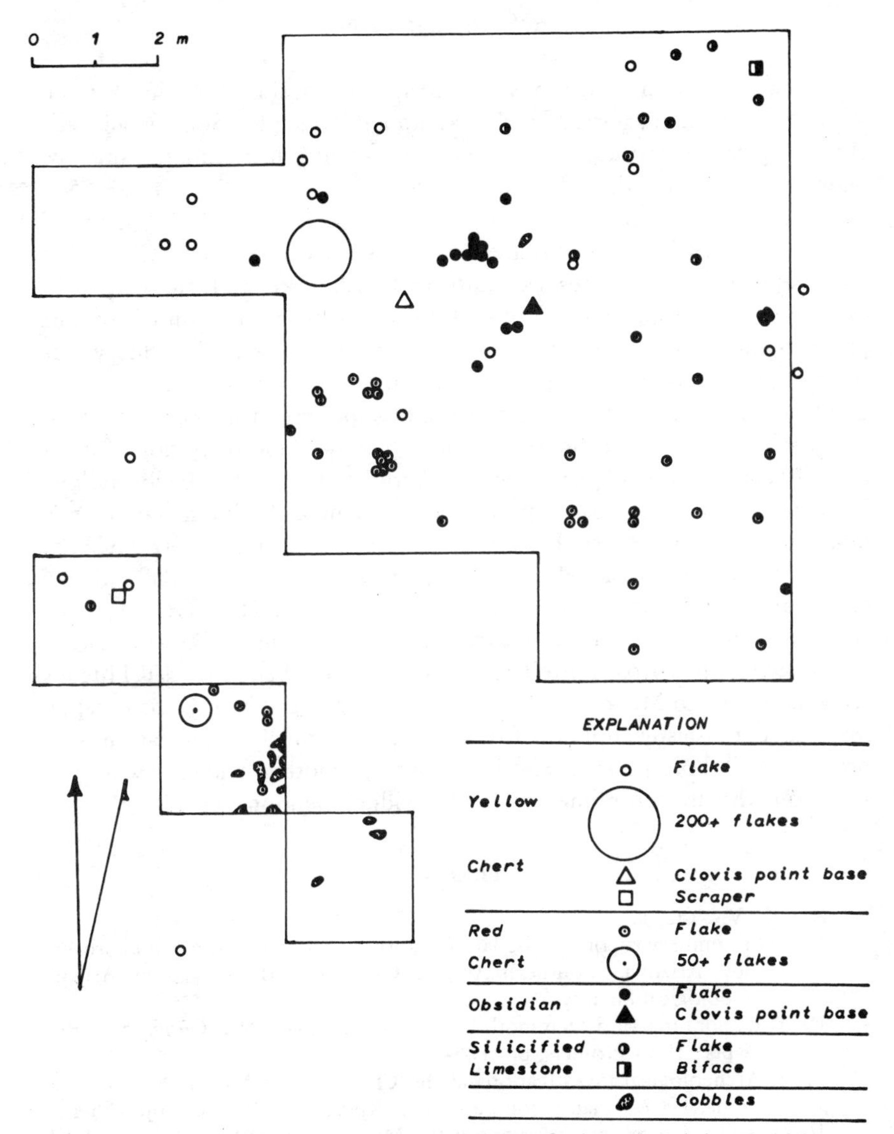

FIG. 2. Map of excavations, area 7, Murray Springs site, Arizona, 1970.

Acknowledgments

Archeological investigations at Murray Springs, since their inception in 1966, have been supported by the National Geographic Society, and geochronological investigations in the San Pedro Valley including the site have been supported by the National Science Foundation (grants GP-5548, GA-1288, and GA-1277).

Deep appreciation is extended to the Kern County Land Co. and its local representatives James McNulty and Jack Porch for allowing us to excavate on its property; to Andrea Cracchiolo for permission to cross his property and to excavate stratigraphic trenches; to the U. S. Military Garrison at Fort Huachuca for access across its property and for aerial photographs of the site; to the Cochise County supervisor for assistance in removing backdirt; to Jim Smith for his expert backhoe operations for the past 5 years; to the Departments of Anthropology and Geochronology, University of Arizona, for supplying equipment and administrative assistance; to Dr. E. W. Haury, University of Arizona, for his expert advice on matters pertaining to Early Man problems in America; to the staff and crew consisting of Dr. Larry D. Agenbroad, assistant director, Gerald Kelso, supervisor, Jonathan Gell, cartographer, Martha A. Ames, Garcia G. Berry, Jr., Peggy Corman, Rosa Portell Ferrer, Steven Haney, and David T. Hughes, crew members; to Mr. and Mrs. Ed Lehner and Mr. and Mrs. Louis Escapule for their enthusiastic support of the project; and finally appreciation is expressed to all those persons who in one way or another made the work possible and who are too numerous for individual mention.

REFERENCES

HAYNES, C. VANCE, JR.

1968. Preliminary report on the late Quaternary geology of the San Pedro Valley, Arizona. Southern Arizona Guidebook III, pp. 79-96. Arizona Geological Society.

1973. Exploration of a mammoth-kill site in Arizona. Nat. Geogr. Soc. Res. Rpts., 1966 Projects, pp. 125-126.

1974. Archeological investigations at the Clovis Site at Murray Springs, Arizona, 1967. Nat. Geogr. Soc. Res. Rpts., 1967 Projects, pp. 145-147.

1976. Archeological investigations at the Murray Springs Site, Arizona, 1968. Nat. Geogr. Soc. Res. Rpts., 1968 Projects, pp. 165-171, illus.

1978. Archeological investigations at the Murray Springs Site, Arizona, 1969. Nat. Geogr. Soc. Res. Rpts., 1969 Projects, pp. 239-242, illus.

HAYNES, C. VANCE, JR., and HEMMINGS, E. THOMAS
1968. Mammoth-bone shaft wrench from Murray Springs, Arizona. Science, vol. 159, pp. 186-187, illus.
HEMMINGS, E. THOMAS
1970. Early man in the San Pedro Valley, Arizona, 236 pp. Ph.D. dissertation, University of Arizona, Tucson.
HEMMINGS, E. THOMAS, and HAYNES, C. VANCE, JR.
1969. The Escapule mammoth and associated projectile points, San Pedro Valley, Arizona. Journ. Arizona Acad. Sci., vol. 5, pp. 184-188, illus.

C. VANCE HAYNES, JR.

Global Physiographic Study of the Ocean Floor

Principal Investigator: Bruce C. Heezen,[1] Lamont Doherty Geological Laboratory, Columbia University, Palisades, New York.

Grant No. 887: In support of a study of global physiographic patterns of sea-floor topography.

The gross form of the floor of the ocean basins was gradually delineated by individual soundings made at widely spaced points. This primitive stage of ocean exploration began in the late 1840's and ended in the 1940's. It has been only since the use of continuously recording echo-soundings that the relief of the ocean floor could be understood in terms of geomorphic features such as valleys, mountains, hills, and plains. The study of deep-sea physiography began at the close of World War II when the first continuous echosounding profiles were recorded. By the early 1950's a sufficient number of profiles had been obtained across the Atlantic to make it possible to begin the serious consideration of physiographic patterns. Certain principles emerged from the study and a physiographic diagram of the North Atlantic, and an accompanying descriptive volume was published in 1959 (Heezen et al., 1959). We next considered the South Atlantic (Heezen and Tharp, 1962) and the Indian Ocean (Heezen and Tharp, 1964).

The late Newman Bumstead of the National Geographic Society's cartographic staff realized the importance of these academic studies to the general public and requested our cooperation in the preparation of a series of ocean-floor panoramas based on our detailed studies (both published and unpublished). The series of ocean-floor panoramas that were in due course published as supplements to the magazine and were later incorporated in the 4th edition of the Society's Atlas of the World are based on our analysis of echosounding profiles made by ships of every maritime nation. Nevertheless, the principal data employed consisted of the detailed precision profiles obtained by research ships supported by the U.S. Office of Naval Research and the National Science Foundation. After 20 years' effort of mapping one ocean after another there came a time when a broader view was required

[1]Dr. Heezen died on June 21, 1977.

not only to present an integrated result to the scientific community and to the public but also as a basis for a more careful consideration of the fundamental meanings of the global pattern of crustal plates.

The National Geographic Society grant made it possible for us to continue on a globe the compilation and analysis originally done exclusively on the Mercator projection. The results of the global physiographic study undertaken under this became the basis for the National Geogaphic Physical Globe painted under our supervision by Society staff artist William H. Bond.

REFERENCES

HEEZEN, BRUCE C., and THARP, MARIE

1958. The floors of the ocean, I: The North Atlantic. Pt. 1: Physiographic diagram of the North Atlantic, in color, 54 by 27 inches. (See also Heezen et al., 1959.)

1962. Physiographic diagram of the South Atlantic Ocean, the Caribbean Sea, the Scotia Sea, and the eastern margin of the South Pacific Ocean, in color, 49¼ by 58¼ inches, scale 1: 10,000,000. Geological Society of America.

1964. Physiographic diagram of the Indian Ocean, the Red Sea, the South China Sea, the Sulu Sea, the Celebes Sea, in color, 49½ by 65 inches, scale 1: 10,000,000. Geological Society of America.

1967. Indian Ocean floor, painted by Heinrich C. Berann. Nat. Geogr. Mag., vol. 132, no. 4, special map supplement.

1968. Atlantic Ocean floor, painted by Heinrich C. Berann. Nat. Geogr. Mag. vol. 133, no. 6, special map supplement.

1969. Pacific Ocean floor, painted by Heinrich C. Berann. Nat. Geogr. Mag., vol. 136, no. 4, special map supplement.

1971a. Arctic Ocean floor, painted by Heinrich C. Berann. Nat. Geogr. Mag., vol. 140, no. 4, special map supplement.

1971b. National Geographic physical globe, painted by William H. Bond, 12- and 16-inch diameters. National Geographic Society.

1971c. Physiographic diagram of the Western Pacific Ocean, in color, 40¾ by 51¾ inches, scale 1: 10,000,000. Geological Society of America.

1975. Ocean floor around Antarctica, painted by Heinrich C. Berann. Pp. 188–189 *in* "Atlas of the World"; scale 1: 25,000,000. National Geographic Society.

HEEZEN, BRUCE C.; THARP, MARIE; and EWING, MAURICE

1959. [Text to accompany the physiographic diagram; see Heezen and Tharp, 1958.] Geol. Soc. Amer. Spec. Pap. 65, 122 pp., illus.

HEEZEN, BRUCE C.; THARP, MARIE; and RYAN, WILLIAM B. F.

1968. The Mediterranean floor, painted by Heinrich C. Berann. Das Stern, 20th anniversary issue.

BRUCE C. HEEZEN

Biologies of Tropical Land Crabs and Their Burrow Associates

Principal Investigators: Charles L. Hogue, Los Angeles County Museum of Natural History, Los Angeles, California, and Donald B. Bright California State University, Fullerton, California.

Grant No. 844: For a study of the biologies of land crabs and their burrow associates.

Since 1967 the authors have been carrying on research on the total biology of tropical burrowing land crabs *(Cardisoma, Gecarcinus, Gecarcoidea, Ucides, Uca,* and *Sesarma)* and the spectrum of arthropods associated with them. The latter live either as members of the aquatic community in the water reservoir of the burrow or as symbionts directly on the host crab's body. The funds made available by the present grant were utilized to carry out field work on the coast of southeastern Brazil with the following objectives: (1) to establish the southern extent of distribution of the land crabs *Gecarcinus lateralis, Cardisoma guanhumi,* and *Ucides cordatus;* (2) to determine the causes for the truncation of range, i.e., the general ecological parameters controlling the lives of the crabs; (3) to reveal and study the bionomics of the burrow associates of these crabs, especially mosquitoes; and (4) to discover and document local cultural practices relative to land crabs.

These objectives were pursued in November and December 1970. The success of our field studies is noted below. In almost all instances we received invaluable assistance from a number of Brazilian biologists whom we wish to acknowledge here. They directed us to the four main coastal localities listed below:

1. *Santos, São Vicente,* and *Itanhaem* (José Guimarães and H. Camargo, Museu de Zoologia da Universidade de São Paulo; Dr. G. Vazzoler, Instituto Oceanografico, Universidade de São Paulo, Santos Office).
2. *Cananeia* (Dr. V. Sadovsky, Instituto Oceanografico, Universidade de São Paulo, Cananeia field station).
3. *Ilhado Pinheiro,* Bahía de Guanabara (Dr. L. de Oliveira, Instituto de Ozwaldo Cruz, Rio de Janeiro).

4. *Guaratiba* and *Restinga de Maranbaia* (Dr. de Oliveira).

A brief account of the significant results of our investigations in these areas (relative to our goals) follows:

1. *Range of Crab Species—Gecarcinus lateralis,* a feeble population discovered at Itanhaem; *Cardisoma guanhumi,* at all localities; *Ucides cordatus,* common at Santos and São Vicente.

   The extremes of range of the last two species were not reached during this trip. From local inquiries we learned that both extend somewhat farther south than we had been prepared to investigate. The most southerly point reached by *Cardisoma guanhumi* is Florianopolis. This was revealed by specimens in the Museu de Zoologia da Universidade de São Paulo and by conducting interviews with a number of local fishermen in each area. Mangrove vegetation, with which *Ucides cordatus* is associated, extends to the border of Uruguay, and the crab probably reaches to approximately that point. These localities represent a range extension of several hundred miles beyond that previously reported in the literature.

2. *Land Crab Ecology*—The habitats in which the three species were found was typical for those generally reported previously in our papers (Bright, 1966; Hogue and Bright, 1971; and Bright and Hogue, 1972):

   Gecarcinus lateralis: Coastal strands.

   Cardisoma guanhumi: Alluvial soils on estuary margins and river deltas.

   Ucides cordatus: Intertidal mangrove mud flats.

   Such habitats occur to and beyond, except for mangrove vegetation, the coastal areas noted under the foregoing section. Thus, at least the first two species potentially could occur farther south than the range reported. However, three factors limiting further dispersal became evident to us in visiting the actual sites.

   a. *Climate.* Between Santos and the southern range extreme of the crabs, winter temperature minima fluctuate around 0° C. Latitude 27° S. may be considered the approximate most southern latitude of the occurrence of frost on the Atlantic coast of South America. These cold temperatures limit the viability of these warm-adapted land crabs.

   b. *Surface Ocean Currents.* Latitude 34°S. marks the approximate limit of the northward-flowing Falkland Current, which would inhibit the marine larval stages of these crabs from dispersion farther south.

c. *Destruction by Man.* It was evident to us that both *Cardisoma guanhumi* and *Ucides cordatus* are under severe survival pressure from both the encroachment of civilization and predation by the local coastal population for food. *Cardisoma* appears to have suffered the most since it is more vulnerable than *Ucides* because of its more accessible burrow habitats. At all localities evidence of human excavation of burrows was noted and the crabs were very difficult to find. Both species are sold locally and in the large markets of São Paulo and Rio de Janeiro.

We noted that housing and commercial developments are resulting in land fills and earth disturbances in the estuarine habitats of the species and certainly are destroying whole populations. Pollution in the Bay of Guanabara (from Rio de Janeiro) has practically annihilated *Cardisoma* from the islands and shores of the Bay.

3. *Bionomics of Burrow Associates*—The arthropod fauna of land-crab burrows at the study sites was found to be poorly developed in comparison to that found in areas we have studied elsewhere, especially Central America. *Deinocerites,* a genus of mosquitoes in which we had particular interest, was not found. We doubt that it exists in the region in spite of the presence of its suitable crab hosts and habitats. The following other mosquitoes were collected; all are common, well-known marine littoral breeders and transient crab-hole inhabitants:

   Aedes taeniorhynchus (Ilha do Pinheiro and Restinga de Maranbaia).
   Culex coronator and *Culex carcinoxenus* (Ilha do Pineiro and Cananeia).

   The only other arthropod associates taken were an unidentified copepod *(Cyclops?* sp.) and a dyticid beetle.

4. *Cultural Aspects*—The coast of Brazil is especially rich in folklore and cultural practices relating to animals from the sea, including land crabs. The reason stems from the long occupation of the coast by a primarily Negro population, which has maintained its African heritage of nature-oriented religions and food practices. Of the former we learned of the "Homenagem do Guaiamu" (homage to the land crab, *C. guanhumi)* in Pernambuco and Homage to the Sea, celebrated in Rio de Janeiro, in which *Cardisoma* plays a significant part; both include veneration of this species.

   Regarding use of these crabs for food we observed and recorded various techniques for catching, trapping, culturing, cooking, vending, and eating. At Santos, we arranged a special trip with the local land-crab fishermen (caranguejeiros) to witness and photograph the collecting procedures for *Ucides cordatus.*

Information acquired on this expedition has been incorporated into only one publication to date (Bright and Hogue, 1972).

REFERENCES

BRIGHT, DONALD B.
1966. The land crabs of Costa Rica. Rev. Biol. Tropical, vol. 15, pp. 183-203.

BRIGHT, DONALD B., and HOGUE, CHARLES L.
1972. A synopsis of the burrowing crabs of the world and list of their arthropod symbionts and burrow associates. Los Angeles County Mus. Nat. Hist. Contr. Sci., no. 220, pp. 1-58.

HOGUE, CHARLES L., and BRIGHT, DONALD B.
1971. Observations on the biology of land crabs and their burrow associates on the Kenya coast. Los Angeles County Mus. Nat. Hist. Contr. Sci., no. 210, pp. 1-10.

CHARLES L. HOGUE
DONALD B. BRIGHT

Current-directed Mechanisms Underlying Movements of *Macrobrachium* Shrimp[1]

Principal Investigator: David A. Hughes, Rosenstiel School of Marine and Atmospheric Science, University of Miami, Miami, Florida.

Grant No. 886: In support of a study of the mechanisms underlying the migrations of *Macrobrachium* shrimp.

Fresh-water shrimps of the genus *Macrobrachium,* widely distributed in the tropical and subtropical regions of the world, are much prized as a gourmet item and represent an important fishery resource in many parts of Asia. Although there is no significant fishery for this group within the United States, there is great interest in the possible cultivation of the potentially valuable members of the group. While techniques have been developed for laboratory rearing of several species of *Macrobrachium* (Lewis, 1962; Fujimura, 1966; Ling, 1967; Costello, pers. comm.), surprisingly little is known of the biology and natural history of the group—knowledge that appears essential for their successful cultivation and conservation.

Laboratory studies have shown that a certain minimum salinity level is essential for the normal development of the larvae of some species occurring in Florida. This dependence on sea water for at least the early stage of their development probably confines these species to river systems having access to the sea, and it is this factor that mitigates against their continued survival in areas such as Florida, where the lower reaches of most rivers and canals are polluted and abound with pesticides and where access to the sea has been blocked by "flood control" measures and dams.

Of particular interest is the mechanism whereby the migrations are carried out. These involve the displacement downriver of sexually mature adults (or perhaps females), or egg-bearing females, to estuaries where spawning occurs, and the subsequent upstream return movements of adults and the newly hatched juvenile stages. These movements are not carried out by all members of the genus *Macrobrachium,* some of which are confined all their life to fresh waters or to estuarine areas; but they appear to be

[1]This report is based largely upon Contribution no. 1630 from the Rosenstiel School of Marine and Atmospheric Science, University of Miami (Hughes and Richard, 1973).

essential components of the life cycle of most larger, commercially important species.

Species of the genus are dependent to varying degrees on saline waters. Whereas some species (e.g., *M. obioni*) are quite independent of the sea and may be found in lakes and ponds no longer connected with the ocean, others, such as *M. carcinus, M. rosenbergi,* and *M. acanthurus,* require waters of low salinity for the successful development of their larval stages (Yutaka Uno and Kwon Chin Soo, 1969; Choudhury, 1970, 1971a, b, c).

Although no study on the movements of members of this group appears to have been conducted, their increased incidence at certain times of the year within estuaries and the lower reaches of rivers suggests that regular breeding migrations are carried out. Furthermore, a study by Hartmann (1958) in Peru showed that annual breeding migrations were carried out by gravid females of *Cryphiops caemantar*, a species differing from *Macrobrachium* only by the absence of an hepatic spine on the carapace (Holthuis, 1952).

In this study, all experiments were carried out in two identical ring-shaped current-chambers housed within light-tight rooms in the laboratory. The current-chambers (described in Hughes, 1969), essentially consisted of two cylinders of plexiglas (60 centimeters high) placed one within the other, so that a ring-shaped channel (15 centimeters wide and with an outer diameter of 61 centimeters) was formed between them. A current was created in this channel by means of recirculating pumps. The current-chamber was filled with fresh water for the experiments with adults and with sea water of varying salinity for those with larvae. The salinity of the water within the chamber could be altered by running either fresh or sea water into the central cylinder so that water diffused into the ring-shaped current chamber through numerous small holes in the wall of the inner cylinder.

Approximately 200 larvae were obtained from captive adults and reared in the laboratory in water of the same salinity as that into which they were placed in the current chambers at the start of the experiments. These larvae, which largely comprised individuals from stages 5 to 7 (Choudhury, 1970), were placed in a current chamber containing brackish water with an initial salinity of 17.5 percent. A current velocity of 5 centimeters per second was maintained. Water samples were siphoned periodically from a point 10 centimeters below the surface and the salinity measured with a Goldberg refractometer. The salinity was varied over a period of several hours, during which 2-minute sample counts were made of the number of larvae swimming in the water column well above the substrate during each 15-minute period.

Most of the gravid and nongravid females used in these experiments were obtained from the laboratory stock of another project. These had been reared in large (approximately 5.0 meters diameter and 1.5 meters deep) indoor tanks supplied with a number of stone refuges on the substrate. We collected other adult females at night from a nearby fresh-water canal, using a flashlight and dip net. Three gravid females were placed in one current chamber and three nongravid females of approximately the same size in the other chamber. A current velocity of 9.0 centimeters per second was maintained in each chamber. Alternating 12-hour periods of light and darkness were imposed for two full days. Five-minute sample counts of transits (upstream or downstream) past an observation port were recorded for each hourly period.

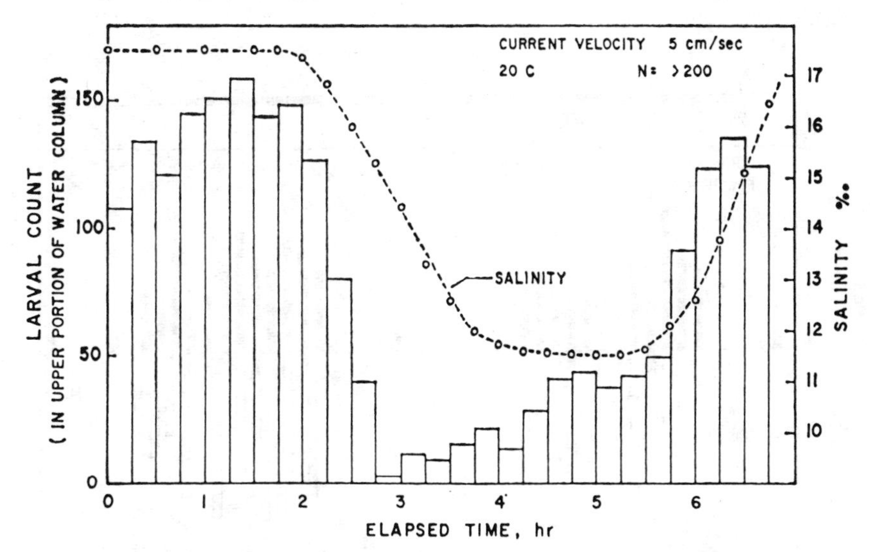

FIG. 1. Occurrence within the upper portion of the water column of larval *Macrobrachium acanthurus* in response to salinity changes. A 2-minute sample count was made during each 15-minute period.

It was found that when salinity within the current chamber was reduced by running fresh water into the central cylinder, larvae dropped rapidly within the water column and remained for some time near the substrate (fig. 1). When salinity was subsequently increased by running sea water into the central cylinder, the larvae returned again to the upper portions of the water column. The experiment was repeated on three occasions with different groups of larvae. Similar results were obtained on each occasion, and only one series is represented in figure 1.

In the initial observations of gravid and nongravid females, the females were obtained from a laboratory stock maintained under artificial conditions. Records of the direction and amount of swimming undertaken in each current chamber (fig. 2) indicated that, whereas nongravid individuals swam primarily in an upstream direction, the gravid individuals swam almost exclusively in a downstream direction. It was also clear from these results that activity was largely confined to hours of darkness.

In further experiments it was shown that the upstream swimming of nongravid individuals was frequently terminated when suitable refuge was offered (in this case, short sections of plastic pipe). The gravid females on the other hand generally continued to swim downstream despite the availability of this same type of refuge.

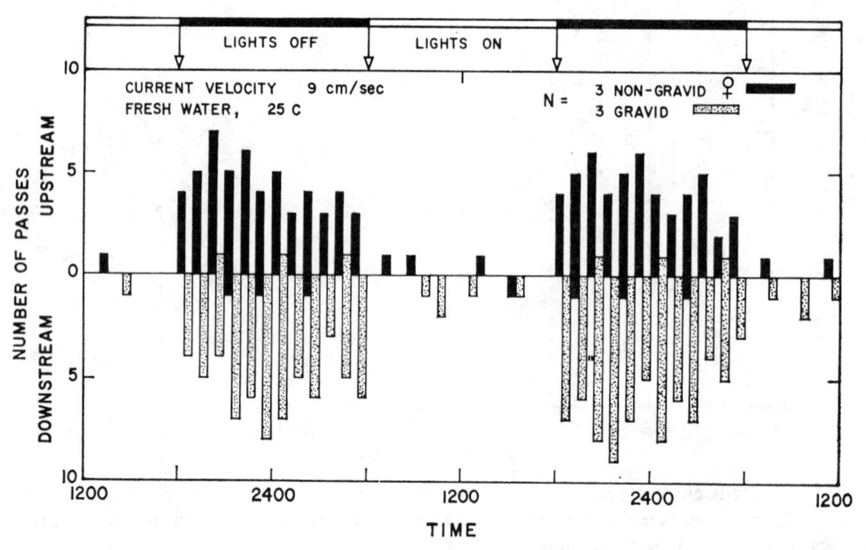

FIG. 2. Current-directed movements of adult *Macrobrachium acanthurus* showing difference between gravid and nongravid females. A 5-minute sample count was made each hour.

In one series of observations two gravid individuals that for three days had been swimming primarily in a downstream direction soon after releasing their larvae began to swim upstream and continued to do so for the two days that they remained within the chamber.

The evidence indicates that larval stages of *Macrobrachium acanthurus* require brackish water to complete their development and will die if maintained in fresh water for longer than five or six days (Choudhury, 1971c). For this reason the adults of this species are generally confined to rivers or ponds with access to the ocean. In the absence of a suitable behavioral mechanism whereby the larval stages could maintain their position within estuaries or river mouths, the larvae would rapidly become dispersed in the sea, and their chances for eventually returning to their normal habitat as juveniles would be negligible. This study indicated one mechanism that would serve to prevent them from being washed out to sea by ebb tides and river effluent waters. In estuarine areas fed by rivers and streams, the waters of the ebb tide are almost invariably of a lower salinity than those of the flood. Therefore, by dropping to the substrate when the salinity of the water in which they are swimming becomes reduced, the larvae will avoid being displaced offshore by the faster moving waters near the surface. The water in the vicinity of the substrate moves more slowly, and whatever offshore displacement occurs during the ebb tide will be more than compensated for by a faster displacement inshore at the time of the flood tide, when the larvae return to the higher reaches of the water column. It is possible that a substantial proportion of early stage larvae originating in the upper reaches of rivers, would be washed downstream rapidly enough to survive until reaching the brackish water they require for further development. Choudhury (1971b) showed that the larvae of *M. carcinus* can survive in fresh water for about five or six days after hatching.

However, the likelihood of the larvae reaching suitably saline waters will almost certainly be improved if the gravid female herself moves downstream to release the larvae in the vicinity of the river mouth or estuary. The information derived from this study indicates that gravid females do indeed move downstream: females bearing eggs are negatively rheotactic but, once they have released their larvae, they, like other nongravid individuals, will generally swim against currents. These findings are in general agreement with those of other investigators studying tidal transport of larvae and various plankters in estuaries (e.g., Jacobs, 1968; Antheunisse et al., 1971).

REFERENCES

ANTHEUNISSE, L. J.; LAMMENS, J. J.; AND VAN DEN HOVEN, N. P.

1971. Diurnal activities and tidal migrations of the brackish water prawn *Palaemonetes varians* (Leach) (Decapoda, Caridea). Crustaceana, vol. 21, p. 2.

CHOUDHURY, P. C.

1970. Complete larval development of the palaemonid shrimp *Macrobrachium acanthurus* (Wiegmann, 1836), reared in the laboratory. Crustaceana, vol. 18, no. 2, pp. 113–132.

1971a. Complete larval development of the palaeomonid shrimp *Macrobrachium carcinus* (L.) reared in the laboratory (Decapoda, Palaemonidae). Crustaceana, vol. 20, no. 1, pp. 51–69.

1971b. Responses of larval *Macrobrachium carcinus* (L.) to variations in salinity and diet (Decapoda, Palaemonidae). Crustaceana, vol. 20, no. 2, pp. 113–120.

1971c. Laboratory rearing of larvae of the palaemonid shrimp *Macrobrachium acanthurus* (Wiegmann, 1836). Crustaceana, vol. 21, no. 2, pp. 113–126.

FUJIMURA, T.

1966. Notes on the development of a practical mass culturing technique of the giant prawn *Macrobrachium rosenbergi.* Indo-Pacific Fish. Council, FAO Reg. Office for Asia and Far East, 12th sess., Honolulu, October 2–17, 1966.

HARTMANN, G.

1958. Apuntes sobre la biología del camarón de río *Cryphiops caementarius* (Molina) (Decapoda, Palaemonidae). Pesca Caza (Min. Agr., Lima, Peru), vol. 8, pp. 15–28.

HOLTHUIS, L. B.

1952. A general revision of the Palaemonidae (Crustacea Decapoda Natantia) of the Americas, II: The subfamily Palaemoninae. Allan Hancock Found. Occ. Pap., no. 12, 396 pp.

HUGHES, DAVID A.

1969. Responses to salinity change as a tidal transport mechanism of pink shrimp *Penaeus duoraraum.* Biol. Bull., vol. 136, no. 1, pp. 43–53.

HUGHES, DAVID A., AND RICHARD, JOSEPH D.

1973. Some current-directed movements of *Macrobrachium acanthurus* (Wiegmann, 1836) (Decapoda, Palaemonidae) under laboratory conditions. Ecology, vol. 54, no. 4, pp. 927–929.

JACOBS, JURGEN

1968. Animal behavior and water movement as co-determinants of plankton distribution in a tidal system. Sarsia, vol. 34, pp. 355–370.

LEWIS, JOHN B.

1962. Preliminary experiments on the rearing of the freshwater shrimp *Macrobrachium carcinus* (L.). Proc. Gulf and Caribbean Fish. Inst., vol. 14, pp. 199–201.

LING, S. W.

1967. Methods of rearing and culturing *Macrobrachium rosenbergi* (de Man). Proc. World Sci. Conf., Mexico, June 12–21, 1967.

YUTAKA UNO AND KWON CHIN SOO

1969. Larval development of *Macrobrachium rosenbergi* (de Man) reared in the laboratory. Journ. Tokyo Univ. Fish., vol. 55, no. 2, pp. 179–190.

DAVID A. HUGHES
JOSEPH D. RICHARD

Anthropological Research in Mali

Principal Investigator: Johan Huizinga, Institute of Human Biology, State University at Utrecht, The Netherlands.

Grant Nos. 902, 1403: For anthropological cave research in Mali (West Africa)[1]; and for study of the Bani-Niger people and their culture.

Cave Research in Mali

The main characteristic of the Niger bend region of Mali is the high cliff of Bandiagara (figs. 1, 2). This vast escarpment contains many natural caves in which small mud constructions, human skeletal remains, and all kinds of remarkably well preserved grave-goods are found. These remains are considered by the Dogon, the present-day inhabitants of the region, as belonging to the Tellem, a population that would have preceded the Dogon in their present habitat.

Until 1907, when Desplagnes's "Le Plateau Central Nigérien" appeared, virtually nothing was known of this region of particular interest for West African history. The material collected by Desplagnes in several caves provided the first evidence of an ancient culture.

From 1931 onward, studies of the oral tradition of the Dogon by French ethnologists of the Griaule School led to the following theory (Griaule, 1938, p. 28). From Mandé, a region southwest of Bamako, the Dogon migrated in a northeasterly direction until, in the 15th century A.D., they came upon a population in the Bandiagara cliff region that they called Tellem. This is supported by the oral traditions of surrounding populations (Izard, 1970) and by the number of Sigui masks found by Griaule in the mask cave of Ibi (Griaule, 1938, pp. 245, 247). On the arrival of the Dogon the Tellem are

[1]This expedition and four subsequent ones, the results of which are here briefly discussed, were made possible by grants to Professor Huizinga from The Netherlands Foundation for the Advancement of Tropical Research (WOTRO), The Hague (1965, 1967); the Wenner-Gren Foundation for Anthropological Research, New York (1966, 1967); the Boise Fund, Oxford (1966, 1967, 1971); and the National Geographic Society, Washington (1970, 1974).

assumed to have moved to the east, to Yatenga, where they now live under the name of Kouroumba (Fulsé).

As no excavations were carried out, the Dogon oral tradition provided the only historical information on this area. It is generally felt that formal traditions rarely penetrate back into time for more than about five centuries from the present (Fage, 1965); consequently, some anthropologists have hesitated to accept this type of evidence. As recently as 1970, Fagg (p. 15) considered that "there is little more warrant for the very existence of the Tellem, outside fairy tales, than for the Trojan origin of the British kingship."

In 1960 and 1962 H. Haan, a Dutch architect-archeologist, toured the whole escarpment on foot in order to survey the situation. The results of his trips were such that the Institute of Human Biology in 1964 decided to equip, in cooperation with Mr. Haan, a multidisciplinary expedition to investigate the area with respect to human biology, ethnology, and archeology. A special hoisting system was designed by Haan to permit investigation of caves often difficult of access.

Geographical Situation

The Bandiagara cliff delimits a sandstone plateau that to the west disappears under alluvial deposits of the Bani-Niger fluvial system. To the east of the cliff extends the vast Gondo plain. The foot of the cliff, 100 to 300 meters high, is buried under a talus of enormous boulders (fig. 3). The total length of the cliff is about 260 kilometers. The horizontally bedded sandstone is honeycombed with shallow erosion caves. These caves are found also in the walls of canyons that pierce the escarpment.

The region is part of the thorn savanna belt (Troll, 1965). The 500-millimeter isohyetic line, which practically coincides with the 15th parallel, bisects the region. Agriculture north of this isohyetic line is impossible without irrigation (Rouch, 1953, p. 146). The water supply of the cliff region is slightly better than that of the surrounding area because of orographic rains (Gallais, 1965, p. 124). Furthermore, 40 percent of the water that falls on the plateau penetrates through fissures in the sandstone until it reaches an impervious schist layer present in the sandstone on the plain level (Palausi, 1959, pp. 119, 163, 174). Therefore sources and pools are mostly situated at the foot of the escarpment. On the other hand, in the Gondo plain 80 percent of the water evaporates before it can penetrate the earth. The soil at the foot of the escarpment between the boulders, as well as the soil of the canyon floors, is much more fertile than the plains soil (Gallais, 1965, p. 129).

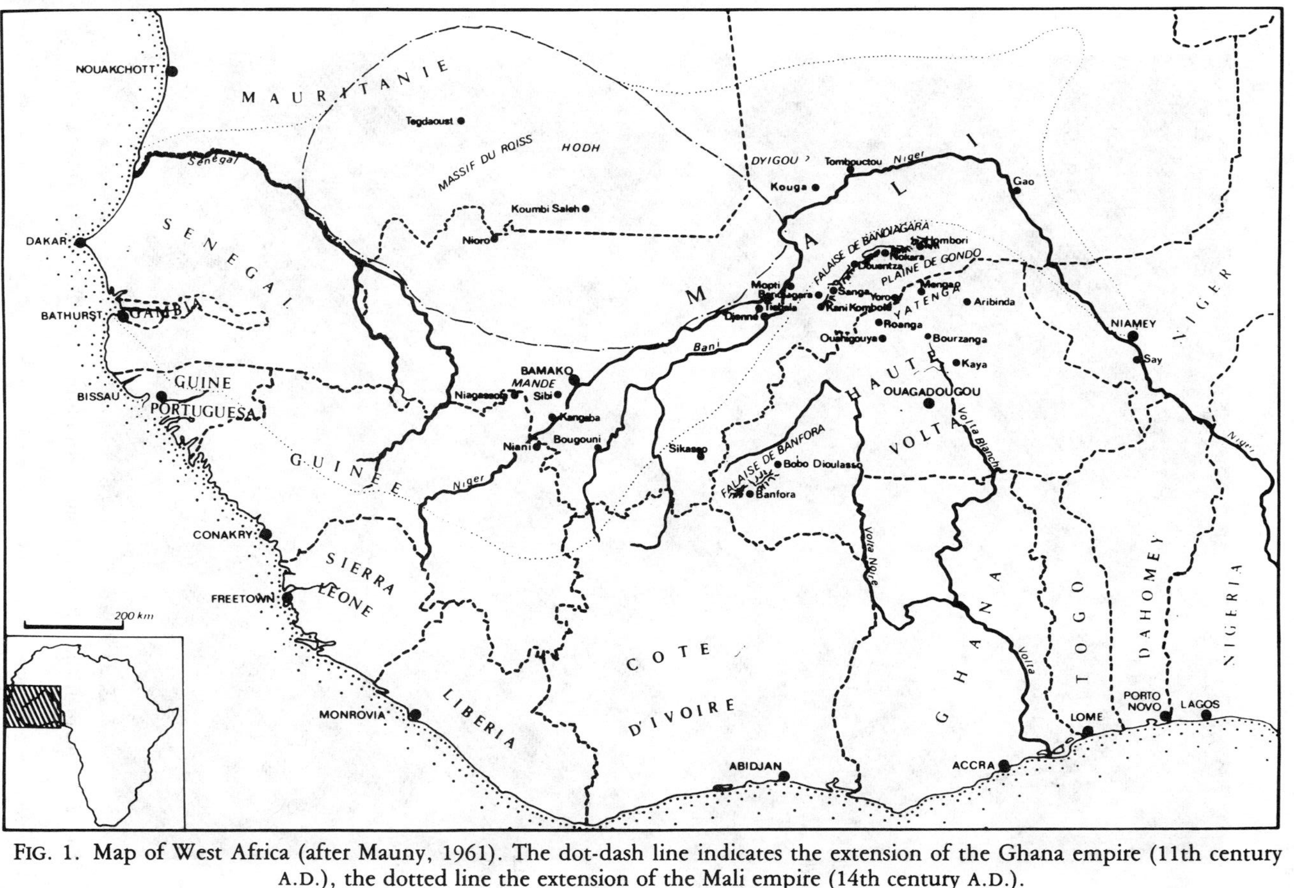

FIG. 1. Map of West Africa (after Mauny, 1961). The dot-dash line indicates the extension of the Ghana empire (11th century A.D.), the dotted line the extension of the Mali empire (14th century A.D.).

FIG. 2. The high cliff south of Pégué with numerous Tellem caves (among others, cave P).

It is thus clear that this region can be considered an ecological niche in comparison with the surrounding areas. The population density is a case in point (Brasseur and le Moal, 1963). In the past the relative advantages of the region for the inhabitants were certainly more important, for the Dogon oral tradition reveals a gradual desiccation of this practically impenetrable region (Griaul, 1938, p. 6).

The Caves

As stated, caves occur along the whole escarpment. Practical considerations (accessibility, presence of a concentration of Dogon, and a relative concentration of caves with remains of previous habitation) led to the choice of two areas for investigation. In the Sanga region 29 caves were examined, in the Nokara region 5 caves. In none of the caves examined was a vertical stratigraphy present.

The caves in the Sanga region are alphabetically identified on figure 3. Caves A to J, inclusive, are situated in the west wall of the Toloy canyon, and K to Z, inclusive, are situated in the high cliff near the village of Pégué. The constructions in the caves are of three major types (Bedaux, 1972):

1. Circular constructions made of wet mud coils with vertical finger imprints on the outside, and with circular entrances closed with a mud coil.
2. Circular and rectangular constructions with rounded edges made of lozenge-shaped mud bricks, or caves closed with a wall of the same bricks, with circular to rectangular entrances, closed with wooden lids or by hinged doors with locks. Sometimes one-storied constructions occur. The constructions may be divided into compartments by low walls.
3. Rectangular constructions made of stones, with rectangular entrances.

The activities performed in the caves are of three kinds. They have been used for burials, for storage of agricultural products, and for ritual practices associated with the burials.

Cave C is one of the biggest (10 by 9 meters) burial caves of the region. Some 2,500 to 3,500 individuals are interred with all kinds of grave-goods behind a mud-brick wall (fig. 4). The grave-goods consist mainly of animal skulls, textiles (clothes and blankets), wooden headrests, bows, quivers, hoes, musical instruments, basketry, leather objects, iron adornments, and carnelian beads. Approximately 9 cubic meters of this ossuary have been excavated (fig. 5). The discrepancies between the number of certain human bones clearly indicate the disorganized character of this cave. Obviously the wrapped skeletons have been displaced, leading to disarticulation and disorganization.

A typical example of a burial-ritual cave is cave D, situated some 12 meters below cave C. The whole cave floor was studded with pottery fragments. Iron objects (bracelets, rings, voluted pins, arrowheads), carnelian beads, and quartz lip-plugs also occurred. The objects were embedded in a thin deposit presumably formed by erosion of former mud-coil constructions, traces of which were still visible against the cave wall. No human skeletal remains were found here. The ritual character of this cave and its relationship with the cemetery cave C are suggested by the nature of the finds, the intentional spatial relationship of some objects, and the fact that this type of association of a cemetery cave with a pottery cave is a recurrent phenomenon (e.g., caves J and G).

Study of the contents of the constructions of cave P proved that they were used for storage of agricultural products. The 38 constructions form a real little village with causeways (fig. 6). Enclosed by these constructions and by the cave wall a little cemetery was found. Fourteen individuals, presumably male, have been buried here. This type of burial is clearly different from that of cave C.

Cave A contained at least 38 constructions made out of mud coils (fig. 7). The constructions r, t, s, and x in the central part of the cave are covered with a thin mud layer, in which all kinds of finger-drawn decorations are found (fig. 8). It is suggested that these particular constructions were used for ritual purposes, in view of the type of decoration (fig. 9). The constructions used for food storage were small and had small entrances. They have been reused later for burial purposes.

In the Sanga region none of the investigated caves showed evidence of habitation, sensu stricto. In view of the relative inaccessibility of the majority of caves, this is perhaps not surprising. Remains of hoisting systems consisting of ropes and poles used as cranes were discovered (see fig. 5). It is suggested that permanent dwellings were situated at the foot of the cliff, on top of the talus unsheltered against the weather.

In order to verify the Dogan oral tradition, which stated that the "Tellem" migrated to the east along the cliff to Yatenga, five caves were examined near Nokara, some 120 kilometers to the northeast of Sanga (see fig. 1). Only one of the caves (Nokara-B) contained human skeletal remains, which were found in a 0.5-meter-high and 60-meter-long slit, in the sandstone escarpment, subdivided by stone walls into 14 compartments. Practically no grave-goods were present. In the other caves (Nokara-A, Nokara-C, Boni-A, Boni-B) circular and rectangular constuctions for storage were found made of stone and/or rectangular mud bricks.

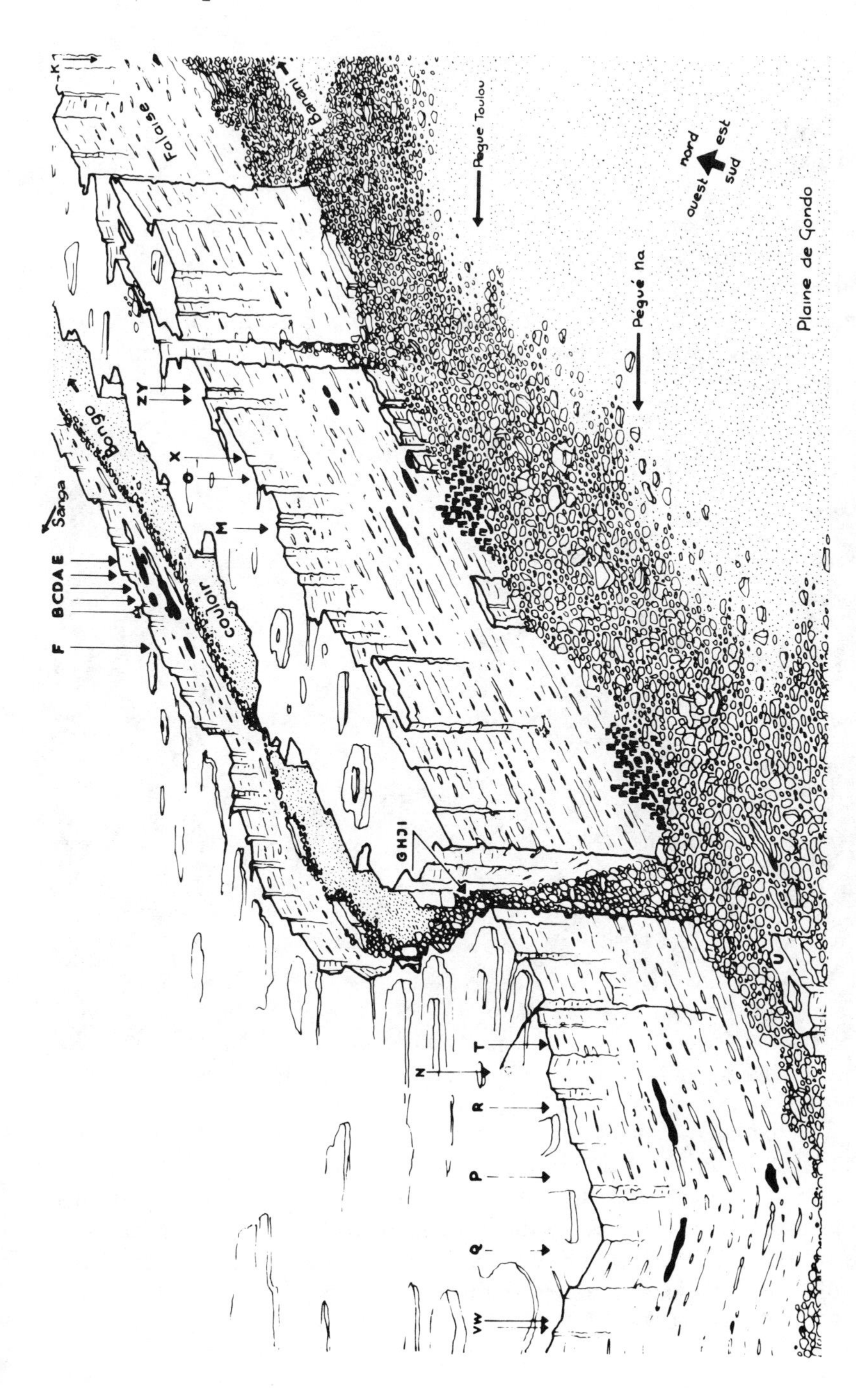

FIG. 3. Bird's-eye view of the high cliff of Bandiagara near Sanga showing the position of the caves.

Chronology

On the basis of architectural details of the constructions in the caves (Bedaux, 1972), a relative chronological order can be established (see fig. 10). The material found in cave D could be related to material found in cave C, which was closed by a mud-brick wall. The material in cave D was placed in a deposit formed by the erosion of mud-coil constructions. Therefore, the constructions of mud coils seem to be earlier than the constructions made out of mud bricks. As stone constructions occur in Dogon traditional architecture (e.g., Banani Ammou), it is suggested that these are later than mud-brick constructions.

FIG. 4. Interior of burial cave C with part of the wall (11th–12th century A.D.).

The temporal sequence of the use of mud coils, mud bricks, and stones as building material is substantiated by 11 carbon-14 datings. The mud-coil constructions are to be dated in the 3d–2d century B.C., the mud-brick constructions from the 11th to the 14th centuries A.D., the stone constructions in the 15th century and later, and the constructions made out of rectangular mud bricks and stones of the Nokara region in the 17th century, and later (Bedaux, 1972).

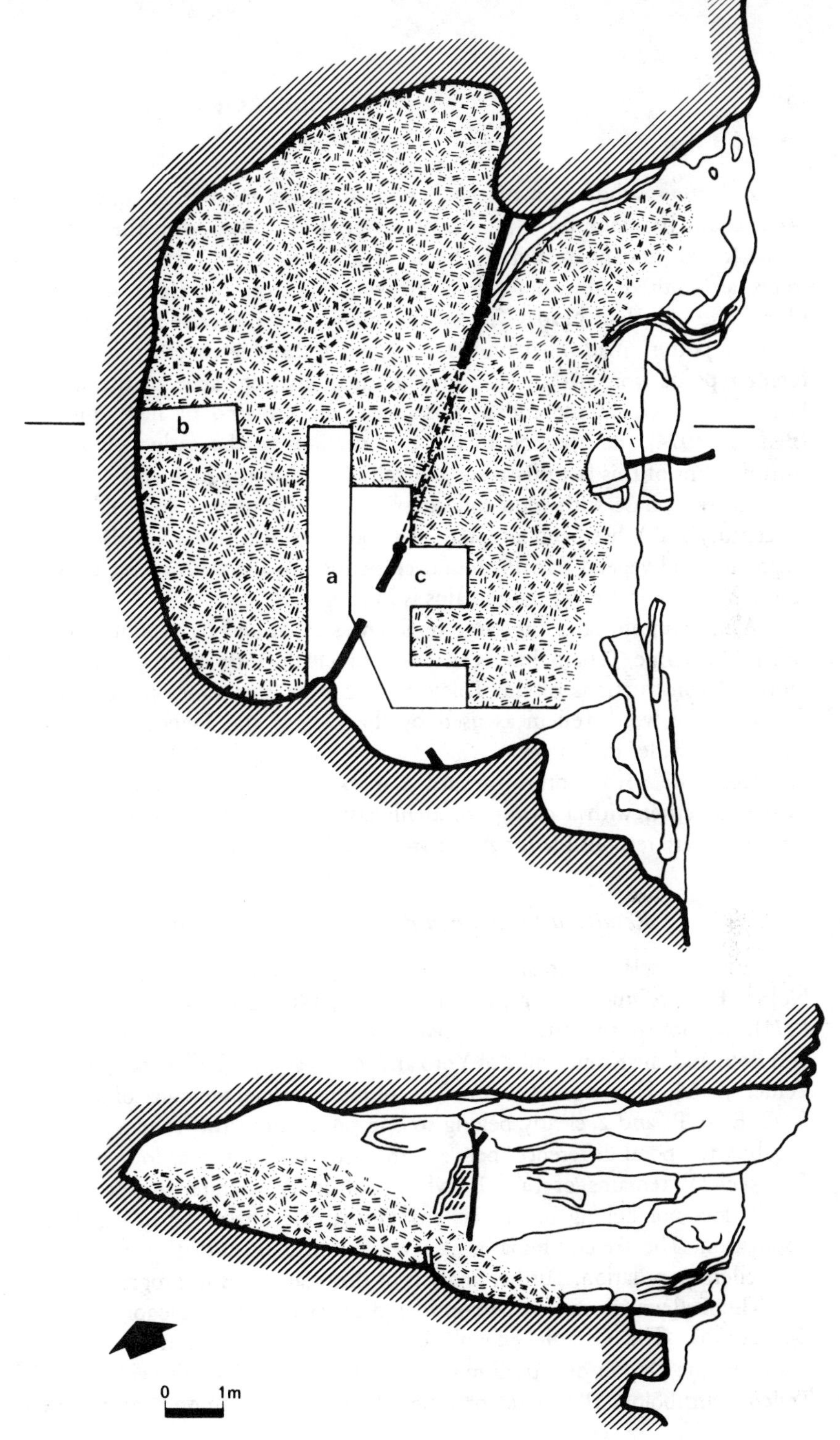

FIG. 5. Plan and section of cave C. Cutting a was excavated in 1965, b in 1966, and c in 1971. Note the pole protruding out of the cave.

A further subdivision of the period in which mud-brick constructions occur could be made on the basis of material associated with the constructions. In the first phase pottery made in a mold occurs together with such items as voluted iron pins, iron arrowheads, iron bracelets, quartz lip plugs, and carnelian beads. The second phase is characterized by the occurrence of pottery made in hammer-and-anvil technique together with a different type of iron arrowhead and a gradual disappearance of the wooden headrests, which, at the end of this phase, are replaced by little iron ones (Bedaux, 1974). As opposed to the constructions of the earlier phases, the constructions of this last phase are generally found in the high cliff.

For the phase with mud-coil constructions the term Toloy culture (3d-2d century B.C.) has been adopted. Attributed to this phase are also pottery fragments and vegetal remains found embedded in the walls of the constructions. Analysis of the vegetal remains is in progress.

A millennium later the same region was inhabited by a population for which the name Tellem has been adopted (11th–15th century A.D.). The mud-coil constructions of the Toloy culture were sometimes reused by the Tellem. (The word Tellem as used by the Dogon and French ethnologists has a much wider meaning.)

From the 15th century onward a marked change in burial ritual occurred, together with a change in architecture. It is strongly suggested that the Dogon are responsible for this change (Bedaux, 1972).

Results of the Human Biological Investigations

Human skeletal remains of nine caves (A, B, C, E, F, H, P, Z, and Nokara-B) were studied (e.g., Huizinga et al., 1967; Huizinga, 1968a; Knip, 1971). A comparative study was made of the present-day Dogon of Sanga and Boni and the Kouroumba of Yoro and Roanga (e.g., Huizinga and Birnie-Tellier, 1966; Huizinga, 1968b). The human skeletal remains of caves A, B, C, E, F, P, and Z clearly belong to one population, the Tellem, notwithstanding temporal differences between the caves of as much as four centuries. The skeletal remains of cave F, which culturally (architecture and burial ritual) does not belong to the Tellem culture, are attributed to the Tellem population. The skeletal remains of caves H and Nokara-B do not belong to the Tellem population. Further analysis of this material is in progress.

The Tellem are not to be considered ancestral to the Dogon or to the Kouroumba. The Griaule School thesis that Tellem equals Kouroumba, based on the Dogon oral tradition, has to be refuted on this evidence. The Tellem morphologically represent a population unique among central West-

African populations. As yet, skeletal remains belonging to the Toloy culture have not been found.

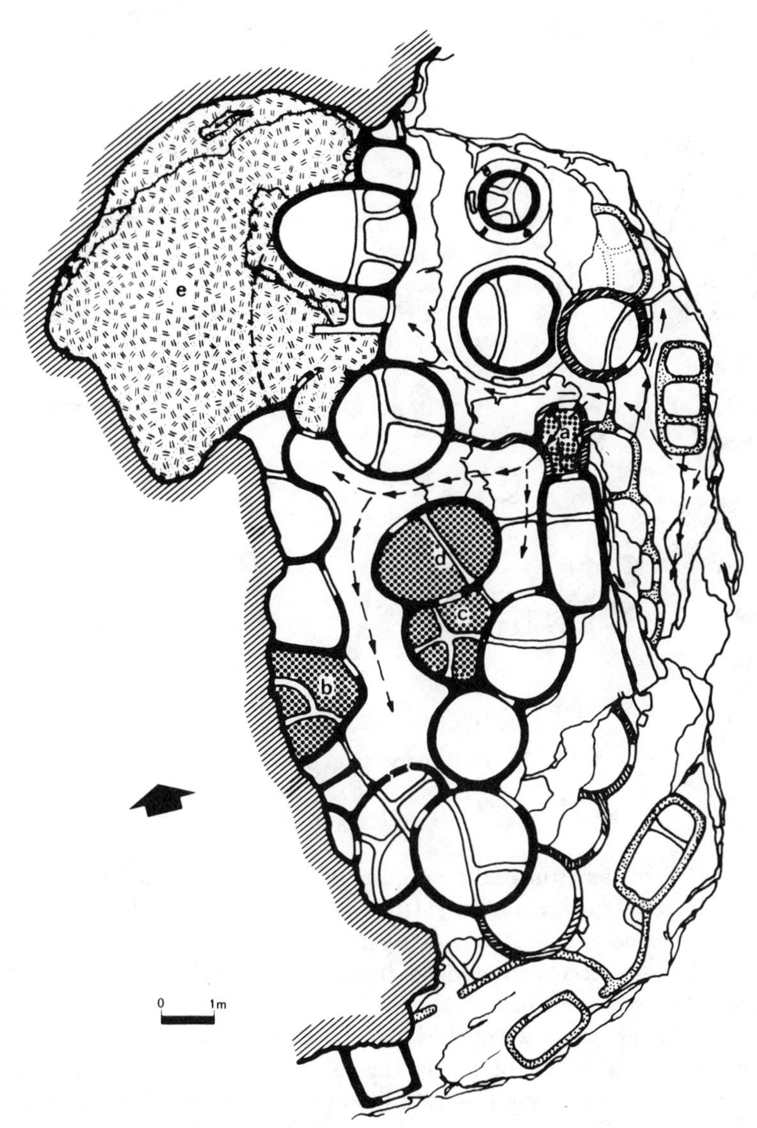

FIG. 6. Plan of cave P. Three levels are distinguished: lowest level, dotted walls; medium level, hatched walls; highest level, plain walls.

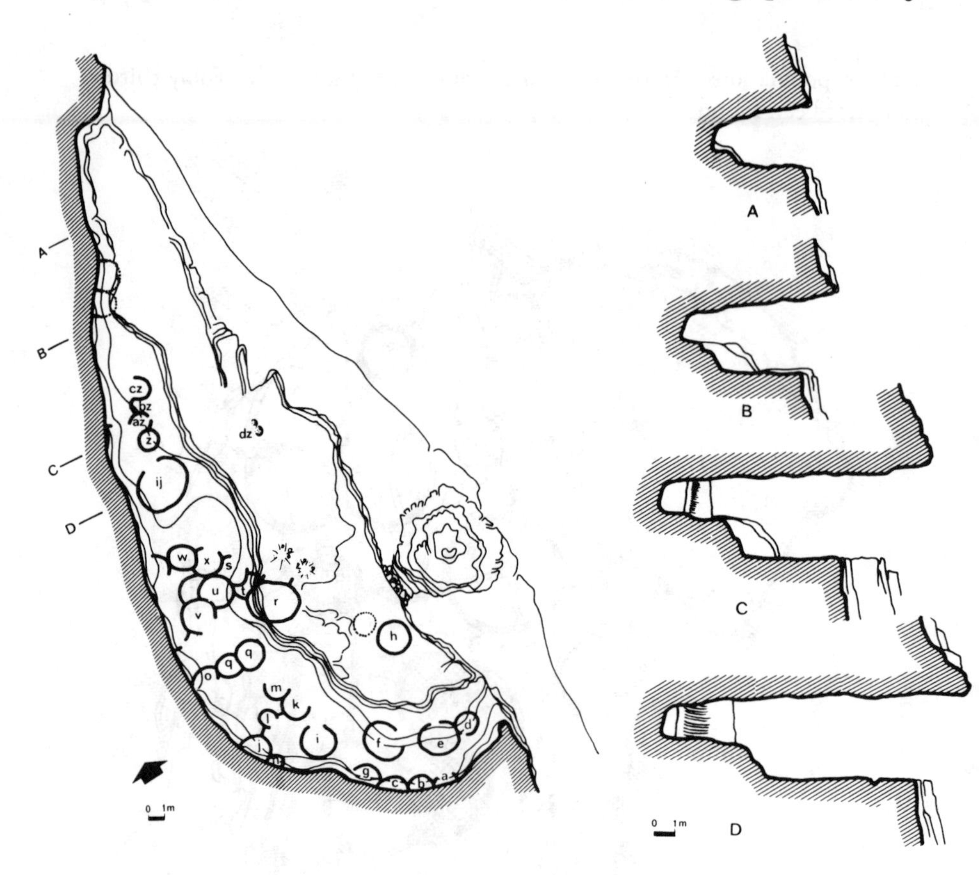

FIG. 7. Plan and sections of cave A.

By means of the estimated total number of individuals buried in cave C in approximately two centuries (11th–12th century A.D.) the population could be estimated to be 1,500–1,600 persons. From that time on the population of the area decreased, judged from the number of skeletal remains found in later caves (Bedaux, 1972).

Practically no skeletal remains of nonadult individuals were found; presumably they were not buried in the caves. In some caves only skeletal remains of one sex were found; in cave P only males, in cave Z predominantly females were buried. In other caves (e.g., C) individuals were buried irrespective of sex.

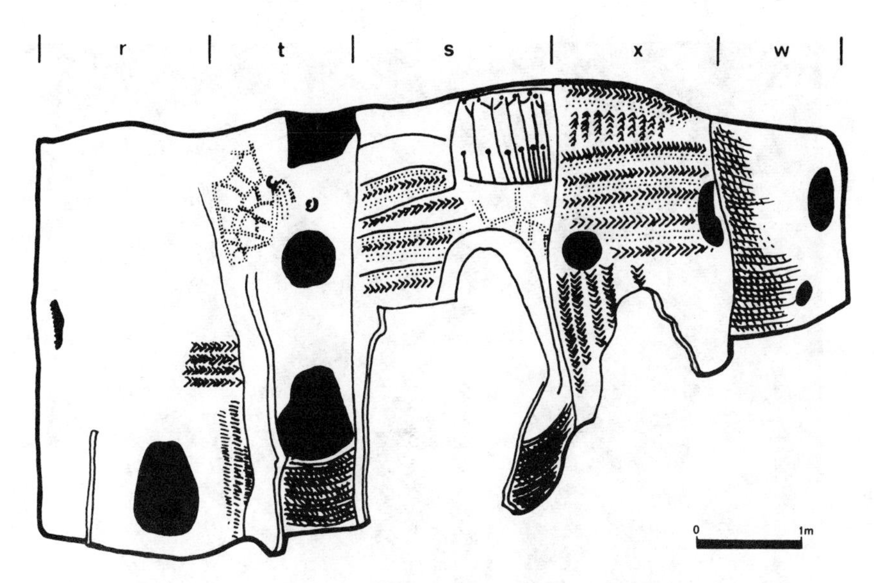

FIG. 8. Wall decoration of construction r, t, s, and x of cave A.

Evidence for Subsistence

The Tellem subsistence (Bedaux, 1972) was based primarily on the cultivation of *Pennisetum typhoïdes,* which was found in the storage constructions of cave P. Hoes were interred together with their deceased possessors. In view of a population of 1,500–1,600 individuals, agricultural techniques must have been fairly well developed.

Gathering provided a substantial supplement to the diet: In cave P were found remains of *Andansonia digitata, Detarium microcarpum, Balanites aegyptiaca, Lannea microcarpa, Celtis integrifolia,* and *Ceiba pentandra*; in cave Q, *Lannea microcarpa* and *Celtis integrifolia.*

Animal husbandry was practiced, judged from skulls of *Aries* and *Bos taurus* in burial cave C and of *Bos taurus* in the cemetery of cave P. These skulls accompanied the dead as grave-goods.

Skulls of hunted animals such as *Tragelaphus scriptus, Hippotragus, Gazella,* and *Syncerus caffer brachyceros* were found as grave-goods only in burial cave C, together with intentionally broken wooden bows and quivers. That skulls of these species were not encountered in later burial caves probably reflects more a change in burial ritual than the disappearance of this game.

FIG. 9. Cave A, construction r (3d–2d century B.C.).

In cave F a skull of *Balearica pavonina* and a shell of *Pelomedusa subrufa,* indicating a Dogon influence, were found (Bedaux, 1972).

Discussion

It is difficult to assume that the origin of the Toloy culture has to be sought in the Sanga region. No vestiges of this culture have been found older than the 3d and 2d century B.C. constructions in caves A, A-2, B-1, D, and L. At the present stage of knowledge of West-African archeology it is probably premature to attribute the origin of this culture to immigration from a certain region. Investigations such as those of Mauny (1950) and Munson (1971) in the Tichitt region (Mauretania) demonstrate dense habitation of that region up to the 4th century B.C. The Toloy culture in the Sanga region has to be dated in the 3d–2d century B.C. A comparative ceramic analysis of the two regions eventually may elucidate relationships. Also, the remarkable resemblances of cave A constructions and constructions discovered by Richir and Robert, (1970) in Rqiss (Mauritania) have to be studied in detail.

As yet, no vestiges of human activities during the millennium separating the Toloy culture and the Tellem culture have been discovered.

The onset of the Tellem culture (11th century A.D.) might be associated with the southward and eastward population movements caused by the decline of the Ghana empire (Fage, 1965). The Berber influence on Tellem architecture (patterned walling) also points to possible contacts with northern regions (Walton, 1960). Ceramic analysis, especially of bowls-on-feet, revealed evidence of contacts before the 11th century A.D. between the Tellem region and Niani, presumed capital of the subsequent Mali empire (Filipowiak et al., 1968). A preliminary distributional analysis of these bowls-on-feet (Bedaux, in press) suggests small scale population movements from Niani to the northeast along the Niger. These population movements are supported by oral tradition (Dieterlen, 1955).

After the 12th century A.D. no bowls-on-feet occur in the Tellem area. In the 13th and 14th centuries, Mali became more and more important. At the same time, the Tellem took refuge in less accessible places in the high cliff. It has to be noted that the Tellem area was never politically controlled by the Mali empire (fig. 1). When after the 14th century the threat from Mali decreased, the Songhay and Mossi raided the cliff area in the 15th and 16th century. Raids by Sonni Ali, Askya Mohammed, and Askya Daoud are mentioned by Rouch (1953, pp. 182, 195, 200, 201). The Mossi raided the country under Naba Rawa and Naba Wumtânago (Izard, 1970, pp. 132, 276, 277, 280, 282). As stated by Gleave and Prothero (1971),

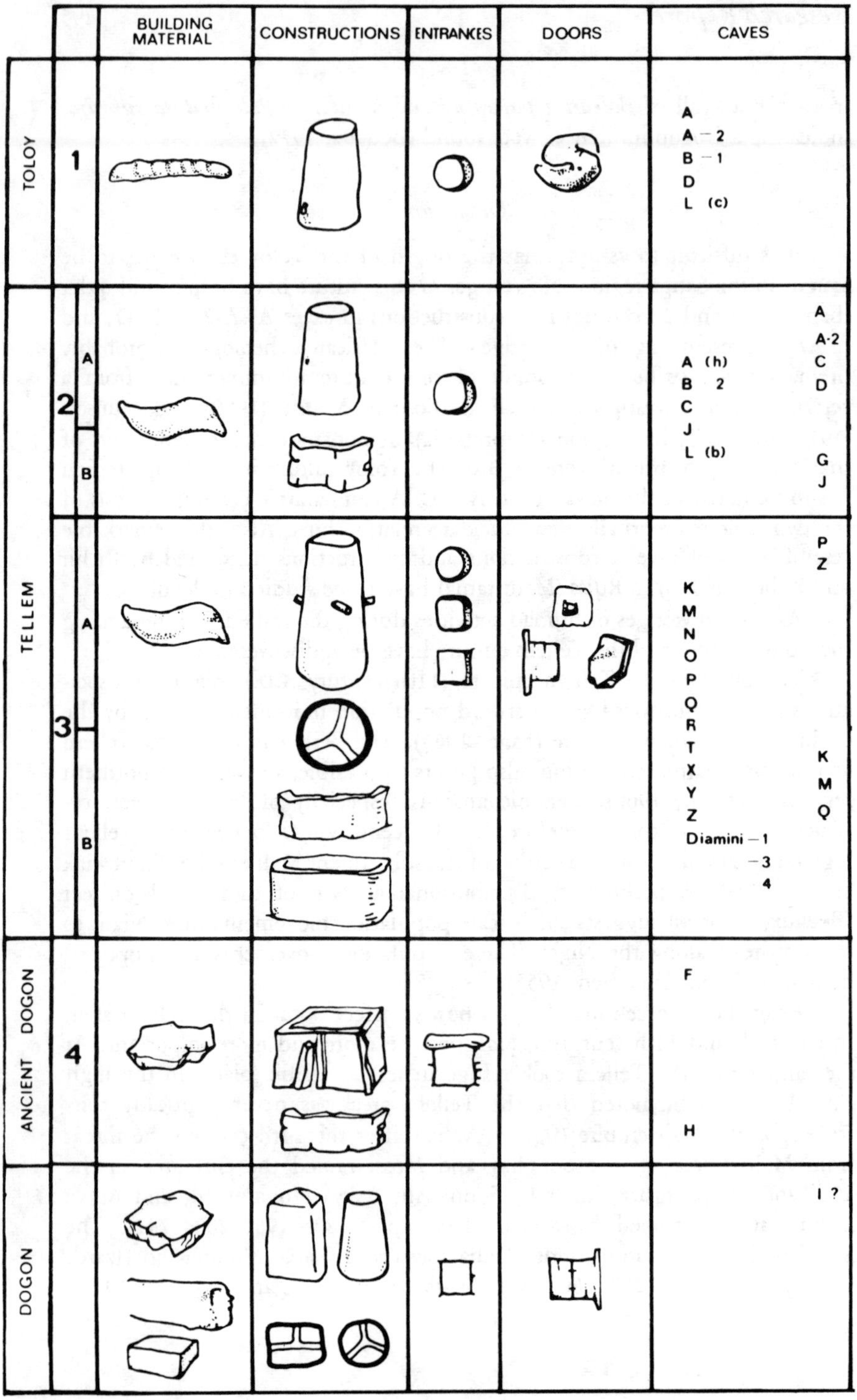

		BUILDING MATERIAL	CONSTRUCTIONS	ENTRANCES	DOORS	CAVES	
TOLOY	1					A A — 2 B — 1 D L (c)	
TELLEM	2 A 2 B					A (h) B 2 C J L (b)	A A-2 C D G J
TELLEM	3 A 3 B					K M N O P Q R T X Y Z Diamini — 1 — 3 4	P Z K M Q
ANCIENT DOGON	4					F H	
DOGON							I ?

FIG. 10. Tentative chronological table for the Sanga region.

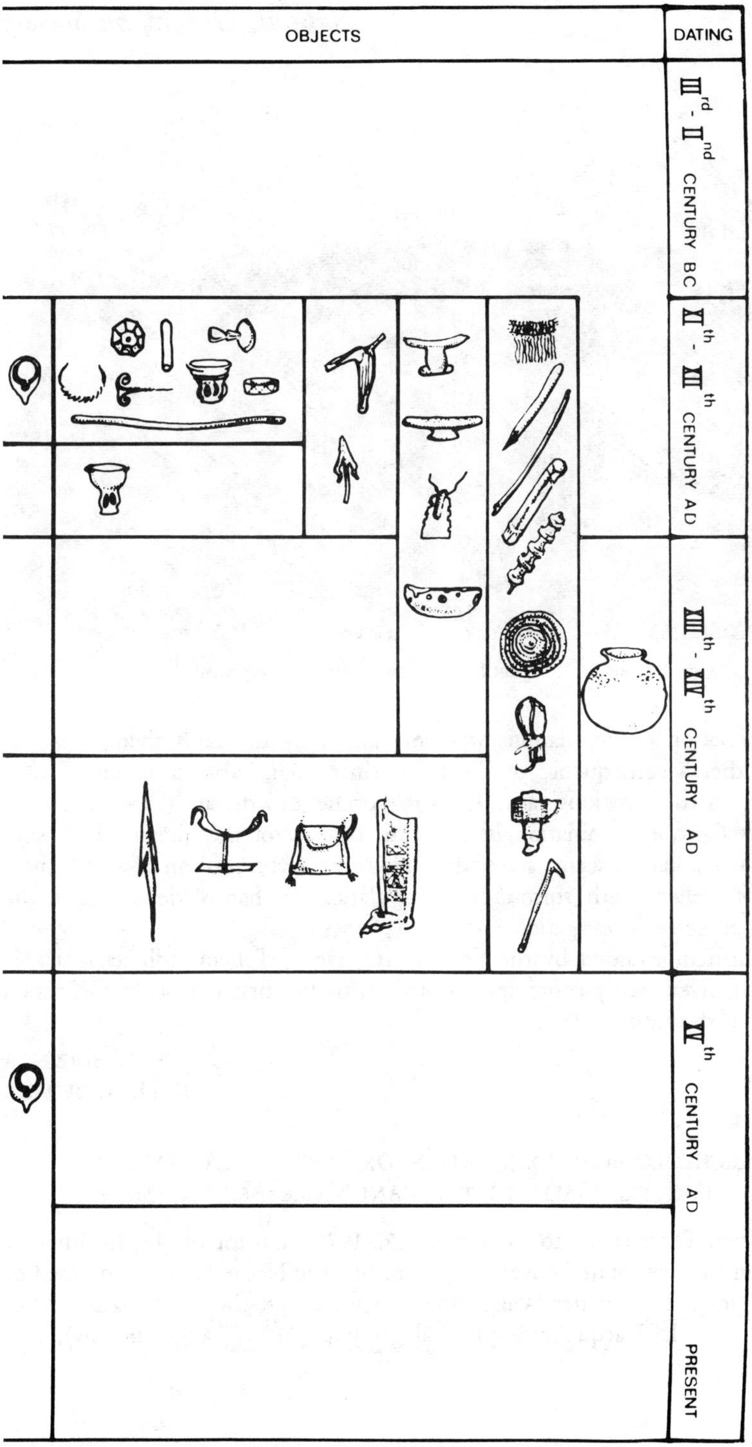

OBJECTS	DATING
	IIIrd - IInd CENTURY BC
	XIth - XIIth CENTURY AD
	XIIIth - XIVth CENTURY AD
	XVth CENTURY AD
	PRESENT

FIG. 11. Toguéré Doupwil: View to the west.

extermination of populations was not caused by the raids themselves but was rather a consequence of the raids, since an instable situation of agriculture in these regions easily leads to famine and disease (Cissoko, 1968). In this light, extermination in the 15th century of the already decreasing Tellem population seems acceptable. However, hybridization of small numbers of Tellem with surrounding populations is hardly demonstrable by anthropometric investigation.

As demonstrated by the findings in cave F, Tellem, still recognizable as such, lived partly contemporaneously with the first Dogon in the region in the 15th century A.D.

JOHAN HUIZINGA
R. M. A. BEDAUX

ARCHEOLOGICAL EXCAVATION OF TOGUÉRÉ DOUPWIL AND TOGUÉRÉ GALIA IN THE BANI-NIGER REGION, MALI

From October 11 to December 15, 1975, a team of the Institute of Human Biology, State University at Utrecht (The Netherlands), composed of Prof. Dr. J. D. van der Waals (archeology), Dr. R. M. A. Bedaux (archeology), Dr. L. Hacquebord (physical geography), G. Lange (botany), and

G. Jansen (photography), excavated two sites in the Bani-Niger region. As representative of the "Institut des Sciences Humaines" (Bamako) K. Sanogo joined the team.

Previous work, from 1964 onward, on the genetic and cultural relationships between recent human groups (Dogon, Kouroumba, Peul) living in the semiarid zone south of the Niger bend on one hand and an extinct population (Tellem) of which cultural and skeletal remains are found in many caves in the high cliff of Bandiagara on the other hand, indicated that (1) none of the groups studied are to be considered as being closely related to the Tellem; and (2) possible relationships to the now extinct Tellem may well be found in groups who lived in the Bani-Niger region. Archeological and human biological information on the Bani-Niger region, of crucial importance to the study of early migrations in western Africa, is lacking. The abundance of sites and the possibility to collect human skeletal material for the study of genetic relationships (if any), offered possibilities for research.

After a survey[1] in November and December 1974 of the riverbanks of the Niger from Mopti to Kouakourou and those of the Bani from Dienné to Mopti, two sites (out of some 40) were selected for archeological excavations.

Toguéré Doupwil (*Sévaré I*)

Situated some 10 kilometers east of Mopti in the floodplain of the Bani-Niger confluence, this is the largest of a series of 5 mounds near Sévaré (fig. 11). The mound is roughly oval in plan. The orientation of the long axis (± 400 meters) is northeast. The short axis is ± 250 meters long. At least two summits are discernible (3.34 meters and 4.08 meters above surrounding plain level). Four sections (A, B, C, D), respectively 4 meters, 3.50 meters, 8 meters, and 2 meters in length, were cleaned. Sections A and B were chosen as close to the summits as possible, section D in the saddle between the two summits. The virgin subsoil in sections A, B, and C appeared approximately at the level of the surrounding plain. In section D, mainly composed of hillwash deposits, the subsoil was found about 60 centimeters under plain level. This may be considered as an indication that the mount initially consisted of small mounds with a permanent (or semipermanent) watercourse in between.

The initial settlement was built on "nucleus terps" (artificial dwelling mounds) built on a natural levee from a gully in the floodplain of the Bani-

[1]Made possible by grants to Prof. Dr. J. Huizinga from the Netherlands Ministry of Cultural Affairs, Recreation and Social Welfare (The Hague) and from the Boise Fund (Oxford).

FIG. 12. Toguéré Doupwil: Section C with coffin-jar.

Niger confluence. One was clearly visible in section C. They are dated in the 11th–12th century (GrN-7944:850 ± 45 B.P., section C; GrN 7943:800 ± 45 B.P., section B). Remains of structures (stumps of walls, floors, pottery-pavements) were visible in all sections, except D. Finds were collected stratigraphically, and included carbonized seeds, and faunal remains. Further samples for C-14 analysis have been submitted for analysis.

In section C a coffin-jar was found (fig. 12) in which one human skeleton was buried in a forced contracted position. An iron bracelet and ankle-ring were found as grave-goods. Two C-14 dates of samples collected during the 1974 survey are pertinent to this burial:

GX-3767: 470 ± 100 B. P. (charcoal sample from section C at a higher level than the burial)

GX-3767: 545 ± 95 B.P. (human bone sample from a nearby coffin-jar)

Thus, a 15th-century date may be assumed for this burial (fig. 13). Other stratified finds included pottery, spindle-whorls, iron objects, and scoriae.

The surface material was much more diversified: earthenware statue, net-weights, cowries, beads, cupreous objects, and flint artifacts. The position of the flint material is not clear. It eventually differed from the flints used in flintlock guns. No flint was found in stratigraphic context.

FIG. 13. Toguéré Doupwil: Human skeletal remains in coffin-jar, section C.

FIG. 14. Toguéré Galia: Section.

FIG. 15. Toguéré Galia: Coffin-jars in section.

Toguéré Galia

The other site excavated was Toguéré Galia near Balé on the right bank of the river Bani, ca. 12 kilometers east of Dienné. Part of the mound has been cut off by the river (fig. 14).

In its present shape the mound is best described as being semicircular. Its north-south long axis (180 meters) is parallel to the river. The remaining east-west axis is 100 meters long. The summit of the mound is 5.3 meters above the Bani level of November 17, 1975. A continuous section in the central part of the mound of 70 meters in length and 3–4 meters high has been studied. The composition of the section was different from Toguéré Doupwil. On the virgin subsoil a core of material deposited by the river and containing some sherds was observed. This may indicate the presence of a nearby settlement at a period in which the riverbanks were still being built up by the river. This layer belongs to the 11th–12th century (GrN-7945:800 ± 80 B.P.). On top was found a homogenous layer, difficult to interpret as no clear structures were visible. These deposits were covered by a continuous stratum of ashes of variable thickness. In the upper part of the secretion, house structures were visible. In the section 10 coffin-jars were visible. The state of preservation of the human bones was bad, as most of the jars were gradually filled with fine silt passing through fissures in the jar or its lid (fig. 15).

Stratigraphically collected finds in the section included pottery, one cupreous ring, iron, baked bricks, and a bead. Faunal and floral remains as well as C-14 samples were also collected.

The surface material of this mound appeared to be more diversified than the surface material from Toguéré Doupwil. Numerous cupreous objects, beads, smoking pipes, fragments of statues, ritual pottery, stone bracelets, spindle whorls, net weights, and iron objects (including an animal figure) were collected. A study was done on modern potterymaking techniques in the village of Seina near Toguéré Galia. Our first impression is that the modern techniques are quite closely related to the pottery techniques used by the old inhabitants of both Toguéré Galia and Toguéré Doupwil

Most of the material collected from Toguéré Doupwil and Toguéré Galia is deposited in the Institute of Human Biology, Utrecht, for further investigation.

A full report of the excavation, including sections on radiocarbon dating, the human skeletal remains, and the floral and faunal remains, is in preparation.

We wish to express our gratitude to the Malinese authorities concerned for their cooperation and their interest in our work.

Grants from The Netherlands Foundation for the Advancement of Tropical Research (The Hague), and from the Boise Fund (Oxford), were awarded to Prof. Dr. J. Huizinga in 1976 to continue research in this area with a human biological study of the Bozo, the oldest living inhabitants of this region.

R. M. A. BEDAUX
J. D. VAN DER WAALS
JOHAN HUIZINGA

REFERENCES

BEDAUX, R. M. A.
1972. Tellem, reconnaissance archéologique d'une culture de l'ouest africain au moyen âge: Recherches architectoniques. Journ. Soc. Africanistes, vol. 42, no. 2, pp. 103–185.
1974. Tellem, reconnaissance archéologique d'une culture de l'ouest africain au moyen âge: Les appuie nuque. Journ. Soc. Africanistes, vol. 44, no. 1, pp. 7–42.
1977. Tellem: Een Bidrage tot des Gescheidenis van de Republiek Mali, 103 pp., illus., with English and French translations. Afrika Museum, Bergen Dal (Netherlands).
____. The geographic distribution of a special type of Tellem bowls. *In* "West African Culture Dynamics: Archaeological and Historical Perspectives," B. Swartz and M. Posnansky, eds. Mouton Publishers, The Hague. (In press.)

BRASSEUR, G., AND LE MOAL, G.
1963. Cartes ethno-démographiques de l'Afrique occidentale, feuilles 3 et 4 nord, 29 pp. Institut Fondamental d'Afrique Noire (IFAN), Dakar.

CISSOKO, S. M.
1968. Famines et épidémies à Tombouctou et dans la Boucle du Niger du XVIe au XVIIIe siècle. Bull. IFAN, ser. B, vol. 30, no. 3. pp. 806–821.

DESPLAGNES, L.
1907. Le plateau central nigérien, 504 pp. Larose, Paris.

DIETERLEN, G.
1955. Mythe et organisation sociale au Soudan français. Journ. Soc. Africanistes, vol. 25, nos. 1, 2, pp. 39–76.

FAGE, J. D.
1965. Some thoughts on migration and urban settlement, Pp. 39–49 *in* "Urbanization and Migration in West Africa," H. Kuper ed. University of California Press, Berkeley.

FAGG, W.
1970. The tribal image, 60 pp. British Museum (Natural History), London.

FILIPOWIAK, W.; JASNOSZ, S.; AND WOLAGIEWICZ, R.
1968. Les recherches archéologiques polono-guinéennes à Niani en 1968. Materialy Zachodniopomorskie, vol. 14, pp. 575–648.

GALLAIS, J.
1965. Le Paysan Dogon (République du Mali). Cahiers d'Outre-mer, vol. 18, pp. 123–143.

GLEAVE, M. B., AND PROTHERO, R. M.
1971. Population density and "slave raiding"—a comment. Journ. Afr. Hist., vol. 12, no. 2, pp. 319–327.

GRIAULE, M.
1938. Masques Dogons. Trav. et. Mém. Inst. Ethnol., no. 33, 896 pp. Paris.

HUIZINGA, JOHAN
1968a. New physical anthropological evidence bearing on the relationships between Dogon, Kurumba, and the extinct West African Tellem populations. Proc. Kon. Nederl. Akad. Wetensch., ser. C, vol. 71, no. 1, pp. 16–30.
1968b. Human biological observations on some African populations of the thorn savanna belt. Proc. Kon. Nederl. Akad. Wetensch., ser. C, vol. 71, no. 4, pp. 356–390.
1974. Comparative survey of African people living in the hot-dry-savanna belt (1964–1972). Pp. 113–117 *in* "The Netherlands Contribution to the International Biological Programme, Final Report 1966–1971." Netherlands Committee for the I.B.P., North-Holland Publication Co., Amsterdam-London.
1977. A comparative survey of African people living in the northern semi-arid zone: A search for a base line. Pp. 241–271 *in* "Population Structure and Human Variation," G. A. Harrison, ed. Cambridge University Press.

HUIZINGA, JOHAN, AND BIRNIE-TELLIER, N. F.
1966. Some anthropometric data on male and female Dogons: The "harmoniously reduced male." Proc. Kon. Nederl. Akad. Wetensch., ser. C, vol. 69, no. 5, pp. 675–695.

HUIZINGA, JOHAN; BIRNIE-TELLIER, N. F.; AND GLANVILLE, E. V.
1967. Description and carbon-14 dating of Tellem cave skulls from the Mali Republic: A comparison with other negroid groups. Proc. Kon. Nederl. Akad. Wetensch., ser. C, vol. 70, no. 3, pp. 338–367.

IZARD, M.
1970. Introduction à l'histoire des royaumes mossi, vol. 1, 2, Recherches Voltaïques, nos. 12, 13, 434 pp. Paris-Ouagadougou.

KNIP, A.
1971. The frequencies of non-metrical variants in Tellem and Nokara skulls from the Mali Republic. Proc. Kon. Nederl. Akad. Wetensch., ser. C, vol. 74, no. 5, pp. 422–443.

MAUNY, R.
1950. Villages néolithiques de la falaise (Dhar) Tichitt-Oualata. Notes Africaines, no. 50. pp. 35–43.
1961. Tableau géographique de l'Ouest africain au moyen âge d'après les sources écrites, la tradition, et l'archeologie. Mémoires de l'IFAN, no. 61, 588 pp. Dakar.

MUNSON, P. J.
1971. The Tichitt tradition: A late prehistoric occupation of the southwestern Sahara, 393 pp. Thesis, University of Illinois. University Microfilms International, Ann Arbor, London.

PALAUSI, G.
1959. Contribution à l'étude géologique et hydrogéologique des formations primaires au Soudan méridional et en Haute-Volta. Bull. Service Géol. et. Prosp. Min., Dakar, no. 33, 209 pp.
RICHIR, Cl., AND ROBERT, D.
1970. Deux agadirs "berbéres" dans le massif du Rqiss (Hodh oriental-Mauritanie). Notes Africaines, no. 127, pp. 75–82.
ROUCH, J.
1953. Contribution à l'histoire des Songhay. Mémoires de l'IFAN, no. 29, 137 pp., Dakar.
TROLL, C.
1965. Seasonal climates of the earth. The seasonal course of natural phenomena in the different climatic zones of the earth. Pp. 15–25 *in* "World Maps of Climatology," H. E. Landsberg et al., eds. Springer Publishing Co., New York.
WALTON, J.
1960. Patterned walling in African folk building. Journ. Afr. Hist., vol. 1, no. 1, pp. 19–30.

Archeological and Paleoecological Investigations at Guadalupe Pueblo, Sandoval County, New Mexico: A Preliminary Report

Principal Investigator: Cynthia Irwin-Williams, Eastern New Mexico University, Portales, New Mexico.

Grant Nos. 865, 963, 1065, 1192. For a study of the structure of Pueblo society on the Middle Puerco River.

This report covers archeological and paleoecological investigations conducted on the Middle Puerco River in northwestern New Mexico (see fig. 1). Final interpretations and conclusions are presented in the doctoral dissertation to be submitted in 1978 by the junior author to the Department of Anthropology, Washington State University.

Guadalupe Pueblo was initially reported by Emma Lou Davis and James Winkler in 1959. Preliminary test excavations were initiated as part of the Puerco River Valley Archeological Project in 1972 after a surface survey of the Guadalupe area by Dorothy Koster Washburn (1974). These excavations were conducted to define the Pueblo's temporal and spatial parameters and they revealed that the site contained remains of two prehistoric occupations. The primary occupation, evidenced through masonry and ceramic styles, represented an intrusive Chacoan population into the Rio Puerco Valley. The secondary reoccupation of the Pueblo was by a local Puercoan population, the extent and nature of which were being studied through a regional survey of the Rio Puerco Valley.

Guadalupe Pueblo was selected for further excavations (1973–1975) for three primary reasons: It represented significant and new information on the late 11th- and early 12th-century Chacoan expansion from Chaco Canyon, New Mexico; it occupied a central and unique position in a cluster of apparently contemporaneously occupied puebloan sites; and it promised to provide excavational and chronological control for 13th-century pueblo occupations within the middle Rio Puerco Valley. The research goals behind these excavations consisted of:

1. Establishment of functional, sociopolitical, religious, and other cultural ties between Guadalupe Pueblo and similar Chacoan outlier communities to the elaborate manifestations in Chaco Canyon;

2. Evaluation of the social influence exhibited by the intrusive Chacoan population and its effect on the local cultural development within the Rio Puerco Valley;
3. Delineation of the cultural-historical relationships of Guadalupe Pueblo and other 13th-century communities in the middle Rio Puerco Valley to prehistoric populations occupying the other Anagazi regions;
4. Exploration of potential environmental and/or sociopolitical forces responsible for 12th- and 14th-century abandonment of Guadalupe Pueblo; and
5. Comparison of the Chacoan community at Guadalupe Pueblo and that established by the subsequent reoccupation of the site.

Explanation and Background of Objectives

The Chacoan Expansion. Chaco Canyon, in northwestern New Mexico, experienced a most sophisticated and complex cultural development between A.D. 930 and 1130 or slightly later. Previous archeological research in Chaco Canyon (Bradley, 1971; Brand et al., 1937; Judd, 1954, 1959, 1964; Hawley, 1934; Kluckhohn and Reiter, 1939; G. Vivian, 1965; Vivian and Mathews, 1965) has outlined three contrasting but contemporary prehistoric community types. R. G. Vivian (1970, pp. 207–281) and Grebinger (1973, pp. 7–15) suggest that the nature of Chacoan society was a response to local environmental factors. Others (Di Peso, 1968, pp. 52–54; Schroeder, 1966, pp. 694–697) feel that direct or indirect contact with the high civilizations of Mexico gave the distinctive flavor to Chacoan communities.

During the late 11th and early 12th centuries populations from Chaco Canyon expanded to outlying areas and created colonial towns duplicating the great Chacoan towns such as Pueblo Bonito and Chetro Ketl. The delineation of prehistoric relationships between these outlying Chacoan settlements to manifestations within Chaco Canyon appears basic to an over-all understanding of Chacoan culture. Although a number of these satellite communities are known, only five such sites have been previously excavated: Lowry Ruin (Martin et al., 1936), Chimney Rock Pueblo (Jeancon and Roberts, 1924), La Plata Site 39 (Morris, 1939, pp. 50–55), Aztec Ruin (Morris, 1919, 1921, 1928), and the Village of the Great Kivas (Roberts, 1932). Excavations are currently being conducted at Salmon Ruins (Irwin-Williams, 1972, in press). The excavations at Guadalupe Pueblo thus provided significant and new information on the relationship between Chaco Canyon and these satellite communities.

Chacoan Influences in the Rio Puerco. A regional site survey (1970–1973) in the middle Rio Puerco Valley (fig. 1), directed by Dr. Cynthia Irwin-Williams, Eastern New Mexico University, and supported by the

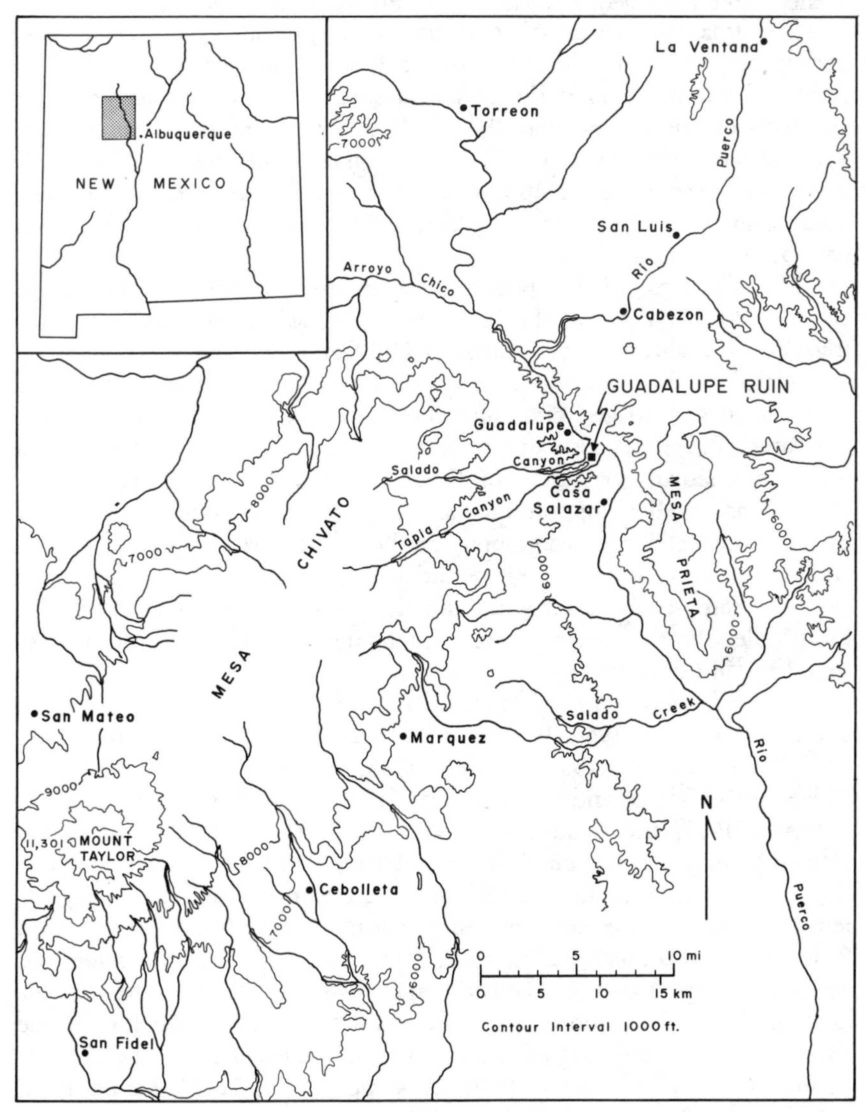

FIG. 1. Map of the Middle Rio Puerco Valley, New Mexico, showing the location of Guadalupe Ruin.

National Geographic Society, established a cultural continuum from the early 10th to the 14th century A.D. This continuum appears characterized by a series of demographic changes that resulted in the clustering of settlements within three geographical areas of the Rio Puerco drainage.

The smallest concentration of prehistoric pueblos occurs near Raton Springs on the Arroyo Cuervo, a tributary of the Rio Puerco. Prieta Vista (Bice and Sundt, 1972) is the only excavated site in this cluster. A larger clustering of sites occurs along the Salado Creek (south) and at its juncture with the Rio Puerco (Fritz, 1972). A small, undated, masonry pueblo slightly north of this settlement group has been interpreted as an intrusive late Mesa Verde community (Davis and Winkler, 1959). No other sites in the group have been excavated.

The largest grouping of prehistoric settlements in the middle Rio Puerco occurs between the historic Spanish towns of Casas Salazar and Guadalupe (fig. 1). Guadalupe Pueblo, situated 160 feet above the valley floor on an isolated sandstone mesa, occupies a central location within this large cluster of sites. Field inspection of ceramic collections from sites surrounding Guadalupe Pueblo suggests that most of these may have been contemporary with the Chacoan occupation of Guadalupe Pueblo. This situation thus afforded an excellent opportunity to study the social influence exhibited by this intrusive Chacoan community on the local Puercoan population. Nevertheless, the attainment of this second goal of the proposed research must await the completion of analytical and test excavation phases of the Puerco River Valley Project now in progress. Therefore, this objective is not further considered in this report.

External Relationships. Despite considerable field work (Dickson, 1973, 1975; Dutton, 1953, 1964, 1966; Ellis, 1975; Ferdon and Reed, 1950; Guthe, 1917; Hibben, 1936, 1937; Holden, 1955; Jeancon, 1929; Judge, 1973; Kidder, 1926; Stubbs and Stallings, 1953; Tichy, 1949; Wetherington, 1968; Worman, 1953) the Coalition Period (A.D. 1200–1325) of northern Rio Grande prehistory is still poorly known. Attempts to relate present Puebloan linguistic groups to prehistoric societies of the San Juan and Chazo regions rely on hypothesized ceramic influences which occurred during the Coalition Period (Ford et al., 1972; Ellis, 1967; Mera, 1935, pp. 8–24; Wendorf and Reed, 1955, pp. 143–149; Wetherington, 1968, pp. 97–99). The strategic location of the middle Rio Puerco Valley immediately west of the Rio Grande Valley, south of the Largo-Gallina drainages, and north of the Acoma-Laguna archeological province (Ellis, 1974, pp. 13–33, 51–99; Rands, 1974; Ruppe, 1953; Ruppe and Dittert, 1952) makes research in this area vital to problems of prehistoric cultural relationships.

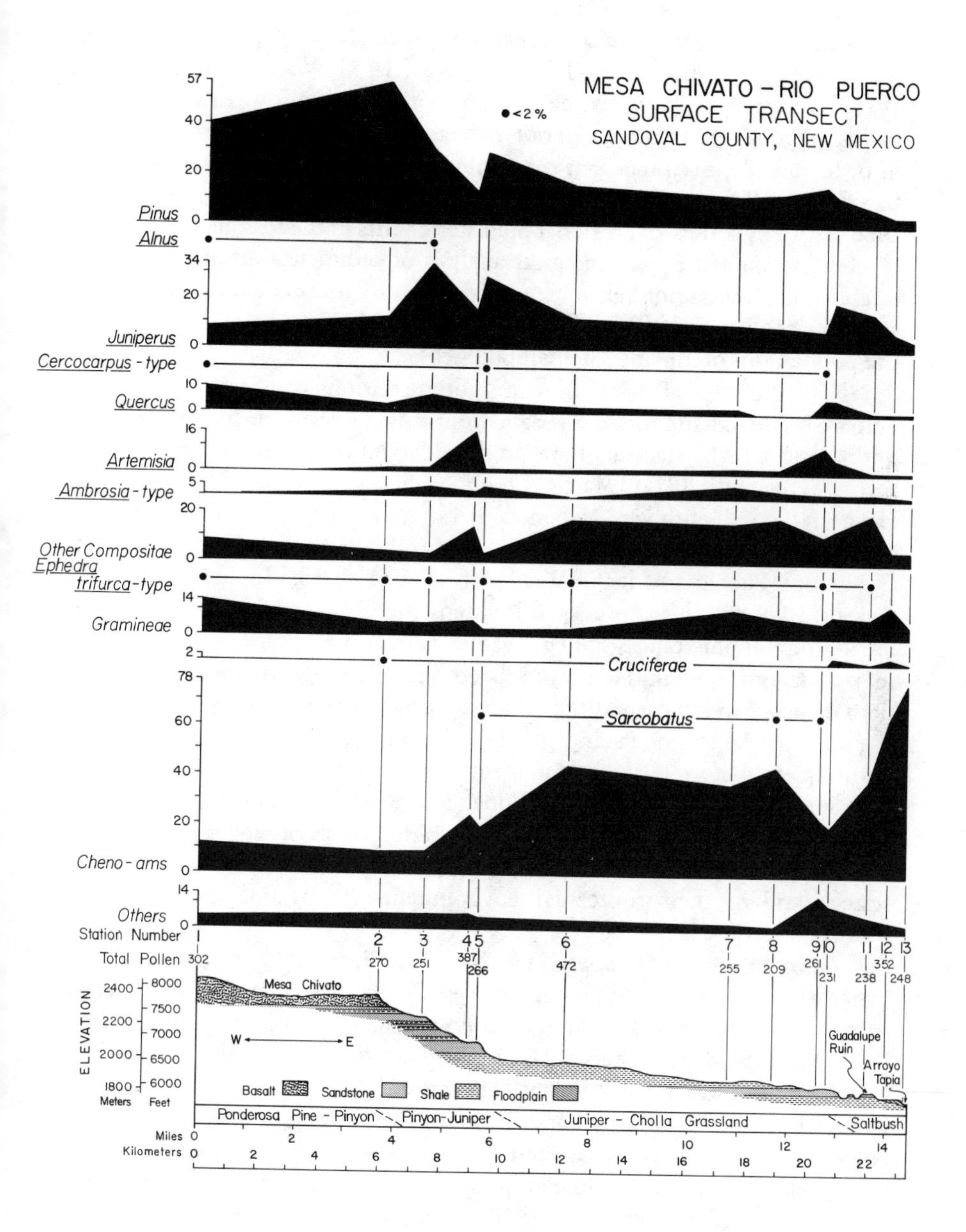

FIG. 2. Modern vegetation and pollen transect from Mesa Chivato to the Rio Puerco Valley floor.

Past Environments and Site Abandonment. Southwestern archeologists (Plog, 1974; Schoenwetter and Dittert, 1968; R. G. Vivian, 1970; Zubrow, 1971) have shown an increasing concern with prehistoric man's adaptation to his physical environment. Prior to statements concerning this relationship, reasonable interpretations concerning past environments must be made. Based on pollen studies of archeological sites, Schoenwetter (1962, 1964, 1966, 1970) hypothesized regional prehistoric shifts in the seasonal distribution of effective moisture. Palynological analysis of sediments within Guadalupe Pueblo were thus undertaken to provide relevant data on these hypotheses and to establish the effect of such hypothesized environmental change on the populations occupying Guadalupe Pueblo.

Nevertheless, paleoenvironmental interpretations based on archeological pollen should be supported by data from nonculturally disturbed deposits. Spring and alluvial deposits have produced significant data on past environments (Freeman, 1972; Martin, 1963; Mehringer, 1967; Mehringer and Haynes, 1965; Mehringer, Martin, and Haynes, 1967). Pollen samples were collected from alluvial sediments in the Tapia and Salado canyons near Guadalupe Pueblo and included as part of our research. In addition, several ancient pack-rat (*Neotoma* sp.) middens were collected. Since *Neotoma* has a limited home range (Finley, 1958; Stones and Hayward, 1968) botanical remains found in its midden, once dated, are extremely useful for interpretations of paleoenvironmental fluxuations (Van Devender, 1973).

It is crucial to understand prehistoric man's articulation with his natural environment before making statements concerning the effects of changing environment on his society. Functional interpretations concerning economic activities at Guadalupe Pueblo were thus aided by palynological, zoological, and botanical analyses of specific artifacts (manos, metates, and whole ceramic vessels) and/or their contextual environments (room floors, archeological features, etc.).

Comparison of Occupations. Bice and Sundt (1972, pp. 104–120) hypothesize a direct cultural link between Prieta Vista and Chaco Canyon based on an identified Chacoan variety of McElmo Black-on-White from Prieta Vista. Ford and others (1972, p. 34) likewise see Chacoan characteristics in the middle Rio Puerco Valley. The secondary occupation at Guadalupe Pueblo is apparently comtemporaneous with Prieta Vista; however, the primary occupation is the clearly characterized by intrusive Chacoan remains. Comparison of occupations at Guadalupe Pueblo would likewise provide insights to varied cultural processes in prehistoric community structure, environmental adaptations, and external relationships.

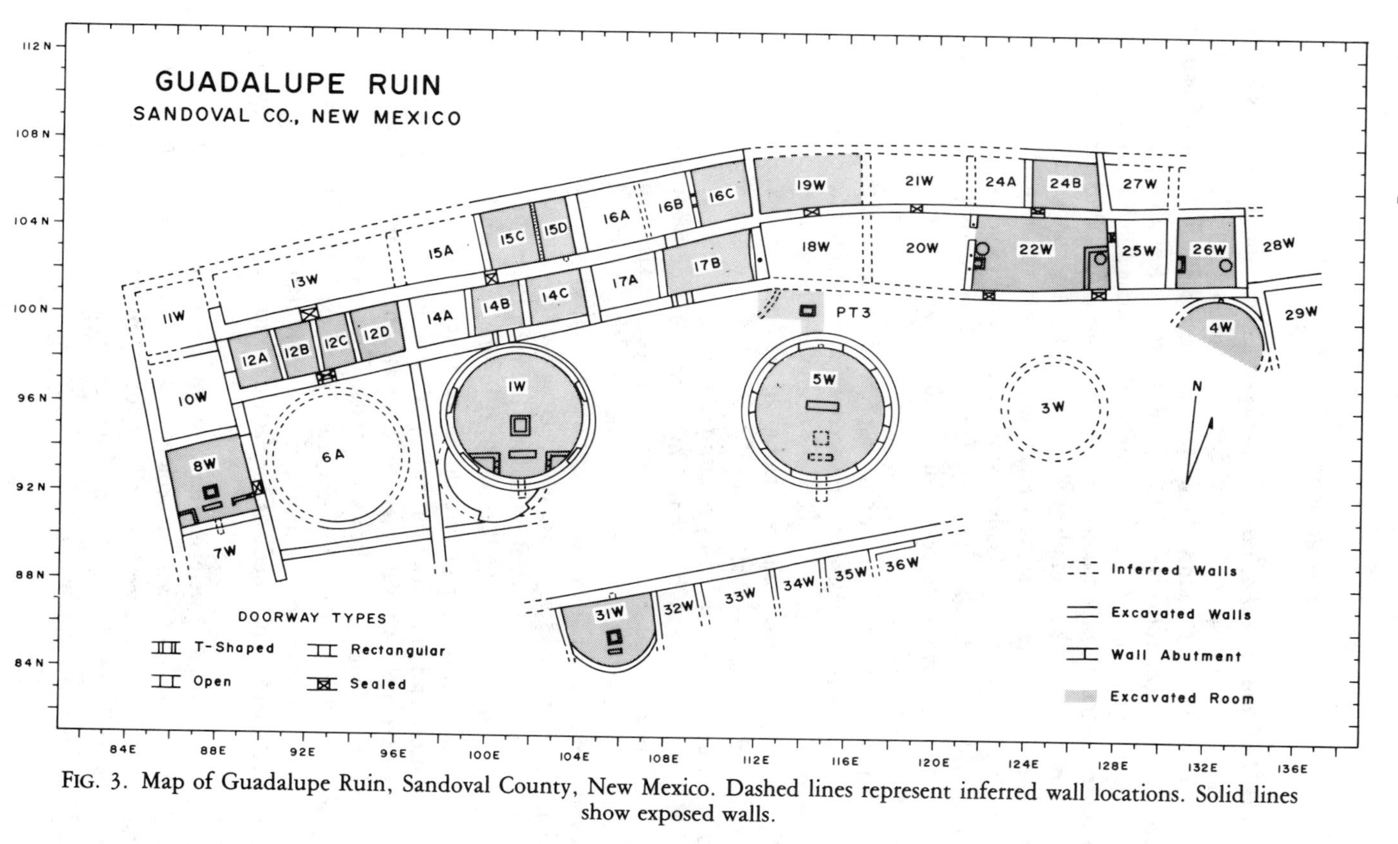

FIG. 3. Map of Guadalupe Ruin, Sandoval County, New Mexico. Dashed lines represent inferred wall locations. Solid lines show exposed walls.

Procedures and Results

Site Location and Present Environment. Guadalupe Pueblo (NW¼ NW¼ sec. 23, T. 15 N., R. 3 W., U.S.G.S. Guadalupe Quad.) is located in southwestern Sandoval County, New Mexico, between the Tapia and Salado arroyos (fig. 1). The ruin (elev. 6,070) is situated 160 feet above the Puerco Valley floor on an isolated sandstone mesa. The middle Rio Puerco drainage is bounded laterally by the basalt-capped mesas Chivato and Prieta and dotted by Tertiary volcanic dikes and plugs (Johnson, 1907). Interfingered Cretaceous bedrock exposures are of Mancos Shale and a lower Mesaverde Formation sandstone equivalent to the Gallup Sandstone (Hunt, 1936, pl. 19; Renick, 1931, p. 5; Sears et al., 1941, p. 112). The valley floor consists of Quaternary alluvium and colluvium deposited up to 50 feet above the present Puerco river bed.

A study of present distributional aspects of modern vegetation and its palynological representation was initiated to aid interpretations of paleo-environments. In addition to collections of modern flora, a series of surface sediment samples were collected along an east-west transect from Mesa Chivato to the Rio Puerco Valley floor (fig. 2). Methodological aspects behind such a transect are discussed by Mehringer (1967, pp. 138–146) and Adam and Mehringer (1975). While it is convenient to divide plant communities into four zonal categories (ponderosa pine-pinyon parkland, pinyon-juniper woodland, juniper-cholla grassland, and saltbush grassland) boundaries between these associations are often obscure and individual species distribution is influenced by substrate, exposure, groundwater, and cultural factors.

Excavations—Excavational procedures followed those outlined by Pippin and Irwin-Williams (Irwin-Williams, 1972) for the San Juan Valley Archaeological Project. Although prehistoric rooms were chosen as the basic unit of excavation and analysis, a metric grid was superimposed throughout the site in attempt to isolate prehistoric intra-room variability. Excavational methods varied with archeological contexts. Thus sediments which related to postoccupational collapse of the ruin were excavated differently than were the floor surfaces of prehistoric rooms. Stratigraphic nomenclature and the general excavational methods for each depositional context are given in table 1.

Excavational areas were chosen through a stratified systematic sample based on research objectives, archeological considerations, and ethnographic parallels. Twenty rooms were partially or totally excavated during the 1973–1975 excavation seasons (fig. 3). Excavated rooms and their individual stratigraphic histories are outlined below.

TABLE 1. STRATIGRAPHIC DESIGNATIONS AND SUGGESTED EXCAVATIONAL UNITS AND PROCEDURES

Designation	*Translation*	*Grid*	*Quad.*	*Screen*	*Max.* depth (cm.)*	*Comment*
A	Present ground surface		X	0	0	No thickness
B	Post-occupational fill		X		60	Variable
C	Structured trash	X		X	10	
D	Artificial fill		X	X	20	Variable
E	Roof surface	X		X	0	Contact stratum
F	Structured roof fall	X		X	10	Articulated roof
G	Occupational fill	X		X	10	
H	Floor surface	X		X	0	Contact stratum
I	Floor structure	X		X	10	Architectural
J	Pre-occupational fill	X			20	Tested only
K	Wall foundation	X			10	Architectural
L	Pit fill	X		X	10	
M	Unstructured trash	X	X	X	20	Variable
O	Zonal floor	X		X	10	

* All strata are separated at natural stratigraphic breaks. Depth refers to maximum arbitrary depth within natural units.

ROOM 1W: Room1W is a circular secondary kiva originally characterized by a masonry deflector, square masonry hearth, and a north-south oriented masonry floor vault occupying the western portion of the kiva. During subsequent remodeling the floor vault was filled and plastered over, and two masonry alcoves were constructed (fig. 3). Samples for archeomagnetic dating were obtained from the ash-filled kiva hearth. Four masonry pilasters supported ponderosa-pine vegas. Five tree-ring cut dates from the burned roof stratum in Room 1 place its construction between A.D. 1264 and 1266. Prior to the kiva roof burning, an infant was interred behind the kiva deflector. Shortly following the roof burning, Room 1 was used for refuse disposal.

ROOM 2: The primary cultural remains belonging to this room were prehistorically disturbed with the construction of Room 1W. Whatever remained of Room 2 between its southern wall and the southern wall of Room 1 was then subsequently disturbed by modern vandals. Nevertheless, the foundation complex of Room 2 was unearthed below the floor of Room 1W. Directly north of this foundation were stratified refuse deposits interpreted as belonging to the initial occupants of Guadalupe Pueblo. These sediments were apparently deposited prior to the construction of the wall foundation for Room 2.

ROOM 4W: The entire southern segment of this circular Chacoan kiva was destroyed through natural slumping from the mesa top. The eastern kiva portion had likewise been disturbed, but by modern vandals. Excavations revealed this kiva to have been reoccupied and modified by the secondary occupation. During reoccupation the lower extent of the kiva wall had been stabilized with basalt cobbles and replastered. Pollen samples were taken from lower and upper wall-plaster layers to aid in the reconstruction of this event. The only remaining feature in Room 4 was a rectangular kiva niche in the northern wall.

ROOM 5W: This large circular secondary kiva was situated in the central plaza area. Its roof level apparently conformed to the original plaza level, the floor levels of Rooms 17, 18, 20, and 22, and the roof levels of Rooms 31W to 36W. A number of small circular adobe-lined hearths and *Meleagris* eggshell fragments were associated with this Chacoan floor. Primary strata were directly overlain by secondary room floors. Each secondary room division presented a similar stratigraphic history with roof fall overlain by post-occupational fill. A noncut tree-ring of A.D. 1279 (SDV-63) places a minimum age for roof construction or modification in Room 12B.

ROOM 14: Two secondary occupation rooms (14B and 14C) of this tridivided primary room were excavated. Lower floor and occupational fill levels in each room may belong to the initial occupation of Guadalupe Pueblo; however, final assignment must await material culture analysis now in progress. Subsequent stratigraphic history of Room 14C is characterized by two secondary floors and their overlying roof strata; whereas secondary occupation in Room 14B consisted of a single floor level, its associated occupational fill, and the overlying roof strata.

ROOM 15B: Room 15B, itself subdivided into Rooms 15C and 15D, is the easternmost secondary subdivision of a larger Chacoan room. Stratified trash deposits underlying the eastern portion of this bilevel secondary room may belong to the primary occupation. A 30-centimeter-high jacal wall separated the eastern raised-floor segment from its western counterpart. Disarticulated human remains were associated with this floor level. A burned roof stratum was continuous above this floor level. Sparse trash accumulation characterized the lower portion of the overlying post-occupational rubble fill.

ROOM 16: The eastern (Room 16C) and central (Room 16B) portions of this tridivided Chacoan room were excavated during the 1975 field season. Stratigraphic histories of both secondary rooms show secondary floor levels constructed directly on artificial fill and overlain by collapsed roof strata. No deposits were found which could be assigned to the initial occupation of Guadalupe Pueblo. A dendrochronological sample from roof fall in Room 16C provided a noncut date of A.D. 1112.

ROOM 17: Initially tested in 1972, the eastern portion (Room 17B) of this secondarily subdivided primary room showed a complex stratigraphic history. Three discontinuous floor levels were each overlain by roof-fall strata. A subfloor grave of an eight-year-old child was found beneath the lowermost floor in the southeastern quadrant of Room 17B. Pollen analysis of sediments within this grave (fig. 4) suggests ritual use of *Zea* and *Typha latifolia* or their pollen. Articulated wall fall along the eastern boundary of Room 17B may indicate that the original Chacoan east wall of Room 17 was later replaced by a secondary wall.

PT 3: A plaza test trench directly north of Room 5 revealed a partially disturbed room floor. A rectangular-slab-lined hearth was found in the southern portion of this floor surface. Overlying strata of vandals' backdirt from Room 18W probably explains the absence of standing walls surrounding this packed adobe floor. This area was designated Room 3.

ROOM 19W: During excavation of a test trench designed to outline the northernmost walls of Rooms 16 and 19W the articulated remains of *Canis familiaris* were found in trash deposits within Room 19. This test trench was thus extended southward to determine the cultural context of this apparent burial. These excavations revealed that the secondary trash stratum was deposited prior to the roof collapse in Room 19W. Excavations did not proceed below the trash stratum.

ROOM 24B: Like Room 16C, the stratigraphic section of Room 24B consisted of a secondary occupation adobe floor directly overlain by zonal roof fall. No primary occupation deposits occurred below the room floor. A single noncut tree-ring date of A.D. 969 from the roof stratum probably belongs to the earlier Chaco occupation.

ROOM 22W: This extremely large secondary-occupation room is characterized by a western jacal wall and southeasterly located masonry alcove. A milling bin and associated subfloor basket occurred adjacent to the jacal wall. A large corregated ceramic vessel was buried within the alcove's floor. Following room abandonment, Room 22W was used as a trash depository. Four tree-ring samples, dating between A.D. 924 and 965, of redeposited timbers were taken from this trash stratum. Mixed primary and secondary occupation ceramics, disarticulated human remains, and the massive internal structure of this trash stratum may indicate secondary disposal. Prehistoric activity within the upper section of this trash stratum is indicated by the remains of a slab-lined hearth later utilized as a milling bin (fig. 4).

ROOM 26W: The secondary occupants of Room 26W completely eradicated the remains of the earlier primary occupants and builders. A subfloor milling

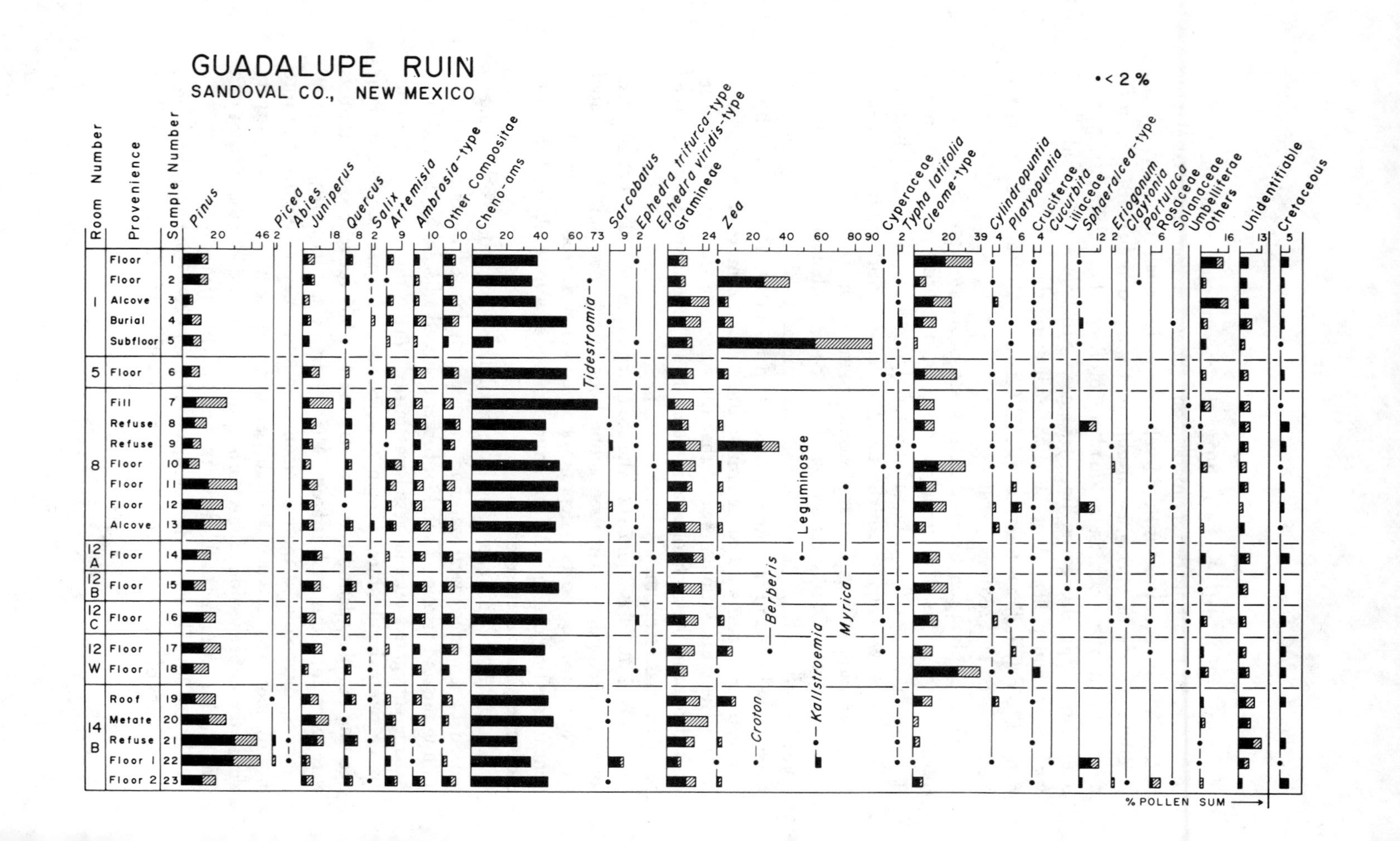
GUADALUPE RUIN
SANDOVAL CO., NEW MEXICO
•< 2 %
Room Number
Provenience
Sample Number
Pinus
Picea
Abies
Juniperus
Quercus
Salix
Artemisia
Ambrosia-type
Other Compositae
Cheno-ams
Tidestromia
Sarcobatus
Ephedra trifurca-type
Ephedra viridis-type
Gramineae
Zea
Leguminosae
Berberis
Croton
Kallstroemia
Myrica
Cyperaceae
Typha latifolia
Cleome-type
Cylindropuntia
Platyopuntia
Cruciferae
Cucurbita
Liliaceae
Sphaeralcea-type
Eriogonum
Claytonia
Portulaca
Rosaceae
Solanaceae
Umbelliferae
Others
Unidentifiable
Cretaceous
% POLLEN SUM
Floor
Alcove
Burial
Subfloor
Fill
Refuse
Roof
Metate
Floor 1
Floor 2
12 A
12 B
12 C
12 W
14 B

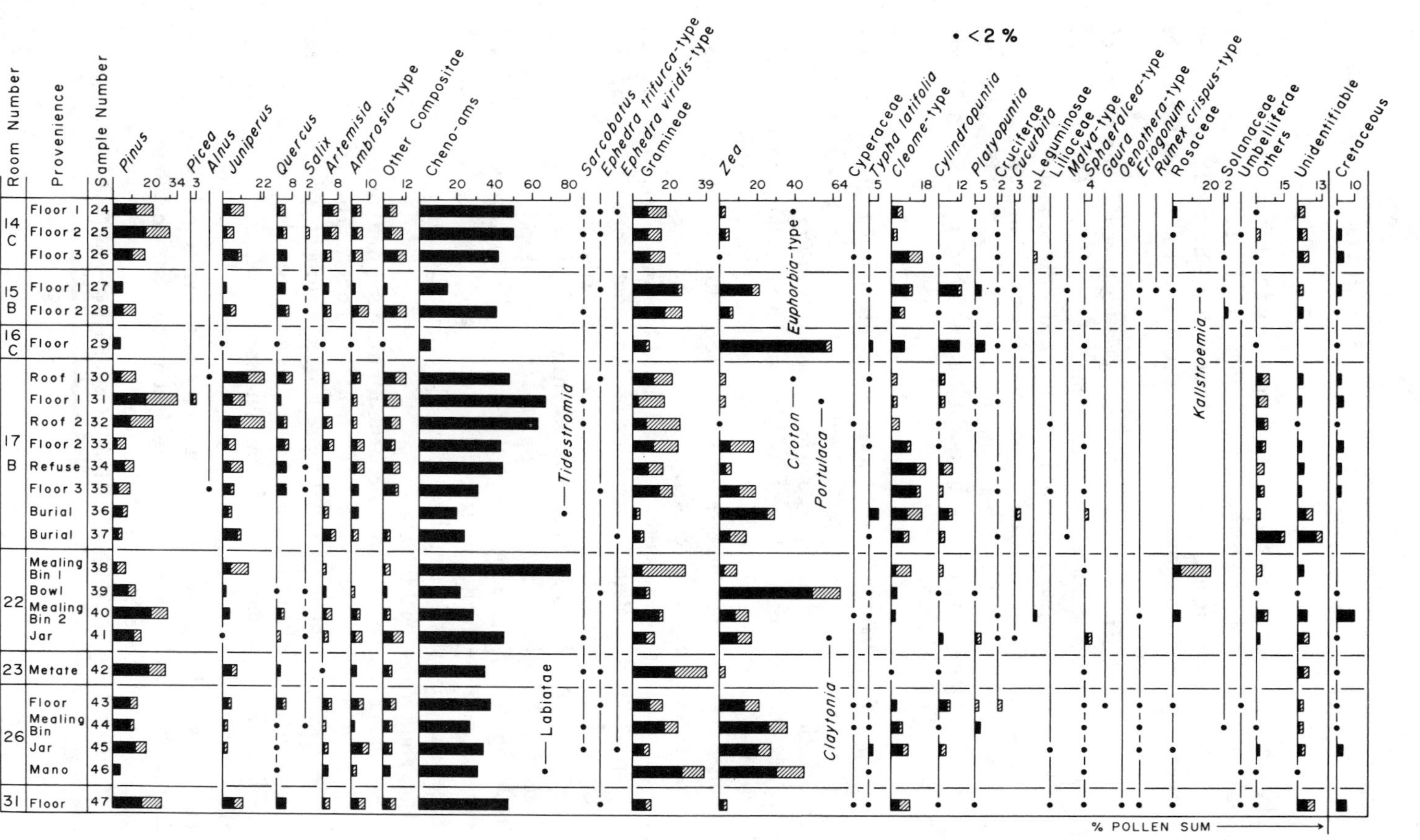

FIG. 4. Pollen diagram of samples from Guadalupe Pueblo. Solid portions show frequencies of all pollen types in first 200-grain count. Lined portions represent frequencies, excluding Cheno-ams, in second 200-grain count.

bin and large corregated ceramic vessel were found within the secondary occupation floor. Two adobe-lined post molds in the northern room half probably belong to roof supports. The floor surface was directly overlain by burned roof stratum. A tree-ring date of A.D. 971 probably dates the earlier Chaco occupation.

ROOM 31W: This secondary D-shaped kiva occupies the eastern end of a row of secondary occupation rooms (Rooms 32, 33, 34, 35, 36) built against a Chacoan retaining wall. The kiva floor overlaid artificial and trash fill. An archeomagnetic sample was taken from the masonry hearth associated with this floor surface and was dated (lab. no. 1148) A.D. 1275 ± 55. Following room abandonment and the subsequent collapse of its roof, Room 31 was partially filled with trash.

Material Culture. Detailed analyses of artifacts recovered during excavation are presently (1977) being conducted at Washington State University. In addition to traditional typological studies of material culture, these analyses will attempt to delimit prehistoric behavioral and organizational patterns of both societies which occupied Guadalupe Pueblo. This approach requires the combined analysis of spatial, contextual, technological, functional, and stylistic attributes of artifacts.

Lithic analysis follows procedures outlined by Irwin-Williams and Pippin (in press). Two analytical categories of lithic remains are recognized—chipped stone artifacts and ground stone tools. Functional studies of ground stone tools, in addition to wear-pattern analysis, are aided by palynological analysis. While present results (see fig. 4) are equivocal, prior studies (Hevly, 1964, pp. 90–91) have shown significant results. Four categories of chipped stone artifacts are analyzed: flake debris, cores and core fragments, utilized flakes and cores, and retouched tools. Flake debris is sampled from room floors and occupational fill strata.

Ceramic analysis is modified from procedures outlined by Bennett (1974) for the San Juan Valley Archaeological Project. This procedure includes attribute analysis of vessel form, surface treatment, paste characteristics, design, and symmetry. The decorated ceramic assemblage associated with the initial occupation of Guadalupe Pueblo consists primarily of Gallup Black-on-White, Chaco Black-on-White, Socorro Black-on-White, and Wingate Black-on-Red. Secondary occupation ceramic wares include but are not limited to a local variety of McElmo-Mesa Verde Black-on-White, Sante Fe Black-on-White, and St. Johns Polychrome.

Pollen Analysis. Pollen analysis of sediments from Guadalupe Pueblo was initiated to:

1. establish a relative pollen chronology for intrasite dating;
2. determine possible prehistoric cultural and economic utilization of plants or their pollen;
3. aid functional interpretations of specific artifacts and/or their contexts of occurrence; and
4. obtain paleoenvironmental information for the period A.D. 900 to A.D. 1300.

Preliminary results of these studies are presented in figure 4. High frequencies of Cheno-ams (80 percent) and Rosaceae (20 percent) pollen in a milling-bin sample (Room 22) probably represent their economic use. *Zea* (29 percent) and *Typha latifolia* (4 percent) in a burial sample (Room 17) are interpreted as culturally introduced plants or their pollen. Pollen types that may represent culturally important plants include *Opuntia*-type, *Sphaeralcea*-type, *Kallstroemia*, and *Sacrobatus*. High frequencies of *Pinus*, *Picea*, and *Abies* from a second-occupation floor in Room 14B probably reflect cultural introduction of these types.

Paleoenvironmental interpretations must await further analysis of pollen samples from the arroyos Tapia and Salado and botanical analysis of pack-rat middens. The introduction of economic pollen types by cultural activities in prehistoric pueblos may mask regional changes in pollen rain. Absolute pollen influx, determined by the addition of tracer pollen to a known weight of sediment, will be used in attempt to alleviate this problem.

Faunal Analysis. The analysis of faunal remains from Guadalupe Pueblo is being conducted by William Gray, a graduate student at Washington State University, who is concentrating on identification and frequency of species represented, prehistoric techniques of food preparation (butchering and cooking), and ecological implications. These data will be used for a M.S. thesis by Gray. Fauna thus far identified from Guadalupe Pueblo are tabulated below (most remains belong to Leporidae, *Cynomys* sp., *Odocoileus* sp., *Ovis canadensis*, and *Antilocapra americana*):

MAMMALIA	
Artiodactyla	
Antilocapra americana	(pronghorn antelope)
Odocoileus hemionus	(mule deer)
Ovis canadensis mexicana	(desert bighorn sheep)
Carnivora	
Canis familiaris	(domesticated dog)
Lynx rufus	(bobcat)
Mephitis sp.	(skunk)
Taxidea taxus	(badger)

Lagomorpha	
Lepus cf. *californicus*	(black-tailed jack rabbit)
Sylvilagus cf. *audubonii*	(desert cottontail)
Rodentia	
Cynomys cf. *gunnisoni*	(white-tailed prairie-dog)
Geomys cf. *bursarius*	(plains pocket gopher)
Neotoma sp.	(wood rat)
Peromyscus sp.	(deer mouse)
AVES	
Falconiformes	
Aquila chrysaetos	(golden eagle)
Galliformes	
Meleagris gallopavo	(wild turkey)
REPTILIA	
Testudines	
Chrysemys picta	(turtle)
PISCES	
Cypriniformes	
Hyboysis gracilis	(flathead chub)

Botanical Analysis. Flotation samples were collected during excavation from archeological features, floor surfaces, and other cultural strata. Analysis of seed and botanical remains found within these samples will aid in economic and paleoenvironmental interpretations. Present results from analysis of samples from Rooms 1, 8, 22, and 26 show occurrence of Cheno-ams, *Opuntia*-type, *Echinocereus fendleri*-type, *Scirpus*-type, *Sporobolus*-type, *Oryzopsis hymenoides, Zea,* Cucurbitaceae, and Portulacaceae.

Corn samples are presently undergoing analysis by Dr. Hugh C. Cutler, Missouri Botanical Garden. Tentative results show that corn from the secondary occupation of Guadalupe Pueblo tends to have more rows of grains and larger ears than that beloging to the initial occupation. Analysis of tree-ring samples by Dr. William Robinson, University of Arizona Tree-ring Laboratory, indicates *Pinus ponderosa* and *Pinus edulis* were the most commonly used timbers. Other species identified include *Pseudotsuga taxifolia, Juniperus* sp., and *Populus fremontii.*

Summary and Conclusions

Completed excavations and in-progress analyses indicate Guadalupe Pueblo was a dual occupation site. The initial occupation was by immigrants from the Chaco Canyon area probably sometime between A.D. 900 and 1130. The initial community of Guadalupe Pueblo was marked by large symmetrically arranged rooms, core and veneer masonry walls, large T-shaped doorways, basalt-cobble wall foundations, and ceramics principally belonging to the Cibola series.

The remains of this initial occupation were later greatly disturbed by the secondary occupants of Guadalupe Pueblo. This secondary occupation probably occurred between A.D. 1264 and 1300. During this time the initial configuration of Guadalupe Pueblo was modified through the asymmetrical addition of new but smaller rooms, subdivisions of existing rooms, construction of jacal walls, and eradication of some existing structures. A later remodeling by this occupation is indicated by superimposed floors and modified features.

Studies of present vegetation and its palynological representation are completed and will aid studies of paleoenvironments now being conducted. Pollen, botanical, and zoological analyses show significant progress and will aid interpretations of prehistoric man's adaptation to his environment. Four of the original five research objectives will be met through current studies. The fifth objective, evaluation of the social influence exhibited by the intrusive Chacoan population, will be met following the completion of the Puerco River Valley Project.

REFERENCES

ADAM, DAVID P., AND MEHRINGER, PETER J., JR.

1975. Modern pollen surface samples: An analysis of subsamples. U.S. Geol. Surv. Journ. Res., vol. 3, no. 6, pp. 733–736.

BENNETT, M. A.

1974. Basic ceramic analysis. San Juan Valley Arch. Proj. Techn. Ser. no. 1, East. New Mexico Univ. Contr. Anthrop., vol. 6, no. 1, 164 pp.

BICE, R. A., AND SUNDT, W. M.

1972. Prieta Vista: A small Pueblo III ruin in north-central New Mexico, 216 pp. Albuquerque Archaeological Society, Albuquerque.

BRADLEY, Z. A.

1971. Site Bc 236, Chaco Canyon National Monument, New Mexico, 127 pp. National Park Service, Division of Archeology.

BRAND, DONALD D., et al.

1937. Tseh So, a small house ruin, Chaco Canyon, New Mexico. Univ. New Mexico Bull., Anthrop. Ser., vol. 2, 174 pp.

DAVIS, EMMA LOU, AND WINKLER, JAMES H.

1959. A late Mesa Verde site in the Rio Puerco Valley. El Palacio, vol. 66, no. 3, pp. 92–100.

DICKSON, D. BRUCE

1973. Settlement pattern stability and change in the pueblo culture of the middle northern Rio Grande area, New Mexico. Ph.D. dissertation, University of Arizona.

1975. Settlement pattern stability and change in the middle northern Rio Grande Region, New Mexico: A test of some hypotheses. Amer. Antiq., vol. 40, no. 22, pp. 159–171.

DI PESO, CHARLES C.
1968. Casas Grandes and the Gran Chichimeca. El Palacio, vol. 75, no. 4, pp. 45–61.
DUTTON, BERTHA P.
1953. Galisteo Basin again scene of archaeological research. El Palacio, vol. 60, no. 10, pp. 339–351.
1964. Las Madres in the light of Anasazi migrations. Amer. Antiq., vol. 29, no. 4, pp. 449–454.
1966. Prehistoric migrations into the Galisteo Basin, New Mexico. Proc. 36th Int. Congr. Americanists, vol. 1, pp. 287–300.
ELLIS, FLORENCE H.
1967. Where did the Pueblo people come from? El Palacio, vol 74, no. 3, pp. 35–43.
1974. Archaeologic and ethnologic data pertaining to Acoma and Laguna land claims, 1958–59. Pp. 9–330 *in* "Pueblo Indians II," D. A. Horr, ed. Garland Publishing Co., Inc., New York.
1975. Life in the Tesuque Valley and elsewhere in the Santa Fe area during the Pueblo II stage of development. Awanyu, vol. 3, no. 2, pp. 27–49.
FERDON, E. N., AND REED, E. K.
1950. A pit-house site near Belen, New Mexico. El Palacio, vol. 57, no. 2, pp. 40–41.
FINLEY, ROBERT B., JR.
1958. The woodrats of Colorado: distribution and ecology. Univ. Kansas Publ. Nat. Hist., vol. 10, pp. 213–552.
FORD, RICHARD I.; SCHROEDER, A. H.; AND PECKHAM, S. L.
1972. Three perspectives on Puebloan prehistory. Pp. 19–39 *in* "New Perspectives on the Pueblos," A. Ortiz ed. University of New Mexico Press, Albuquerque.
FREEMAN, CHARLES E.
1972. Pollen study of some Holocene alluvial deposits in Dona Ana County, southern New Mexico. Texas Journ. Sci., vol. 24, no. 2, pp. 203–220.
FRITZ, V. D.
1972. Settlement patterns in the Salado Canyon, New Mexico: Pueblo I–III (850–1350 A.D.), 103 pp. Master's thesis, Eastern New Mexico University.
GREBINGER, PAUL
1973. Prehistoric social organization in Chaco Canyon, New Mexico: an alternative reconstruction. The Kiva, vol. 39, no. 1, pp. 3–23.
GUTHE, CARL E.
1917. The pueblo ruin at Rowe, New Mexico. El Palacio, vol. 4, no. 4, pp. 33–39.
HAWLEY, F. M.
1934. The significance of the dated prehistory of Chetro Ketl. Univ. New Mexico Monogr. no. 2, 80 pp.
HEVLY, R. H.
1964. Pollen analysis of Quaternary, archaeological and lacustrine sediments from the Colorado Plateau. Ph.D. dissertation, University of Arizona.

HIBBEN, FRANK C.
1936. The excavation of a pre-Biscuit ware ruin in the Chama Valley. El Palacio, vol. 41, nos. 8, 9, 10, pp. 48–53.
1937. Excavation of the Riana Ruin and Chama Valley survey. Univ. New Mexico Bull., Antrop. Ser., vol. 2, no. 1, 60 pp.

HOLDEN, JANE
1955. A preliminary report on Arrowhead Ruin. El Palacio, vol. 62, no. 4, pp. 102–119.

HUNT, CHARLES B.
1936. Geology and fuel resources of the southern part of the San Juan Basin, New Mexico, pt. 2: The Mount Taylor coal field. U. S. Geol. Surv. Bull. 860-B, pp. 31–80, illus.

IRWIN-WILLIAMS, CYNTHIA, ed.
1972. The structure of Chacoan society in the northern Southwest: investigations at the Salmon site—1972. East. New Mexico Univ. Contr. Anthr., vol. 4, no. 3, 60 pp.
____. The structure of Chacoan society in the northern Southwest: II (in press).

IRWIN-WILLIAMS, CYNTHIA, AND PIPPIN, LONNIE C.
____. Introduction to lithic analysis. San Juan Valley Archaeological Project Technical Series, East. New Mexico Univ. Contr. Anthrop. (in press).

JEANCON, J. A.
1929. Archeological investigations in the Taos Valley, New Mexico, during 1920. Smithsonian Misc. Coll., vol. 81, no. 12, 29 pp.

JEANCON, J. A., AND ROBERTS, FRANK H. H., JR.
1924. Further archaeological research in the northeastern San Juan Basin of Colorado, during the summer of 1922. Colorado Mag., vol. 1, nos. 3–6, pp. 108–118, 163–173, 213–224, 261–276.

JOHNSON, D. W.
1907. Volcanic necks of the Mount Taylor region, New Mexico. Bull. Geol. Soc. Amer., vol. 18, pp. 303–324.

JUDD, NEIL M.
1954. The material culture of Pueblo Bonito. Smithsonian Misc. Coll., vol. 124, 398 pp.
1959. Pueblo del Arroyo, Chaco Canyon, New Mexico. Smithsonian Misc. Coll., vol. 147, no. 7, 222 pp.
1964. The architecture of Pueblo Bonito. Smithsonian Misc. Coll., vol. 174, no. 1, 349 pp.

JUDGE, W. J.
1973. The University of New Mexico 1973 season field session in archaeology. Awanyu, vol. 1, no. 4, pp. 19–21.

KIDDER, ALFRED V.
1926. Early Pecos ruins on the Forked Lightning Ranch. El Palacio, vol. 21, no. 10, pp. 272–283.

KLUCKHOHN, CLYDE, AND REITER, PAUL, Eds.
1939. Preliminary report on the 1937 excavations, BC 50–51, Chaco Canyon, New Mexico. Univ. New Mexico Bull., Anthrop. Ser., vol. 3, no. 2, 190 pp.

MARTIN, PAUL S.

1963. The last 10,000 years: a fossil pollen record of the American Southwest, 87 pp. University of Arizona Press, Tucson.

MARTIN, PAUL S.; ROYS, L.; AND VON BONIN, B.

1936. Lowry Ruin in southwestern Colorado. Field Mus. Nat. Hist., Anthrop. Ser., vol. 23, no. 1, 216 pp.

MEHRINGER, PETER J., JR.

1967. Pollen analysis of the Tule Springs area, Nevada. Pp. 130–200 *in* "Pleistocene Studies in Southern Nevada," H. M. Wornington and D. Ellis, eds. Nevada State Museum Anthrop. Pap., no. 13.

MEHRINGER, PETER J., JR., AND HAYNES, C. VANCE, JR.

1965. The pollen evidence for the environment of early man and extinct mammals at the Lehner Mammoth site, southeastern Arizona. Amer. Antiq., vol. 31, no. 1, pp. 17–23.

MEHRINGER, PETER J., JR.; MARTIN, PAUL S.; AND HAYNES, C. VANCE, JR.

1967. Murray Springs, a mid-postglacial pollen record from southern Arizona. Amer. Journ. Sci., vol. 256, pp. 786–797.

MERA, H. P.

1935. Ceramic clues to the prehistory of north central New Mexico. Lab. Anthrop. Techn. Ser. Bull. 8, 43 pp.

MORRIS, EARL H.

1919. The Aztec ruin. Amer. Mus. Nat. Hist. Anthrop. Pap., vol. 26, no. 1, pp. 7–108.

1921. The house of the great kiva at the Aztec Ruin. Amer. Mus. Nat. Hist. Anthrop. Pap., vol. 26, no. 2, pp. 113–138.

1928. Notes on excavations in the Aztec Ruin. Amer. Mus. Nat. Hist. Anthrop. Pap., vol. 26, no. 5, pp. 261–420.

1939. Archaeological studies in the La Plata District, southwestern Colorado and northwestern New Mexico, 298 pp. Carnegie Institution of Washington.

PIPPIN, LONNIE C.

1973. Excavations at the Salmon ruin. Pp. 15–25 *in* "The Structure of Chacoan Society in the Northern Southwest," C. Irwin-Williams, ed., Eastern New Mexico Univ. Contr. Anthr., vol. 4, no. 3.

PLOG, FRED T.

1974. The study of prehistoric change, 199 pp. Academic Press, New York.

RANDS, ROBERT L.

1974. Laguna land utilization. Pp. 205–396 *in* "Pueblo Indians, IV," D. A. Horr, ed. Garland Publishing Co., Inc., New York.

RENICK, B. C.

1931. Geology and ground-water resources of western Sandoval Country, New Mexico, U.S. Geol. Surv. Water-Supply Pap. 620, 117 pp.

ROBERTS, FRANK H. H., JR.

1932. The village of the Great Kivas on the Zuni Reservation, New Mexico. Bur. Amer. Ethnol. Bull. 111, 197 pp.

RUPPE, REYNOLD J., JR.

1953. The Acoma culture province: an archaeological concept. Ph.D. dissertation, Harvard University.

RUPPE, R. J., JR., and DITTERT, A. E., JR.
1952. The archaeology of Cebolleta Mesa AND Acoma Pueblo: a preliminary report based on further investigation. El Palacio, vol. 52, no. 7, pp. 191–217.
SCHOENWETTER, JAMES
1962. The pollen analysis of eighteen archaeological sites in Arizona and New Mexico. Pp. 168–209 *in* "Chapters in the Prehistory of Eastern Arizona, I," P.S. Martin et al. Fieldiana, Anthrop. 53.
1964. The palynological research. Pp. 63–118 *in* "Alluvian and Palynological Reconstruction of Environments, Navajo Reservoir District," J. Schoenwetter and F. W. Eddy. Mus. New Mexico Pap. Anthr., no. 13.
1966. A re-evaluation of the Navajo Reservoir pollen chronology. El Palacio, vol. 73, no. 1, pp. 19–26.
1970. Archaeological pollen studies of the Colorado Plateau. Amer. Antiq. vol. 35, no. 1, pp. 35–48.
SCHOENWETTER, JAMES, AND DITTERT, A. E., JR.
1968. An ecological interpretation of Anasazi settlement patterns. Pp. 41–66 *in* "Anthropological Archeology in the Americas," Betty J. Meggers, ed. Anthropological Society of Washington, Washington, D.C.
SCHROEDER, ALBERT H.
1966. Pattern diffusion from Mexico into the Southwest after A.D. 600. Amer. Antiq., vol. 31, no. 5, pp. 683–704.
SEARS, J. D.; HUNT, C. B.; and HENDRICKS, T. A.
1941. Transgressive and regressive Cretaceous deposits of the southern San Juan Basin, New Mexico. U.S. Geol. Surv. Prof. Pap. 193-F, pp. 110–121.
STONES, ROBERT C., and HAYWARD, C. L.
1968. Natural history of the desert woodrat, *Neotoma lepida.* Amer. Midl. Nat., vol. 80, pp. 458–476.
STUBBS, S. A., AND STALLINGS, W. S., JR.
1953. The excavation of Pindi Pueblo. Lab. Anthrop., Sante Fe, School of Amer. Res. Monogr. 18, 165 pp.
TICHY, M. F.
1949. Ancient burial near Sante Fe's Public Welfare Building. El Palacio, vol. 56, no. 3, pp. 80–81.
VAN DEVENDER, T. R.
1973. Late Pleistocene plants and animals of the Sonoran Desert: a survey of ancient packrat middens in southwestern Arizona, 179 pp. Ph. D. dissertation, University of Arizona, Tucson.
VIVIAN, GORDON
1965. The Three-C Site: an early Pueblo II ruin in Chaco Canyon, New Mexico. Univ. New Mexico Publ. Anthrop., no. 13, 48 pp.
VIVIAN, GORDON, AND MATHEWS, T. C.
1965. Kin Kletso, a Pueblo III community in Chaco Canyon, New Mexico. Southw. Monum. Assoc. Techn. Ser., vol. 6, no. 1, pp. 1–115.
VIVIAN, R. G.
1970. Aspects of prehistoric society in Chaco Canyon, New Mexico, 313 pp. Ph.D. dissertation, University of Arizona, Tucson.

WASHBURN, DOROTHY KOSTER
1972. An analysis of the spatial aspects of the site locations of Pueblo I–III sites along the middle Rio Puerco, New Mexico, 262 pp. Ph.D. dissertation, Columbia University, New York.
1974. Nearest neighbor analysis of Pueblo I–III settlement patterns along the Rio Puerco of the east, New Mexico. Amer. Antiq. vol. 39, no. 2, pp. 315–335.
WENDORF, FRED, AND REED, E. K.
1955. An alternative reconstruction of northern Rio Grande prehistory. El Palacio, vol. 62, nos. 5–6, pp. 131–173.
WETHERINGTON, RONALD K.
1968. Excavations at Pot Creek Pueblo. Fort Burgwin Res. Cent. Monogr. no. 6, 104 pp.
WORMAN, F. C. V.
1953. A report on the cache of obsidian artifacts from the Pajarito Plateau, El Palacio, vol. 60, no. 1, pp. 12–15.
ZUBROW, E. B. W.
1971. Carrying capacity and dynamic equilibrium in the prehistoric Southwest. Amer. Antiq., vol. 36, no. 2, pp. 127–138.

CYNTHIA IRWIN-WILLIAMS
LONNIE C. PIPPIN

Conservation of the Kyrenia Ship, 1970–71

Principal Investigator: Michael L. Katzev, Oberlin College,[1] Oberlin, Ohio.

Grant No. 875: In support of research on conservation of the shipwreck near Kyrenia, Cyprus.

A Greek merchant ship of the 4th century B.C. was dismantled and lifted from the sea bottom off Kyrenia, Cyprus, in autumn 1969. This brought to a conclusion the University of Pennsylvania Museum's 3-year campaign of survey and excavation on the site. Following directly upon it, Oberlin College undertook the second phase of this archeological project—to preserve the original timbers of the Greek ship, so that she could be reassembled for exhibition, and to consolidate the merchantman's cargo for museum display.

The most challenging problem before us was how best to conserve the ship's timbers, waterlogged for more than 2,200 years. Approximately two-thirds of the original hull remained; but its state of cellular breakdown was such that if left to dry normally the water loss would cause the wood to shrink and distort, making eventual reconstruction of the ship impossible. Hence, some method had to be found for treating the wood so that, upon drying, its dimensions would not be altered. To permit time for experiments toward this end, the disassembled timbers were kept constantly wet. Most of the merchantman—its ribs, outer planks, and keel—was placed in a

[1] With the very kind permission and support of the Department of Antiquities of the Republic of Cyprus, the conservation of the Kyrenia ship was begun in 1970 under the auspices of Oberlin College. In addition to that institution's sponsorship, financial aid was received from the National Endowment for the Humanities, the Cyprus Mines Corporation, the National Geographic Society, the John Brown Cook Foundation, the Louise Taft Semple Foundation, the Dietrich Foundation, and the Ford Foundation through a grant administered by the University of Pennsylvania Museum. The Cyprus Mines Corporation also continued to render considerable aid through its facilities on the island; the United States ambassador to Cyprus, David H. Popper, and his staff frequently provided needed assistance to the project; and Avo Mangoian, a professional photographer in Nicosia, graciously helped us in a multitude of ways. Furthermore, an expression of gratitude is extended to our personnel, to whom the accomplishments here reported are directly accountable.

20- × 40-foot concrete tank of fresh water (fig. 1) inside the Crusader Castle at Kyrenia. More delicate items such as the ship's thin flooring boards, mast step, and rigging members remained in five shallow storage tanks at the expedition house. To protect the wood from bacterial attack, the Dow Chemical Co. donated its fungicide "Dowicide A," which was added afresh at each monthly draining and cleaning of the storage tanks. This "holding action" in fresh water served not only to protect the timbers but also to leach out accumulated salts and bottom silt.

With the wood in safe storage, expedition architect Miss Laina Wylde set about a 10-month project of measuring and describing each of the timbers. Her catalogue will serve as the primary guide in the ship's reassembly. At the same time conservator Miss Frances Talbot and assistant director Robin Piercy began experiments in conserving the wood through immersion in a solution of polyethylene glycol (PEG), a water-soluble waxlike compound. This method, the most widely published and successful treatment for preserving waterlogged wood, promised also to be the least expensive. In theory, if the wood could be made to absorb a sufficient amount of the polyethylene glycol, then this wax, upon drying, would bulk the wood's cells and prevent them from collapsing. From October 1969 to June 1970 selected samples from the Kyrenia ship were immersed in solutions of PEG in a program of experiments that varied these factors: the molecular weight of PEG (1,000 to 4,000), the concentration of the solution (30 to 100 percent), temperature of the solution (20° to 80°C.), and the time of immersion (6 weeks to 6 months).

The first results were discouraging. After treatment and upon drying the wood failed to retain dimensional stability under the procedure recommended by consultants from the U.S. Forest Products Laboratory, where the major research in PEG treatment of wood has been carried out in this country. The Kyrenia timbers, more than 22 centuries old, riddled with the shells of marine borers, carrying heavy accumulations of sea silt, and in an advanced state of cellular breakdown, obviously posed problems in the absorption of PEG not yet encountered by the U.S. scientists. They had advised using PEG 1,500 and increasing the concentration to 30 percent. Miss Talbot began to increase the concentration markedly and thereby obtained more encouraging results. By June 1970 she and Mr. Piercy had also found that by using PEG 4,000 the successful treatment for all the Kyrenia timbers could be assured.

Before we started to process the ship's timbers some basic questions remained to be answered: How might we best implement our small-scale test findings to treat 3.5 cubic meters of wood? How would we approach reassembling the ship once treatment was finished? And had recent research in

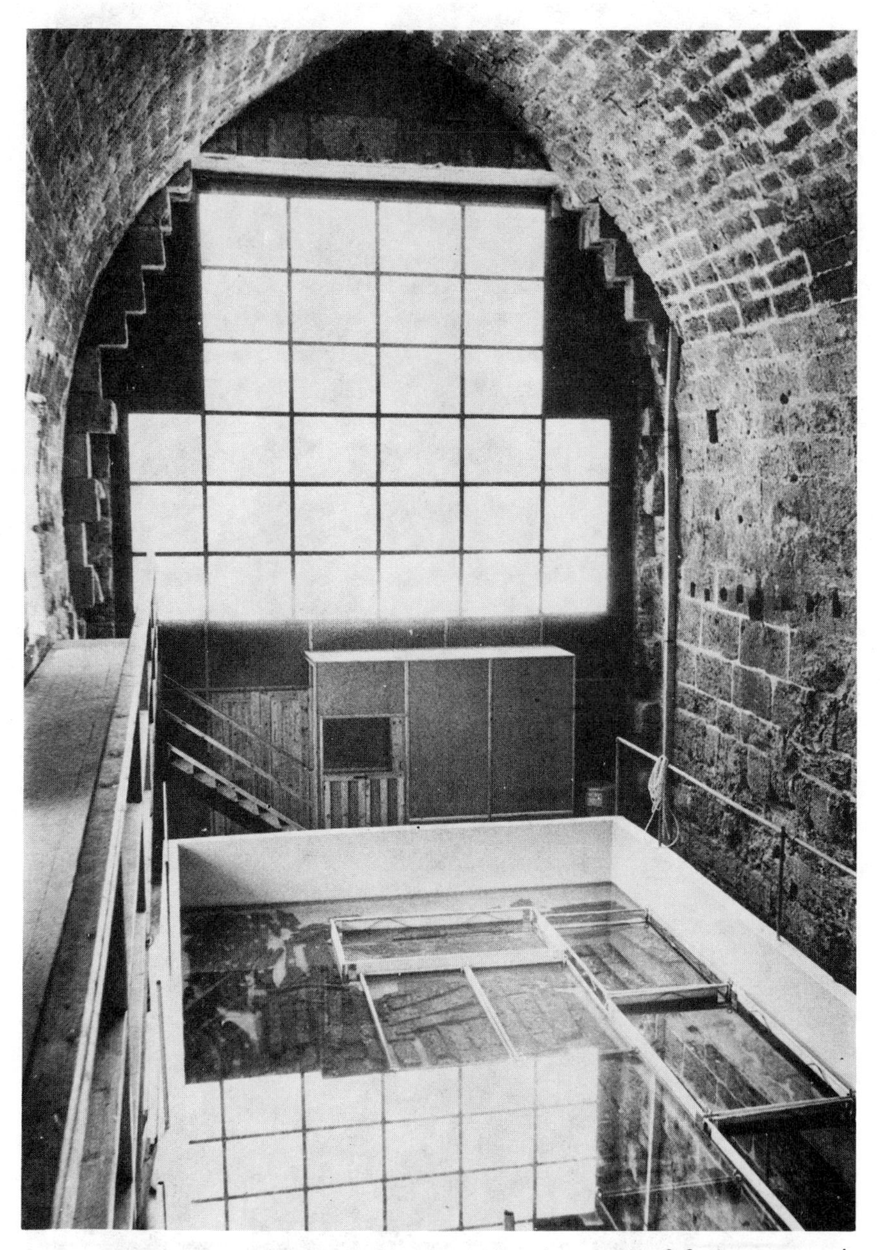

FIG. 1. In Kyrenia Castle trays of ship's timbers in a tank of fresh water await preservation.

FIG. 2. One of two large immersion tanks built within the Ship Gallery in Kyrenia Castle to treat the major portion of the hull.

wood conservation provided any yet unpublished methods that would be better suited to preserving the Kyrenia wood? Early in June Mr. Katzev attended the International Institute for Conservation's New York Conference on the Conservation of Stone and Wooden Objects. It was then opportune to inspect at first hand those laboratories and museums most actively at work on ship preservation and display. Hence, in late June and early July Miss Talbot, Mr. Katzev (funded by a H. H. Powers Travel Grant from Oberlin College), and Mrs. Katzev visited the Central Research Laboratory for Objects of Art and Science in Amsterdam, the British Museum Research Laboratory in London, the Norsk Sjöfartsmuseum in Oslo, the Vasa Museum in Stockholm, and the Research Laboratory of the Swiss National Museum in Zurich. We learned of experiments in such new processes as freeze-drying, radiation polymerization, and resin treatment. In each case, however, the technique proved either too risky or far too expensive for large-scale application. The experimenters were unanimous in advising us to proceed with the PEG method. During our interviews Miss Talbot particularly gained valuable advice on the final surface treatment of PEG-treated timbers. A cause of much concern to us had been the very waxy surface and black color of the Kyrenia test pieces. Safe methods were outlined for cleaning and then surface bleaching the timbers back to their pretreatment appearance.

Our questions on the mechanics of large-scale treatment were best answered at the laboratory of the Danish National Museum in Brede, where five Viking ships of the 10th century A.D., comparable in size to the Kyrenia ship, are being treated by PEG immersion. Here appropriate processing tanks were examined as models for building our own tanks from local materials on Cyprus. Of especial interest was the opportunity to see one of these ships being reassembled in the new museum that the Danes have built to house the vessels near their find spot in Roskilde Fjord. Methods being used there to reshape, join, scaffold, and exhibit these PEG-treated ships offered us excellent guidelines for the 1972–73 reconstruction work at Kyrenia. The value of making 1:1 tracings of every piece of wood prior to treatment was also made clear by the Danish example. Laborious as this may seem, such tracings are an instant check on a given timber's dimensions after treatment. More importantly, the drawings serve as keys for reshaping back to original curvature the ship's flattened outer planking.

On return to Kyrenia in mid-July Miss Talbot placed into treatment a small group of the ship's floor timbers to serve as a final check on her method. The schedule called for immersion in PEG 4,000 and gradually increasing the solution from 30 to 90 percent concentration at a constant temperature of 60 °C. over a period of 6 months. The excellent rate of PEG absorption in these final tests signaled that the time for full-scale treatment was at hand. Mr. Piercy and a local blacksmith meanwhile had constructed two large immersion tanks (fig. 2) that would serve for processing the bulk of the ship's wood in Kyrenia Castle. At the time of this writing these tanks are fully operational. Contained in them are the ship's keel, ribs, and the thickest of the planking—the outer wales. They form the first of two treatment cycles that will be required to process all the timbers. It was decided to treat these heaviest members first, since they will in turn require the longest drying period. By the time the second and final batch of timbers comes out of treatment, the keel and ribs should be totally dry and ready to serve as the skeleton in the ship's reassembly.

Before its treatment each piece is given a final cleaning (fig. 3), then drawn to full scale, placed on a shelving rack, and lowered into the treatment tank. This process of loading a single 3- × 1- × 1-meter tank takes approximately four weeks. The drafting system involves laying the timber on a flat surface, then setting over it a plexiglas "drawing board." The plastic film Melinex is spread over the plexiglas, and on it with sharp crayon pencils are drawn in varying color codes the timber's outline and surface details such as nails, dowels, notches, and mortises and tenons. Since the Melinex is transparent, the person drafting can align his eye, the crayon point, and the reflected image of his eye on the Melinex in constant position over the edge he is drawing.

As noted earlier, these drawings will serve beyond being a check for shrinkage and distortion. The ship's planking is soft and worm-riddled. Since the hull was dismantled, the planks have settled out of their curvature, and they will emerge from treatment further flattened. Fortunately, the PEG process allows for such waxen timbers to be softened by heat and reshaped to their original contours. In so doing, the Melinex drawings are of considerable help. From them "dummies" of the planks can be cut from flexible composition board. Then once the ship's skeleton of keel and ribs is fixed in reassembled position, the "dummy" planks may be flexed to recreate the original curvature against the ribs. With these properly contoured "dummies" used as a guide, the original planks, bulked with wax, may be heated and reformed to their original shape.

Paralleling the treatment process at Kyrenia Castle is a similar program to deal with the wood kept in our expedition house. Five smaller treatment units are in operation there, and an extension of the expedition's lease on the building now guarantees that all the wood stored in the house can be processed there, thus obviating the danger of transporting these fragile pieces to the Castle for preservation.

1970 saw a most fruitful cooperation between ourselves and the Cyprus Department of Antiquities toward educational use of the ship material. Following the opening of a temporary museum (fig. 4) to display selected

FIG. 3. A portion of the ship's keel receives its final cleaning before going into bath of polyethylene glycol for six months.

FIG. 4. Small exhibition room opened in 1970 by the Cyprus Department of Antiquities to display segments of the ship's cargo and cabin wares.

finds from the ship, the number of visitors to Kyrenia Castle increased by more than 60 percent over the preceding year. In fact, among the island's historic monuments the Castle is now second in popularity, headed only by the Roman city of Salamis. Restoration work by the Department of Antiquities on the vaulted gallery in which the ship's timbers are housed has contributed to this interest. Now, from a mezzanine balcony visitors may view the wood in its holding tank and observe the drawing and conservation work below. The Department has pledged further restoration work. In January they began vaulting, flooring, and tuck-pointing two additional large galleries adjacent to the ship room. These will become the principal exhibition rooms for the ship's cargo and will feature a small theater for scheduled showings of the excavation story through slides or film.

During the summer the Antiquities Department made available the courtyard of Kyrenia Castle for the Cyprus "premier" of the expedition film "Antiquity from the Sea." The event, sponsored by the United States Information Service with the permission of the National Geographic Society, was expected to draw an audience of approximately 1,000. Over 2,500 Cypriots and tourists attended, most of them standing through the 60-minute presentation. Because of this interest, I was asked to narrate a second showing in Nicosia to an audience numbering about 2,000, and, in cooperation with the Cyprus Broadcasting Corporation, "Antiquity from the Sea" was aired on television in September with narration in Greek. It should be mentioned in this regard that the 16-millimeter film was made by camerman Bob Dunn and the Lecture Department of the National Geographic Society. The Society officially premiered it last March at Constitution Hall, in Washington, D.C. Means are now being sought to gain education distribution of the film in this country.

During the year, whenever time and weather permitted, the expedition staff made dives on the wreck site to raise the "dump" material that had been set aside during our seasons of excavation. From the recovery, to date (1971), of approximately two-thirds of these discarded sherds, several welcome additions to the ship's amphorae and plain-ware pottery came to light. Miss Talbot virtually finished her conservation of the small finds and has begun to restore from hundreds of fragments a sizable portion of the ship's lead sheathing for exhibition.

Considerable progress was made toward final publication of the Kyrenia material, for which the Clarendon Press has invited a manuscript. Photographic coverage of the 404 amphorae, which were the vessel's principal cargo, was completed. Also, the many examples of cabin pottery that had been mended from sherd material over the previous winter were catalogued, drawn, and photographed. All epigraphical evidence in the form of coins, graffiti, stamped amphora handles, and mason's marks on the millstones was photographed for publication. Unfortunately time did not permit us to complete the photographic catalogue of the grain-mill blocks and many of the smaller finds or restoration of the iron objects recovered from the excavation. These tasks remained to be undertaken the following summer.

With the formidable task of inventorying the ship's timbers accomplished, Miss Wylde was able to draft the final site plans and two restored sections of the ship's hull. Study of her preliminary drawings over the winter raised the distinct possibility that the Kyrenia ship carried some form of fore-and-aft sail, rather than the square rig so long associated with the Greek world. The forward location of the mast step strongly suggests the use of a sprit or lateen rig. If this hypothesis is correct, we would have in the Kyrenia ship evidence for an unexpected advance in sailing technology by the ancient Greeks.

In conclusion, the 1970–71 season at Kyrenia saw the problems of conserving the ship's timbers answered and the final treatment set well under way. To the staff at Kyrenia—Miss Talbot, Miss Wylde, and Mr. Piercy—go my deepest thanks for their patient and inventive skills, which have brought about this achievement. To our sponsors we all extend our most sincere gratitude for their conviction that the Kyrenia ship merits this effort. With a very great sense of relief and enthusiasm I am able to report that the timbers of the Kyrenia ship will be preserved and ready for reconstruction by the summer of 1972.

REFERENCES

KATZEV, MICHAEL L.

1970. Resurrecting the oldest known Greek ship. Nat. Geogr. Mag., vol. 137, no. 6 (June), pp. 840–857, illus.

1973. Resurrecting a Greek ship 2,300 years old. Pp. 35–40 *in* "Men, Ships, and the Sea," by Alan Villiers, 436 pp., illus. National Geographic Society, Washington, D.C.

1974. Cyprus underwater archeological search, 1967. Nat. Geogr. Soc. Res. Rpts., 1967 Projects, pp. 177–184, illus.

1978. Cyprus underwater archeological search, 1968. Nat. Geogr. Soc. Res. Rpts., 1968 Projects, pp. 178–188, illus.

1977. Cyprus underwater archeological research, 1969. Nat. Geogr. Soc. Res. Rpts., 1969 Projects, pp. 289–306, illus.

KATZEV, MICHAEL L., and KATZEV, SUSAN W.

1974. Last harbor for the oldest ship. Nat. Geogr. Mag., vol. 146, no. 5 (Nov.), pp. 618–625, illus.

MICHAEL L. KATZEV

The Art of the Washo Indians

Principal Investigator: Norval Kern, Trenton State College, Trenton, New Jersey.

Grant No. 859: For field research on the art of the Washo Indians, Nevada and California.

The purpose of this investigation was to present a series of photographs of baskets to Washo informants in an effort to determine verbal meanings of designs employed on baskets and the use and function of the baskets, especially ceremonial use, and also to determine if the designs used were commonly "owned" by the tribe as a whole or by individual families, moieties, or bands.

The utilitarian crafts—basketry, ceramics, and textiles—common throughout the primitive world often reached a high level of proficiency and great beauty in their designs. These designs have often been compatible with, and perhaps grew out of, the techniques. In cultures with highly developed art forms the decorative designs on utilitarian objects were sometimes applied with no other reason, meaning, or function than esthetic pleasure.

It is also true that no culture, however crude it appears on the surface, has not produced an art form. As for the Washo Indians, all evidence points to the fact that their highly developed basketry art was essentially their only form of artistic expression. It is also evident, since Washo basketry is acknowledged to be technically perhaps the finest in the world, that this art form is a result of a long and exacting period of apprenticeship and training that involved the fashioning of tools with which to prepare weaving materials, the knowledge of location, time of gathering, and preparation of the basic materials used in the weaving, and the knowledge of designs.

Since the Washo Indians were a hunter-gatherer group following a seasonal migratory route, the easily carried basket was essential to their culture and was adapted for ceremonial purposes. Enough is known of Washo culture and history to make the motivation and function of the basketry art sufficiently clear; the precise meanings of the designs or what they specifically represent, however, have not been recorded. We know how the objects served to implement the functions that led to their having been created, but we do not have consistent information concerning the content or subject matter, if any, embodied in the designs occurring in the baskets.

The meanings of art forms lie deep in the cultural heritage, but these, unfortunately, because of lack of recorded traditions, are often lost in the shallow cultural context in which they can now be studied. The triangle is a basic form used by the Washo and almost all American Indians. Used alone or with appendages, it generally has meaning associated with it in other Indian tribes. Meanings are often subjective and can vary broadly depending on application. They can even be interpreted with variation within a tribe. However, a general consensus of meaning is generally evident and obtainable among Indian groups.

In an earlier work I (1968) had studied several hundred Washo baskets (variously located at the Smithsonian Institution; the Museum of the American Indian, Heye Foundation; the Nevada State Museum; the Nevada Historical Society; and the Lowie Museum) and had identified 14 isolated design characteristics employed by the Washo Indians (see fig. 1). The Lee collection at the Nevada State Museum was the primary resource, as each item is variously documented in a journal containing date of purchase, Washo artist, provenance, and many interesting anecdotes.

S. A. Barrett (1971) listed 22 names of basketry designs and included illustrations of a number of designs I did not find on the several hundred early Washo baskets examined. He qualified his findings, however, with the statement: "Much more elementary designs appear in the older baskets, indication, as is borne out by the information obtained from the Washo, that many of these elaborate designs are copied from the basketry of other tribes or from trade objects and are used in these baskets to make them more saleable." The names and designs listed in Barrett's paper were not used in determining the Washo design alphabet in this study.

Otis T. Mason (1908) reported meanings of designs on Washo baskets acquired from Abe Cohen, a Nevada dealer in Indian artifacts. According to Cohen, all designs represented some legend of the Washo tribe; some descriptive titles, however, do not bear out this assertion. Mr. Cohen supplied his purchasers with documentation of Washo baskets, including meanings of the designs (see fig. 2). In contrast, Dr. Simon Lee writes in his journal (n. d., unpublished) regarding a basket he had acquired:

> 253. Made by Lena Dick, of Topaz, Mono Co. Cal. Lena is a pure-blooded Washo, 31 years old, married and has one child, a daughter, 9 years old. She says she worked 3 months on this basket with the exception of 3 days only. 18 stitches to the inch.
>
> She and her husband both said that the ornamentation had *no* significance, that it is to "make it pretty" only.
>
> She attended school for four years. Her mother was a skilled basket maker. (3 stick). Price paid $20.00. June 24, 1921.

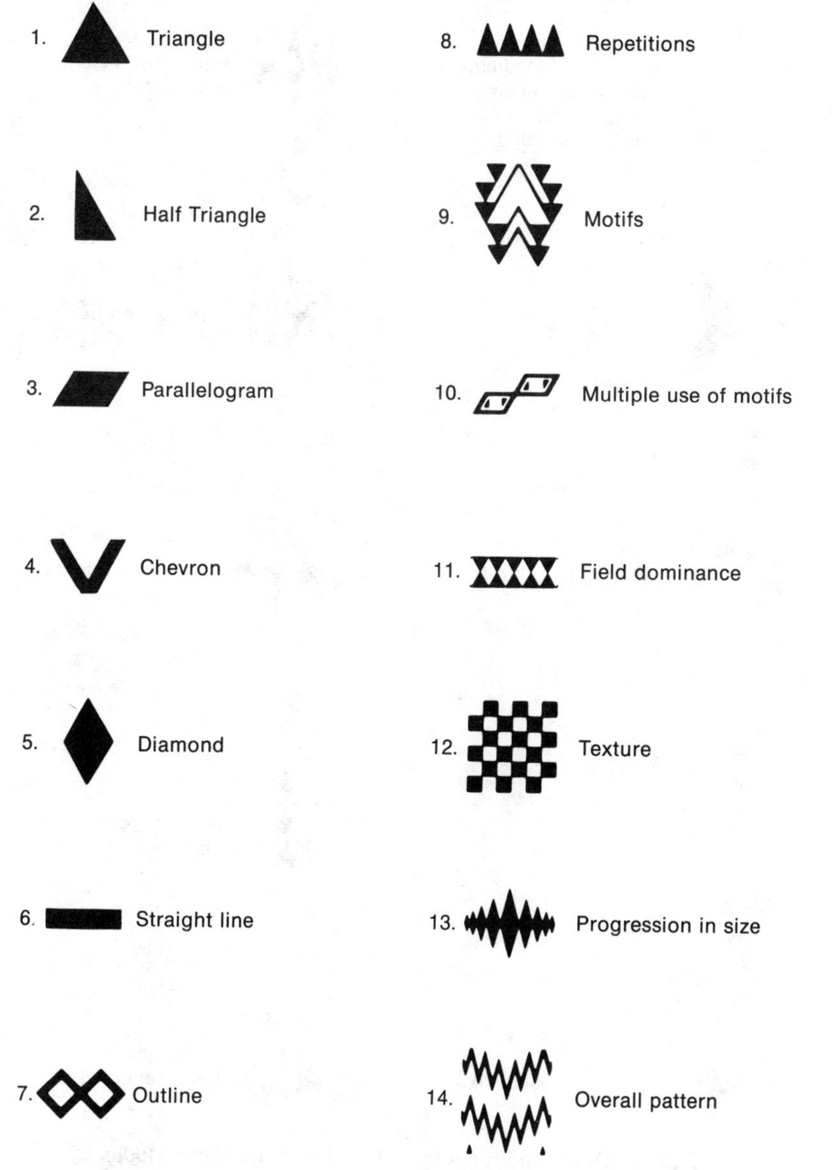

FIG. 1. The Washo design alphabet.

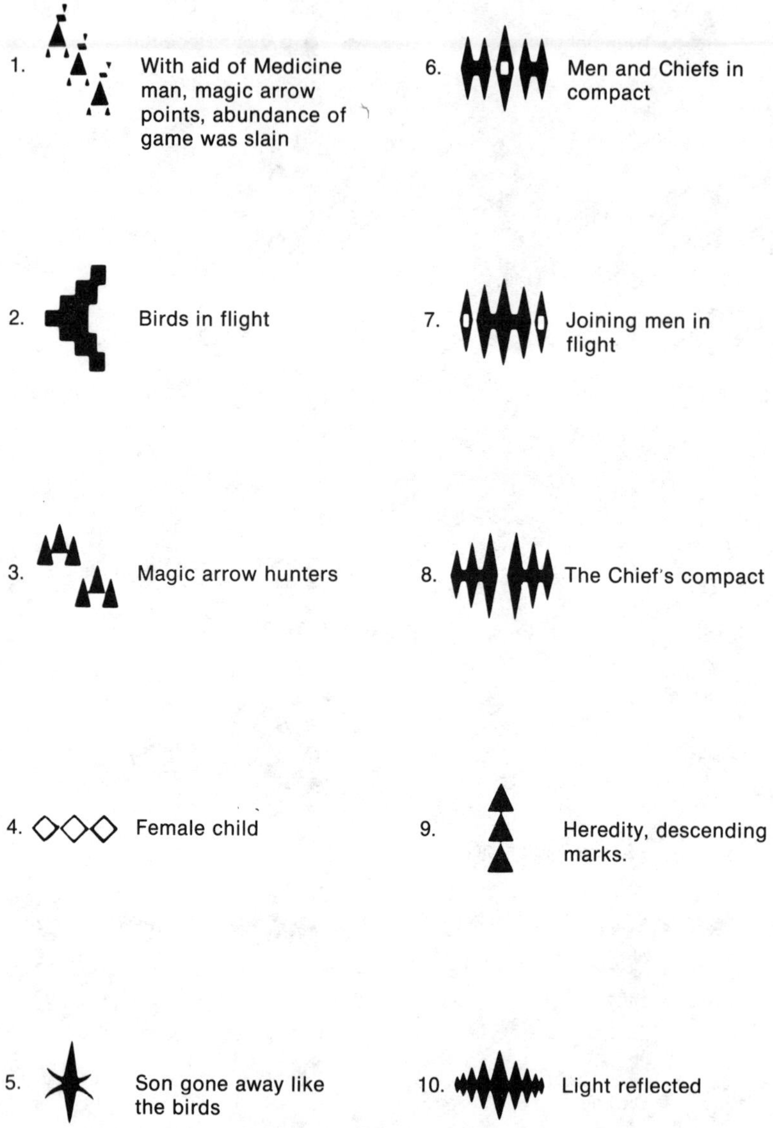

1. 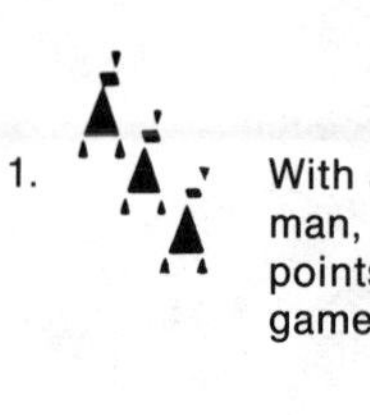 With aid of Medicine man, magic arrow points, abundance of game was slain

2. 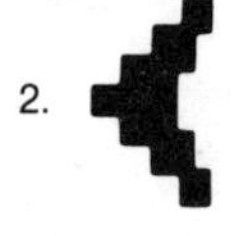 Birds in flight

3. 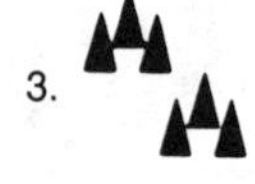 Magic arrow hunters

4.  Female child

5.  Son gone away like the birds

6. Men and Chiefs in compact

7. Joining men in flight

8. The Chief's compact

9. Heredity, descending marks.

10. Light reflected

FIG. 2. Design meanings from A. Cohen, after Mason (1908).

The Museum of the American Indian, Heye Foundation, lists some titles of Washo basketry designs in their collection as ''Quail Design'' or ''Turtles and Trees,'' indications that the designs represented natural forms (fig. 3). Perhaps even abstract designs were associated with natural phenomena.

A Washo birth ceremony involved the preparation of a basket to be used in ritual cleansing of the newborn child. Six baskets were prepared for a puberty ceremony; baskets were used in death ceremonies. Small baskets were used in ''Indian medicine.'' Would such special purpose baskets be somehow unique in form or design?

Six questions were formed to elicit data from informants:

1. What was the meaning of 14 isolated ''design alphabet'' characters used in Washo basketry?
2. What was the meaning of particular, common design arrangements of the ''design alphabet'' characters?
3. Could these design arrangements be associated with particular bands within the tribe, or were they held in common?
4. Did they represent natural phenomena?
5. Were the designs pure abstractions whose possible earlier meaning had been lost?
6. (A major objective of the interviews.) If informants could identify baskets by designs, size, or form, were they made for ceremonial functions and, if so, what factors determine the ceremonial identification?

It should be noted that the great majority of Washo baskets, other than those in the Lee collection at the Nevada State Museum and those obtained from the Nevada dealer, Abe Cohen, are not documented. In the Lee collection only one (fig. 4) is mentioned as being used for a specific ceremony, and even so it was not specially made for that purpose.

Originally I proposed to interview in the Washo territory for 14 days, but the number of informants was larger than I had supposed, and so the time was extended to a total of 21 days, August 8 to 28, 1970. The principal informants were (ages are my estimates, generally supported by other informants): Clara Frank, 90, and Fred Richards, 70, of Dresslerville, Nevada; Elaine Christianson, 35, Belma Jones, 50, and Jessie Wade, 50, of Woodsford, California; John Frank, 95, and Jim Frank, 40, of Carson City, Nevada; and Tom Barber, 85, of Alpine, California. There is a Washo colony at Reno, but I could not identify or locate anyone there with knowledge of basketry. Of the six known Washo who at present sporadically produce baskets, Clara Frank and Jessie Wade were the only persons with work in progress at the time of my visit whom I was able to contact.

I was disappointed to discover a substantial resistance to picture-taking from some of the Washo. Others refused to be tape-recorded. Generally, I was allowed to photograph work and persons and to record our conversations. I managed to take 111 slides and to record approximately 16 hours of conversations (in case of reticence to be taped, this consisted of my summary immediately following the interviews).

The procedure followed was simple and was maintained as consistently as possible with each person. I first secured from the acting Washo Council Chairman Jim Frank and the individual colony chiefs permission to visit members of the tribe. From these men I obtained leads and directions to individual homes. After a social period of becoming acquainted, I explained my purpose in visiting and posed the six questions before looking with informants at the unlabeled 8- × 10-inch photographs of baskets. I also discussed various Washo ceremonies with each of them. The Washo are a warm, friendly people and were anxious to discuss other matters as well. Some were very willing to show me personal collections of baskets; others were reticent and unwilling, denying that they owned any. The following briefly summarizes my findings with respect to each question:

1. The informants consistently denied any meaning at all to the "design alphabet" characters, although they were consistent in agreeing that they were typical of Washo design.

2. The informants attributed meanings to designs by other local tribes but denied that the Washo ever applied verbal meaning to their art work. Several scoffed and laughed at the very idea.

3. It was consistently affirmed that simple designs and complex patterns could be identified by band. While the "design alphabet" was held in common, the manner of use was the property of bands and jealously protected. Informants described anger and disputes occurring should one basketmaker trespass by using designs not the property of her band. These designs could be elaborated with complex patterns and still remain within the bounds of the designs owned by the band. Informants were able to identify a sufficient number of baskets by maker or band to substantiate band-ownerships of designs, even on baskets that had no discernible literal meaning. Time and the small number of informants now available would no doubt preclude any possibility of broadly establishing the band-ownership of designs and motifs of the past.

4. That designs represent natural phenomena was denied. Informants suggested that a design element might be descriptively called an arrowhead. However, it was never intended to represent an arrowhead.

5. That designs are pure abstractions whose possible earlier meaning is lost was agreed to be true. Designs are meaningless and are used to enhance the form, to make the basket beautiful to see, own, and use. Informants could not recall any tradition in the tribe that would in any way assign meaning to any design.

6. Informants denied that a basket could be identified as having been made for a particular ceremonial function, either by design, form, or size, or that any particular qualities were embodied in ceremonial baskets. Most recalled and consistently described the ceremonies and the role of the baskets

FIG. 3. *Top*, coiled basket, height 4 inches, with red and black decoration representing quail design. *Bottom*, coiled basket, height 7 inches, with red and black decoration representing turtle and tree designs. (Photos courtesy Museum of the American Indian, Heye Foundation.)

in them. However, they denied that there was a difference, either in designs or form, between a "treasure basket" made to hold small belongings, a gift basket, or a basket made for its intrinsic value, which could be used for gambling or trade. Function could be determined only by size. Informants agreed that the ceremonial baskets were quite like traditional ordinary baskets except that they were no doubt better made and more elaborate.

A photograph of a basket from the Lee collection (fig. 4) was one used in the interviews; neither the design nor the form drew any special response from informants, except that it was a cooking basket. This would support the Washo contention that Washo ceremonies did not require specifically designed basketry. The small basket (fig. 5), perhaps used in "Indian medicine," also elicited no special response.

There is thus no evidence available to indicate that the geometric Washo designs are the product of a transition from pictographic or realistic forms that graphically conveyed meaning, or that the abstract designs were becoming more representational. If the geometric patterns found on Washo objects used in ceremonial functions perhaps had specific meaning at one point in time, it is disappointing to discover that within the cultural context of the contemporary Washo Indians these meanings, if they ever existed, can no longer be obtained. Like meanings in the art of many ancient cultures they have been left in the past.

The decorative art forms of a specific object from a group generally are in agreement stylistically with the design principles and motifs of the culture as a whole. This is true of the Washo. While great variation exists within the identified work of the tribe, consistencies exist that allow the work to be positively attributed to the Washo. This design vocabulary no doubt stems from deep in the Washo culture heritage, which Davis (1967) indicates may have existed for thousands of years in the same general territory. As meaning disappears, design forms are made to fit the form or surface on which they are applied.

Informants substantiated the use of six baskets prepared specifically for a puberty ceremony, but they denied any specific meaning attributed to the designs used on these specially prepared baskets other than to make them "pretty" for the occasion. A basket was prepared by the mother during the maternity period to be used in a ceremony at the child's birth, and informants denied meaning to the designs used on the special baskets as well.

The informants indicated that the only design with verbal meaning was the abstract design of the hood of a cradle board. This could take various forms but was a series of single linear motifs when intended for a girl, and this was repeated in reverse for a boy, forming diamonds or chevrons.

The Washo have a vocabulary of standard basketry forms. Baskets created for ceremonial purposes, gifts, dances, and "prizes," as well as for purely functional purposes, all fall within the parameters of this vocabulary

FIG. 4. This basket, height 6½ inches, width 11 inches, from the Lee collection in the Nevada State Museum, was thus described by Dr. Lee in his journal:

> "Singa ming." (A small Basket, Washo.) Made by Susie, wife of Washo Johnnie has been in use about 10 years; bought in 1898. About this time tourists commenced buying up the Indian work and in consequence their products greatly increased in value.
>
> Johnnie and Susie had recently lost a young son, Harvey, by death at the Carson Indian School, and this basket had been buried with him; but Susie, no doubt excited through the soaring prices of baskets prevailing, exhumed the one intended to hold food for her departed son on his pilgrimage to the "happy-hunting grounds" and took it to Miss Mary Bray, her patron, and said she would take $3.00 for it, but instructed her never to tell of whom she bought it. I became the possessor.
>
> One day Johnnie came to my office to pawn another basket for $4.00 and at once his eyes lighted upon this mortuary one. He was *wild*, and with blood fairly oozing from his eyes asked, "*where* did you get that basket?" I was so surprised at his conduct that I was at a loss for a proper answer, but upon a repetition of his question I told him I had bought it. He said, "you know when my lillee (little) Harvey died?" I nodded. He continued, "that basket was buried with him. Somebody stole him. I like perty dam well who did it, someday I find out, then I tell you." So I thought best to tell of whom I bought it. Next day he brought Susie in and made her look at it and then turned loose upon her the vials of his wrath—no doubt. As he spoke in his native tongue I lost the force of it, but neither one seemed to so desire the basket as to return my $3.00; so it remained.

of forms. Informants denied that any particular form could be associated solely with a special ceremonial use, with the possible exception of a small basket used in "Indian medicine." This type of basket could be left on the exterior of the dwelling and contain offerings to the spirit world. I presented a photograph of a basket I presumed to have this function, but informants could not comment on the "medicine" use of such a basket, although I observed two similar baskets attached to the exterior of homes. Such baskets are also referred to as gift or trinket baskets.

When Lake Tahoe and the general territory occupied by the Washo became an attraction for tourists and visitors, apparently any "meanings" of basketry designs were made up on the spot for the benefit of the purchaser. The merchandizing of baskets by Abe Cohen in Carson City, especially those of the Washo Indian woman Dot-So-La-Lee, seems to have contributed to the confusion about meanings. One of the informants in this study, a niece of this famous basketmaker, denied any meaning to Dot-So-La-Lee's designs other than to make them salable. In fact, she suggested that Abe Cohen may have made up the meanings, since the Washo attach none to their designs.

Apparently this practice was not very widespread at the time Barrett (1917) investigated the Washo and listed some general terms for design elements. When questioned, informants denied Barrett's earlier statements of meanings, such as "arrowheads"; although they agreed that such a descriptive term might be associated with the triangle, the designs did not represent arrowheads. The terms Barrett obtained from the Washo regarding their basketry designs were purely descriptive, such as "straight line" or "zigzag" and they apparently gave him no further meanings.

It is evident that basketry formed a conspicuous and important position in the lives of the Washo Indians, and, since this is their only art form, it follows that these designs probably were at some point in their cultural history filled with meaning. Since meaning now is completely disavowed by informants, it appears that the significance of their traditional designs stems from other factors.

The aboriginal Washo tribe was divided into "bands," and the remaining Washo are still grouped in this manner to a certain extent. The most significant discovery of this investigation was that these bands, or family groups, "owned" designs and symbols that were used on baskets they produced. This is a phenomena that occurs also among the peoples of Western New Ireland in Melanesia. As with the Washo bands, each New Ireland clan "owned" a number of design forms which were used in creating wooden sculptures for Malagan ceremonies.

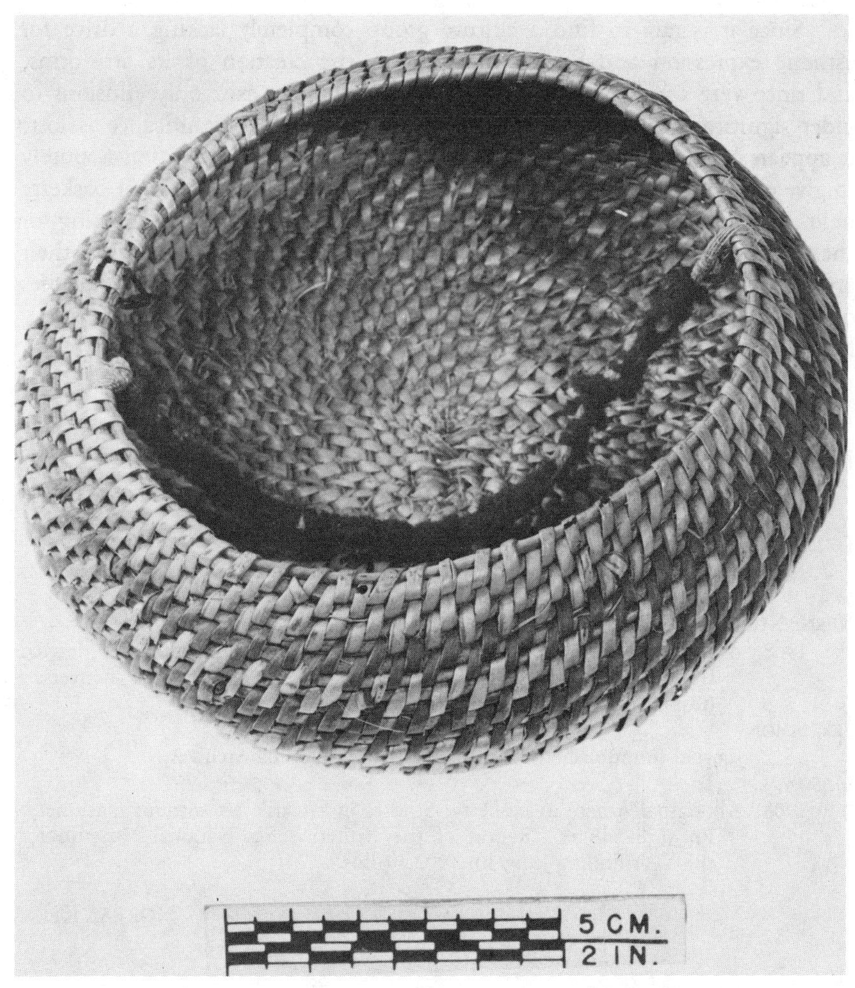

FIG. 5. "Bowl," 5 inches wide. (Photo courtesy Smithsonian Institution.)

The design restriction imposed on a basketmaker limited to "owned" forms often results in a rare degree of creativity and inventiveness in the elaboration of a simple theme, since the "new" designs are by necessity elaborations and innovations of a limited number of traditional motifs and elements. This limitation, a strong factor in the development of the incredible wood sculptures of New Ireland, no doubt was a powerful factor in Washo basketry.

Since it is rare to find a culture group completely lacking a drive for esthetic expression and artistic meaning in the creation of its art forms, and since very ancient art forms can alter until there exist only allusions to older significant meanings, and eventually the original significance is lost, it appears at this point that the meaning of the Washo decoration is purely to give esthetic pleasure. Certainly this is the position regarding their basketry held by the Washo informants, who vehemently deny any meaning of their designs having existed in their traditions and memories. Clearly, their art is an example of a primitive group designing purely for esthetic purposes on their functional and ceremonial artifacts. What once surely had meaning has become art for art's sake.

REFERENCES

Barrett, Samuel A.
1917. The Washo Indians. Bull. Public Mus. Milwaukee, vol. 2, no. 1 (May), pp. 21–22.

Davis, Wilbur A.
1967. Outline of central Sierra archaeological research, 1966–67. University of Nevada, Reno. (Mimeographed.)

Kern, Norval
1968. A presentation of sculpture: A synthesis of a design alphabet derived from the art forms of a primitive people. New York University (unpublished doctoral dissertation).

Lee, Simon
____. Journal (unpublished). State Museum of Nevada Archives.

Mason, Otis T.
1908. Aboriginal American basketry: Studies in a textile art without machinery. Pp. 178–548 *in* "Report of the United States National Museum for the Year Ending June 30, 1902," illus.

Norval Kern

A Comparison of the Spacing Patterns of Polar Bears on Islands and Mainland Coasts in Hudson and James Bays

Principal Investigator: Brian M. Knudsen, University of Manitoba, Winnipeg, Manitoba, Canada.

Grant Nos. 871, 990: For a study of the behavior and ecology of polar bears (*Ursus maritimus*), Northwest Territories, Canada.

Polar bears (*Ursus maritimus*) on North Twin Island in James Bay have been found to space themselves either randomly or uniformly during the summer and fall (Knudsen, 1973, 1976). Differences between populations of mobile animals with respect to their spacing patterns can reflect more complex differences between the biology of the populations (Brown and Orians, 1970). The dispersion of polar bears along 806 miles of coast on western James Bay and Hudson Bay was measured as a preliminary indicator of possible differences between these bears and the bears on North Twin Island.

On October 3 and 5, 1971, two pilots and two observers conducted an aerial census of the above coast in a twin-engined aircraft (DC-3) flying at an altitude of 250 to 300 feet. Throughout the flight, the ground speed (varying between 120 and 140 knots) and time (to the nearest half minute) at which each bear was sighted were noted. Distances between bears were then calculated for all bears sighted along the 806 miles of coast. Distances less than 1 mile were estimated visually to the nearest quarter mile.

A total of 167 bears was seen. Each family was treated as if it were a single bear, for cubs do not wander from the mother. The result was that only 142 points were considered. I simulated a randomly dispersed population of bears along the coastline by utilizing the formula that MacArthur (1957) used to generate his broken-stick model for species abundance, in which a unit length line is broken into random length segments and the length of the rth shortest unit segment is

$$\frac{1}{n} \sum_{i=1}^{r} \frac{1}{(n - i + 1)}$$

where n = the total number of segments. The whole function was multiplied by 806.25 to expand the line from unit length to the exact length of the coastline. The number of segments (*n*) was set at 142.

A computer program was written that carried out the 142 repetitions of the calculation and therefore produced a ranked series of 142 distances to the nearest neighbor for a random dispersion along a line. A comparison of observed and random dispersions was made by ranking the distances to the nearest neighbor for the 142 observed points. The customary logarithmic arrangement (MacArthur, 1960; Preston, 1948) was used, presenting the data in octaves rather than in arithmetic intervals (table 1).

The "0" column of table 1 shows that the bears on this coastline were highly aggregated; there were 57 bears less than one-fourth mile from their nearest neighbor. In a random dispersion only 3 bears would have been that close to their nearest neighbor.

The significance of these groups, which contrast so sharply with the uniformly and randomly dispersed bears on North Twin Island, is still a matter of speculation. The grouping could be a result of the localization of some important factor such as freedom from insects, the presence of kelp or sea ducks as food, cooling from some deep water a short distance offshore, or beaching points for whale or seal carcasses. Alternatively, the groups could have a function independent of location. Relationships could be established in these groups that might influence mating or home range behavior. If these groups are sites where fights occur and dominance hierarchies are established, the latter hypothesis is conceivable. Future observations on the abundance of key resources and the behavior of animals within the groups will clarify the significance of aggregations of bears and will make aerial surveys even more useful in orienting research into the differences between populations of polar bears.

TABLE 1. FREQUENCIES OF DISTANCES TO NEAREST NEIGHBOR FOR AN OBSERVED POPULATION OF POLAR BEARS ON THE JAMES BAY AND HUDSON BAY COASTS AND A RANDOMLY DISPERSED SIMULATED POPULATION.

	Octave (distance to nearest bear in miles)								
	0	¼	½	1	2	4	8	16	32
Observed frequency	57	7	11	18	27.5	12.5	4	4	1
Expected frequency	3	6	8	16	25	34	33	15	2

REFERENCES

BROWN, JERRAM L., and ORIANS, GORDON H.
1970. Spacing patterns in mobile animals. Pp. 239–262 *in* "Annual Review of Ecology and Systematics," vol. 1, Richard F. Johnston, ed. Annual Reviews, Inc., Palo Alto, California.

KNUDSEN, BRIAN M.
1973. The ecology of polar bears on North Twin Island, Northwest Territories, 60 pp. M. A. thesis, University of Montana.
1976. Behavior and ecology of polar bears on North Twin Island, Northwest Territories. Nat. Geogr. Soc. Res. Rpts., 1968 Projects, pp. 199–200.

MACARTHUR, ROBERT H.
1957. On the relative abundance of bird species. Proc. Nat. Acad. Sci., vol. 45, pp. 293–295.
1960. On the relative abundance of species. Amer. Nat., vol. 94, pp. 25–36.

PRESTON, FRANK W.
1948. The commonness, and rarity, of species. Ecology, vol. 29, pp. 254–283.

BRIAN M. KNUDSEN

Distribution and Host-tree Orientation of Bagworm Parasites

Principal Investigator: Herbert M. Kulman, University of Minnesota, St. Paul, Minnesota.

Grant No. 904: In support of a study of the distribution and host-tree orientation of the parasites of the bagworm (*Thyridopteryx ephemeraeformis*).

This research is concerned with the geographical distribution, abundance, and host-tree orientation of parasites of the bagworm *Thyridopteryx ephemeraeformis* (Haworth). Similar information can be simultaneously collected for bagworm fecundity. The bagworm is a common foliage-eating lepidopteran occurring in the eastern half of the United States south of a line from Nebraska to Pennsylvania.

The basic principles being investigated are the influences of geographical location and host-tree species on the fecundity of the bagworms and the parasite complex attacking the bagworms. Because the bagworm overwinters in the egg stage within the old pupal case and most of the parasites or evidence of their previous activity can be found in overwintering cocoons on the trees, collections were made in the fall or winter.

In previous studies (Kulman, 1965; n.d.) it was established that certain parasites attack bagworms only on evergreen or deciduous trees. Differences were also found between tree species in each group. The goal of the study supported by the National Geographic Society was to determine if the relationship holds true for other tree hosts and parasites of the bagworm in other geographical locations.

I completed the field-work part of the study by collecting and rearing parasites from the western edge of the bagworm's range from Nebraska to Texas, and from Louisiana to Illinois, from Ohio to western Florida, and back up the Atlantic coast to Pennsylvania. Collections were made at about 150-mile intervals along all four north-south routes. Whenever possible, collections of 100 bagworms from each of three locations 1 to 10 miles apart were made separately for up to three species of trees. The material was packed in plastic bags and sent to Minnesota and stored at 5 °C. After 90 days (diapause requirement) the bagworm pupal cases were opened. All except the normal egg-bearing pupal cases were placed in separate rearing vials for parasite emergence. Dead pupae and eggs were examined for cause of death. With my large reference collection of bagworm pupae and eggs parasitized by known species, it has been possible to identify many of the previously emerged parasites by a combination of emergence holes, exuvia, and other artifacts. After parasites are identified, the data from these collections will be put on data cards. We have data from about 150,000 bagworms covering about 35 locations. These data should give us a quantitative picture of the geographical and host-tree range of various bagworm parasites and information on bagworm fecundity on several different host trees.

The literature on orientation of insect parasites to the plant host of their phytophagous prey has been recently reviewed (DeBach, 1964). The important unique factor in my study is that the same species of phytophagous insect host, the bagworm, occurs on many different tree species in various parts of the insect's range. The species of parasites of the bagworm differs between host trees because initial host-finding activity of insect parasites is based on habitat (trees in this case) and only after they are on the appropriate host tree do they seek out the host insect. Part of the Virginia data is worked up. It shows that *Itoplectis conquistor* attacks pupae on coniferous and deciduous trees, but *Phobetes thyridopterigis* and *Spilochalcis mariae* attack pupae only on deciduous trees. *S. mariae* restricted most of its activity to sycamore and boxelder. With insects with a narrow host range, the host tree and phytophagous insect factors would be confounded since each tree species or species group would have a different species of phytophagous insect.

It may be several years before the study will be completed because some of the parasites are difficult to identify; indeed some will probably have to be described as new species.

REFERENCES

DEBACH, PAUL, ed.

1964. Biological control of insect pests and weeds, 844 pp. Reinhold Publishing Corp., New York.

KULMAN, HERBERT M.

1965. Natural control of the bagworm and notes on its status as a forest pest. Journ. Econ. Ent., vol. 58, pp. 863–866.

——. Preference on parasites for bagworms feeding on various tree hosts. (In preparation.)

HERBERT M. KULMAN

Archeological and Paleontological Investigations at Olduvai Gorge, Tanzania, 1970

Principal Investigator: Mary D. Leakey, Centre for Prehistory and Palaeontology, Nairobi, Kenya.

Grant Nos. 837, 839: In further support of the Leakeys' Olduvai Gorge archeological and paleontological project in East Africa.[1]

The 1970 season at Olduvai Gorge was devoted mainly to investigation of the upper part of the sequence, that is, Beds III and IV, in order to continue the story unearthed in Beds I and II during previous field work.

Bed III proved unrewarding since it contains few living sites of Early Man, possibly because of the dry and inhospitable conditions at the time. Excavations in Bed IV, however, yielded interesting stone industries and associated human fossils. Bed IV can now be subdivided into two parts. The lower part, Bed IV proper, is represented by riverine deposits and remains of small, temporary lakes. The Olduvai region appears to have been widely populated by Early Man at this time, and numerous living sites along the river channels are known.

There is now evidence indicating that this part of Bed IV probably spans the period between 700,000 and 500,000 years ago. The deposits formerly known as Bed IVb have now been given separate status and are known as the Masek Beds. They represent, on the whole, a period of dry, desertic conditions but also include a number of river channels. One of these was excavated and found to contain a living site with an abundance of large, beautifully made quartz handaxes. These belong to the most recent stage of the Acheulean, or handax, culture known at Olduvai and probably date to between 200,000 and 250,000 years ago.

A series of hitherto unexplored sites on the south side of the gorge, where the marker Tuff IVb is preserved, provided well-documented evidence as to the relationship of the stone industries of Bed IV. Excavations were

---

[1] Brief accounts of the Leakeys' investigations at Olduvai Gorge, under National Geographic Society grants beginning in 1960, may be found in earlier volumes of these *Reports*.

carried out at four sites in this area, and it was found that two distinct industries existed side by side. One of these consisted of a classic Acheulean in which handaxes and cleavers made on large flakes predominate. This industry is virtually indistinguishable from the Early Acheulean known from middle Bed II. The second stone industry is composed of a variety of small tools with a few diminutive handaxes. There are no cleavers, but there are numbers of artificially pitted stones or anvils.

A human femur and hip bone were found in association with the Acheulean industry. The bones are extremely massive and have been assigned to *Homo erectus*. Since this is the first time that any part of a human pelvis older than Neandertal man has been found, the significance of the Olduvai specimen cannot be assessed at present, but it will certainly supply valuable information concerning the mode of locomotion and stance of *Homo erectus*. No human remains were found in association with the second industry.

For many years prehistorians have been aware of the existence of two cultural traditions in tool-making during the Middle Pleistocene, both in Europe and in Africa. Various hypotheses have been put forward in explanation, but direct evidence of contemporaneity and associated hominid material had not come to light prior to these discoveries at Olduvai.

Laboratory Work

The crushed skull of *Homo habilis* that was found in 1968 was finally taken apart, cleaned of its matrix, and pieced together by R. J. Clarke. This is a remarkable achievement and has probably never been paralleled with any other fossil skull.

The Olduvai Museum

Grants from the Antiquities Department of Tanzania and the Wallace Genetic Foundation made possible the preparation of exhibits in the museum building that was erected by the Society several years ago.

Excellent fiber-glass casts, obtained from the National Museum in Nairobi, are being used to demonstrate the fossil fauna, the stone industries, and the fossil hominids from the various levels at Olduvai. There is also a large explanatory label on the geology. Subsidiary exhibits include a colored diagram of the faulting, plans of the living floors, and a distribution map of the raw materials used for making tools. Preparation of the exhibits progressed well, and it was hoped to open the museum to the public at the end of the year or in January 1971.

Visitors

During 1970 visitors to the gorge totaled 15,466, in addition to just under a thousand students and others in educational parties. Their Majesties Queen Margarethe and Queen Ingrid of Denmark were among some of the most interested and enthusiastic visitors.

MARY D. LEAKEY

Lower Pleistocene Hominids from Lake Turkana, North Kenya, 1970–1972

Principal Investigator: Richard E. F. Leakey, National Museums of Kenya, Nairobi, Kenya.[1]

Grant Nos. 828, 909, 931, 1001, 1017, 1079. For continuing paleontological and archeological research in the vininity of Lake Turkana, Kenya.

During June–August 1970, the National Museums of Kenya organized a further expedition to the extensive fossil beds lying to the east of Lake Turkana. The 16 specimens collected during this season brought the total collection of hominids from Koobi Fora to 23 (table 1). Among the 1970 finds are 5 specimens of postcranial material.

The hominid and other vertebrate material has been collected from two principal areas, which are referred to as Ileret and Koobi Fora. A preliminary report on the geology of Koobi Fora area was published by Anna K. Behrensmeyer (1970). During 1970, Miss Behrensmeyer continued geological work in this locality, and a geological team from Iowa State University—Drs. Carl Vondra, Gary Johnson, and Bruce Bowen—undertook a preliminary investigation of the Ileret area. A definite correlation between the deposits of Ileret and Koobi Fora has yet to be confirmed. The faunal evidence shows that the two areas do overlap to some extent, but until further work is completed fossil material will be referred to locality sections only.

Further archeological work on the area has been undertaken by Dr. G. L. Isaac and several new sites have been located. A detailed report on this aspect of the 1970 expedition has been published elsewhere (Isaac et al., 1971).

The eight mandibles collected in 1970, with the exception of two, KNM-ER 730 and 731, seem to represent variations of one type and are similar to the two mandibles collected in 1968. The most complete of the

[1]The continuing program of research at Koobi Fora has been possible as a result of the support from many but in particular from the National Geographic Society; the National Science Foundation; Mr. Robert Donner, Jr., and the William H. Donner Foundation (through NGS grant 1063); and the National Museums of Kenya. I thank also the members of the expedition for their work in the field and in the laboratory and, in particular, my wife, Meave, for her constant help at all levels.

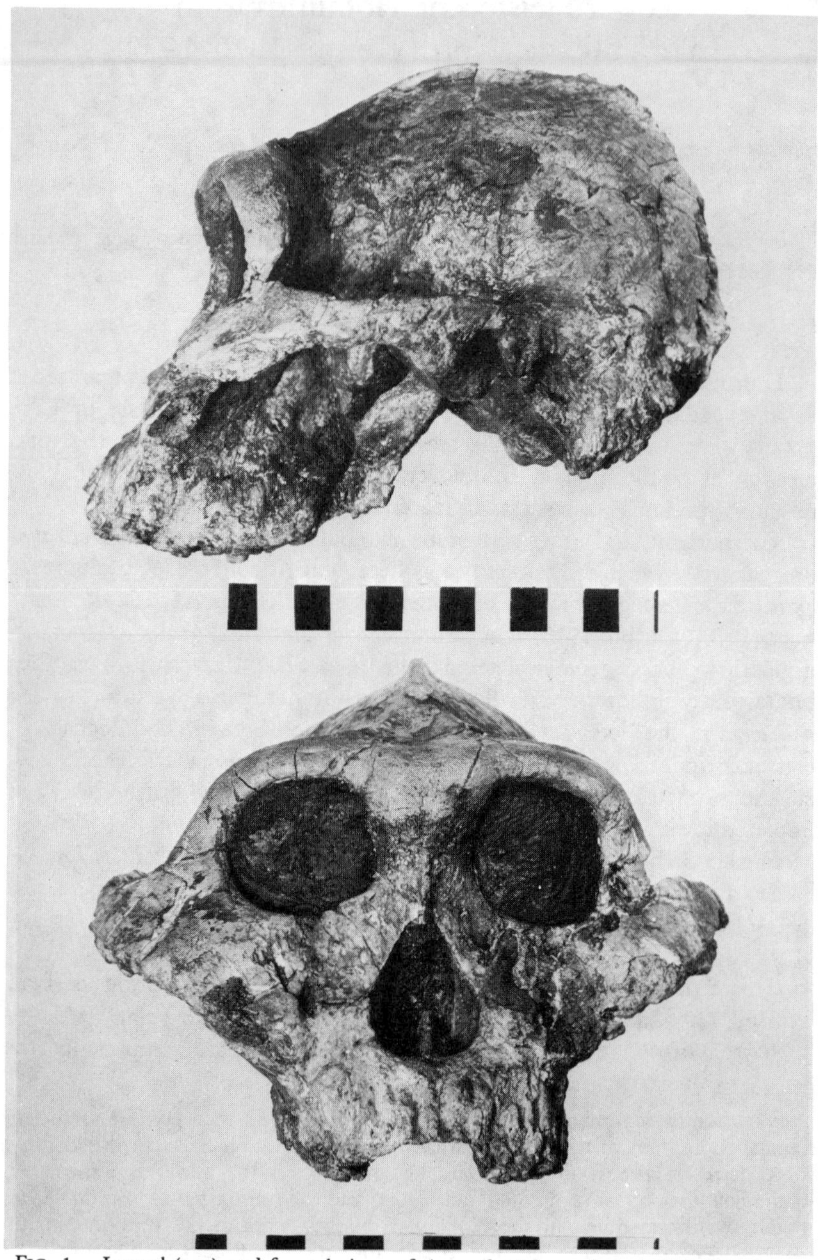

FIG. 1. Lateral (top) and frontal views of *Australopithecus boisei*, KNM-ER 406.

eight is KNM-ER 729, which was discovered by Dr. P. I. Abell. This specimen consists of a robust corpus with P_4 through M_3 on the right side and M_2 and M_3 on the left side. The left third and fourth premolars have complete crowns, but the roots are damaged and so these teeth are separate from the mandible. The left ascending ramus is missing, but the right ramus is fairly complete and lacks only the coronoid process and mandibular condyle.

When compared with robust australopithecine mandibles from South Africa, the Peninj mandible from Lake Natron in Tanzania and the specimens from the Omo Valley of Ethiopia, there is a striking uniformity of the over-all morphology. The specimens do vary, but it is likely that these variations are merely individual differences which might be expected within such a sample. In the absence of additional evidence KNM-ER 725, 726, 727, 728, 729, and 733 and the two mandibles collected in 1968, KNM-ER 403 and 404, are referred to *Australopithecus* cf. *boisei.*

The two remaining mandibles, KNM-ER 730 and 731, collected in 1970 are striking in their contrast to the six mandibles I have just discussed. KNM-ER 730 was discovered by Dr. Meave Leakey and is the more complete. This specimen consists of the left side of the mandible with M_3 and M_1 extending through the symphysis to the right corpus, which is broken at the fourth premolar. The teeth show heavy wear and the alveolar region shows reabsorption, which is most advanced in the anterior part of the mandible.

It is clear that KNM-ER 730 is unlike the typical robust australopithecine mandible from the same stratigraphic level at Koobi Fora. KNM-ER 731 is very similar to KNM-ER 730 and both are to be provisionally referred to the genus *Homo* cf. *erectus*.

An almost complete right half of a cranium KNM-ER 732, a parietal fragment KNM-ER 734 and associated cranial, and mandibular fragments KNM-ER 733 were also collected.

KNM-ER 732 is of particular interest. The specimen is broken through the sagittal plane and no fragments of the left side were located. The right half is fragmented but sufficiently complete to provide a great deal of information. The teeth have been broken along the alveolar margin and, apart from a portion of the right fourth premolar, no crowns were recovered in spite of excavation and intensive sieving.

On the basis of its morphology there is little doubt that KNM-ER 732 is an australopithecine, but in the absence of further material and taking into account the strong possibility of marked sexual dimorphism, I refer it to *Australopithecus*.

The five postcranial fragments were compared with *Homo sapiens*, *Pan*, and *Gorilla* in a provisional manner at the time of the first report. The left femoral diaphysis KNM-ER 737 lacks epiphyses but is otherwise complete and is apparently free from distortion. It is interesting that it resembles the *Homo sapiens* femur in several respects.

The left femoral diaphysis KNM-ER 736 has been broken anteriorly just above the lesser trochanter and distally some distance below the estimated midpoint, and it therefore lacks both epiphyses. The diaphysis is markedly robust, and there is no evidence of curvature to the shaft. The specimen is quite unlike *Homo*, *Pan*, and *Gorilla* material.

The left femoral diaphysis with proximal epiphysis preserved, KNM-ER 738, consists of just more than half the shaft represented by a large splinter of the medial surface and the proximal region, which is complete except for the greater trochanter. The join between the two pieces shows interlock of irregularities on both the medullary and external surfaces which leave no doubt that this is a true contact. The shaft bears evidence of having been broken and subsequently healed during life, and this has resulted in thickening of the bone in the region above the commencement of the linea aspera. This thickening is most pronounced on the anteromedial aspects.

The left tibia KNM-ER 741 consists of the proximal epiphysis and approximately half the length of the shaft. Its morphology is of considerable interest and will require detailed examination. Until this is done, superficial comparison with extant models is considered to be of little value. The anterior border of the shaft and the tuberosity are mesiolaterally compressed, resulting in wide and flat medial and lateral surfaces. The medial condyle is powerfully buttressed. The shaft shows considerable torsion in relation to the transverse axis of the condyles.

The right humerus KNM-ER 739 is complete except for the proximal epiphysis. The bone is robust and of large size, and the muscle attachments are powerfully developed.

In 1971 more early hominid material was recovered from the Koobi Fora area; the number of specimens totaled 45 (see table 2). The collection further confirmed the contemporaneity of *Australopithecus* and *Homo* during the Lower Pleistocene in East Africa. The exact location of each hominid find is marked in the field by an embedded concrete post, and geological investigations have allowed all the specimens to be related to stratigraphic sections. Several excavations were undertaken to recover further material associated with surface finds.

Preliminary reports of geological investigations in 1969 and 1970 in the two principal collecting areas at East Rudolf Koobi Fora and Ileret have been published (Vondra et al., 1971; Vondra and Bowen, 1973), but until 1971 no stratigraphic correlations between the two areas had been obtained.

Dr. Bruce Bowen of Iowa State University continued geological investigations in both areas in 1971, and in addition to obtaining more detailed stratigraphic correlations between the principal fossiliferous localities in each area he was also able to obtain a probable stratigraphic correlation between the two areas.

It should be noted here that the stratigraphic position of the two crania KNM-ER 406 and KNM-ER 407 are from a horizon that is above rather than below the Ileret correlate of the KBS tuff. All the hominid material recovered so far from Koobi Fora and Ileret seems to be younger than 2.6 million years.

Collection of samples for radiometric dating was undertaken during 1971 by Ian Findlater (Birkbeck College, London), and Dr. A. Brock undertook systematic paleomagnetic investigations to complement this dating program. Until these results are known and more precise information on the age of the hominid specimens is available the hominid material should be considered as being from a range of deposits aged from approximately 2.5 to 1.0 million years.

A team led by Dr. Vincent J. Maglio investigated the faunal evidence from Koobi Fora in 1971 and collected samples of fossil vertebrates from many of the more important localities (Maglio, 1971).

A large collection of artifacts was recovered in 1971 in situ by Prof. Glynn Isaac and is described elsewhere (Isaac, 1975). Several new artifact localities were discovered, and these will considerably broaden the evidence of early Pleistocene paleotechnology.

A further 38 fossil hominids were collected during 1972, bringing the total now known from this locality to 87 (tables 3 and 4). The collection includes cranial and postcranial material. Several specimens recovered from deposits that are below the KBS Tuff are of particular interest in view of the presence of at least two distinct forms of hominid at this early period. I believe that the final analysis of the hominids from Koobi Fora should be based on as large a sample as can be reasonably available, and there is every indication that further material will be recovered with the continued investigation of the area.

The paleontological investigations in 1972 were directed by Dr. J. M. Harris of the Kenya National Museum, and further specimens of several taxa were collected. Some specimens collected from below the KBS Tuff should prove of considerable interest and value regarding the interpretation of the lower Pleistocene genera. With the extension of exploration, a unified system of locality numbers designating collecting areas has been devised by Dr. Maglio.

Archeological exploration and excavations were continued under the

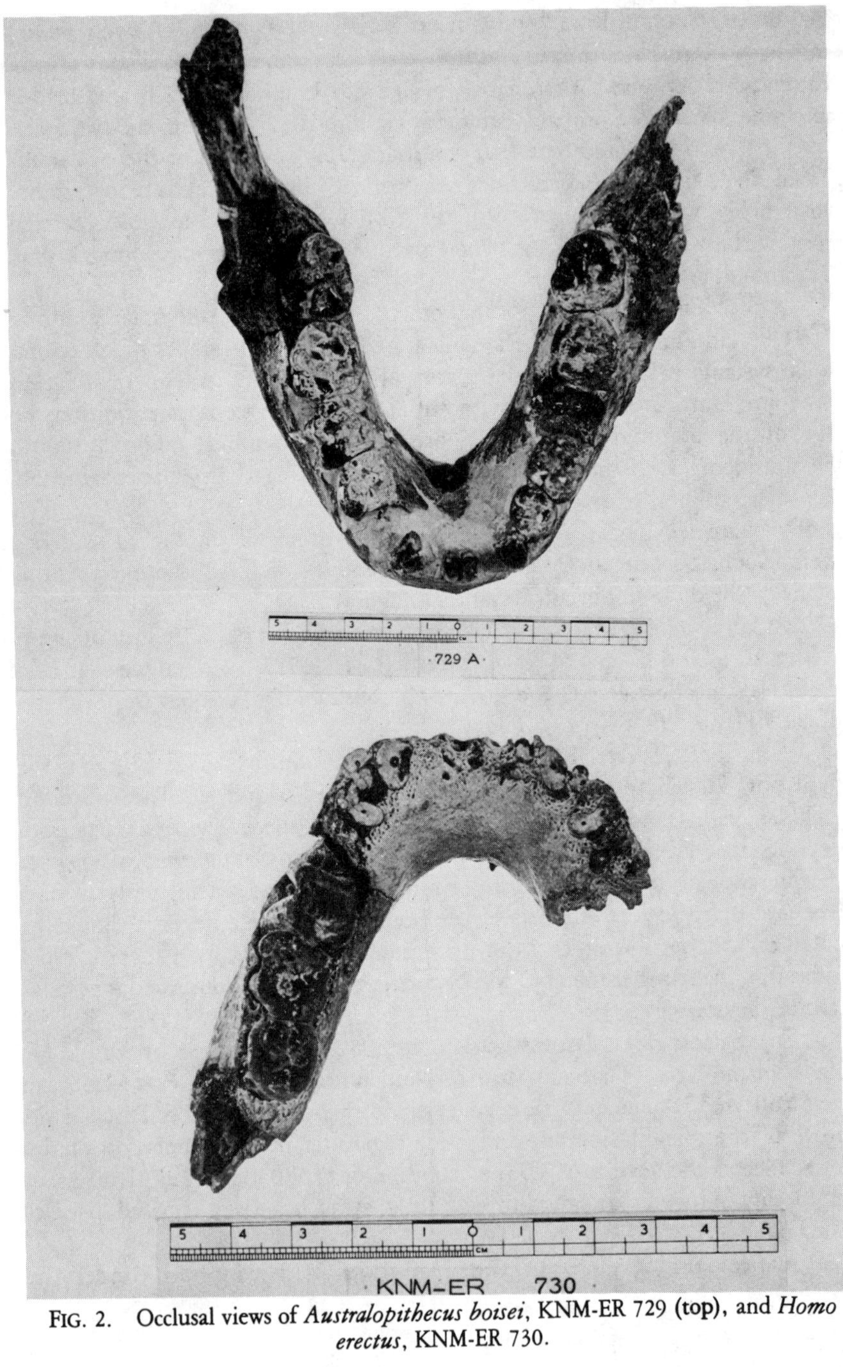

FIG. 2. Occlusal views of *Australopithecus boisei*, KNM-ER 729 (top), and *Homo erectus*, KNM-ER 730.

supervision of Dr. Isaac, assisted by graduate students. The excavations within the KBS Tuff were examined; a large collection of artifacts was recovered from several preliminary excavations. A detailed report on the archeological activities will be presented elsewhere.

Dr. Bruce Bowen extended the geological survey and mapping south of the Koobi Fora ridge and has established the broad continuity of the sequence from the lowest deposits at Kubi Algi, about 4.5 million years, to the uppermost deposits at Ileret, about 1.0 million years.

Ian Findlater continued the field investigation and mapping of volcanic events. In spite of meticulous collecting and rigorous laboratory analysis, however, dates for the tuffaceous horizons continue to prove unreliable. Some intriguing technical problems indicate that depositional complications are causing the conventional techniques of radiometric age determinations to give inconclusive results. The continued paleomagnetic studies by Dr. A. Brock together with faunal correlations provide useful additional data. The stratigraphical correlation of the areas 119, 121, 123, 127 south of the Koobi Fora ridge is uncertain and this information is omitted for specimens from these areas. Specimens 1510 and 1590 to 1593 were discovered after the 1972 expedition and closed its principal research activities; these specimens, although important, are therefore only listed in the tables and not mentioned further. The *Homo* specimens, KNM-ER 1470, 1472, 1475, and 1481, will be given particular attention in order to allow adequate treatment of these important finds.

Hominine Material. Sixteen individuals, listed in table 4, are represented by the material collected during 1972. Evidence of *Homo* at levels below the KBS Tuff horizon will be put forward on the basis of some remarkable new material.

A fragment of parietal, KNM-ER 1466, is notable; it is thick boned and bears a marked temporal ridge, features that are reminiscent of the calvaria from Olduvai Gorge (Leakey and Leakey, 1964). The specimen is unfortunately incomplete and cannot provide any conclusive evidence for the presence of *Homo erectus* at Ileret but is certainly a strong indication.

Four specimens collected in 1972 are provisionally attributed to the genus *Homo*. One, a cranium, KNM-ER 1470, is of particular interest.

The following specimens are of special interest: (1) a cranium, KNM-ER 1470; (2) a right femur, KNM-ER 1472; (3) a proximal fragment of a second right femur, KNM-ER 1475; and (4) an associated left femur, distal and proximal fragments of left tibia, and a distal left fibula, KNM-ER 1481. They were all recovered from area 131 and from deposits below the KBS Tuff.

TABLE 1. HOMINID SPECIMENS FROM KOOBI FORA AND ILERET (1970)

Year	*Locality*	*KNM-ER No.*	*Details of specimens*
1968	Koobi Fora	403	Right mandibular corpus—fragmented dentition
1968	Koobi Fora	405	Maxilla—very weathered without dentition
1968	Ileret	404	Right mandibular corpus—fragmented dentition
1968	Ileret	417	Fragment of parietal
1969	Ileret	406	Cranium—no dentition (see fig. 1)
1969	Ileret	407	Cranium—lacking facial and maxillary region
1969	Koobi Fora	164	Fragment of parietal
1970	Ileret	725	Left mandibular corpus—no dentition
1970	Ileret	726	Left mandibular corpus—no dentition
1970	Ileret	727	Right mandibular corpus—no dentition
1970	Ileret	728	Right mandibular corpus—no dentition
1970	Ileret	729	Mandible with dentition—ascending rami damaged (see fig. 2)
1970	Koobi Fora	730	Left mandibular corpus with M_1 to M_3 through symphysis to right P_4 (see fig. 2)
1970	Ileret	731	Left fragment of mandibular corpus
1970	Ileret	732	Right side cranium; maxilla, frontal, parietal to mastoid (see fig. 3)
1970	Ileret	733	Cranial fragments; maxilla fragment and left mandibular corpus
1970	Koobi Fora	734	Parietal fragment
1970	Koobi Fora	736	Left femur—shaft
1970	Koobi Fora	737	Left femur—shaft
1970	Koobi Fora	738	Left femur—proximal end and shaft
1970	Ileret	739	Right humerus—distal end and shaft
1970	Ileret	740	Left humerus—fragment of distal end
1970	Ileret	741	Left tibia—proximal end and shaft

Area 131 consists of approximately 30 square kilometers of fluviatile and lacustrine sediments. The sediments are well exposed and show no evidence of significant tectonic disturbance; there is a slight westward dip of less than 3°. Several prominent marker horizons provide reference levels and have permitted physical correlation of stratigraphical units between area 131 and other areas in the Koobi Fora locality. An account of the geology is given by Vondra and Bowen (1973).

At present, analysis of samples collected for dating from the KBS Tuff in area 131 has proved inconclusive.

The cranium KNM-ER 1470 and the postcranial remains KNM-ER 1472, 1475, and 1481 were all recovered as a result of surface discovery. The unrolled condition of the specimens and the nature of the sites rule out the

TABLE 2. SPECIMENS FROM THE 1971 COLLECTION FROM EAST OF LAKE TURKANA

Locality	*KNM-ER No.*	*Details of specimens*
Koobi Fora	164*	Two metacarpi and two cervical vertebrae
Ileret	801*	Right mandibular corpus—M_2, M_3 in place and isolated right I_2, left M_2, and M_3
Ileret	802*	Isolated adult teeth—lower left P_4, M_1, M_2, M_3 and right P_4, M_1, M_3; upper left C, P^3, and right M^2
Ileret	803	Upper canine, medial incisor, and associated postcranial parts—including fragments of the diaphyses of femur, tibia, ulna and fibula, fragments of distal fibula, talus, second metatarsal, and several phalanges
Ileret	805	Left mandibular corpus—lacking dentition
Ileret	806	Isolated teeth—M_1, M_2, two P_4s, and two M_3s
Ileret	807	Fragment left maxilla—M^3 and partial M^2
Ileret	808	Isolated upper teeth—lateral incisor, premolar, and M^1
Ileret	809	Fragments isolated teeth
Koobi Fora	810	Left mandibular corpus through symphysis—M_3
Koobi Fora	811	Fragment parietal
Koobi Fora	812	Immature left mandibular corpus
Koobi Fora	813	Right talus and fragment tibia diaphysis
Koobi Fora	814	Cranial fragments—including frontal and parietal
Ileret	815	Left femur—proximal end lacking head
Koobi Fora	816	Isolated left upper canine and fragments of molars
Koobi Fora	817	Left mandibular corpus—lacking dentition
Ileret	818	Left mandibular corpus—P_4 to M_3
Ileret	819	Left mandibular corpus—lacking dentition
Ileret	820	Immature mandible—permanent incisors and first molars and deciduous canines and molars. The unerupted permanent premolars and canines are in the crypts
Ileret	992	Mandible—lacking three incisors and parts of the ascending rami
Ileret	993	Right femur—diaphysis and distal epiphysis
Koobi Fora	996	Isolated lateral incisor
Koobi Fora	997	Proximal metatarsal
Ileret	1170*	Skull fragments
Ileret	1171*	Isolated juvenile teeth—lower left P_4, M_1, M_2, and right M_1, M_2; upper left M^1, M^2, and right C, P^4, M^2

possibility of secondary deposition—there is no doubt in the minds of geologists that the provenance is as reported. All the specimens are heavily mineralized and the adhering matrix is similar to the matrix seen on other fossils from the same sites. In due course, microscopic examination of thin sections of matrix taken from the site and on the fossils might add further evidence.

Cranium KNM-ER 1470 was discovered by Bernard Ngeneo, a Kenyan,

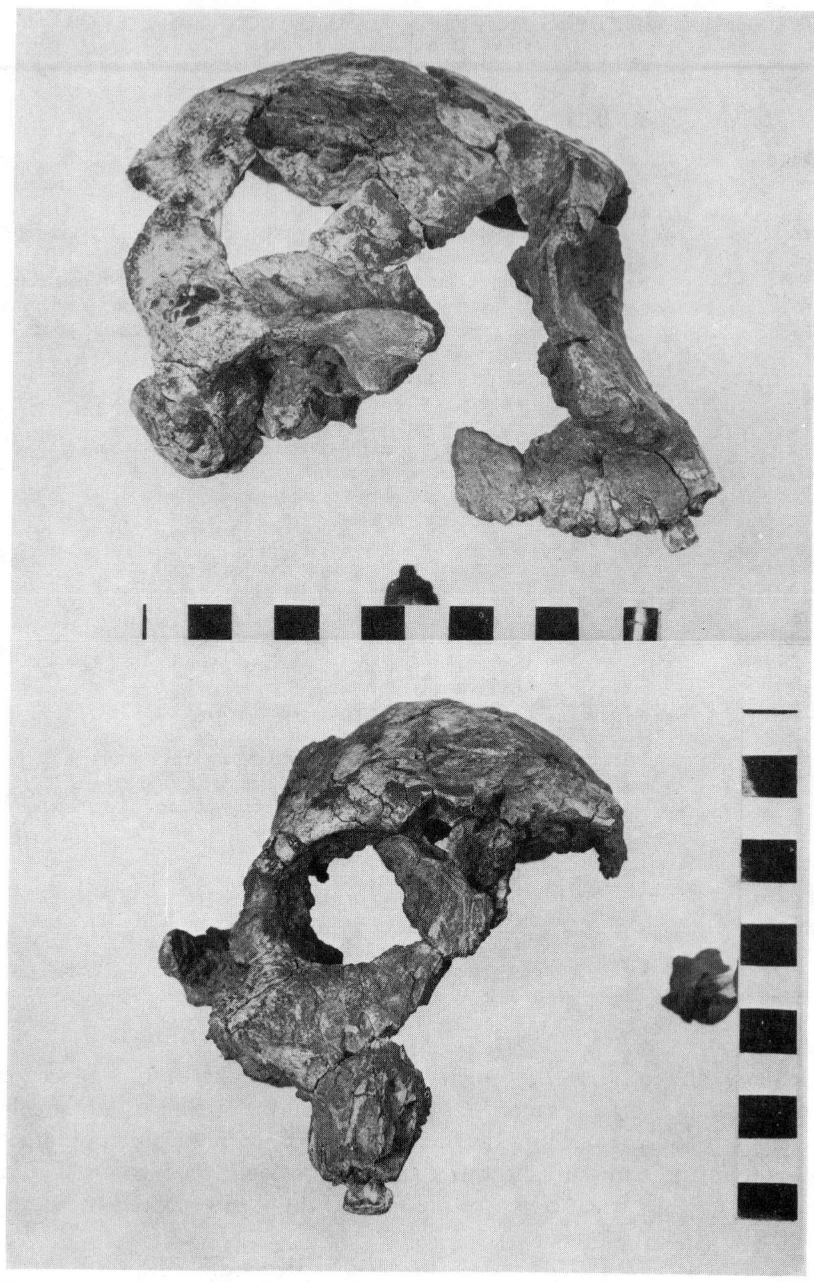

FIG. 3. Lateral (top) and frontal views of *Australopithecus* cf. *boisei*, KNM-ER 732.

who noticed a large number of bone fragments washing down a steep slope on one side of a gully. Careful examination showed that these fragments included pieces of a hominid cranium. An area of approximately 20 by 20 meters was subsequently screened and more than 150 fragments were recovered.

The skull is not fully reconstructed. Many small fragments remain to be included, and it may be some time before the task is completed. At present the cranial vault is almost complete and there are good joins between the pieces. The face is less complete and although there are good contacts joining the maxilla through the face to the calvaria, many pieces are still missing. The orientation of the face is somewhat uncertain because of distortion of the frontal base by several small, matrix filled cracks. The basicranium shows the most damage and is the least complete region.

The cranium shows many features of interest. The supraorbital tori are weakly developed with no continuous supratoral sulcus. The postorbital waisting is moderate and there is no evidence of either marked temporal lines or a temporal keel. The vault is domed with steeply sloping sides and parietal eminences. The glenoid fossae and external auditory meati are positioned well forward by comparison with *Australopithecus*. The occipital area is incomplete but there is no indication of a nuchal crest or other powerful muscle attachments.

In view of the completeness of the calvaria, it has been possible to prepare in modeling clay an endocranial impression, which has been used to obtain minimum estimates for the endocranial volume. Six measurements of the endocast by water displacement were made by Dr. A. Walker and gave a mean value of 810 cubic centimeters. Further work by Dr. R. Holloway gave a more precise volume of 775 cubic centimeters.

The palate is shallow, broad, and short, with a nearly straight labial border that is reminiscent of the large *Australopithecus*. The great width in relationship to the length of the palate does contrast markedly, however, with known australopithecine material. The molars and premolar crowns are not preserved, but the remaining roots and alveoli suggest some mesiodistal compression. The large alveoli of the anterior teeth suggest the presence of substantial canines and incisors.

KNM-ER 1472, a right femur, was discovered as a number of fragments by Dr. J. Harris. It shows some features that are also seen in the better preserved left femur, KNM-ER 1481, but other features, such as the apparently very straight shaft and the bony process on the anterior aspect of the greater trochanter, require further evaluation.

The proximal fragment of femur, KNM-ER 1475, was discovered by

Table 3. 1972 Material Attributed to Australopithecus

KNM-ER No.	*Specimen detail*	*Area*
1463	Right femur diaphysis	1A
1464	Right talus	6
1465	Proximal fragment left femur	8
1467	Isolated M_3	3
1468	Right mandible	8
1469	Left mandible, M_3	131
1471	Proximal half right tibia	131
1476	Left talus, proximal tibia and fragment tibia shaft	105
1477	Juvenile mandible with teeth	105
1478	Cranial fragments	105
1479	Fragments isolated molars	105
1500	Skeletal elements	130
1503	Proximal right femur	123
1504	Distal right humerus	123
1505	Proximal fragment femur and fragment of shaft	123
1506	Right mandible, M_1, M_2, and isolated P^4, P^3	
1509	Isolated teeth, P_4-M_3	119
1592	Distal half femur	12

Table 4. 1972 Material Attributed to Homo

KNM-ER No.	*Specimen detail*	*Area*	*Stratigraphic position where known*
1462	Isolated m_3	130	Below KBS Tuff
1466	Parietal fragment	1	Below upper Tuff
1470	Cranium	131	Below KBS Tuff
1472	Right femur	131	Below KBS Tuff
1475	Proximal right femur	131	Below KBS Tuff
1480	Isolated molar	105	Above KBS Tuff
1481	Left femur, proximal tibia, distal tibia, and distal fibula	131	Below KBS Tuff
1483	Mandible fragments	131	Below KBS Tuff
1501	Right mandible	123	—
1502	Right mandible with molar	123	—
1507	Juvenile left mandible with teeth	127	—
1508	Isolated molar	127	—
1510	Cranial fragments	119	—
1590	Cranial fragments with juvenile dentition	12	Below KBS Tuff
1591	Humerus lacking head	12	Above KBS Tuff
1593	Cranial and mandibular fragments	12	Below KBS Tuff

Kamoya Kimeu. Its condition is such that a final taxonomic identification will be difficult and it is therefore included only tentatively in this report. This fragment shows some features such as a short, more nearly cylindrical neck, which are not seen in the femurs of *Australopithecus*.

A complete left femur, KNM-ER 1481, associated with both ends of a left tibia and the distal end of a left fibula were also discovered by Dr. J. Harris. The femur is characterized by a very slender shaft with relatively large epiphyses. The head of the femur is large and set on a robust cylindrical neck which takes off from the shaft at a more obtuse angle than in known *Australopithecus* femurs. There is a marked insertion for gluteus maximus and the proximal region of the shaft is slightly flattened anteroposteriorly. The femoro-condylar angle is within the range of *Homo sapiens*. When the femur is compared with a restricted sample of modern African bones, there are marked similarities in those morphological features that are widely considered characteristic of modern *H. sapiens*. The fragments of tibia and fibula also resemble *H. sapiens* and no features call for specific comment at this preliminary stage of study.

The taxonomic status of the material is not absolutely clear, and detailed comparative studies which should help to clarify this problem have yet to be concluded. The edocranial capacity and the morphology of the calvaria of KNM-ER 1470 are characters that suggest inclusion within the genus *Homo* cf. *habilis*.

Conclusions

The 1970 through 1972 field seasons at Lake Turkana provided vast quantities of new data on hominid evolution. The analysis of the fossils and artifacts will take many years and the contributions from this study will be far reaching.

Although previous work at other African localities had indicated the coexistence of *Homo* and *Australopithecus* cf. *boisei*, the fossils from Koobi Fora and Ileret are so much more complete and provide critical evidence. The coexistence of more than one species raises many questions that will be considered in future years of research at Lake Turkana.

REFERENCES

BEHRENSMEYER, ANNA K.
1970. Preliminary geological interpretation of a new hominid site in the Lake Rudolf Basin. Nature, vol. 226, pp. 225–266, illus.

ISAAC, GLYNN L.
1975. Earliest man and environments in Lake Rudolf Basin, pp. 552–564. University of Chicago Press.

ISAAC, GLYNN L.; LEAKEY, RICHARD E. F.; and BEHRENSMEYER, ANNA K.
1971. Archeological traces of early hominid activities east of Lake Rudolf, Kenya. Science, vol. 173, pp. 1129–1134, illus.

LEAKEY, LOUIS S. B., and LEAKEY, MARY D.
1964. Recent discoveries of fossil hominids in Tanganyika: at Olduvai and near Lake Natron. Nature, vol. 202, pp. 5–7, illus.

MAGLIO, VINCENT J.
1971. Vertebrate faunas from the Kubi Algi, Koobi Fora and Ileret areas, East Rudolf, Kenya. Nature, vol. 231, pp. 248–249.

VONDRA, CARL F., and BOWEN, BRUCE E.
1973. Stratigraphical relations of the Plio-Pleistocene deposits, East Rudolf, Kenya. Nature, vol. 242, pp. 391–393, illus.

VONDRA, CARL F.; JOHNSON, GARY D.; BOWEN, BRUCE E.; and BEHRENSMEYER, ANNA K.
1971. Preliminary stratigraphical studies of the East Rudolf Basin, Kenya. Nature, vol. 231, pp. 245–248, illus.

RICHARD E. F. LEAKEY

Studies of Irish Moss, *Chondrus crispus* Stackhouse

Principal Investigators: Esther L. McCandless and Elizabeth M. Gordon-Mills, McMaster University, Hamilton, Ontario, Canada.

Grant No. 892: For studies of the alga *Chondrus crispus* in natural and artificial habitats.

Irish moss, a marine red alga, grows in abundance on the coasts of the North Atlantic (fig. 1). Its economic importance to the Maritime Provinces of Canada lies in its content of carrageenans, sulphated galactose polymers, which have been used for generations in making puddings and which continue to be of importance primarily in the food industry. These constitute 60 to 70 percent of the dry weight of the seaweed, from which they are easily extracted by hot water.

The present report summarizes work carried out between October 1970 and 1972 on this alga, with the aid of grants from the National Geographic Society and the National Research Council of Canada. The research has involved two different approaches, a histochemical and ultrastructural study of the alga, carried out by Elizabeth M. Gordon-Mills, and a biochemical investigation by Esther L. McCandless. To obtain live material for both aspects of the investigation, a number of field trips to Nova Scotia were taken by either or both of the grantees. Plants were collected during low tide from shaded areas (see figs. 2, 3) in Peggy's Cove (October 1970; January, June, and October 1971), Paddy Head (January 1971); Ketch Harbor (October 1970; January, May, and June 1971); and Portuguese Cove (October 1970), Nova Scotia, all points within easy access of Halifax and the Atlantic Regional Laboratory of the National Research Council of Canada.

The field trips afforded the opportunity for the grantees to become acquainted with the marine phycologists of this laboratory and of Dalhousie University. The advantage of more direct communication among various laboratories working on *Chondrus crispus* became apparent and led to a plan for a conference on morphology, ecology, physiology, and biochemistry of this alga, which culminated in a panel discussion held June 22, 1972, as part of the joint meetings of the Canadian Botanical Association and Canadian Society of Plant Physiologists in Halifax, Nova Scotia. The proceedings of this session contain an expanded version of the histochemical and ultrastructural studies in the present report and has been published as a supplement to volume 27 (1973) of the Proceedings of the Nova Scotian Institute of Science.

In continuation of the biochemical work of 1970–71, E. L. McCandless spent a 6-month sabbatical leave (January to July 1972) in the Atlantic Regional Laboratory of the National Research Council in Halifax, Nova Scotia.

Histochemical and Ultrastructural Studies

Recent work on the chemical and physical characteristics of κ- and λ-carrageenans derived from the marine alga *Chondrus crispus* Stackhouse (Rees, 1969) stimulated interest in the locations and functions of these polysaccharides in the living plant. This led to the investigation of the structure of the plant at both the light-microscope level, using histochemical techniques applied to brown algae of the genus *Fucus* by McCully, fluorescence microscopy, and polarization microscopy, and at the ultrastructural level, using transmission electron microscopy and freeze-etching techniques. The plants used were collected on the field trips, carried back to the maritime laboratory in plastic bags, and fixed immediately in glutaraldehyde-formaldehyde or kept at 0–4° until they could be placed in culture tanks. Stock cultures were maintained in Hamilton, Ontario, in "Instant Ocean" (Aquarium Systems, Inc.) at 10°–15° under 130–175 lux illumination and 12-hour day length.

As the histochemical reactions of κ- and λ-carrageenans are similar, we had thought to distinguish them by using a specific technique borrowed from animal histochemistry, the fluorescent antibody reaction, suggested by the production of antibodies to the two carrageenans in this laboratory (Johnston and McCandless). Unfortunately, attempts to produce specific antibody to λ-carrageenan for the present experiments were unsuccessful. It should be pointed out also that the discovery that plants of the two stages of life cycle produce different carrageenans (*vide infra*) was made subsequent to the work reported in this section. Much of the histochemical work used nonsporulating plants, hence plants of unknown stage. Carposporic plants of this species are known to predominate in the areas of collection and presumably predominate in this study as well. This is the stage that produces μ- and κ-carrageegans. Further work has since been carried out upon tetrasporic plants (Gordon-Mills and McCandless, 1975).

Two main areas of cells are usually distinguished in the histological description of the thalli of *C. crispus,* an outer cortex containing densely packed small cells and an inner medulla of large cells imbedded in an intercellular matrix; the two regions are not discrete but grade into each other.

Electron-microscope studies with both thin sectioning and freeze-etching techniques showed that the immediate cell walls have microfibrils arranged circularly around the cell (fig. 4). It is probable that they occur in a reticulate surface-view pattern as in the cell walls of other red algae. Hand sections of living *Chondrus* tissue examined under polarized light showed a brilliant positive birefringence in the immediate cell walls, most probably due to the orientation of the microfibrils (fig. 5). The cortical cells contain one reniform chloroplast and one nucleus together with organelles similar to other red algae. Microfibrils similar to those occurring in the wall were observed in golgi vesicles. Subcortical and medullary cells are multinucleate with a highly

FIG. 1. *Chondrus crispus* Stackhouse (Irish moss). Herbarium specimen, collected at Peggy's Cove, Nova Scotia, October 4, 1971. Actual size.

FIG. 2. *Chondrus cripus* bed, central zone (*Laminaria* to left and in right foreground, *Fucus* and *Ascophyllum* on higher rocks at right), Peggy's Cove, Nova Scotia, low tide, October 15, 1970.

lobed chloroplast and large vacuoles, which possibly contain carrageenan. These differences from cortical cells appear to develop progressively as one approaches the medulla.

Carposporangia and tetrasporangia are uninucleate and contain densely packed plastids and starch grains. They are also surrounded by a fibrillar cell wall.

In many previous descriptions of plant-wall substances carrageenan has been assigned a nonstructural role as a mucilaginous substance. The most common structural polysaccharide in plant cell walls, cellulose, is present in *C. crispus* only as 2 percent of the dry weight. With the traditional histochemical reaction using concentrated sulphuric acid and iodine solution cellulose could not be demonstrated in the present studies. This would lead one to suspect that cellulose is not the structural wall substance in *C. crispus.*

Light-microscope studies using the metachromatic staining reactions with toludine blue and alcian blue were carried out to determine the locali-

FIG. 3. *Chondrus crispus* bed (*Laminaria* at top of photograph), Peggy's Cove, Nova Scotia, low tide, October 15, 1970.

zation within cells and in the intercellular spaces of the carrageenans, which react by virtue of their sulphate content. The strongest metachromasia occurred mainly in the intercellular regions as a halo around the cells, particularly in the subcortex; this indicated that the most highly sulphated polysaccharide occurs here, or that this area is most concentrated in carrageenans. There is also a thin layer of sulphated material between the cytoplasm and immediate cell wall. A positive periodic acid Schiff's reaction, which should indicate the presence of μ carrageenan, occurs in the intercellular matrix of cortical cells but outside the areas of high sulphate concentration; in reproductive tissue in particular it is found also around cells in the medulla. This type of polysaccharide has been postulated to be the precursor of κ-carrageenan.

Immunofluorescence studies using a specific antisera against κ-carrageenan, prepared in a goat, showed that this polysaccharide probably occurs mostly in the immediate walls of all cells, i.e., just outside the cytoplasm.

Concomitant considerations of evidence from toluidine blue, immunofluorescent, and PAS staining support the idea that the microfibrils observed in thin sections and freeze-etched replicas of *C. crispus* are composed of κ-carrageenan. Rees (1969) has reported that this polysaccharide forms a double helix under certain conditions, and these helices undergo aggregation, which presumably is the form in which they appear as microfibrils. Rees has also described "kinks" in the helices, which result from the presence of D-galactose-6 sulphate rather than anhydrogalactose units in the polymer molecules. It may well be that this conformation is important in the formation of aggregates in microfibrils in the native state.

For many years it has been recognized that the pectic and hemicellulose substances occurring as the middle lamellae between primary cell walls of higher plants are composed of acidic polysaccharides; these substances probably occur in an amorphous form that is not birefringent. In *C. crispus* the most highly sulphated compounds are found also in the intercellular regions of the subcortex and as halos around the medullary cells.

Rees (1962) suggested that the possible functions of cell-wall mucilages in marine algae are (1) providing a cation exchange barrier between protoplasm and sea water, (2) providing a highly hydrophilic reservoir of moisture that would reduce the dangers of desiccation during low tide, and (3) serving as a cushion to protect the cells from physical buffeting. This last factor is probably most important in reference to κ-carrageenan. Rees and Conway (1962) analyzed the porphyran in samples of *Porphyra perforata* from various localities differing in degree of exposure to wave action. The percentages of 3,6-anhydrogalactose suggested that the greater the exposure, the higher the 3,6-anhydride content. These data support the hypothesis of the basically structural function of κ-carrageenan, which also contains 3,6-anhydrogalactose units.

Biochemical Studies

Preliminary studies of carrageenan biosynthesis were carried out upon alga harvested in several locations off the southern coast of Nova Scotia and air-shipped at 0° to Hamilton. For the experiments in 1970–71, nonsporulating fronds were usually chosen and incubated in a small container of artificial seawater ("Instant Ocean," Aquarium Systems, Inc.) containing 1 mc. $NaH^{14}CO_2$/liter, at about 4°, under 1,200 lux supplied continuously or on a 12/12 hr light/dark cycle. Samples were removed sequentially, air dried, extracted, and analyzed.

Incorporation of radioactivity into the carrageenan followed a similar

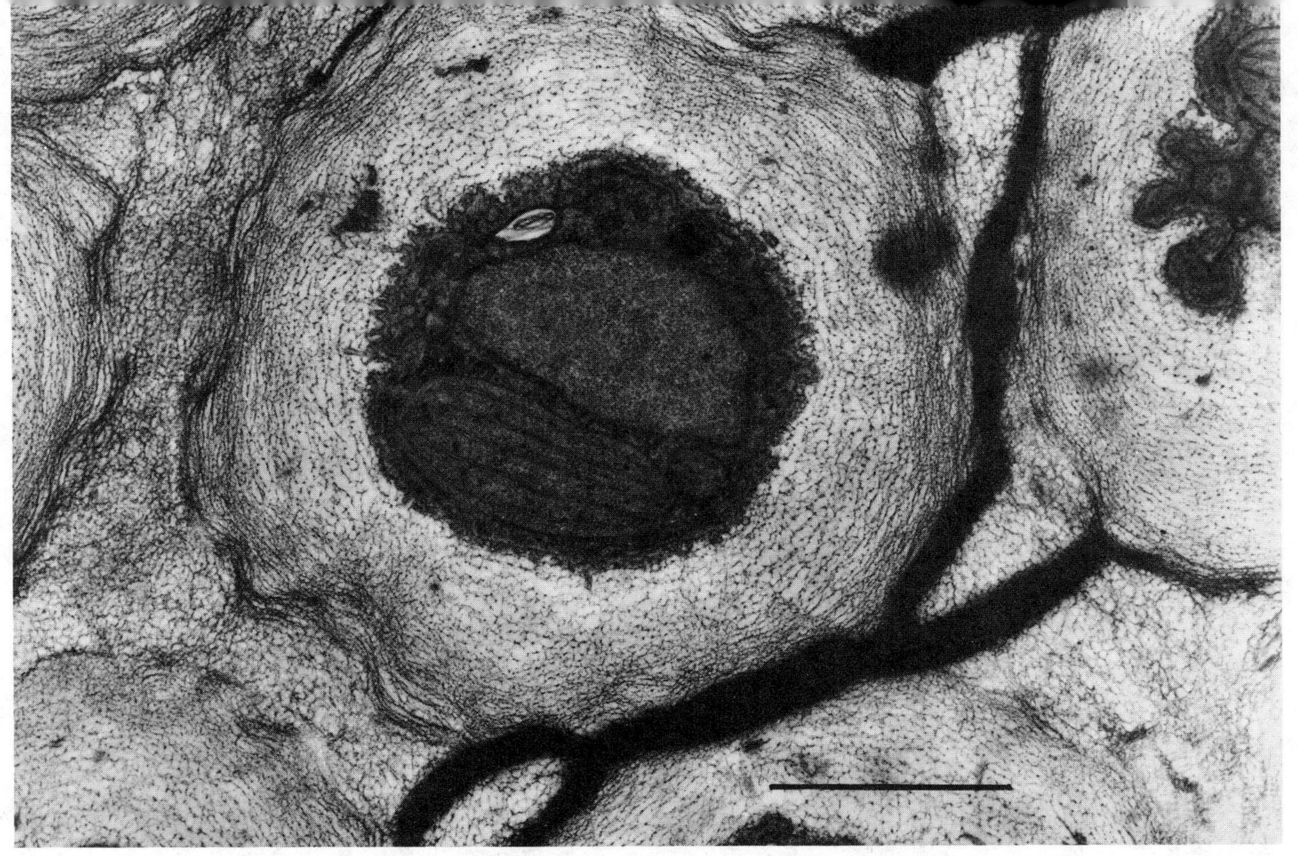

FIG. 4. Section of cell of young thallus, showing fibrillar wall, chloroplast, and nucleus. (The line = 1μ.)

pattern in all experiments, with rapid uptake of labeled ^{14}C into a carrageenan fraction, which was soluble in KC1, and very slow incorporation into the insoluble fraction. The highest specific activity of the KC1 soluble carrageenan was obtained at later time intervals (72 hours) in the two October experiments, but the initial slope of uptake was similar in all cases. The specific activity of the insoluble fraction was very low in all experiments and almost negligible in those carried out in January.

A primary problem of these experiments was the variable recovery of carrageenan from the fractionation process and the variation in proportion of the two polymers. A similar problem has been reported by other workers and discussed extensively by Black et al. When the preliminary results of the present investigation were presented at the VIIth International Seaweed Symposium in Sapporo, Japan, in August 1971, three possible sources of variation were mentioned, (1) season, (2) region or habitat, both investigated by Black et al., and (3) stage of the life cycle. This last possibility was suggested by our chance observation that several samples with tetrasporangia upon them had a very high content of KCl soluble or "lambda" carrageenan, and almost no KCl insoluble carrageenan.

The second series of experiments was carried out in Halifax, with the collaboration of J. S. Craigie of the Atlantic Regional Laboratory. This time the problem was attacked initially by limiting the experimental material with respect to origin and stage of life cycle, using only carposporic material from Fink Cove, and by planning to study this throughout the year. ^{14}C incorporation into the carrageenans was studied at 13° rather than at 4°, and the light intensity was increased a hundredfold, to optimize photosynthetic activity of the plants. The experiments were performed in enriched, filtered seawater. The extraction method was greatly improved and the fractionation procedure simplified.

By April it was apparent that the KCl soluble fraction of carposporic plants was unusual, as it contained 7 to 12 percent anhydrogalactose, a structural element thought to confer KCl insolubility and hence to belong to the so-called "kappa" carrageenan; it was also relatively low in sulphate relative to the values given by Rees (1968) for "lambda" carrageenan. This carrageenan constituted only 13 to 22 percent of the total carrageenan. The most abundant polymer in all instances in the carposporic plants was KCl insoluble, the analysis of which was characteristic of "kappa" carrageenan. This constituted 69 to 85 percent of the total carrageenan. There was little variation in biochemical analysis of carposporic plants at different times of the year. As in the earlier experiments, the initial slope of ^{14}C incorporation into the carrageenans was similar at various times of year.

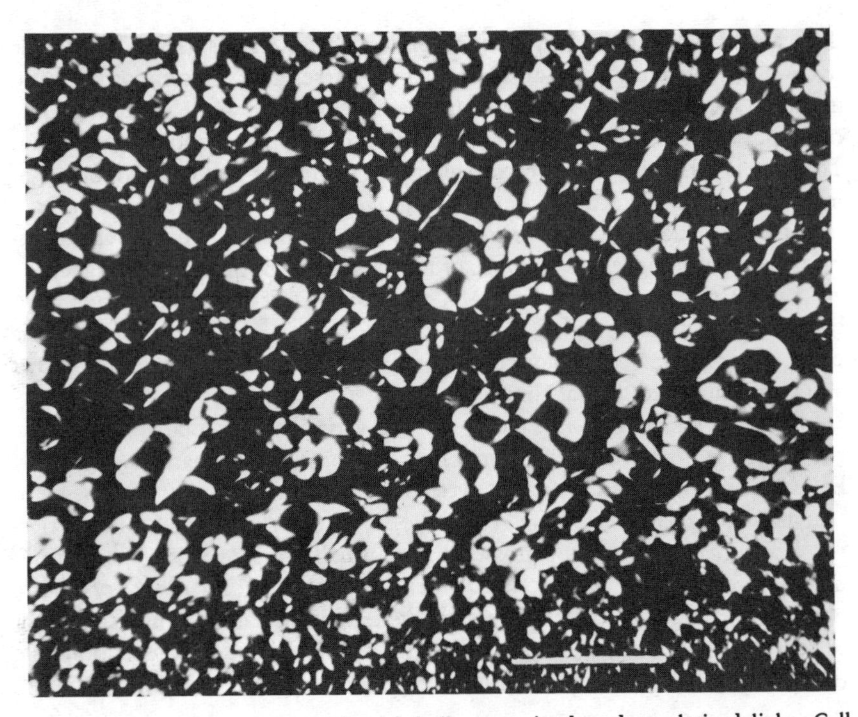

FIG. 5. Handcut transverse section of thallus examined under polarized light. Cell walls are birefringent. (The line = 40μ.)

This information and the earlier observation of high "lambda" carrageenan content of tetrasporic plants led to two experiments upon this stage of the life cycle. In all instances (6 extractions), tetrasporic plants were characterized by high yields (83 and 89 percent in the two experiments) of a very viscous KCl soluble carrageenan, the analysis of which suggested that it was lambda carrageenan. A small amount (10 to 15 percent) of insoluble material was obtained, but this was obviously not kappa carrageenan, as its anhydrogalactose content was negligible.

All four fractions, viz, carposporic KCl soluble and insoluble and tetrasporic KCl soluble and insoluble, have been characterized by infrared spectroscopy by John A. Walter of the Atlantic Regional Laboratory. The spectra indicate that the polymers insoluble in KCl (kappa carrageenan?) in the two stages of the life cycle are different and that the KCl soluble polymers (lambda carrageenan?) in the two plants are also distinct species. The two polymers from a given stage of the life cycle bear a closer relationship than would be suggested by their solubility characteristics. The KCl soluble fraction of the tetrasporic alga most closely resembles in composition and infrared spectrum the lambda carrageenan of Rees and coworkers; the carposporic KCl insoluble carrageenan is probably his kappa carrageenan. The first is a highly viscous component, the latter the gelling component of most *Chondrus* extractives. Lambda carrageenan is believed to exist as a rather rigid ribbon and shows no tendency to form helices, which is characteristic of kappa carrageenan. Because of this characteristic of kappa carrageenan, we had assumed (Gordon and McCandless) that it was the "structural" or cell wall component of *C. crispus.* Yet it is not present in the tetrasporic plant. This discovery was made shortly before the panel discussion on *Chondrus* and was announced at that time.

In the case of *Chondrus crispus*, the variation in proportion of these two polymers observed on a seasonal basis and on a habitat basis can probably be explained by the stage of life cycle most prominent in that season, or in that habitat. That the two stages of the life cycle of a single plant species, specimens of which are not grossly distinguishable except when sporulating, make rather different principal polymers is a very exciting discovery. Quite obviously, two stages possess the same genetic information. This is thought to represent the first description of such a difference, but it seems probable that a similar difference exists in other red algae as well.

REFERENCES

ANDERSON, N. S.; DOLAN, T. C. S.; LAWSON, C. J.; PENMAN, A.; and REES, D. A.
1968. Carrageenans, V: The masked repeating structures of λ- and μ-carrageenans. Carbohydr. Res., vol. 7, pp. 468–473.

ANDERSON, N. S.; DOLAN, T. C. S.; PENMAN, A.; REES, D. A.; MUELLER, G. P.; STANCIOFF, D. J.; and STANLEY, N. F.
1968. Carrageenans, IV: Variations in the structure and gel properties of κ-carrageenan, and the characterization of sulphate esters by infrared spectroscopy. Journ. Chem. Soc., vol. 100, pp. 602–606.

BLACK, W. A. P.; BLAKEMORE, W. R.; COLQUHOUN, J. A.; and DEWAR, E. T.
1965. The evaluation of some red marine algae as a source of carrageenan and of its κ- and λ- components. Journ. Sci. Food Agr., vol. 16, pp. 573–585.

GORDON, ELIZABETH M., and MCCANDLESS, ESTHER L.
1973. Ultrastructure and histochemistry of *Chondrus crispus* Stackhouse. Proc. Nova Scotia Inst. Sci., vol. 27, suppl., pp. 111–133.

GORDON-MILLS, ELIZABETH M., and MCCANDLESS, ESTHER L.
1975. Carragreenans in the cells walls of *Chondurs crispus* Stack. (Rhodophyceae, Gigartinales. I: Localization with fluorescent antibody. Phycologia, vol. 14, no. 4, pp. 275–281, illus.

JOHNSTON, K. H., and MCCANDLESS, ESTHER L.
1968. The immunologic response of rabbits to carrageenans, sulfated galactans extracted from marine algae. Journ. Immun., vol. 101, pp. 556–562.
MCCANDLESS, ESTHER L., and CRAIGIE, J. S.
1974. Reevaluation of seasonal factors involved in carageenans production by *Chondrus crispus:* Carrageenans of carposporic plants. Botanica Marina, vol. 17, pp. 125–129.
MCCANDLESS, ESTHER L.; CRAIGIE, J. S.; and WALTER, J. A.
1973. Carrageenans in gametophytic and sporophytic stages of *Chondrus crispus.* Planta, vol. 112, pp. 201–212.
MCCANDLESS, ESTHER L., and RICHER, S. M.
1972. 14 C studies in carrageenan synthesis. Proc. VII Int. Seaweed Symposium, Sapporo, Japan, 1971, pp. 491–498.
MCCULLY, MARGARET E.
1970. The histological localization of the structural polysaccharides of seaweeds. Ann. New York Acad. Sci., vol. 175, pp. 702–711.
REES, D. A.
1962. Some properties of the cell-wall mucilage of marine algae. Brit. Phycol. Bull., vol. 2, pp. 180–181.
1969. Structure, conformation, and mechanism in the formation of polysaccharide gels and networks. Adv. Carbohyd. Chem. Biochem., vol. 24, pp. 267–332.
REES, D. A., and CONWAY, E.
1962. The structure and biosynthesis of porphyran: A comparison of some samples. Biochem. Journ., vol. 84, pp. 411–416.

ESTHER L. MCCANDLESS
ELIZABETH M. GORDON-MILLS

Speciation among Small Mammals of the Apostle Islands

Principal Investigator: Richard R. Meierotto, College of St. Thomas, St. Paul, Minnesota.

Grant Nos. 863, 1002, 1206. To study speciation among small mammals of the Apostle Islands, Lake Superior.

This study was initiated to determine whether small mammals on the different islands in the Apostle group had been isolated long enough to have developed genetic differences. The Apostles (fig. 1) are a group of about 22 islands located off the northern shore of Wisconsin in Lake Superior, from several to 25 miles from the mainland. The smallest island included in the study was about 20 acres in size, while the larger ones were over 10,000 acres.

During the summers of 1968 and 1969, I sampled the small mammals on a number of islands using snap-traps. One species, *Clethrionomys gapperi*—the red-backed vole—was found on all but one of the islands sampled. In addition, several other species were relatively common. With some assurance that at least one species could be taken on most islands, a proposal was sent to the National Geographic Society for funds supporting a study of possible speciation among the small mammals. Dr. Ulysses S. Seal, a biochemist at the Veteran's Hospital in Minneapolis, agreed to do the necessary electrophoresis work on the plasma.

Live-trapping began during the summer of 1970. Equipment was moved to a convenient camping area, usually a part of the shoreline with a sandy beach that permitted easy landing. A small laboratory was set up near the camp. An island would be trapped until a representative sample of small mammals was captured. This required four to seven days. Then the camp would be moved to the next island and the procedure would be repeated. Some of the islands had no suitable beaches or campsites, and these were trapped by "commuting" from a nearby island.

Having to rely on a boat to reach a trap-line was difficult when onshore winds caused large waves. This problem was solved by acquiring a large anchor from a local fisherman. When the anchor was thrown overboard before reaching shore it would hold the boat just beyond rocks or shallow water until the traps were checked.

In total, four summers were spent trapping 19 of the islands and selected areas of the mainland. A portion of the succeeding three summers was devoted to obtaining additional specimens from islands where the initial trapping success was poor and to collecting animals for a laboratory population.

After 1974, the islands became part of the Apostle Islands National Lakeshore Park, and permits were required for collecting.

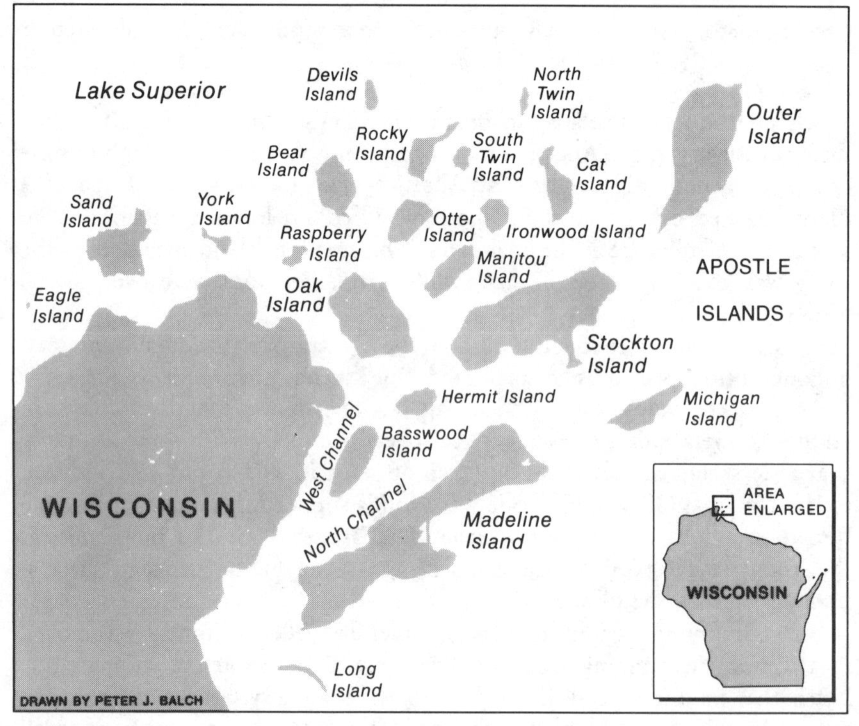

FIG. 1. Map showing location of Apostle Islands in Lake Superior.

Materials and Methods

The boat used in the study was a 16-foot Boston Whaler. It is very stable in rough water and can float in shallow water, making it an excellent craft for this type of activity. A fiber-glassed cedar-strip cabin was constructed on the front when it became apparent that large waves would regularly splash over the bow and wet everything in the boat.

Small mammals were taken with both metal and wooden live traps. During cold, wet weather the wooden traps proved superior because there was a lower loss due to exposure. Peanut butter was used as bait.

Traps would be set along a transect across an island. Between 100 and 150 traps were used. They were checked each morning and evening. When an animal was captured, it was placed in a holding can and the trap was reset.

At the camp, blood would be taken by cardiac puncture with a disposable heparinized needle and syringe. The blood was placed in a 5-cc. plastic vial and centrifuged. A portable gas-powered alternator supplied the current for a standard laboratory centrifuge. When separation between cells and plasma was complete, the plasma was transferred to a clean 5-cc. plastic vial with an airtight cap. The plasma was then frozen on dry ice.

The dry-ice cooler was constructed with several layers of insulation; however, one week was about the maximum time plasma could be kept with a load of dry ice. It was then transferred to a freezer in Bayfield or on one of the islands. Coast Guard stations on Devils and Raspberry Islands had freezers and would hold the plasma. Periodic trips were made to the Twin Cities in order to turn the plasma over to Dr. Seal at the Veteran's Hospital in Minneapolis.

Dr. Seal ran gel electrophoresis tests on the plasma samples. They were stained for esterases and serum proteins. Polaroid photos were taken of the gels showing migration patterns. The patterns of *Clethrionomys gapperi* were compared from one island to another and with the mainland.

In order to obtain a population of *Clethrionomys* with known genetic patterns, an attempt was made to establish a laboratory population. The first gravid females were taken to Dr. C. Jannis at the University of Minnesota, who was interested in studying milk proteins in various animals. After he had finished I was to obtain the families for the winter. The voles raised their young successfully. The young appeared to be growing very well when they began to die.

The following year a number of gravid females were brought back to St. Thomas College. Correspondence with Richard Bueck at the North Central Forest Experiment Station in Rhinelander, Wisconsin, indicated that they had had some success in raising *Clethrionomys* in the laboratory. His suggestions were followed as to the size of breeding cages and other equipment.

When the young reached 20 grams in weight, pairs representing crosses between different islands were placed in cages. Light was controlled on a 16/8 light/dark cycle because indications are that *Clethrionomys* breeds only during summer months. After several weeks some of the animals began to

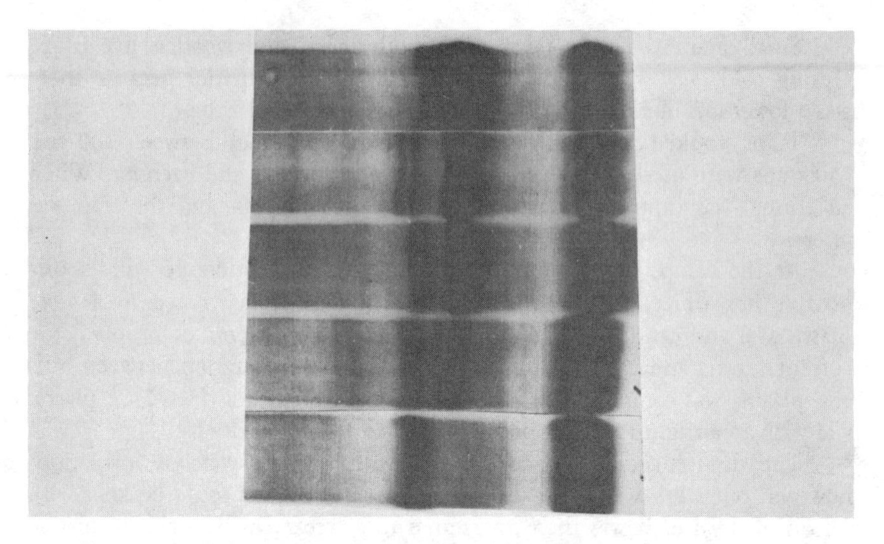

FIG. 2. Variation in serum proteins for *Clethrionomys* on Raspberry Island.

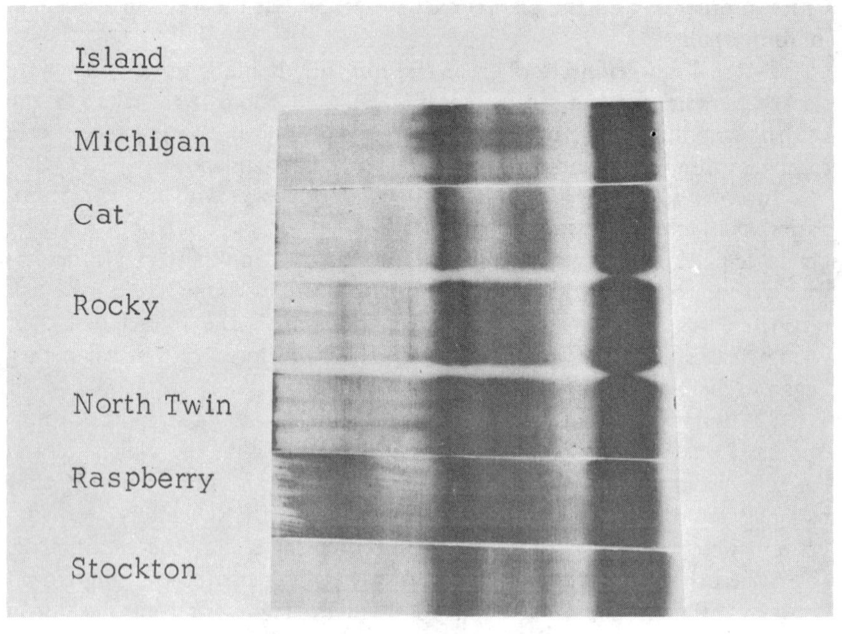

FIG. 3. Serum proteins from *Clethrionomys* taken on different islands showing similarities.

die. Before the winter was over, all the animals had died and no young had been produced.

Thinking that it might be impossible to raise the young during the winter, we made an attempt to raise them on one of the islands the following year. Adult females from some islands were placed in isolation until it was certain they were not going to have young. They were then placed in a cage with an adult male. At the end of the stay on the islands for the summer, about a month, there were still no young.

Another group of gravid females was brought back to the Twin Cities, but again there was no success. Variations of bedding, food, and cleaning cages often vs. leaving them alone, etc., produced no results, and again they all died during the winter.

The species appears to do well when confined to cages, becoming quite tame. The experience in this study, however, is that they do not survive very long in captivity and their reproductive activity is altered.

Results

Live-trapping on the islands and the mainland resulted in the capture and taking of blood samples from 558 small mammals. Of these, 441 were *Clethrionomys gapperi*, the species used in the comparative study (table 1).

Figure 2 shows some of the serum proteins for *Clethrionomys* captured on Raspberry Island. For both the transferrins (ff) and albumins (al) there were some alleles in common, and others that were distinct.

Figure 3 illustrates the similarity in alleles for transferrin from animals taken on different islands. These islands represent a good geographic spread of those sampled.

Figure 4 is included to indicate the great similarity of two specimens on Cat Island to some of those on Michigan Island. By comparison, some of those on Michigan Island have fewer alleles in common.

Meristic characteristics checked were ear length, body length, tail length, and length of the hindfoot. The animals were classified as adult or juvenile and the averages for these measurements were obtained for each age group.

There were no significant deviations found for any of the measurements that would indicate morphological variability between islands.

Electrophoresis studies were not made on species other than *Clethrionomys*. The measurements from the other species, *Microtus pennsylvanicus* and *Peromyscus maniculatus gracilis,* did not indicate significant variation. However, the number of these species taken was too small to be a valid sample.

Discussion

The red-backed vole, *Clethrionomys gapperi*, appears to have a great deal of variation with regard to serum proteins and esterases (Canham and Cameron, 1972). The results of the electrophoresis studies on the voles captured in this study also show many variations. It was thought that any polymorphism might be exhibited as allele differences for each island or for the mainland population. In reality, there was a great deal of polymorphism within the population on each island. This variation seemed to be as great as that found between animals captured on different islands.

An explanation for this might be the small home range of most mice and voles. Selander et al. (1971) found that the distance necessary to cause genetic isolation was small. Because of the nature of the trapping method in this study, a transect system, it is possible that members of distance-isolated populations were captured on each island.

Also, if the initial animals introduced to the islands had similar origins, it would cause the similarities in alleles between *Clethrionomys* found on islands and the mainland.

TABLE 1. ANIMALS FROM WHICH BLOOD SAMPLES WERE OBTAINED

Island	*Clethrionomys gapperi*	*Microtus pennsylvanicus*	*Peromyscus maniculatus gracilis*	*Blarina brevicauda*	*Sorex cinereus*
Eagle		7			
Sand	2		9		
York	1				
Raspberry	35				1
Bear	29				
Devils	35				
Rocky	38	2			1
Otter	35				
Oak	22		12	1	
Manitou	29				
Ironwood	22	2			
South Twin	31	3			
North Twin	18				
Cat	22				
Stockton	18	3	23	1	1
Hermit	23	2			
Basswood	17	2			
Michigan	20				
Outer	19	10	18		
Total	416	31	62	2	3

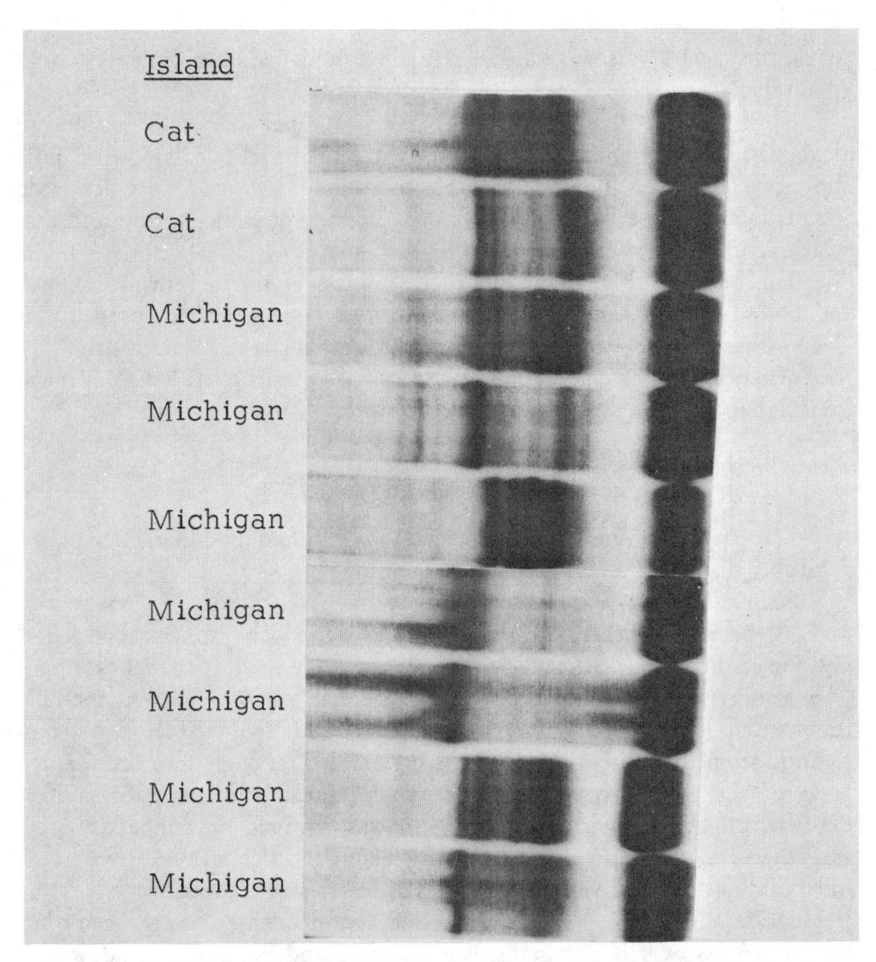

FIG. 4. Similarity and differences in serum proteins not correlated with islands.

Historically, the most likely time and source of large introductions would be the logging operations of the late 1800's and early 1900's. Since horses were used extensively and most logging was done during the winter, much hay was hauled over the ice to the islands. Hay and other materials stored on the mainland awaiting ice formation would attract mice, which could then be easily transported to various islands.

During the first summer a test was made to determine how long an animal the size of a large mouse would be able to swim in Lake Superior water. Several large animals, both *Microtus* and *Clethrionomys,* were captured and taken offshore in the boat. In several trials during calm weather, the maximum time a vole was able to stay afloat and maintain progress was 17 minutes. During rough weather the time was only 10 minutes.

Some studies (Beer et al., 1954) have indicated that mice are able to travel about one-quarter of a mile over ice. This travel is enhanced if loose snow covers the ice and they are able to tunnel. The snow cover between islands in Lake Superior is usually limited because of strong winds, and that which accumulates is usually packed by the wind.

The belief is that at present there is little or no movement of small mammals between islands; however, the time elapsed since widespread introduction has not been sufficient to erase the similarities in allele distribution. The distance between populations on an island appears to have had as much genetic-barrier effect as the water or ice between islands.

General Considerations

Trapping data from the various islands resulted in some information regarding distribution and presence of mammals.

Microtus pennsylvanicus, the meadow vole, was captured in grassy areas such as abandoned fields, sedge areas around lagoons, bogs, or stream deltas. On one of the islands, Eagle, *Microtus* was the only small mammal captured. The island is rather small and is heavily wooded. Very likely it was the only mouse that had gained access to the island, and in the absence of competition from the red-backed vole it had extended its range into the wooded areas of the island. Another case involving possible interspecific conflict occurred on Otter Island where *Microtus* was captured only in grassy areas near shore. *Clethrionomys* was captured inland in large numbers near some old buildings. Several years later, the same area was trapped for laboratory population animals and only *Microtus* was found in the clearing. It appears that *Clethrionomys* is dominant over *Microtus* and keeps the meadow vole out of its territory. This has been reported by several investigators (Clough, 1964; Calhoun, 1959).

Clethrionomys gapperi, the red-backed vole, was found in forest areas especially where there was considerable underbush or windfalls.

Peromyscus maniculatus gracilis was found frequently but none were captured on some of the islands. They were taken in open forest areas typical of the preferred habitat of this animal.

Other animals captured include *Tamiascurus hudsonicus,* the red squirrel; *Blarina brevicauda,* the short-tail shrew; *Sorex cinereus,* the masked shrew; *Mustela vison,* the mink; and *Mustela frenata,* the weasel.

An interesting aspect of mammal distribution was the difference between an island and a mainland species checklist. No island observations of chipmunks, skunks, woodchucks, or raccoons were made. These animals are all common on the mainland. Since the animals are either true or false hibernators, it is tempting to speculate that this characteristic is a barrier to dispersal to the islands. This theory is supported by the presence of many red squirrels and snowshoe hares on the islands, animals of comparable mobility and body size. The absence of porcupines on the islands is likely a function of mobility. This animal has the potential of crossing the ice but is so slow that it may never begin such a journey.

Raccoons and gray squirrels are recent migrants to northern Wisconsin. After a number of years if the gray squirrel (a nonhibernator) gains access to the islands while the raccoon (a false hibernator) does not, it would lend credence to an ice-bridge means of dispersal.

The presence of deer on some islands and the absence on others have been noted during the course of this study. Plans are being made to continue an investigation of the impact of deer on vegetation and of deer distribution.

REFERENCES

BEER, JAMES R.; LUKEUS, P.; and OLSON, D.
1954. Small mammal populations of State Islands, Basswood Lake, Minnesota. Ecology, vol. 35, no. 4, pp. 437–445.

CALHOUN, J. B.
1959. Revised sampling procedure for the North American census of small mammals (NACSM). National Institute of Mental Health, Bethesda, Maryland.

CANHAM, R. P., and CAMERON, DAVID G.
1972. Variation in the serum proteins of the red-backed mice *Clethrionomys rutilus* and *C. gapperi* and its taxonomic significance. Can. Journ. Zool., vol. 50, pp. 217–227.

CLOUGH, GARRETT C.
1964. Local distribution of two voles: Evidence for interspecific interaction. Can. Field-Nat., vol. 78, no. 2, pp. 80–88.

SELANDER, ROBERT K.; SMITH, MICHAEL H.; YANG, S. Y.; JOHNSON, W. E.; and GENTRY, J. B.
1971. IV. Biochemical polymorphism and systematics in the genus *Peromyscus*. I. Variation in the old-field mouse (*Peromyscus polionotus*). Studies in Genetics VI. Univ. Texas Publ. 7103, pp. 49–90.

RICHARD R. MEIEROTTO

Breeding Biology of Cackling Geese and Associated Species on the Yukon-Kuskokwim Delta, Alaska

Principal Investigator: Peter G. Mickelson, University of Michigan, Ann Arbor, Michigan.

Grant Nos. 850, 919, 1044. In support of a study on breeding biology of cackling geese on the Yukon-Kuskokwim Delta.

The Yukon-Kuskokwim Delta is the breeding grounds of nearly the entire species population of the cackling goose (*Branta canadensis*) and of the emperor goose (*Philacte canigica*). They nest in a narrow zone of coastal habitat, which is the breeding grounds also of half the estimated population of black brant (*Branta nigricans*). The entire Pacific Flyway population of white-fronted geese (*Anser albifrons)* and most whistling swans (*Olor columbianus*) nest on the Yukon-Kuskokwim Delta. Farther inland on the Delta, Taverner's Canada geese (*Branta canadensis taverneri*) nest in smaller numbers (Gabrielson, 1952; King and Lensink, 1971).

My study was conducted from early May to September from 1969 to 1972 on a 4-square-mile study area located 24 miles southeast of Hooper Bay, Alaska. The primary objectives of my field research were (1) to determine phenology during four breeding seasons, (2) to describe the nesting habitat of cackling geese in comparison with that of other geese and eiders, (3) to determine reproductive success, (4) to determine the effect of predation, and (5) to determine the factors affecting production of geese and eiders.

The study area chosen has excellent breeding habitat for cackling geese as well as good nesting habitat for black brant, emperor geese, white-fronted geese, and spectacled eiders (*Lampronetta fischeri*). A lowland floodplain interpersed with many shallow (wadeable) ponds and meandering tidal sloughs characterizes the study area. Most ponds are smaller than 2 acres, have many small islands, and have irregular shorelines. Ponds and sloughs make up approximately 50 percent of the study area. Much of the land area is best described as wet meadow approximately 1½ feet above mean high tide. *Carex rariflora, C. mackenziei,* and *Poa eminens* are the most abundant plants.

Methods

During the latter half of the egg-laying period and in the early incubation period I systematically searched the islands and peninsulas of each pond for cackling-goose nests. Nests of other species were found during this initial search, but most nests were located in the mid or late incubation period. Nest searching probably accounted for 95 percent of all goose and eider nests started.

For each nest found, a description of the following was recorded: the nest site; the nest; the number, incubation stage, and size of eggs; and the fate of the eggs.

Observations of brood sizes were made daily throughout the brood season. Most counts I made while watching from blinds on top of wooden towers 10 feet high, from my camp and while cruising sloughs in a motorized skiff.

Flightless cackling geese (young birds and adults molting their flight feathers) were captured by driving them across land and sloughs into a corral made of fish net. Geese were sexed, aged, and leg-banded with a colored-plastic band and a standard U.S. Fish and Wildlife monel band.

Food habits of geese and eiders were studied by collecting birds known to be feeding and then examining esophageal contents. Also, geese and eiders were observed feeding. To determine the quality of available plant species commonly used as food by geese and eiders, I collected samples of plants. Pooled vegetation samples were sent to the WARF Institute of Madison, Wisconsin, for nutrient analyses.

Banding data for cackling geese were provided by the Migratory Bird Populations Station at Laurel, Maryland, and the Klamath Basin National Wildlife Refuges, Tulelake, California. Only banding and recovery data for normal, wild birds were used. Procedures outlined by Bellrose and Chase (1950) were followed for creation of life tables.

Results

Geese and spectacled eiders breeding on the study area arrived as pairs in the last 3 weeks of May. All breeding geese and some eiders had copulated prior to arrival on the nesting grounds. Nesting began as soon as habitat was snow-free and dry, in the last week of May in 1969 and 1970 and in the first week of June in 1971 and 1972.

An average of 204 cackling geese, 32 black brant, 20 emperor geese, 19 white-fronted geese, and 42 spectacled eiders nested on the study area each year. All goose species exhibited territoriality; black brant were involved in the most territorial disputes. Cackling geese and black brant preferred to nest on islands. There was little interspecific competition for nesting islands. Other species generally nested on the shorelines of ponds or along sloughs. Most geese and eiders showed a tendency to nest in or near previously used sites. In all species the female selected the nest site.

The onset of nesting was highly synchronous—most cackling-goose nests were started within a period of 10 days. The average incubated clutch size for cackling geese was 4.65, 3.63 for black brant, 4.63 for emperor geese, 4.61 for white-fronted geese, and 4.69 for spectacled eiders. The incubation period averaged 26 days for cackling geese and about 24 days for black brant and spectacled eiders. All nesting hens were quite attentive to their duties, but they did leave their nests at least once daily, to drink, bathe, feed, and preen. Male geese remained near their mates throughout incubation. Male spectacled eiders deserted their mates by midincubation. Nesting success averaged 67.6 percent for cackling geese, 44.6 percent for black brant, 88.9 percent for emperor geese, 84.4 percent for white-fronted geese, and 68.0 percent for spectacled eiders. The average clutch for successful nests was 4.26 for cackling geese, 2.93 for black brant, 4.21 for emperor geese, 4.08 for white-fronted geese, and 4.41 for spectacled eiders. Hatching for all species was quite synchronous; most eggs hatched within 8 days.

The average brood size for fully feathered young was 3.70 for cackling geese, 2.49 for black brant, 3.29 for emperor geese, 4.00 for white-fronted geese, and 3.54 for spectacled eiders. There was little interspecific brood mixing. Broods were raised on the study area or within a radius of 4 miles. Young geese and eiders grow rapidly. Cackling-goose and black-brant goslings needed 40 to 46 days to gain flight, emperor goslings needed 50 to 60 days, young white-fronted geese required 55 to 65 days, and spectacled-eider ducklings, 45 to 55 days.

The molting period for geese covered a 6-week period from the second week of July through the third week of August. Most geese molted on or nearby the study area; however, I recorded a molt migration by yearling and nonbreeding emperor geese in 1971 and 1972. Adult cackling geese and black brant regained flight in 3 weeks, while emperor geese and white-fronted geese required 4 weeks for full flight-feather replacement. Adult female spectacled eiders did not molt on the study area. They probably molted in September along the Bering Sea coast.

The majority of cackling geese and black brant regained flight by the first or second week of August. Black brant migrated south during the next 3 weeks and were rarely seen in September. Cackling geese began migrating south in the third week of August. Most had left the Kashunuk River area by September and all had departed by late September. Emperor geese and white-fronted geese began flying south in the last week of August. Most migrated by the second week of September. Spectacled eiders migrated to the Bering Sea in late August.

Discussion

Several factors may have important effects on the production of cackling geese on my study area and the Delta. Food was abundant. Geese are predominantly grazers and utilize *Carex rariflora* and *C. mackenziei* shoots and fruits. Seeds of *Calamagrostis deschampsiodes* are also taken during July and August. Only the young goslings, less than 3 weeks old, took a significant amount of terrestrial insects. By mid-August geese and eiders began to include *Empetrum nigrum* berries in their diets. Eiders are aquatic feeders, taking primarily animal matter, especially chironomid larvae.

Certainly cool temperatures and cloudy weather during May of 1971 and 1972 reduced production. This resulted in a lower nesting density of geese, a reduction in the frequency of large clutch sizes, a reduction in average clutch size hatched by successful nesters, and finally a decreased number of young reaching flight stage.

High-quality habitat was not a characteristic of all parts of the study area. Undoubtedly some cackling geese were forced by territorial pairs to nest in lower-quality habitat. Those cackling geese that did nest on islands had a significantly greater clutch size and nesting success than those cackling geese nesting at other sites. I concluded that territoriality was the ultimate factor limiting nesting density of cackling geese on my study area. Other species were limited by nesting habitat and, in the case of spectacled eiders, probably by competition from cackling geese for nest sites.

Breeding by 2-year-old cackling geese was not as common as reported for other Canada goose populations. Less than 25 percent of the 2-year-olds bred. Geese and eiders laid continuation clutches if the first clutch was destroyed in the laying period. No cases of renesting were found.

Predation accounted for the loss of 17 percent of the eggs laid by cackling geese and most of the loss of young cackling geese. Other species suffered a slightly lower rate of predation on eggs. Predation was the cause of 65.8 percent of all losses of goose and eider eggs. The loss of young from the downy stage to flight stage ranged from 8.4 percent for cackling geese (an average of 0.33 young lost per brood) to 34.1 percent for black brant (an average of 1.25 young lost per brood). Glaucous gulls were the most important predator on eggs and young. At least one-half of all predation losses were the result of human activity disrupting nesting geese or separating goslings from parents, thus leaving the young vulnerable to gulls.

No losses of eggs, adults, or young geese due to activity of Eskimos were recorded for my study area. However, there was some spring hunting, egging, and loss of molting cackling geese, black brant, and white-fronted geese in the Kashunuk River area. This loss of cackling geese was not substantial.

The major mortality of both young and adult cackling geese was due to hunting, especially on the wintering grounds in California. The mortality rate (based on Yukon Delta bandings) for young cackling geese was 48.5 percent, for yearlings was 40.91 percent, and ranged from 23.37 to 32.65 percent for adults. Hunting pressure on cackling geese is lower than recent hunting kills of dusky Canada geese (Chapman et al., 1969) or Great Basin Canada geese (Hanson and Eberhardt, 1971). According to estimates made along the migration route, the population of cackling geese is about the same as the late 1950s (240,000 to 375,000).

Cackling geese and other waterfowl should be given continued protection as afforded by the Clarence Rhode National Wildlife Range and other refuges along migration routes and on wintering grounds. Major developments, such as associated with the oil industry, should be prohibited on the breeding grounds. Human activity both on the nesting and brood rearing grounds should be limited to the gathering of nesting and brood data necessary to indicate yearly trends in production. Banding of cackling geese on the wintering and molting areas and of other species on molting and brood-rearing areas should be continued to provide information on the breeding status of the populations and the yearly kills. Hunting pressure should be adjusted to provide healthy populations that both maintain themselves and provide sport hunting.

REFERENCES

BELLROSE, FRANK C., and CHASE, ELIZABETH B.

1950. Population losses in the mallard, black duck, and blue-winged teal. Illinois Nat. Hist. Surv., Biol. Notes, no. 22, 27 pp.

CHAPMAN, JOSEPH A.; HENNY, CHARLES J.; and WIGHT, HOWARD M.

1969. The status, population dynamics, and harvest of the dusky Canada goose. Wildl. Monogr., no. 18, 48 pp.

GABRIELSON, IRA N.

1952. Alaskan waterfowl and their management. Selected Papers of the Alaska Science Conference..., 1950. Arctic Inst. North Amer., Special Publ. no. 1, pp. 292–305.

HANSON, W. C., and EBERHARDT, L. L.
1971. A Columbia River Canada goose population. Wildl. Monogr., no. 28, 61 pp.
KING, JAMES G., and LENSINK, CALVIN J.
[1971.] An evaluation of Alaskan habitat for migratory birds. U.S. Bur. Sport Fish. and Wildl., 46 pp. (Unpublished.)

PETER G. MICKELSON

Behavior and Ecology of Feral Asses (*Equus asinus*)

Principal Investigator: Patricia D. Moehlman, University of Wisconsin, Madison, Wisconsin.

Grant Nos. 862, 1056: For a study of the social organization and communication behavior of feral burros.

The behavior and ecology of feral populations of *Equus asinus* were studied in the Northern Panamint Range of Death Valley National Monument for 20 months in 1970 to 1973.

Seasonal population size and distribution were determined by individual identification and by road, aerial, and watering-source censuses. The peak density in the Wildrose study area occurred during the spring and summer months. In the fall and winter approximately 60 percent of the population moved out of the 310-square-kilometer study area. The high density within 3.2 kilometers of Wildrose Spring during the summer months was probably related to water resource needs. Individuals showed a seasonal pattern of movement, and their home ranges varied from 1.3 to 31.3+square kilometers.

Feral asses were primarily browsers in the Death Valley study area. Individuals drank approximately once every 24 hours during the hot dry summer. Females with young foals (less than 1½ months old) drank several times a day. The peak periods of drinking for the population were between 1900 and 2100 hours in the summer months. Diurnal activity was distributed among feeding (51 percent), resting (17 percent), standing (19 percent), walking (9 percent), and social, grooming, and elimination behavior (4 percent). A sample 24-hour watch on one territorial male showed activity both day and night, with 12 feeding bouts separated by resting intervals of 1 minute to 2.2 hours.

The only stable groups in this population were composed of an adult female and her offspring. Groups in which individuals were associated for at least 2 hours and less than one week were classified as "temporary groups." The sex and age composition of these groups included: 1, all-male groups; 2, two or more females and offspring; 3, mixed groups of adult males and adult females and offspring; and 4, yearling groups. Individuals were solitary in 23.9 percent of the observations, and 57.8 percent of the groups observed contained 2 to 4 individuals. Large aggregations (8 to 21) occurred rarely

(3.3 percent) and were associated with scarce resources, i.e., water and/or estrous females.

Interindividual spacing within groups was recorded at 5-minute intervals. Females and young foals were the only animals that spent most of their time within 1 meter of one another. The majority of adult-to-adult spacing distances were greater than 10 meters. Genetically related females, however, spent 69.2 percent of their time within 1 to 4 meters of one another. Female-to-male spacing decreased when the female was in estrus. Then, the most dominant male would generally stay within 1 to 4 meters of the female, while the subordinate males were at distances of 15+ meters from the female.

In general the feral population in Death Valley National Monument had a territorial social system similar to that reported by Klingel (1972) for native *Equus asinus* in the Danakil Desert of Ethiopia. The only stable social group consisted of mother and offspring, and territorial males were the sole males to be involved in breeding on their territory, although they did tolerate the presence of all conspecifics on their area. The Death Valley population differed, however, in that nonterritorial breeding did take place. This seemingly atypical behavior is most likely due to selective domestic breeding. Territorial behavior is generally considered to be an unfavorable trait for facilitating domestication (Hale, 1969) and may have been selected against during the potentially two thousand generations subjected to man's breeding program. Attempts at nonterritorial breeding have been observed in Grevy's zebra (Klingel, 1969), but fighting between courting males was nearly continuous and no successful copulations were observed. Dominance relationships in the Death Valley population were sufficiently established to facilitate access by an individual male to an estrous female on nonterritorial areas. The dominating male would usually threaten the nearest male, who in turn would threaten all other males away.

The intense competition among males for an estrous female on a nonterritorial area interfered with the female's normal daily activity pattern. When an estrous female was on a territorial area copulation frequency was low (e.g., once in 8 hours) and the rate of feeding was similar to the population mean. The copulation frequency of estrous females associated with males on nonterritorial areas was much higher (e.g., 6 in 35 minutes) and the rate of feeding would drop as low as 23.3 percent of hourly activity. In this study such reduced feeding did not seem to affect the reproductive success and survival of the female; but in a more marginal habitat the potential stress might be critical.

The reproductive success of males in the Death Valley population appeared to depend on two distinct strategies: 1, obtaining a territory near the main water source and copulating with all estrous females that entered therein; and 2, remaining nonterritorial and copulating with estrous females when they were off territories. Female asses were in estrus for 7 to 9 days, and ovulation occurs near the end of estrus. During this time copulation repeatedly took place. Without specific genetic determination of parentage, the relative success of these two strategies cannot be truly determined. However, observations of the spatial distribution of estrous females suggest that dominant males that hold territories do most of the effective mating. Unfortunately, this problem is impossible to investigate further, since the National Park Service is presently cropping the population with the goal of total elimination.

In an attempt to examine the range of behavior and social organization within *Equus asinus* in North America, short-term observations (one month) were made on a feral population in a very different habitat, Ossabaw Island, Georgia. This island is characterized by lush vegetation and a warm humid climate. There were approximately 40 feral asses on the island, with a density greater than one per square kilometer. Although the Ossabaw observations were limited, they do illustrate the plasticity possible in the social behavior and organization of feral asses. Contrary to the situation in Death Valley there were stable groups. At the south end of the island there was a stable group that exhibited all the characteristics of a harem group. At the north end of the island was a group of 13 asses that were associated in 63.6 percent of the observations. In this group the dominant male did all the courting and copulating.

Genus *Equus* is characterized by two distinct types of social organization. The harem or uni-male group has been described for Burchell's zebra (Klingel, 1972), Hartmann's zebra (Klingel, 1968; Joubert, 1972), and feral horses (Feist, 1971). The territorial form of social organization with stable bonds occurring only between mother and offspring has been described for Grevy's zebra (Klingel, 1969) and for the African ass (Klingel, 1972). Thus feral ass populations in two very different types of habitat exhibited the two types of social systems found within the Equidae. These two types of social organization also constitute what appear to be the extremes of a social organization continuum ranging from a system in which territoriality plays an important role and social bonding is limited, to the more socially organized and cohesive family groups. Fisler (1969), Crook (1970), Jarman (1974), and Kaufman (1974) have all discussed and speculated on the interrelationship between environment and social organization. The types of social organization observed in Death Valley and Ossabaw Island are consistent with some of the trends suggested by these authors.

Many factors appear to be important in the determination and/or reenforcement of a social system. In particular, data on home range, demography, and resource availability and its effect on behavior and social bonding appeared to be the critical factors in determining the type of social organization exhibited in the two locales.

Demography

In Death Valley individuals moved over large areas, with some minimal home ranges being as large as 31.3 square kilometers. Ossabaw Island asses were much more limited in potential home range and tended to restrict their movements to about 20 square kilometers. Individuals were in a higher density on Ossabaw Island (greater than 1 per square kilometer). Inter-individual spacing in Death Valley reflected the general lack of group cohesion. Female to female spacing was mostly at 10+ meters (65.2 percent), and distances female to male (63.6 percent at 15+ meters), and male to male (61.6 percent at 15+ meters) were even greater. By contrast within the Ossabaw Island harem group, the two females spent a majority (74.1 percent) of the observations within 4 meters of each other. The two adult males spent 63.9 percent of the observations within 9 meters, and male to female spacing was also relatively close (60.6 percent within 9 meters).

Resource Availability and Development of Social Bonds

Death Valley is characterized by a hot dry climate with low and sporadic rainfall. The vegetation in the study areas was primarily browse. This was a relatively unstable habitat in which water sources were of prime importance during the summer months. The feral asses exhibited low sociability, had small group size and large home ranges, and for most the year were distributed at a low density and charactercally exhibited a territorial type of social system. During periods of heat stress the population tended to be clumped around water sources. At these times territorial males were in residence adjacent to the water source, thereby enhancing their chance of copulating with estrous females.

Ossabaw Island was hot and humid with lush vegetation and readily available water supplies. The population was in higher density, had smaller home ranges, and exhibited greater sociability and group cohesion. One group of five operated as a harem.

A basic element of the daily activity pattern, percentage of time spent feeding, was quite different in the two populations. In Death Valley the asses were primarily browsers and spent 51.0 percent time feeding. By contrast, Ossabaw Island asses were primarily grazers and spent 38.1 percent time feeding. Jarman (1974) has emphasized the importance of feeding ecology in the determination of ungulate social organization. Low sociability tends to occur among browsing species, with grazers forming the more social end of the continuum. A determining factor in this trend may be the proportion of time required for feeding.

A critical resource in Death Valley was water. Mothers, presumably because of fluid stress, showed a high threat and rejection rate when foals attempted to nurse. Nursing rejections began on the first day and increased in intensity as the foal grew older. Rarely did a foal attempt to nurse without being threatened by its mother. Until the foal was a month old its nursing success per attempt was 0.82 percent. By the time it was 3 to 4 months old the success rate had diminished to 0.35 percent. This rejection was similar to weaning behavior in other equids, and differed mainly in that it commenced when the foal was so young. The lactating female is under more severe fluid stress than other adults in the population. This was reflected in their higher frequency of watering during the hot months (2 to 3 times per day as opposed to per day for other adults). While foals ate vegetaion, they did not drink water until they were about 3 months old. Thus the mother provided the foal with most of its fluid intake during that period. This provided certain safeguards for the foal, since it didn't have to compete for water at the springs. However, it increased the fluid stress on the mother in what was already an arid and difficult environment. Thus, the mother may have needed to regulate the interval of nursing so as to moderate fluid stress. This physiologically based behavior may then operate as a mechanism to stimulate independent and aggressive behavior on the part of the foals, and may thereby contribute to the lack of bonding between adults in this population. Foals were threatening conspecifics by the second day of age, particularly when another animal attempted to approach its mother.

The Ossabaw Island population exhibited almost no aggressive behavior. In particular, females rarely threatened their foals and the nursing success rate was much higher (3 to 4 months, 0.88 percent). This was probably directly related to the lactating female's reduced exposure to water stress.

Three categories of behavioral interactions that might have contributed to social bonding and grouping cohesion were greeting, mutual grooming, and social play. In Death Valley greeting behavior occurred mainly between adult males (60.2 percent) and often involved aggressive behavior (63.3 percent). Following the general trend of low frequency of association and lack of aggressive interactions, female to female greetings were rare (1.7 percent). Foals were involved in 34.0 percent of the greetings, of which they initiated 15.6 percent. Greeting behavior was rare on Ossabaw Island, which may simply be another indication that individuals were well known to each other and relationships were clearly established.

Social grooming is usually considered to be important for group cohesion (Sparks, 1967). In Death Valley the general pattern of low sociability was also reflected in the frequency of mutual grooming (0.3 observation per hour). Ossabaw Island asses had a much higher frequency of grooming (1.5 observations per hour). There were also three categories of grooming partners that were not observed in Death Valley, e.g., male-female, female-nonoffspring foal, male-foal. This behavior is consistent with the general pattern of a cohesive group, relatively small interindividual spacing, and a low level of aggressive behavior.

Social play was the other behavioral category that might have contributed to social bonding. Interestingly enough, this type of interaction was not observed between foals in the Death Valley population. These foals only exhibited solitary play consisting of such activities as picking up (in mouth) and dropping objects, running in spurts, quick stopping in front of adults, pivoting and running away, and biting and mounting their mothers. In a more social equid (New Forest ponies, Tyler, 1972) foals were playing with other foals and/or yearlings in their third week and by the sixth week social play constituted 55 percent of their play. On Ossabaw Island two male foals spent many hours engaged in social play which usually consisted of play-fighting. These foals were the same age and regularly associated; all of which facilitated social play.

Plasticity of Social Behavior

Within equids, there appears to be an upper limit for group size in which individuals can express and maintain stable relationships and bonds. The maximum size of permanent groups in Hartmann's zebra (Joubert, 1972) is about 13, with 65.2 percent of the groups being between 4 and 7 animals: Klingel reported an average size of 4.5 to 7.5 for this zebra (1967). Average size for harem groups in feral horses (Feist, 1971) was 5, with a maximum of 21. Thus, when feral asses did form permanent groups they followed the pattern for Equidae.

From the behavioral and ecological information on the two feral populations of asses, it appears that although *Equus asinus* normally displays low sociability, they do have the behavioral plasticity, given a favorable environment, to form highly social and stable harem groups.

REFERENCES

CROOK, J. H.
1970. Social organization and the environment: Aspects of contemporary ethology. Anim. Behav., vol. 18, pp. 197–209.
FEIST, J. D.
1971. Behavior and feral horses in the Pryor Mountain wild horse range, 129 pp. Master's thesis, University of Michigan. (Unpublished.)
FISLER, GEORGE F.
1969. Mammalian organizational systems. Los Angeles County Mus. Contr. Sci., no. 167, pp. 1–32.
HALE, EDGAR B.
1969. Domestication and the evolution of behavior. Pp. 23–42 *in* "The Behavior of Domestic Animals," E. S. E. Hafez., ed. Williams & Wilkins Co., Baltimore.
JARMAN, P. J.
1974. The social organization of antelope in relation to their ecology. Behaviour, vol. 48, pp. 215–267.
JOUBERT, E.
1972. The social organization and associated behavior in Hartmann zebra, *Equus zebra hartmannae*. Madoqua, ser. 1, no. 6, pp. 17–56.
KAUFMAN, J. H.
1974. Social ethology of the whiptail wallaby, *Macropus parryi*, in northeastern New South Wales. Anim. Behav., vol. 22, pp. 281–269.
KLINGEL, H.
1967. Soziale Organization und Verhalten von Freilebender Steppenzebras. Zeitschr. Tierpsychol., vol. 24, pp. 580–624.
1968. Soziale Organization und Verhalten von Hartmann und Berg Zebras (*E. zebra hartmannae* und *E.z. zebra*). Zeitschr. Tierpsychol. vol. 25, pp. 76–88.
1969. Zur Soziologie des Grevy-Zebras. Zool. Anz. Suppl., vol. 33, pp. 311–316.
1972. Social behavior of African Equidae. Zool. Africana, vol. 7, pp. 175–186.
SPARKS, JOHN H.
1967. Allogrooming in primates: A review. Pp. 148–175 *in* "Primate Ethology," Desmond Morris, ed. Weidenfield & Nicolson, London, and Aldine Publishing Co., Chicago.
TYLER, STEPHANIE
1972. The behavior and social organization of the New Forest ponies. Animal Beh. Monogr., vol. 5, no. 2, 196 pp.

PATRICIA D. MOEHLMAN

The Chan Chan–Moche Valley Archeological Project, Peru

Principal Investigators: Michael E. Moseley, Peabody Museum, Harvard University, Cambridge, Massachusetts, and Carol J. Mackey, San Fernando Valley State College, Los Angeles, California.

Grant Nos. 847, 923, 1050, 1165, 1166,[1] *1342, 1415*[1]. In support of studies of prehistoric urban-rural relationships on the north Peruvian coast: the Chan Chan–Moche Valley Project.

With support from the National Geographic Society and the National Science Foundation the Chan Chan–Moche Valley Project carried out a continuous program of archeological field studies in Peru from June 1969 until December 1974. By the time of termination the project had grown into the largest archeological endeavor ever undertaken in Andean South America. The following report succinctly summarizes the development of the project. It then critiques some of the problems encountered in the course of field studies in the hope of saving future investigators frustration.

Aims and Goals

As the project was initially conceived of in 1967, the aim was simply to map Chan Chan, the vast adobe ruins of the capital of Chimor or the coastal Chimu empire. At that time archeological investigations of urbanism were in fashion in other areas of the world, and this seemed an appropriate venture to initiate at Chan Chan because of the excellent preservation of the ruins and because other prehispanic Andean cities were largely unstudied. The plan was simply to trace the configuration of the standing architecture off aerial photo enlargements and check unclear details with ground survey. Presumably, the undertaking could be done within a year's time because the emphasis was on mapping, not interpretation. In hindsight, the scheme was tenable only because the project's future directors had spent but a few days at the site and were unaware of the great spread and complexity of the ruins.

---

[1]Grant Nos. 1166 in 1973 and 1415 in 1974 were for publication of maps resulting from the Chan Chan Project.

The idea was presented to Profs. John H. Rowe and Gordon R. Willey, who subsequently served as advisers to the project. They reacted favorably to the mapping, but not to the lack of interpretation. Chan Chan had a long and complex history and a meaningful investigation would have to contend with how the city functioned as well as with the history of its rise and fall. Rowe pointed out the likelihood that stratigraphic deposits within the ruins would be complicated and mixed and suggested that a ceramic chronology would be most easily established by seriating Chimu artifact assemblages found at small rural sites with short occupations.

Thus, there was more to Chan Chan than mapping. Interpretation demanded understanding of how architecture was used and chronological control, as well as exploration of rural settlements. Additional study of aerial photos and further visits to the site underscored the complexity of the archeological phenomena awaiting study.

Specificity of research goals as well as field methods was called for in 1968 when the first grant proposal was written to secure funding. Subsequently, a major proposal was written for each year of work. While onerous, this practice forced annual stocktaking of concepts, work completed or in progress, priority programs, timetable, and expenses. This was particularly useful because the project changed substantially as it developed, and an annual assessment of direction was vital.

The broad research goal was "to provide a basic understanding of the history and functioning of a major Andean city in relation to its rural sustaining communities." Chan Chan was a rigidly sectioned and compartmentalized city, and the aim was "to examine the sociological implications of this formal planning and to develop a history of the occupation of the settlement." A second focus of study was "to examine the nature and extent of the ties between Chan Chan and its rural sustaining communities" in the Moche Valley (Moseley, 1968). Small sites would provide assemblages for seriation, while excavations at longer-lived settlements would yield stratigraphy for a local cultural chronology. Thus, in 1968, the proposed research had three target areas: Chan Chan, sustaining communities, and chronology.

Background literature was insufficient to compensate for the lack of first-hand knowledge of the valley or its principal sites. Therefore the proposal formulated few specific, testable hypotheses, but outlined general problems. At Chan Chan it was possible to be specific about the ten major compounds. They had been hypothesized to be either quarters of craft guilds or alternatively quarters of royal lineages. Additional general study problems included residence patterns, occupational specialization, the circulation of goods and services, city planning, and urban renewal, as well as population size and its distribution through time.

Less was known about the valley occupation, and the proposal outlined only three problem sets: subsistence patterns, function of rural sites, and irrigation or water management. There was one testable hypothesis: urbanism and city life on the north coast were intrusive phenomena introduced via foreign military invasion. In 1968 this tenet was dogma, and a statement that the proposition would be tested was deliberately left out of the proposal.

Prior to the start of field work expectations were that Chan Chan would resemble an Old World type of preindustrial city and that local settlement patterns would basically resemble those previously outlined for the adjacent Virú Valley by Gordon Willey (1953). Over the next five years these expectations were continually modified.

The project was now conceived of as requiring two years, with a possible wind-down period at the end. A great deal of work and data had to be contended with. The decision was made to "subcontract" work in the form of Ph.D. and B.A. theses. Candidates were assigned specific problems and assumed responsibility for excavation, analysis, and reporting. Ultimately about 18 individuals worked on doctoral degrees and about 9 on bachelor degrees.

Of particular importance to the undertaking was standardizing data recording and indexing. In 1968, a 59-page "Field Manual" was drawn up so that the work of different investigators might be comparable in organization, recording, and terminology. This manual proved invaluable in maintaining continuity over five years of study.

Field Operations

Field work began in June 1969, and the experience proved educational as well as often humorous in retrospect. (See Mackey and Moseley, 1976, for an account of the first field season.) At Chan Chan people engaged in reconnaissance survey kept getting lost! For the novice the ruins were too vast and the mud walls too high to maintain easy orientation and sense of location. The site was soon nicknamed "The Adobe Monster" because of swallowing up new staff members for several hours.

The first three months of field operations at Chan Chan and in the Moche Valley were basically exploratory. Things proved to be so entirely different from what was anticipated that revised research hypotheses could not be formulated until some understanding of the archeological potential was at hand.

This reconnaissance allowed the 1969 research proposal to be more specific about problems and methods. At Chan Chan the range of archeological phenomena included both unique materials and repetitive materials that formed recognizable patterns. Patterning was most evident in the monumental architecture and major compounds. As construction decreased in size and elaboration, recurrent features were progressively harder to recognize. This had two lasting effects on the project's strategy. First, study of repetitive phenomena was emphasized over investigation of unique phenomena. Second, work began first on the major compounds—because they were in many ways easier to deal with—and in subsequent years moved down the architectural continuum into smaller, less formally arranged constructions. The basic approach pursued was to isolate patterning by survey and mapping; to excavate one or more recurrent structures of a pattern; and then to refer the results back to the unexcavated constituents of the pattern.

In 1969 it was recognized that the large enclosures were of two general types, compounds of irregular plan and ciudadelas with an internal tripartitate division. In the fall, excavations were started in Ciudadela Rivero (Day, 1974). This work defined a substantial number of architectural patterns. Many were given further study in subsequent years, including audiencias (Andrews, 1972), burial platforms (T. Pozorski, 1971; Conrad, 1973), canchones (McGrath, 1973), annexes (Hart, 1976), and friezes (Fang, 1975).

At the start of field operations two exploratory excavations were opened outside the compounds in areas of small, irregular, agglutinated rooms, or "S.I.A.R." (J. Topic, 1970, 1977). These provided some definition to the lower end of the Chan Chan structural continuum. The middle of the continuum was simply referred to as "intermediate architecture" for descriptive convenience. It included a great deal of monumental construction, but of a lesser scale than the compounds (Klymyshyn, 1976). The only problem with dividing the ruins into categories of monumental compounds, intermediate architecture, and S.I.A.R. was the subconscious impression that the site represented a three-class social hierarchy.

Mapping was the other activity initiated at Chan Chan in 1969. To maintain accuracy, a scale of 1:500 was selected for the approximately six square kilometers covered by the compounds, intermediate architecture, and much of the S.I.A.R. Procedures consisted of measuring ground-control points and using these to scale 1:500 enlargements of extant aerial photographs. The enlargements were traced and the tracings checked and corrected with ground survey and measurement. The corrected tracings were then redrafted and copied to form a final map, which was a composite of 22 sheets. The entire operation took approximately 24 months, and the results were published at a scale of 1:600 (Moseley and Mackey, 1974).

Initial exploration of the Moche Valley revealed a substantial number of sites of different ages. Consequently, the 1969 project proposal planned to expand survey activities to include not only Chimu communities but also earlier sites. The survey was concerned with charting the distribution of sites in space and time, as well as establishing the types of activities that took place at different settlements. To examine correlations between specific configurations of remains and particular types of activities the "small site methodology" was formulated. This methodology emphasized the use of small, short-lived settlements for establishing activity patterns because such sites were more likely to be functionally specific and less complex than larger sites with long occupations (Moseley and Mackey, 1972). An excavation program was designed to explore activity patterns at rural settlements as well as chronological problems. In 1969 Lithic Stage sites (Ossa, 1973), sites associated with prehispanic roads (Bankes, 1971), and the intervalley Chicama–Moche canal (Kus, 1972) were subjects of excavation.

By June 1970 the project assumed the general structure retained until the end of field operations. Chronology, Chan Chan, and the occupation of the lower valley were principal themes of concern. In terms of methodology the focus on patterning and repetitive architecture at Chan Chan was retained, as was the small-site methodology in the valley survey. Work at Chan Chan consisted of moving down the architectural scale, as well as out across the compounds and intermediate architecture to define patterning and its implications. In the valley, attention to irrigation continued (T. Topic, 1971; Farrington, 1974). Systematic site survey, skirting large settlements, began on the south side of the valley and moved inland to the valley neck where major canals had their intakes. The survey then crossed the river and moved downvalley and out onto the plains surrounding Chan Chan. This course was one of advancing from simple, less well-preserved to complex and better-preserved archeological phenomena. Excavations were opened at five outlying Chimu settlements in 1970 for purposes of establishing site function and chronology (Keatinge, 1973). The undertaking successfully met the project's original concern with Chan Chan—contemporary urban-rural relationships. Except for continuing studies of diet (Griffis [S. Pozorski], 1971; S. Pozorski, 1976), burial structures, and input from site survey there was no subsequent large-scale work at Chimu sites.

The scope of the project changed significantly in 1971 with the decision to work on large sites other than Chan Chan. Settlements covering 2 square kilometers or more had been bypassed in survey. They were nonetheless of major importance in establishing the urban antecedents of Chan Chan and in disproving the contention that city life was a foreign introduction stemming from military conquest. Investigations were therefore undertaken at the Caballo Muerto complex (Moseley and Watanabe, 1974; T. Pozorski, 1976),

Cerro Arena (Mujica, 1975; Brennan, 1977), Huacas Sol and Luna (T. Topic, 1977), and Galindo (Bawden, 1977), in addition to an ethnohistorical study of Trujillo (Lynch, 1973). Given the vast size and complexity of these settlements, their archeological potential could only be sampled. Yet, by the close of the project only two large sites—Cerro Orejas and Puerto Huanchaco—had not received detailed consideration.

Research Problems

The project encountered a number of significant problems that deserve comment. These can be discussed in terms of the three principal research foci.

Dating. Temporal correlations with archeological sequences and phenomena outside the Moche Valley are difficult to make with precision, and the greater the spatial separation the greater the difficulties. Ideally, the soundest approach is that advocated by Rowe (1960). This consists of cross-tying to a sequence of periods of relative time established in the south coastal Ica Valley on the basis of a "master" sequence of changes in pottery style derived from funerary ceramics. Unfortunately, cross-dating can be done only by two means. The first is by radiocarbon dates. These have inherent problems that become progressively more acute with the increasing antiquity of the phenomena under consideration. The second cross-dating method lies in finding Ica Valley materials in direct physical association with Moche Valley materials. With more than 800 kilometers separating the two valleys, such associations are rare or absent. This forces reliance on secondary levels of association. Here materials not made in either area that can be cross-dated to one valley must be found in association with remains from the other valley. These "bridging associations" are also rare and considerable inference surrounds their interpretation.

These problems make it difficult to dovetail the Moche Valley occupation with the broader prehistory of the Andean region on anything but a very general level.

In the Andean area archeological dating has traditionally been based on changes in the styles of ceramics found with burials. A frequent assumption is that changes in pottery are concomitant with changes in other aspects of culture. The project did not subscribe to this monovariant approach to culture change. Rather, the working assumption was that culture change can be calibrated only by establishing independent developmental sequences for multiple cultural variants and seeing how these change in relation to one another.

Within the valley ceramics and architecture provided large samples of remains that were used for dating purposes and for calibrating cultural change. Ceramics can be conceptualized as falling into two overlapping categories. The first entails domestic and utilitarian vessels that comprise the folk ceramics utilized by a majority of Moche Valley inhabitants. If a viable project chronology is established in this medium, dating will be most reliable for the last two millennia and most generalized for earlier times. The core of the sequence will come from excavations at Huacas Sol and Luna, Galindo, and Chan Chan, as well as three rural Chimu settlements excavated in 1970–71.

"Status" wares comprise the second category of ceramics. Basically these are art objects with esthetic properties executed in varying degrees of refinement and elaboration. Status ceramics are known principally from graves, but their original function was of broader scope and paralleled the roles played by fine fabrics among the Inca empire. A five-phase sequence exists for Mochica or Moche type ceramic grave accompaniments. The sequence is based upon the form of the spouts of stirrup-spout vessels, with additional attributes assisting in phase and subphase distinctions. At present this is the most precise ceramic chronology applicable to the Moche Valley; however, its utility is highly circumscribed. The sequence is based only on limited attributes found on a certain type of status vessel. Therefore, the chronology works best for graves and looted cemeteries. Alternatively, it is of little or no use at small residential sites, such as farmsteads, whose inhabitants had infrequent access to fine pottery.

The experience of the project indicates that status ceramics provide pottery sequences with narrow dating intervals that are of limited applicability; whereas, folk ceramics provide sequences with wider intervals that are of broad applicability.

Establishing chronological controls at Chan Chan was challenging. A ceramic sequence will emerge from strata cuts in areas of S.I.A.R. occupation. However, this sequence may not bracket all phases of occupation or encompass all ceramic forms employed at the site, for three reasons. The first is simply the problem of securing a "representative" set of sequential ceramic assemblages from a settlement of vast size in which activity areas changed both their nature and location through centuries of habitation. The second problem is one of locating stratified deposits in which the original depositional processes can be isolated and the mixing of materials can therefore be controlled. The southern third of the site has deep archeological deposits. However, these are products of complex sequences of residential and other activities often entailing constructions that leveled or removed earlier structures, as well as the use of artificial, artifact-bearing fill derived from unknown contexts. The third problem is the construction of *wachaques* and immense sunken gardens that were excavated down to about water-table level. Within the area of habitation millions of cubic meters of sediments were deliberately moved from one area to another. Natural and cultural deposits were mixed, transported, dumped, leveled, built upon, and occasionally moved again. This problem is particularly critical in the southeast quadrant of the site in the vicinity of the Chaihuac compound and Huaca Higo, which are among the oldest monumental constructions. The first occupation of Chan Chan may have begun in this region. However, most areas surrounding the two monuments have been cut away by construction of sunken fields.

Thus, the earliest monumental construction at Chan Chan is not necessarily synonymous with the first occupation of the site. Nor is there any guarantee that the first occupation was not largely removed by subsequent *wachaque* construction. Therefore, any ceramic sequence for Chan Chan will be weakest and most problematical at its early end.

The initial phase of research at Chan Chan began with a program of collecting surface sherds and artifacts from the monumental architecture on a structure-by-structure basis. It was assumed that such collections would produce chronological and functional information. The program was shortly abandoned for the following reasons. First, many sherds derived via erosion from their inclusion within mud bricks forming walls, and the origin or context of this pottery prior to incorporation within the adobes could not be controlled. Second, many sherds derived from eroding, unconsolidated fill in benches, platforms, or surfaces upon which structures were built, and again there was no control over the origins of these materials. Third, with abandonment the monumental architecture was subjected to a secondary "squatter" occupation by people utilizing Chimu ceramics and artifacts. Fourth, beginning with the secondary occupation and continuing into recent times, canals were intruded into the site, and farming in courts, plazas, and rooms mixed the wall, fill, and "squatter" materials with whatever survived of the original content of the structures. Fifth, and finally, excavation indicated most monumental architecture was kept clean of refuse during the primary occupation, and with abandonment most goods and items in use were systematically removed. Had Chan Chan not been in a desert, rain, erosion, and farming could have leveled the settlement to a point where inferences drawn from the statistical sampling of surface artifacts would be highly ambiguous if not misleading.

Complex stratigraphy and mixed surface remains forced the project to explore architecture as a chronological source. Here the underlying assumption is that if structures can be dated by means of inherent properties, then dating problems stemming from uncertain artifact associations can be avoided.

The great compounds formed the backbone of the project's endeavors, which were undertaken from four separate perspectives. First, the compounds were seriated on the basis of layout and general morphological constituents (Day, 1974). Second, a sequence was proposed on the basis of changes in the form of audiencias and their variants (Andrews, 1972, 1974). Third, burial platforms suggested another sequence (Conrad, 1973). Fourth and finally, changes in height/length/width and mold marks of adobe bricks provided another means of dating (Kolata, 1978). The adobe brick chronology is the most viable. It reverses the order of the original audiencia sequence and can accommodate most burial platforms without conflict. The brick chronology also extends to Galindo and earlier settlements, securely anchoring the beginning of the sequence.

Chan Chan. Exploring architectural patterning is an economical and justifiable approach to a settlement of the size and nature of Chan Chan. One error in research design may lie with the published plans of the site (Moseley and Mackey, 1974). About six square kilometers of standing architecture was mapped at a scale of 1:500 on the assumption that good structural preservation warranted accuracy. Hindsight indicated that perhaps 70 percent of the structures and features that were recorded did not have surface preservation warranting a 1:500 scale. Therefore mapping at this scale gave the misleading impression of better preservation and accuracy than were inherent in the surface remains. There were also numerous publishing problems that proved expensive and resulted in printing the plans at 1:600, as well as printing in monotone as opposed to the originals, which were bitone.

It is profitable to think of mapping as potentially directed toward two ends at large sites with complex architecture. The first end is locating a structure in relation to other structures, and the second is recording the dimensions of a structure. These two ends do not always call for or warrant the same degree of investment. An alternative strategy for the project would have been to map at 1:1,000 or 1:2,000 for locational purposes, and then to map critical features at 1:100 for dimensional purposes.

Valley Studies. In exploring the valley occupation excavations at small- or moderate-sized settlements with good preservation and short occupations proved extremely productive for purposes of establishing chronology or site function. However, out of more than 300 sites surveyed only about 10 percent of the smaller settlements warranted intensive work. Excavation and mapping programs at large or urban settlements were necessarily more superficial than the work at Chan Chan, and each large site investigated was the focus of but a single Ph.D. thesis. Yet, these undertakings are a major strength of the project because they bring both the valley occupation and Chan Chan into historical focus.

The settlement-pattern survey attempted to locate and record all prehistoric sites in a 250-square-kilometer area stretching from the coast to the valley neck. The goal was only partially met because of factors affecting site preservation and the methods of survey.

Preservation is governed by site location, size, and construction activities. Agriculture is the principal determinant of where people reside in the valley; and the tendency is to live along canal courses, generally on unfarmed land above the water channels. Through time, canals were cut at progressively higher elevations as progressively more land was reclaimed. This brought many early sites formerly outside the confines of agriculture into areas under cultivation. These sites were then farmed over and, more importantly, silted over by irrigation-laid sediments. This means that small sites within the confines of modern cultivation are lost owing to burial. Alternatively, large sites, such as mounds, situated in the same area project above the surrounding fields, although the bases of the structures are buried by silt. Thus, the Moche Valley site sample is biased toward large sites and toward late sites. During the Moche and Chimu occupations canals and settlements were pushed into desert regions well beyond areas of contemporary farming. Here there is good preservation of large and small settlements, and this has weighted the study of the valley occupation very heavily toward the Moche and Chimu settlements.

Beyond the limits of modern fields all areas of prehispanic cultivation and adjacent unreclaimed land were surveyed on foot and by vehicle, as were all major dry washes, passes, and routes leading to the valley, along with summits and slopes of flanking hills.

The chronological outlines of the valley occupation could have been established simply by recording the larger sites that survive. Yet, more than 50 percent of the sites recorded by the project were small one- or two-room structures, looted cemeteries, surface-sherd scatters, and lithic scatters. This was time consuming and many small sites no doubt escaped detection. However, the utility of recording many small sites is that, collectively, they provide chronological control over features such as ancient roads and canals.

Summary

The Chan Chan–Moche Valley Project expanded scope during its years of field operations. This was due to the local archeological potential outstripping original expectations. Expansion was an agglutinative process that entailed letting increasing numbers of "subcontracts" in the form of B.A. and Ph.D. theses. These theses, as they reach fruition, constitute the final reports of the project's undertakings. They make the data and interpretations available without investing in a costly publication program.

The problems encountered by the project were largely owing to the archeological phenomena under study being more complex than expected. Establishing chronological controls proved the most critical problem and one which deprives local sites and remains of their full analytical potential. Nonetheless, the project did achieve its original aim of understanding Chan Chan in the context of its rural sustaining communities. It then went on to place these findings in the context of man's 10 millennia occupation of the Moche Valley.

REFERENCES

ANDREWS, ANTHONY P.

1972. A preliminary study of U-shaped structures at Chan Chan and vicinity, Peru. Unpublished B.A. thesis, Harvard University.

1974. The U-shaped structures at Chan Chan, Peru. Journ. Field Arch., vol. 1, no. 3/4, pp. 241–264, illus.

BANKES, GEORGE H. A.

1971. Some aspects of the Moche culture. Unpublished Ph.D. thesis, London University.

BAWDEN, GARTH

1977. The Moche V occupation of Galindo. Unpublished Ph.D. thesis, Harvard University.

BRENNAN, CURTIS

1976. The Salinar occupation of Cerro Arena. Unpublished Ph.D. thesis, University of Arizona.

CONRAD, GEOFFREY W.

1973. Burial platforms and related structures on the north coast of Peru: Some social and political implications. Unpublished Ph.D. thesis, Harvard University.

DAY, KENT C.

1974. Monumental architecture at Chan Chan, Peru: Ciudadelas and compounds. Unpublished Ph.D. thesis, Harvard University.

FANG, MADELEINE

1975. The marine theme of Chimu friezes. Unpublished M.A. thesis, University of California, Los Angeles.

FARRINGTON, IAN S.

1974. Irrigation and settlement pattern: Preliminary research results from the north coast of Peru. Chap. 8 (pp. 83–94) *in* "Irrigation's Impact on Society," 181 pp., illus., Theodore E. Downing and McGuire Gibson, eds. University of Arizona Press, Tucson.

GRIFFIS, SHELIA
1971. Excavation and analysis of midden material from Cerro la Virgen, Moche Valley, Peru. Unpublished B.A. thesis, Harvard University.

HART, ELIZABETH
1976. Ciudadela associated structures: Form and function. Unpublished B.A. thesis, Harvard University.

KEATINGE, RICHARD W.
1973. Chimu ceramics from the Moche Valley, Peru: A computer application to seriation. Unpublished Ph.D. thesis, Harvard University.

KLYMYSHYN, ALEXANDRA
1976. Intermediate architecture in Chan Chan, Peru. Unpublished Ph.D. thesis, Harvard University.

KOLATA, ALAN
1978. An adobe brick chronology for the Moche Valley. Unpublished Ph.D. thesis, Harvard University.

KUS, JAMES S.
1972. Selected aspects of irrigated agriculture in the Chimu heartland, Peru. Ph.D. thesis, University of California, Los Angeles. University Microfilms, Ann Arbor, Michigan.

LYNCH, PATRICIA
1973. Settlement patterns of the Moche Valley, Peru: A preliminary synthesis and analysis. Unpublished B.A. thesis, Harvard University.

MACKEY, CAROL J., and MOSELEY, MICHAEL E.
1976. The Chan Chan–Moche Valley archeological project: The first field season. Nat. Geogr. Soc. Res. Rpts., 1968 Projects, pp. 317–324.

MCGRATH, JAMES E.
1973. The canchones of Chan Chan, Peru: Evidence for a retainer class in a preindustrial urban center. Unpublished B.A. thesis, Harvard University.

MOSELEY, MICHAEL E.
1968. Prehistoric urban-rural relationships on the north Peruvian coast. Unpublished research proposal, Harvard University.

MOSELEY, MICHAEL E., and DAY, KENT C.
——. The Andean desert city. School of American Research, Santa Fe, New Mexico (in press).

MOSELEY, MICHAEL E., and MACKEY, CAROL J.
1972. Peruvian settlement pattern studies and small site methodology. Amer. Antiq., vol. 37, no. 1, pp. 67–81.
1974. Twenty-four architectural plans of Chan Chan, Peru: Structure and form at the capitol of Chimor, [10] pp. + 24 folded sheets in case. Peabody Museum Press, Cambridge, Massachusetts.

MOSELEY, MICHAEL E., and WATANABE, LUIS
1974. The adobe sculptures of Huaca Los Reyes: Imposing artwork from coastal Peru. Archaeology, vol. 27, no. 3, pp. 154–161, illus.

MUJICA, ELIAS
1975. El occupación del Cerro Arena. Unpublished B.A. thesis, San Marcos University.

OSSA, PAUL P.
1973. A survey of the lithic preceramic occupation of Moche Valley, north coastal Peru: With an overview of some problems in the study of the early human occupation of West Andean South America. Unpublished Ph.D. thesis, Harvard University.
POZORSKI, SHELIA G.
1976. Prehistoric subsistence patterns and site economics in the Moche Valley, Peru. Unpublished Ph.D. thesis, University of Texas, Austin.
POZORSKI, THOMAS G.
1971. Survey and excavations of burial platforms at Chan Chan, Peru. Unpublished B.A. thesis, Harvard University.
1976. Caballo Muerto: A complex of early ceramic sites in the Moche Valley, Peru. Unpublished Ph.D. thesis, University of Texas, Austin.
ROWE, JOHN H.
1960. Cultural unity and diversification in Peruvian archaeology. Pp. 627–631 in "Men and Cultures," selected papers of Fifth International Congress of Anthropological and Ethnological Sciences, Philadelphia, September 1–9, 1956.
TOPIC, JOHN R., JR.
1970. A lower class residential area of Chan Chan: Initial excavations. Unpublished B.A. thesis, Harvard University.
1977. The lower class at Chan Chan: A qualitative approach. Unpublished Ph.D. thesis, Harvard University.
TOPIC, THERESA L.
1971. Preliminary studies of selected field systems, Moche Valley, Peru. Unpublished B.A. thesis, Harvard University.
1977. Excavations at Moche. Unpublished Ph.D. thesis, Harvard University.
WILLEY, GORDON R.
1953. Prehistoric settlement patterns in the Virú Valley, Peru. Bur. Amer. Ethnol. Bull. 155, 453 pp., illus.

MICHAEL E. MOSELEY

Sperm-whale Capture and Acoustics

Principal Investigator: Kenneth S. Norris, University of California, Santa Cruz, California.

Grant No. 833: For bioacoustic studies of the sperm whale.

A theory about the production of burst-pulsed sounds by the sperm whale (*Physeter catodon*) was developed by Dr. George Harvey and me (Norris and Harvey, 1974) that required for a definitive test the recording and analysis of sounds from a sperm whale of known length. The gist of the theory is that the complex anatomy of the sperm-whale forehead, which includes two vertically placed air sacs that find the ends of the huge oil-filled spermaceti case, is used to produce packets of sound by reverberation. The sound is proposed to travel in the spermaceti and to bounce off the air mirrors. Then, at the front of the spermaceti organ some sound escapes with each such traverse, through an upper lip, where contact with the tissue of the anterior forehead is tightly maintained, thus allowing sound passage. The anatomy of the air-sac system allows recycling of air and thus sound production deep in the sea, which has been observed in deep-swimming whales (Backus and Schevill, 1966). The test proposed was to catch a sperm whale by normal head-netting methods and to "drydock" it in a specially built inflatable rubber raft, using the means I developed for the first live-whale capture (Norris, 1974). In this method the netted whale is partially immobilized alongside the capture vessel by means of nooses run around its tail and secured on deck, the uninflated raft slid under it, inflated with compressed gas. The whale is thus both immobilized and supported on a "waterbed" and can be manipulated at will, or towed to port.

It was planned to listen in to the forehead of the whale with a contact microphone, measure its length and other dimensions, and to note any behavioral correlates of phonation. In this way it was hoped to see if the dimensional features of the animal matched projected travel times in the spermaceti organ, and to determine the exact locus of sound emission, and to note whether or not such emission was under the control of the animal.

Records from the hand-whaling industry indicated a prominent sperm-whaling grounds in the vicinity of the lower Hawaiian islands, though modern strandings and other records there were uncommon. Thus it was decided to attempt capture in this area.

The various gear needed for such an effort were assembled or constructed; special contact hydrophones, built of lead zirconate titanate discs, were built and tested; and recording gear was assembled and calibrated. A special 30-foot inflatable raft was built to specifications and brought to Hawaii. Arrangements were made with the Oceanic Institute research vessel *Hiki No* to stand by, should animals be located, to serve as the collection and towing vessel. The captured animal was to be brought into the lee of the nearest island for tests in the raft, before a decision was made to bring it into captivity altogether or release it. Special head-netting gear suitable for netting up to a 30-foot sperm whale was built. Lines and other gear were readied, as were measures designed to protect the vessel and crew from a possible irate adult.

Arrangements were made with a local charter service, the Royal Hawaiian Air Service, to fly transects offshore from Maui, Lanai, Kahoolawe, and Hawaii, in search of whale schools. Though more than 5,000 air miles were flown in this way no sperm whale was sighted, though many other cetaceans of several species were located and recorded. The effort was stopped because of exhaustion of the allocated funds.

Since this attempt, some partial corroboration of the theory has come from recordings made of a very large old sperm whale trapped briefly in a fiord in the Faroe Islands. Measurements of it were made by dropping a measured disc near it and photographing the disc. Sounds were then recorded, back-calculated, and matched to proposed length, the time relations in the sound packets being considered as reflecting the dimensions of the spermaceti organ. This correspondence was close (Bertel, Mohl, pers. comm.), but, to date, no direct recordings from sperm whales have been made. Our work has not been reinstituted, primarily because of the expense of the collecting ship that is required to stand by but which is no longer available to us. The existence of the northwest Hawaiian sperm-whale grounds is suspect in my mind, and may reflect more the needs of whalers who had been at sea for many months than any concentration of whales.

REFERENCES

BACKUS, RICHARD H., and SCHEVILL, WILLIAM E.

1966. *Physeter* clicks. Chap. 22 (pp. 510–528) *in* "Whales, Dolphins, and Porpoises," Kenneth S. Norris, ed. University of California Press.

NORRIS, KENNETH S.

1974. The porpoise watcher, 250 pp. W. W. Norton & Co., New York.

NORRIS, KENNETH S., and HARVEY, G. W.

1974. Sound transmission in the porpoise head. Journ. Acoust. Soc. Amer., vol. 56, no. 2, pp. 659–664.

KENNETH S. NORRIS

Natural History and Ecology of the Falkland Islands, with Emphasis on Bird Life

Principal Investigator: Olin Sewall Pettingill, Jr., Laboratory of Ornithology, Cornell University, Ithaca, New York.

Grant No. 893: In support of research on the natural history and ecology of the Falkland Islands.

The Falkland Islands, an archipelago in the South Atlantic 300 miles east of the tip end of South America, comprise a British colony of 2,300 people, practically all British or of British descent. Sheep-farming is their principal industry. About half of the population lives in Stanley, the capital and only town; the other half is scattered among some 30 settlements on the larger islands. Each settlement is headquarters for a particular farm, which is either privately owned or owned and operated by the London-based Falkland Islands Co. (FIC).

Knowing that the Falklands are the only place in the world where one may live with people and be in the vicinity of at least three kinds of penguins as well as hosts of other sea birds, I induced Walt Disney to send Mrs. Pettingill and me to the islands in 1953–1954 to film penguins, other wildlife, and the activities of the Falklanders. The results of our five months of work—and experiences—later appeared in the Disney film "Islands of the Sea," in an article for the *National Geographic* (March 1956), and in Mrs. Pettingill's book "Penguin Summer" (1960). Anxious to make another film, this one for myself, with the addition of sound, and to undertake an ecological and natural history study of the islands, with emphasis on bird life, we planned the 1971–1972 expedition, supported in part by a research grant from the National Geographic Society.

Whereas in 1953–1954 we concentrated our efforts on two productive spots, Kidney Island and New Island, this time, with the assistance of Maurice Rumboll, a young naturalist from Argentina, we worked in many ornithologically rewarding parts of the archipelago. Except for two stays at Kidney Island, we based ourselves in different settlements, reaching them by government-operated Beavers, float planes admirably suited for short lifts. Words cannot adequately express our indebtedness to the several farm managers and their families for their hospitality and for their great generosity in providing transportation by Land-Rovers to the sea-bird colonies on their respective properties.

We arrived in the Falklands on November 8, 1971, and our work in the succeeding 4 months proceeded without a hitch. My special interests centered on the relationships of the 57 species of breeding birds to the peculiar environment of the islands and, in the great sea-bird colonies, to the interactions of the associated species and the behavior of each species.

As I have reported earlier (Pettingill, 1960), the Falklands have a cool, equable climate the year round with persistently strong winds, often reaching gale force. This factor, coupled with a totally treeless terrain, except for plantations about settlements, restricts the number of terrestrial species of birds able to colonize the islands.

Only nine passerine species are native and breed regularly. Of these, three—a pipit (*Anthus correndera*), a meadowlark (*Sturnella loyca*), and a finch (*Melanodera melanodera*)—occupy the interior of the two large islands, which are mainly covered with grass interspersed (depending on drainage) with dwarf shrubs. A fourth species, a ground-tyrant *(Muscisaxicola macloviana)*, survives successfully in the shelter of rocky outcrops and sea cliffs where it finds a sufficient supply of insects.The other five species—two wrens *(Cistothorus platensis* and *Troglodytes aedon)*, a furnariid *(Cinclodes antarcticus)*, a thrush *(Turdus falcklandii)*, and a small finch *(Spinus barbatus)*—tend to concentrate in tussock grass *(Poa flabellata)*, which grows in dense clumps, 8 to 10 feet high, on many small islands such as Kidney Island, providing a unique habitat.

I have reported at length (Pettingill, 1974) on our observations of all nine passerine species, giving our impressions and interpretations of behavior, including vocalizations, presenting data on nests and nesting habits, and contributing information on habitat selection, food, and postnesting activities. I stressed the relationships of the species to the Falkland environment—geographical features, climate and weather, human settlement and industry, vegetation, and animal life. I found that the populations of all nine species were sparse in all areas of the Falklands, owing to the paucity of insect food, except on tussock islands and about human settlements. The nesting season for passerines was confined to three or four months despite a remarkable equable climate all year that would seem to permit a longer season. I obtained no evidence of passerines migrating to the South American mainland.

We devoted much time to the marine birds nesting along the coasts. Few places in the Southern Hamisphere rival the Falklands in the variety and numbers of penguins, procellariiform (tube-nosed) birds, cormorants, waterfowl, shorebirds, and gulls.

We paid considerable attention to the two oystercatchers, *Haematopus leucopodus* and *H. ater.* Both were equally common—an unusual situation since few coasts in the world have more than one breeding species. How they were ecologically and behaviorally different, and hence reproductively isolated, I shall discuss in detail in a forthcoming paper. Briefly, the species *ater,* the blackish oystercatcher, restricted itself to rocky coasts where it foraged primarily for mussels and limpets and nested well above the tideline, while *leucopodus*, the Magellanic oystercatcher, stayed on or in the vicinity of sandy beaches where it probed for sandworms and small clams and nested in grassy places back from the sea. We saw the two species together only when *leucopodus* chose to forage for mussels and limpets on the rocky coasts frequented by *ater.* Neither species showed any concern about the presence of the other. The species *ater* was the more vociferous, seemingly making up in vocalizations what it lacked in striking coloration. Both species performed their particular "piping" displays as do other species of oystercatchers elsewhere. I obtained a good photographic record of these displays, and in a future publication I will give my views on their social significance.

The abundantly breeding black-browed albatross (*Diomedea melanophris*) gave me an excellent opportunity to record by direct observation and photography its rich variety of displays. I now have an ample basis for comparing its displays with those of several other albatross species, notably those of the Laysan albatross *(Diomedea immutabilis)*, which I once studied at Midway Islands in the North Pacific. In a forthcoming paper I shall point the similarities and differences between the displays of the species and show that the displays of the black-browed albatross are more simplified or less evolved.

I was able to augment my information on the breeding behavior of the king and rock cormorants (*Phalacrocorax albiventer* and *P. magellanicus*) obtained in 1953–1954. I now have substantial material for a paper on their behavior and breeding biology as well as their ecology. The two species differ widely. King cormorants forage in deep, offshore waters, the rock cormorants in shallow, inshore waters. The kings nest in large colonies among rockhopper penguins, the rocks in small isolated colonies on the shelves of cliff walls.

Our sole disappointment was the scarcity of birds of prey and our consequent inability to learn more about them. Although they were no less scarce than in 1953–1954, I had hoped for better luck in finding nests. I can say only that they are holding their own, and this statement includes the peregrine falcon. Compared to the way it is declining in the Northern Hemisphere, it seems to be faring well!

We were delighted to discover that, in the 18 years since our first stay in the Falklands, the populations of penguins—the gentoo (*Pygoscelis papua*), rockhopper (*Eudyptes crestatus*), and Magellanic (*Spheniscus magellanicus*)—had markedly increased. At New Island, the gentoo colony inland from North Harbour had doubled in size to 50,000 individuals, and the rockhopper colony west of the settlement had doubled to perhaps 250,000 individuals. We were also delighted to find a few pairs of macaroni penguins (*Eudyptes chrysolophus*) nesting in some of the rockhopper colonies and to learn of six gentoo colonies in which king penguins (*Aptenodytes patagonicus*) were nesting. In five of the colonies there were only a pair or two of kings, but in the colony at Volunteer Beach, which we visited in December and again in February, we noted as many as 40 full-grown kings at one time, including 10 adults, each with an egg or chick.

The increase in penguins is due partly to greater protection afforded by the Falklanders. While they still take penguin eggs under license, many people have come to recognize penguins as a tourist attraction and consequently have either stopped or greatly curtailed the practice. The Falkland Islands Government has helped by setting aside, as nature reserves, a number of small islands and areas on the main islands, East Falkland and West Falkland, where penguins nest.

At the conclusion of our work toward the end of February 1972, we ran into the problem of reaching the mainland of South America for a flight home. The Falklands had no landing field for planes. Thus the only means of transportation to and from the islands was by ship. We arrived in the Falklands from Montevideo on the RMS *Darwin*, owned and operated by the Falkland Islands Co. While we were there, the firm decided that it could no longer afford to operate the ship without a government subsidy. The government, crying poverty, held back on providing funds. And so we waited. At long last, five weeks after our work was completed, the FIC and the government reached a compromise, and we sailed on the *Darwin* on March 24 for Comodora Rivadavia, Argentina, the nearest port on the South American mainland. From there, on March 27, we took a commercial flight north to Buenos Aires and beyond.

REFERENCES

PETTINGILL, ELEANOR RICE

1960. Penguin summer: An adventure with the birds of the Falkland Islands, 198 pp., illus. Charles N. Potter, Inc., New York.

PETTINGILL, OLIN SEWALL, JR.

1956. People and penguins of the faraway Falklands. Nat. Geogr. Mag., vol. 109, no. 3, pp. 387–416, illus.

1960. The effects of climate and weather on the birds of the Falkland Islands. Proc. XIIth Int. Orn. Congress, Helsinki, 1958, pp. 604–614.

1974. Passerine birds of the Falkland Islands: Their behavior and ecology. Living Bird, vol. 12, pp. 95–136, illus.

OLIN SEWALL PETTINGILL, JR.

Sea-lion Vibrissae—an Acoustic Sensor

Principal Investigator: Thomas C. Poulter, Biological Sonar Laboratory, Fremont, California, and Stanford Research Institute, Menlo Park, California.

Grant No. 888: To study acoustic vision by ears and vibrissae in sea-lion sonar.

We in the Biological Sonar Laboratory have been conducting extensive studies of the sonar of the marine mammals since 1962 and have published more than 80 papers in this and related fields. We were the first to show that the pinnipeds use a system of echolocation (Poulter, 1963a, b; 1965; 1966), that they use a double click containing a silent or listening period of less than 10 milliseconds duration and so located timewise as to receive echoes from targets at a range up to 25 feet with an accuracy of ±4 centimeters (Poulter, 1963b; Shaver and Poulter, 1967).

We also showed that their echolocation clicks may not necessarily come from their vocal cords but many come also from a point near the posterior end of the larynx (Poulter, 1965). We further postulated as a result of many experiments that their hearing is cut off whenever they are generating a signal (Poulter, 1963b); thus they have not been listening to a loud click just before listening for a very weak echo. At their normal rate of clicking of up to 25 per second and with 12 animals echo ranging on the same fish, the probability that the echo of another animal's click would fall within this silent period is only 1 in 15. This, combined with the fact that the exact waveform of each animal's clicks is specific for that animal, leads us to believe that they can identify those echoes which result from their own click.

This provides them also with an uncanny ability to cope with interfering or jamming type signals. On one occasion a circulating pump in an adjacent tank was introducing high-frequency squeaks into the water at a rate of about 10 per second while we were feeding California sea lions in total darkness and recording their clicks. For a short time they superimposed a series of randomly spaced and random frequency clicks over this background of squeaks, then got in step with them and introduced about three or four clicks between successive squeaks of the pump (Poulter, 1963b). From an analysis of their signals we determined what the probable accuracy is with which they can determine the range and bearing of a target (Shaver and Poulter, 1967), and Dr. Seville Chapman (1969) has shown that they can obtain an accurate acoustic image of the shape and size of a target. They are thus able to discriminate between two very similar targets such as a fish and a piece of beef cut to the same size and shape; therefore they can discriminate between targets of different texture (Poulter and Jennings, 1969). We have demonstrated that the California sea lion uses almost a white noise click for fish over 6 inches long and predominantly a two-tone click for the same species of fish less than 5 inches in length (Poulter and Jennings, 1969).

These studies were conducted in an anechoic bioacoustical sonar research tank, which has better anechoic characteristics than any other tank constructed to date of comparable size (Poulter, 1968). It is 80 feet long by 18 feet wide and 5 feet deep and has a reverberation decay rate in excess of 5,000 decibels per second for frequencies as low as 300 Hz.

The pinnipeds are not limited to their own vocalization as a source of sound for their sonar but they can use the cavitation clicks from their swimming through the water, as is the case of the fur seals and penguins. It has been demonstrated also that the sonar capability of the pinnipeds is an innate ability and not a learned technique (Poulter, 1969).

A study of the manner in which the California sea lion manipulates its vibrissae and uses its sonar even in daylight while exploring an anechoic tank into which it has been placed for the first time suggests that the vibrissae are being used in some manner in conjunction with their sonar. This led to a careful examination of the nerves at the base of the vibrissae by means of both optical and electron microscope. This investigation was conducted by Robert J. Stephens, Ph.D., Irvin J. Beebe, M.D., and Thomas C. Poulter, Ph.D., in 1972. In general the conclusions of that investigation are as follows:

1. The nerve system at the base of the vibrissae of the California sea lion is vastly more complex than they are for the hairs along the center line sensitive area of the shark.
2. The vibrissae may be flexed slowly over a wide angle without generating a signal but should generate a large signal if flexed at a high rate.
3. The vibrissae should respond to the very high repetition rate, even the vocalization of *Tursiops* (270 kHz) or *Platanista* (380 kHz).
4. The vibrissae should respond to very low intensity signals.

This by no means should detract from their use as normal tactile organs. In fact, I have held my hand out to "Whiskers," a 7-year-old, 750-pound

California sea-lion bull, and he came up close to my hand and advanced the vibrissae of one side of his face through about 80° until they touched my fingers without moving the vibrissae on the other side of his face.

Implants for cochlear microphonic studies have been attempted in the pinnipeds on several occasions, but because the bulla is so completely filled with cardiovascular tissue (Odend'hal and Poulter, 1966) no successful im-

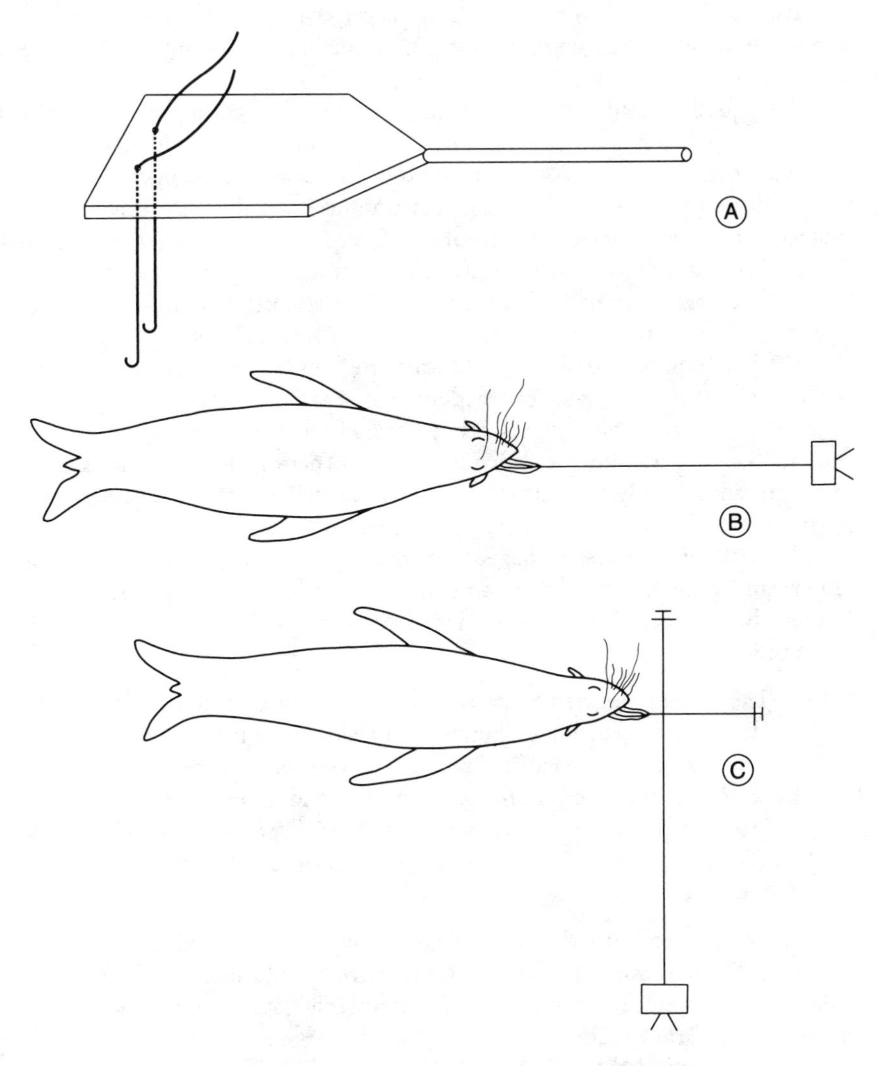

FIG. 1

plant has been completed and further work needs to be done to develop a satisfactory surgical technique. Tentative or partially successful implants have, however, given spectacular results from acoustic, mechanical, and even electromagnetic stimuli.

With an opening in the bulla it is not necessary that the electrode be in actual contact with the edge of the round window, but if it is in contact with the tissue in the vicinity of the opening, a very strong cochlear microphonic signal will be obtained from a tuning fork contacting almost any place on the animal's head.

An equally strong signal is obtained merely by tapping the animal's head with a pencil or a surgical instrument or by thumping it with the finger. However, most spectacular was the response from an extremely weak modulated electromagnetic field, which was produced by the very tiny coil removed from an ear-plug-in-type speaker. This coil minus all other parts from the speaker was energized by the output signal from a magnetic tape recorder. With this coil at a distance of more than 2 feet from the electrode implant, a good quality cochlear microphonic signal could be picked up.

We have demonstrated that California sea lions have the ability to resolve and make use of vastly shorter time intervals than can man. They will, for instance, send out echolocation clicks at a rate of 60 or even 75 per second and react to the echoes from the individual clicks. There is no reason to believe that this cannot apply to their tactile organs as well as to their hearing, and it would certainly enhance their ability to cope with jamming in their sonar.

Chapman (1969, 1971) has shown that the size and shape of a sonar target can be determined with some accuracy and that the factors that influence the accuracy by means of sonar of this determination and their effects are as follows:

1. The higher the frequency of the signal, the greater the resolution.
2. Multiple frequencies are better than a single frequency.
3. Fluctuating frequencies are better than constant frequencies.
4. Motion of the receiver also enhances size and shape recognition.
5. Multiple point reception greatly enhances shape and size recognition.
6. Wider separation in the multiple point reception greatly enhances identification.

In Dr. Charles E. Rice's study of the use of sonar by blind people at the Biological Sonar Laboratory, he showed that they could identify some three-dimensional targets if the targets were alternately rotated about two right-angle axes at a known rate.

Since the blind dolphin from Pakistan employs frequencies up to 380 kHz in its sonar and, if it takes advantage of its tactile detection of sound in water, it should have as accurate an image of a sonar target as man would have a visual image on a television screen except for color.

As of the time of this report three experiments have been conducted employing gross electrode implants on or near the facial nerve leading from the vibrissae to the brain and one experiment employing a microelectrode in a single nerve cell.

In the first three cases moderate to very strong positive results were obtained and in the case of the single cell electrode the results were questionable to negative. This range of results was not too surprising because of the preponderance of nerves in this vicinity and the problem of selecting the proper nerve. In the first experiment an incision was made on the right side of the face of a 1-year-old anesthesized California sea lion in order to expose a section of one of the facial nerves about 4 centimeters in length.

A pair of electrodes had been prepared from 20-mil, 90-percent plat-

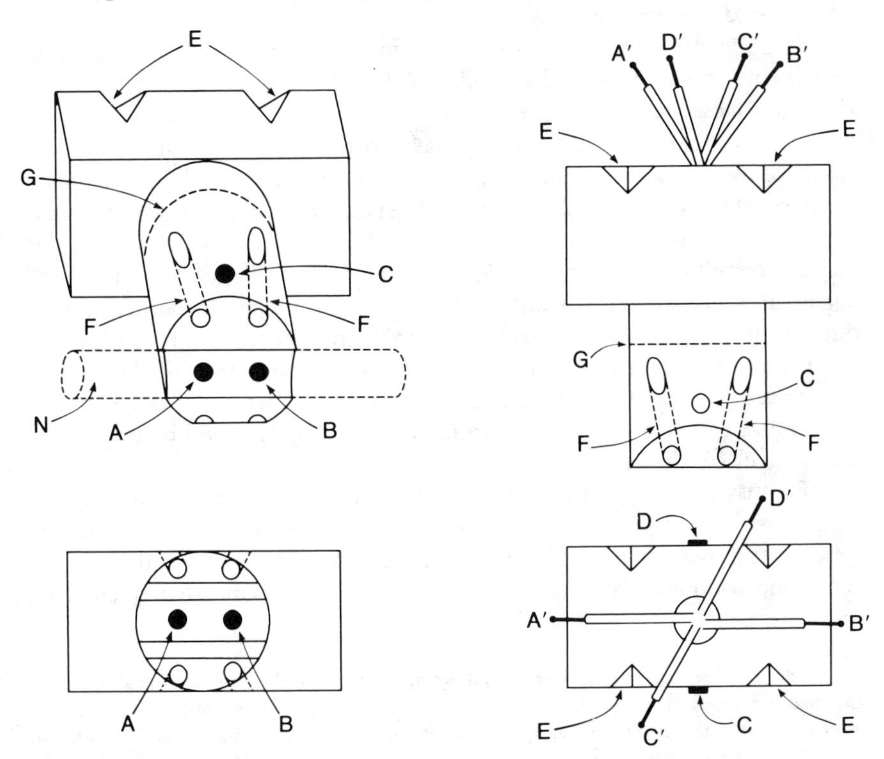

FIG. 2

inum, 10-percent rhodium wire. The electrodes first had a small sphere fused on one end, and these electrodes were coated with an insulating material except for about 5 millimeters on each end. The end of the electrodes with the sphere was bent into the form of a hook, and the other end was attached to a frame of lucite as shown in figure 1A.

This pair of electrodes was hooked under the facial nerve forming two contacts separated by about 2 or 3 centimeters. With the electrodes in place the ends of the vibrissae on the right side of the animal's face were brought together and taped to one end of a 5-foot-long, 5-mil nylon fiber, the other end of which was attached to the moving coil of a loudspeaker from which the cone had been removed, as shown in figure 1B.

The nylon fiber[1] used to transmit the motion of the moving coil to the vibrissae was made 5 feet long to ensure that the electromagnetic field from the moving coil would not overlap the implanted electrodes. This 5-foot length of nylon fiber was surrounded by a skeleton framework just to protect it from accidental damage.

The signal used to energize the moving coil of the speaker in the first experiment was generated by a Model 4204A Hewlett-Packard oscillator amplified by a Sony TC 200 tape recorder. The signal, which went to the speaker coil driving the nylon fiber, was also recorded on Channel 1 of the Model SP 300 Ampex magnetic tape recorder, and the signal picked up by the electrodes shown in figure 1 was recorded on Channel 2. The input signals started at 400 Hz and were increased in 100 Hz intervals up to 1 kHz and then in the following steps: 1, 2, 3, 4, and 8 kHz. Oscillograms of the input signals and that picked up on the nerve electrodes show a faithful reproduction of the input signals, and the signal strength was such that no preamplifier was necessary between the electrode and the input of the Ampex tape recorder. Since the animal had already been under anesthesia for more than 2 hours, it wad decided to terminate the experiment and design a more favorable electrode system.

Because good signals had been picked up when the electrodes were in contact with the tissue adjacent to the nerve and because of the ability to pick up the cochlear microphonic signals at some distance from the edge of the round window in an attempted round window implant even when using

---

[1]To confirm that such a nylon fiber would accurately transmit the necessary signal, a similar array was assembled in which the nylon fiber was 100 feet long; one end of this 100-foot fiber was connected to the moving coil and the other end to the normal speaker cone. With such an assembly, the signals were sufficiently clear that an animal species could be identified from the transmitted signal.

a tuning fork as a sound source, it was decided to conduct a simple test in which two electrodes were implanted without surgery merely by introducing them through a large hypodermic needle in the vicinity of the facial nerve and then remove the needle over the electrode after the electrode was in place.

It will be observed from figure 1B that the direction of motion of the vibrissae would be parallel to the vibrissae rather than flexed sideways, or normal to its axis. Judged from the innervation of the vibrissae as shown by Stephens et al. (1973), this would not be the most sensitive direction in which to flex the vibrissae.

For this the second test, the vibrissae were taped together and pulled straight forward by means of a light tension on a rubber band. Then at a right angle to this was a second rubber band and in a straight line with the second rubber band was the 5-foot-long nylon fiber and speaker coil as shown in figure 1C. While some excellent signals were obtained by this arrangement using a great variety of input signals, there was appreciably more background noise than had been obtained on the previous electrode assembly and since this animal had been under anesthesia for another purpose for approximately 2 hours, this experiment was terminated.

In the third vibrissae test, it was decided to place two electrodes on the facial nerve and two on the tissue about 6 millimeters above the nerve and separated by about 1 centimeter in a direction normal to the axis of the nerve. An electrode assembly as shown in figure 2 was constructed. This electrode contains four platinum-rhodium electrodes, A, B, C, and D. To form these electrodes a small sphere was fused on the end of the 20-mil wire. This sphere was then flattened into a disc normal to the axis of the wire and about 2 millimeters in diameter. When the facial nerve N was exposed, two sutures were fed under the nerve with their ends fed up through the holes F in the lucite block and into the notches E and tied so as to hold the nerve in contact with the electrodes A and B.

This brought the skin of the animal's face to the level G on the electrode assembly. The incision was then sutured shut by placing a suture on each side of the lucite block holding the electrodes, thereby bringing the tissue in contact with electrodes C and D.

In this case the same signal input system was used as is shown in figure 1C. The input signals covered a wide range of pure tones and complex signals including the human voice and a great variety of marine mammal vocalization. The output signals were not only high quality analog reproductions of the input signals but the signal strengths were as high as 80 millivolts and some good quality copies of magnetic tape recordings were made through this system. If the nylon fiber was clamped tightly between the thumb and the finger, the signal would almost completely disappear. The same electrode was implanted on a 22-pound cat with completely negative results.

Relatively little is known about the physiology of these marine mammals. The intro-orbital is very much larger than in any comparable size land mammal. The very large nerve to the vibrissae complex as shown by the electron microscope examination further points out this difference. In fact these differences can best be expressed in contrasts rather than minor differences. Therefore, because both positive and negative results are obtained, much more work remains to be done before these phenomena are well understood.

REFERENCES

CHAPMAN, SEVILLE

1969. Size and shape of sonar targets. Proceedings of the Sixth Annual Conference on Biological Sonar and Diving Animals, Stanford Research Institute, Menlo Park, California, pp. 63–67.

1971. Size, shape, and orientation of sonar targets measured remotely. Amer. Journ. Physics, vol. 39, pp. 1181–1190.

ODEND'HAL, STEWART, and POULTER, THOMAS C.

1966. Pressure regulation in the middle ear cavity of sea lions: A possible mechanism. Science, vol. 153, pp. 768–769.

POULTER, THOMAS C.

1963a. Sonar signals of the sea lion. Science, vol. 139, pp. 753–755.

1963b. The sonar of the sea lion. IEEE Trans. Ultrasonics Engin., vol. UE-10, no. 3, pp. 109–111.

1965. Location of the point of origin of the vocalization of the California sea lion, *Zalophus californianus.* Status report, 8 pp.

1966. The use of active sonar by the California sea lion, *Zalophus californianus* (Lesson). Journ. Auditory Res., vol. 6, pp. 165–173.

1968. Echoranging signals. Progress report, SRI Project 6830, NIH Contract NBO4736-05 and 0551 and Subcontract ONR-371, 400 pp.

1969. Sonar of penguins and fur seals. Proc. California Acad. Sci., vol. 36, no. 13, pp. 363–380.

POULTER, THOMAS C., and JENNINGS, R. A.

1969. Sonar discrimination ability of the California sea lion. Proc. California Acad. Sci., vol. 36, no. 11, pp. 381–389.

SHAVER, H. N., and POULTER, THOMAS C.

1967. Sea lion echo ranging. Journ. Acoust. Soc. Amer., vol. 42, no. 2 (August), pp. 428–437.

STEPHENS, ROBERT J.; BEEBE, IRVIN J.; and POULTER, THOMAS C.

1973. Innervation of the vibrissae of the California sea lion, *Zalophus californianus.* Anat. Rec., vol. 176, no. 4 (August), pp. 421–442.

THOMAS C. POULTER

Ecology of Large Calcareous Foraminiferida, Queensland Shelf and Great Barrier Reef, Australia

Principal Investigator: Charles A. Ross, Western Washington University, Bellingham, Washington.[1]

Grant No. 883: To study the ecology of large calcareous Foraminifera of the Queensland Shelf and Great Barrier Reef, Australia.

For a number of years I have studied extinct large calcareous Foraminiferida (Protozoa) of the superfamily Fusulinacea, which is widely distributed in late Paleozoic strata and is extensively studied because of a rapid evolutionary history for correlation purposes (Dunbar and Skinner, 1937; Rauser-Chernousova et al., 1959; Ross, 1963; Thompson, 1948, 1954). The primary aim of my research in fusulinaceans has been to decipher their evolutionary changes and to relate these changes to past environments and to the timing, magnitude, and extent of their geographic dispersals and extinctions. This series of inquiries has led to investigating the possible biological basis for fusulinacean patterns of occurrence and distribution in both time and space. Because this group is extinct (and has been for about 200 million years) and has no closely related surviving descendants, much of the interpretations must be made by analogy with extant Recent foraminifers that show similar or analogous morphological structures and lived in similar physical environments. One major problem in comparing extinct and Recent large calcareous foraminifers is that, in addition to the fact that we do not fully understand

[1]I thank the many persons and institutions who helped to make this study possible and aided in its completion. Travel funds and several items of equipment for the study were generously subsidized by the National Geographical Society grant. Prof. C. E. Marshall, Prof. W. G. H. Maxwell, Dr. David Taylor, Dr. Edgar Frankel, and others at the Department of Geology and Geophysics, University of Sydney, Australia, kindly made facilities and collections available and helped in many arrangements. The Queensland Department of Primary Industries and its Crown-of-Thorns Research Station at Mourilyan Harbour also aided the study in many invaluable ways. Robert Pearson, director of the Research Station, and John Bloomfield and Miss Julia Henderson of the station staff were most helpful and cooperative in collecting the material and in the laboratory work. The study was completed during a sabbatical leave from Western Washington University.

the paleobiology of the extinct groups, we have relatively little knowledge of the biology of Recent groups. Most of the effort in studying Recent and fossil Foraminiferida has been directed toward describing and identifying taxa and locating biostratigraphic or environmental guide fossils. Relatively few studies have examined the biological aspects of the living foraminiferal organism or its life history, and of these studies most have concentrated on the smaller species living in temperate marine waters or have cultured them in nearby laboratories (Bradshaw, 1957, 1961). The purpose of the research performed under the present grant was to expand our knowledge of the ecological requirements of Recent large calcareous foraminifers with the aim of applying this information to interpreting the shell morphology of Recent and fossil representatives.

The tropical Indo-Pacific marine province contains the greatest diversity of large calcareous Foraminiferida, and Myers (1942, 1943) had made biological observations on several living species from that region but apparently had not cultured or studied them. My previous work in 1961 at the Heron Marine Laboratory at the southern end of the Great Barrier Reef, Australia, and in 1964 and 1965 at the Lerner Marine Laboratory, Bimini, B.W.I., indicated that it should be possible to collect and culture large calcareous foraminifers and to determine some of their ecological requirements and more of their natural-history and growth relations.

I spent a year in Australia studying the distribution and ecology of Recent large calcareous Foraminiferida in the inter-reef and inner shelf areas of the Queensland shelf. This area is broadly similar to many late Paleozoic carbonate shelves and is one of the few locations in the world today that has a long coastline behind an extensive barrier reef and carbonate shelf system. It is also unique in having a great variety of large calcareous foraminiferid species (about 24), including the family Alveolinidae, which is a homeomorph of Fusulinacea in size, shape, and mode of coiling. The only definitive systematic study of Foraminiferida from this area is by Collins (1958), who identified 382 species from collections made by the *Challenger* and 1928–29 Great Barrier Reef expeditions. Maxwell (1968) and his coworkers have shown that foraminiferid debris is commonly a dominant sediment type in the inter-reef and inner shelf areas and that much of this debris is reworked from older deposits. A necessary part of the research was collecting and staining samples in order to identify the living specimens and separate them from empty shells or those eroded from older deposits and redeposited. Measurement of the major physical environmental parameters, sedimentary relations and reef topography, and a taxonomic inventory of associated benthos assisted in determining community associations.

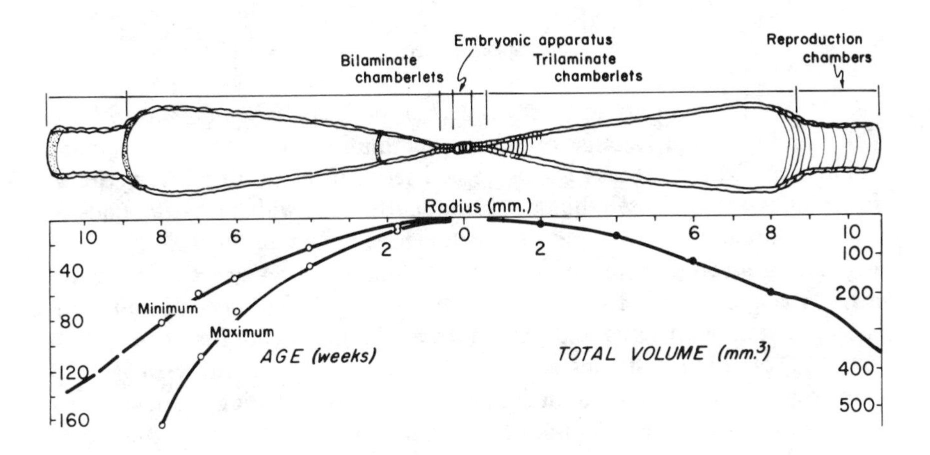

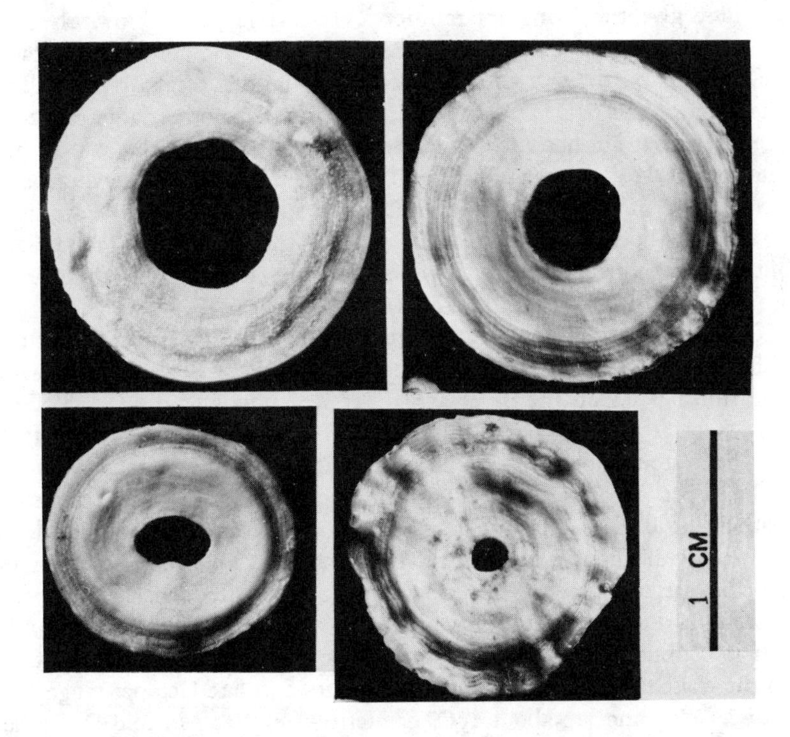

FIG. 1. Cross section of shell of *Marginopora vertebralis* Quoy and Gaimard from Great Barrier Reef, Australia, showing growth stages and external view of shell.

Marginopara vertebralis

One of the common and easily collected species is *Marginopora vertebralis* Quoy and Gaimard, a large calcareous Foraminiferida adapted to euphotic sedimentary basins associated with tropical reefs. It lives with other species of foraminiferids and loosely binds substrate sediments with its pseudopods to reduce erosion by waves and currents. Three stages of shell construction (fig. 1), embryonic, laminate, and reproduction chamber stages, characterize major changes in the growth of individuals. A well-developed flexostyle in the embryonic apparatus and reproductive chambers was first reported in Ross (1972a) in this species and genus. Reproduction in *M. vertebralis* is primarily asexual, and reproductive activity is greatest during the late spring on the Great Barrier Reef. Reproductive maturity requires a year and commonly longer. *M. vertebralis* is host to one or more species of zooxanthellae-dinoflagellates, of which the most common is *Gymnodinium rotundatum* in its motile form. These zooxanthellae are abundant in the protoplasm of *M. vertebralis*, give the living foraminifer a distinctive yellow-brownish green color, and apparently are symbiotic. The symbionts are generally similar to those that inhabit the soft tissues of several of the reef corals and contribute to the color of the tissues. *M. vertebralis* and perhaps other large calcareous foraminifers that are hosts to similar zooxanthellae-dinoflagellates may have an important ecologic relationship to hermatypic corals in serving as an alternate host in the life cycle of this symbiotic group. Such a symbiotic and alternate-host relationship may explain the similar geographic distributions of large calcareous foraminifers and reef-building hermatypic corals (Ross, 1974, 1977; Ross and Ross, 1978).

Collections studied came from three reefs off the Queensland coast near Innisfail and from near the mouth of the Don River near Bowen, Queensland. In the Innisfail region the inner and outer reef trends of the central Great Barrier Reef are within a few miles of one another and are accessible by power boat from Mourilyan Harbour. In this region, individual reefs lack well-developed lagoons and reef growth is concentrated on the eastern or "weather" side. The tidal range is nearly 3.5 meters, and at midtide on a calm day with minor wind drift tidal currents are 2 to 4 meters per minute across the eastern crest of the reefs. Strong, short-frequency storm waves are common during the austral winter, and more gentle, but deeper, wave action is common during the rest of the year. Surface-water temperatures from the coast to the outer edge of the reef tract in late October range from 25° to 26.5°C. and are about 1°C. greater 6 weeks later in mid-December. Average annual water temperature ranges about 5.5°C. During sunny calm days the water is warmed 1° to 2°C. over the back reef area and forms a warm surface layer 1 to 2 meters deep on an outgoing tide.

The reef crest is a useful height datum surface, which is partially exposed by very low tides. The surface and slopes of the reef are broken by depressions and surge channels that have floors of coarse calcareous sediment. A series of poorly defined submerged terraces form the eastern and southeastern sides of these reefs. The dimensions, depth, and orientation of these depressions in relation to the reef front and direction of wave action influence the rate and amount of accumulation of calcareous sediment.

About 60 percent of the grains in depressions below 5 or 6 meters in depth are living Foraminiferida and are sufficiently abundant to bind the upper several centimeters into a loosely cohesive aggregate that withstands minor wave and current action. The abundance of living Foraminiferida on the upper surface of substrates relates in part to their ability to work their way upward through sediment and to maintain a position on the surface. Wave action from local winter storms is apparently sufficiently strong to dislodge substrate Foraminiferida and other grains from shallower basins, and it is unusual to find a wide size range in *M. vertebralis* at depths shallower than 15 meters. The standing crop of large living *M. vertebralis* (12 millimeters or larger in diameter) is patchy, averaging about 20–30 individuals per square meter in most sediment-filled depressions below 10–15 meters.

A series of collections was taken from a number of different depths to study the changes in foraminiferal assemblages and growth. A collection was made on October 28, 1970, from a reef debris basin at 8–9 meters depth at the south end of Peart Reef (fig. 2). Visual examination and vital staining indicated that most of specimens of *M. vertebralis* were alive. Many specimens and about 2 liters of substrate material were collected and returned to the laboratory, where this collection was the source for most of the living specimens used for observation in this study. Another collection was made on October 29, 1970, from a debris-filled depression at about 15 meters depth at the southeastern end of Feather Reef. This collection contained about a dozen large *M. vertebralis* specimens, a few reaching 25 millimeters in diameter. A deeper collection was made on December 16, 1970, from a large depression about 22 meters in depth at the north end of Feather Reef. This collection included specimens of *M. vertebralis* that reached 36 millimeters in diameter.

In the laboratory most of the collections of *M. vertebralis* were spread in a layer of calcareous debris 1–2 centimeters thick in the bottom of screen baskets and the baskets were then suspended from styrofoam floats in sea water. The living specimens of *M. vertebralis* worked their way to the top of the substrate, and 50 specimens of different sizes and growth stages were selected, measured, and transferred to screen-covered bottles submerged in sea water. After about a week a second set of 60 large specimens was measured and placed in two screen-basket floats without a sandy substrate. The sea-water system in which the specimens were maintained was part of the aquarium circulation system at the Queensland Crown-of-Thorns Research Station at Mourilyan Harbour. The water is partially flushed and refilled frequently from Mourilyan Harbour at high tide. This arrangement maintained the salinity between 34.5 to 35.0 ppt, the pH between 8.0 and 8.2, and the temperature between 26° and 29°C., although the temperature was usually between 26.5° and 27.5°C. The water and tanks supported a rather diverse microbiota including bacteria and many smaller invertebrates.

Taxonomic Clarification

Marginopora vertebralis Quoy and Gaimard was described and illustrated in encyclopedic works edited by de Blainville (1830, 1834). For many years the species was erroneously referred by many authors to *Orbitolites complanata* Lamarck, an Eocene species. There is still confusion concerning the characters that distinguish *M. vertebralis*, the type species of *Marginopora*, *Sorites marginalis* Lamarck, and *Amphisorus hemprichii* Ehrenberg, the type species of *Amphisorus*; interestingly, each species appears to be the only valid Recent species assigned to its respective genus. Both *M. vertebralis* and *A. hemprichii* are abundant in several collections. The most obvious difference is the bilaminate arrangement of chamberlets throughout *A. hemprichii* and the trilaminate arrangement of chamberlets in *M. vertebralis* after 2 millimeters diameter of growth. *S. marginalis* has simple chamberlets. *M. vertebralis* has a large discoidal and biconcave shell that generally reaches 10–12 millimeters and occasionally more than 30 millimeters in diameter before undergoing reproduction. Most shells lose their early portions by solution so that they have a characteristic central hole that makes it impossible to separate microspheric and megalospheric individuals in an adult population. The shell is high magnesium calcite (about 12.5 percent magnesium carbonate).

Three main growth stages are recognized (fig. 1), an embryonic stage, a cyclical chamberleted stage, and a chambered reproductive stage. The embryonic stage is formed within the reproductive chambers of the parent and is released after it is fully formed. It consists of a proloculus, a well-defined flexostyle, and a single nonsubdivided, equatorial chamber.

After being released from its parent the young adds a series of small chamberlets as parts of cyclic chambers around the circumference of the

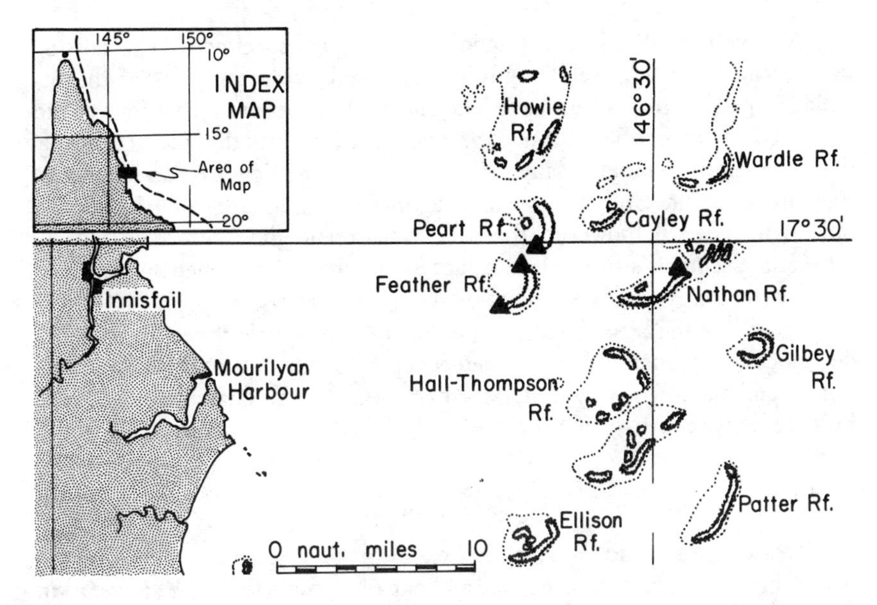

FIG. 2. Map of a part of the central Great Barrier Reef, Australia, locating several named reefs.

shell. The initial chamberlets are small and added in two layers. This mode of chamberlet addition continues for 5–8 cyclic chambers and calcification proceeds in several cycles at one time. After these chambers are completed, more complex chamberlets are formed consisting of large main chamberlets that form between smaller lateral chamberlets. These lateral chamberlets are half a cycle out of phase with the main chamberlets and their outer walls are thin and transparent. Lateral chamberlets are connected by a pore to the main chamberlet half a cycle below and by another pore to the main chamber half a cycle above.

The final growth stage has 4–9 reproduction chambers that are about 0.3 millimeter high and that are not subdivided into chamberlets. Reproduction chambers are coarsely porous. Sixty to more than 150 embryonic apparatus form in these reproduction chambers. The apparatus are released when the coarsely porous peripheral margins burst. The fragile lateral walls of these reproduction chambers commonly remain only for a short time after this release and are usually rapidly broken by movements of other animals so that a jagged fringe of the first reproduction chamber remains. The empty shell becomes encrusted with epibiota within a few days.

A large central hole is common in most larger specimens. The missing parts include the thin-walled early portions and also some parts of the trilaminate portion that would have had thick walls. These early portions would be relatively susceptible to breakage and abrasion, but this seems unlikely since the samples contain many other large and more delicate Foraminiferida that are complete and unbroken. The mechanism that forms the central hole is not known; however, the wide variation in the size of the hole in different specimens and the lack of abrasion marks on the shell suggest that this is a solution feature controlled by the individual.

Variations in size of mature (reproducing) individuals appear to be depth dependent. Specimens from 8–9 meters depth usually start to form reproduction chambers when they reach 13–15 millimeters in diameter and those from 22-meter depth when they reach 25–30 millimeters in diameter.

Growth Rates

Measurements and observation made on 150 specimens were used to determine rates of growth, life span, and rate of reproduction in *M. vertebralis*. Specimens larger than 15 millimeters in diameter usually had reproduction chambers and several released young megalospheric individuals during the study. Specimens between 12 and 15 millimeters in diameter were thought to be from a single reproductive season. Measurements were made for this size range shortly after the specimens became established in the laboratory; they were remeasured 6 weeks later. The young megalospheric individuals were measured more frequently. From the differences in diameter of the specimens their average and maximum rate of diameter increase was calculated (fig. 1). Calcification continues for a week or 10 days, and growth in young individuals is rapid enough that the next cycle of chamberlets is added at 4- or 5-day intervals and before calcification is entirely complete in the previous one or two cycles. Larger specimens without reproduction chambers show a lesser amount of diameter increase, although their volume increase is more rapid. Specimens with reproduction chambers have a wide range of diameter growth because the addition of only a few of these high chambers increases the shell diameter markedly.

In order to investigate the volumetric changes and estimate the age of individuals from their diameters, a cross section of a shell was constructed from a composite of 10 or 12 individuals from collection 3 (fig. 1) and the geometry of a chamber reduced to the equation $v = \pi (r_2^2 - r_1^2) t$, where v is volume, r_1 is shell radius before chamber addition, r_2 is shell radius after chamber addition, and t is the average distance through the chamber from

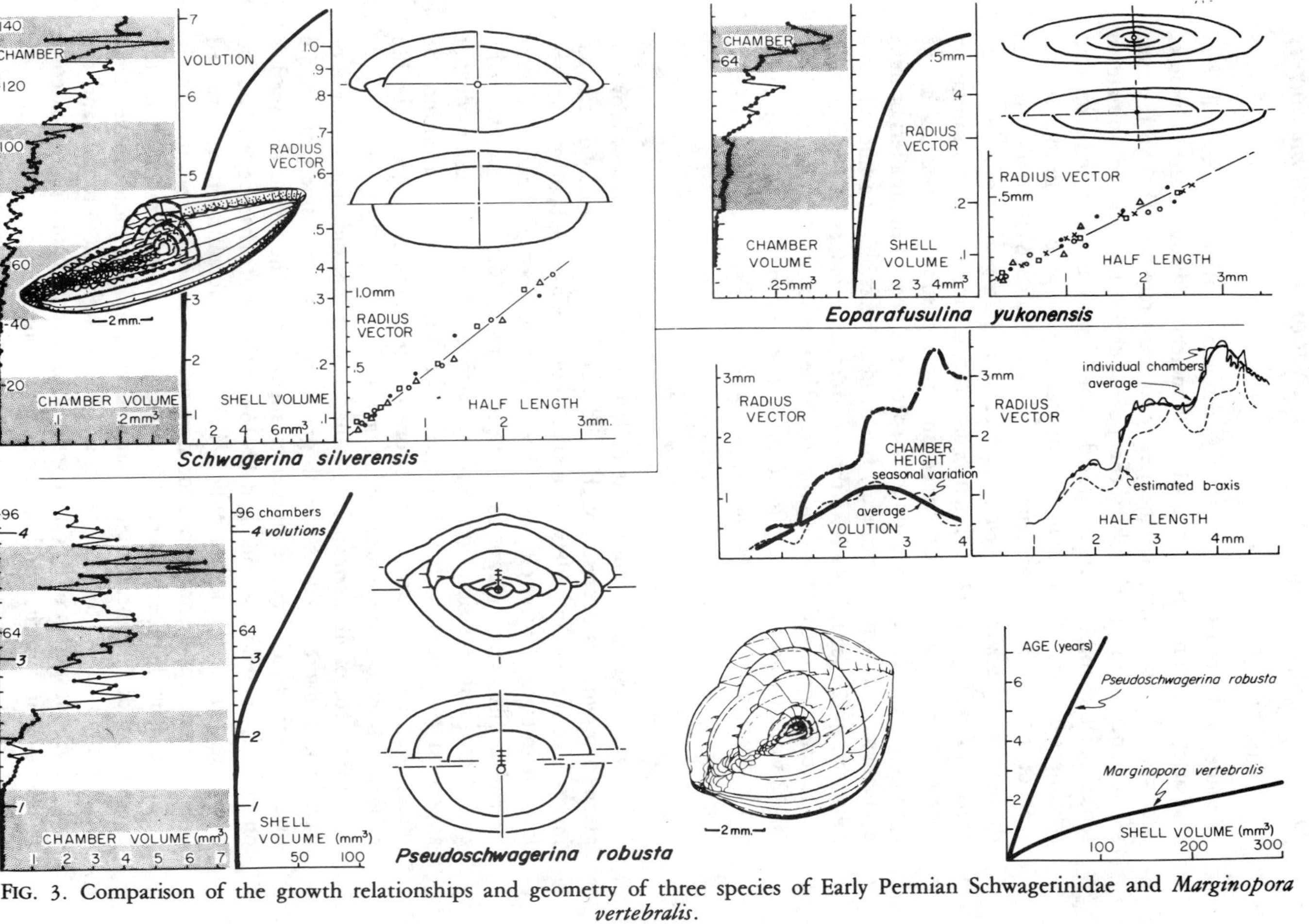

FIG. 3. Comparison of the growth relationships and geometry of three species of Early Permian Schwagerinidae and *Marginopora vertebralis*.

one side to the other. The volumes at different locations in the shell show that after a specimen reaches 12–13 millimeters in diameter the volume of successive chambers increases at a nearly constant rate even though the cross section and height of chambers change markedly from the trilaminate to reproductive chamber form of growth. The age/radius curve indicates that specimens that are 12–16 millimeters in diameter are probably in their second year of growth and that reproducing individuals 16–19 millimeters in diameter are probably in their second or even third year of growth. A few specimens as small as 11 millimeters in diameter included a 1.5-millimeter reproduction chamber growth stage and were possibly reproducing at the age of one year, but most reproducing specimens were 15 millimeters or more in diameter and therefore probably two or more years old. Specimens from a collection at 22-meter depth have three diameter size modes, 3–5 millimeters, 14–18 millimeters, and 25–31 millimeters. The smallest mode represents about 10–12 weeks of growth; the middle mode one to two years; and the largest mode two or more years, and has reproduction chambers.

Symbionts

Marginopora vertebralis in the collections studied is a yellow-brownish green color, which is the result of ellipsoidal bodies that are widely distributed inside most of the chamberlets, particularly in the thin-walled lateral chamberlets. Six to eight of these ellipsoidal bodies generally occupied each chamberlet and at first were thought to be captured food. However, they show no evidence of disintegration from digestive activity, their outer casings do not appear in the excretion material, their distribution is regular within the foraminifer, and they are apparently one of the nonmotile stages in the life cycle of a dinoflagellate-zooxanthella organism.

Specimens of *M. vertebralis* that had lain on one side for a couple of days became darker yellow-brownish green on their upper side than on the undersurface, which became lighter cream colored. The lateral chamberlets on the well-lighted upper side had 12–16 symbionts per chamberlet, and the poorly lighted lower side had only 2–4. When the foraminifers were turned over, the new upper surface became dark yellow-brownish green in a couple of days and its chamberlets were filled with about 12–16 symbionts and the new lower side became lighter colored. The symbionts either move freely in, or are moved by, the endoplasm and are strongly phototrophic, and the clear, thin, transparent outer calcite walls of the lateral chamberlets apparently have evolved into calcite windows for the symbionts.

Symbiosis between various algae and various invertebrates is widely known and has been reviewed by Buchner (1965), Droop (1963), Yonge (1963), and McLaughlin and Zahl (1959). Symbiotic relations between Foraminiferida and algae also are known but only incompletely recorded and studied (Hedley, 1965). Except for several planktonic species such as *Globigerinoides ruber* (d'Orbigny), which also contains zooxanthellae symbionts, published records of Foraminiferida containing symbionts are mainly from the family Soritidae. To these records *Alveolina quoyi* (d'Orbigny) of the family Alveolinidae should be added as this species has intracellular bodies that resembled those found in *M. vertebralis*. Bütschli (1886) reported symbionts from *Peneroplis* and *Orbitolites duplex* (= *Amphisorus hemprichii*). Winter (1907) described an ovate, biflagellated, green symbiont, *Cryptomonas schaudinni*, from *Peneropolis pertusus*, and Lee and Zucker (1969) illustrated *Chlamydomonas* sp. from *Archaias angulatus*. Doyle and Doyle (1940) found symbiotic dinoflagellates in *Amphisorus hemphrichii* similar to the nonmotile stages of *Symbiodinium microadriaticum,* the dinoflagellate-zooxanthella described by Freudenthal (1962) from the coral *Cassiopea frondosa*. Symbionts of the dinoflagellate-zooxanthella type occur also in the planktonic species *Globigerinoides ruber* as reported by Rhumbler (1909) and Lee and others (1965), as well as in *M. vertebralis* specimens observed in this study.

Physiologic problems associated with metabolism within single-celled calcareous foraminifers having a great volume of protoplasm and thick shell continue to be poorly understood. However, the presence in large calcareous foraminifers of numerous symbionts similar to those in hermatypic corals, and a similar geographic distribution of these foraminifers and reef-building hermatypic corals, suggest that symbionts may affect the metabolism of these two widely different groups in much the same manner. McLaughlin and Zahl (1957, 1959, 1966) and Zahl and McLaughlin (1957, 1959) established that zooxanthella symbionts in corals stimulated the host's metabolic activity by rapidly consuming normal "animal" waste products, and Goreau (1959) suggested that stimulation may also include secretion of vitamins and hormones. Growth in hermatypic coral skeletons is 10 times more rapid in normal light with zooxanthellae than in the dark without zooxanthellae and is related to the rapid withdrawal of CO_2 and H_2CO_3 by zooxanthellae from the calcium bicarbonate-calcium carbonate equilibrium reaction inside the tissues of the corals (Goreau, 1959).

Other Large Calcareous Foraminiferida

Ten Recent families of Foraminiferida in the tropics and subtropics have subfamilies, genera, and species that reach volumes greater than 3 cubic millimeters and some exceeding 500 cubic millimeters. These large, and even gigantic, dimensions in a single-celled marine organism appear related to rapid growth rates (Ross, 1972a). These Foraminiferida normally live within the photic zone and are associated with coral reefs. They commonly contribute 15 percent or more of the skeletal debris incorporated in Recent reefs (Maxwell, 1968).

In the paleontological record, large calcareous Foraminiferida are represented by 13 additional families. Large individuals evolved in 5 families during the Carboniferous and Permian, 2 families during the late Triassic and Jurassic, 10 families during the Cretaceous, and 6 families during the Cenozoic. Eight of these are closely related to the 10 Recent families having large calcareous representatives (Loeblich and Tappan, 1964). Accumulation of shells of these Mesozoic and Cenozoic Foraminiferida in carbonate sediments is similar to that of living representatives and, at times, may have been considerably greater.

Fusulinacean Shells

Comparison of the construction of Recent *Marginopora vertebralis* with shell construction in the extinct superfamily Fusulinacea (Ross, 1972b) (Carboniferous to Permian, 310 m.y.a.-225 m.y.a.) reveals a number of similarities and some differences.

The fusulinacean shell has a proloculus and a series of chambers added around an axis of coiling. Most individuals are megalospheric. In some genera the outer volutions may become irregular. The spiral wall has fine closely spaced pores. In detail, construction of the spiral wall varies considerably in different families but basically is an outer, thin, organic-rich layer, the tectum, and an inner, thicker, calcareous layer, the diaphanotheca, or in some groups a honeycomblike structure, the keriotheca. Septa are nearly planar to strongly folded.

A tunnel is formed by resorption of the septa near the midplane of the shell and extends from the earliest formed chamber to all but the last three or four chambers. Several genera have multiple tunnels. Where septal folds of adjacent septa touch, resorption is also common and forms passageways (cuniculi) that connect alternate chambers in the shell. Secondary deposits are also present in many fusulinacean shells and include thin layers that coat all or part of the floor, roof, and sides of chambers; chomata, which are thick, organic-rich deposits at the sides of the tunnel; and other secondary deposits that fill or heavily coat various portions of the chambers often with characteristic patterns.

Fusulinacean shells were measured for height, depth, and volume of individual chambers, the variation in thickness of the spiral wall, growth rates, total volume, relationship of radius vector and half length, geometric approximation of shell form, and variation in mode of shell construction in order to make comparison with the Recent *Marginopora vertebralis*. As the chamber is the smallest increment of growth, sagittal sections that show each chamber are particularly useful.

Three Early Permian fusulinacean species were selected for analysis: *Schwagerina silverensis* Sabins and Ross from southwestern Arizona; *Eoparafusulina yukonensis* (Skinner and Wilde) from northern Yukon Territory; and *Pseudoschwagerina robusta* (Meek) from western Texas. Each has certain geometric features that represent a portion of fusulinacean shell diversity, each is from a different locality so that localized paleoecological conditions should not be repeated, and each is from a different fusulinacean subzone within the Early Permian.

The shells of these three species closely approximate a simple geometric construction. The plot of half length versus radius vector (distance from center of proloculus to outer edge of the spiral wall) forms a set of points through which a line can be constructed that can be used to estimate the length, given only the radius vector. Predictions of related variables is a problem in inflated genera of Schwagerinidae; for example, in *Pseudoschwagerina robusta*, where growth relations change at different ontogenetic stages. Both the height and depth of chambers vary considerably at different points in the shell. The volume of each chamber and that of the total shell were estimated on the basis that the inner and outer outlines of a chamber are halves of two unequal ellipses. The equivalence in area in the calculated ellipses is within 5 percent of the generalized specimen. Volume is equal to area of the chamber times one-half the depth of the chamber. The total volume of a fusulinacean shell can be calculated for any radius vector or half length by treating the shell as quarters of four different-sized ellipsoids.

In *Pseudoschwagerina robusta* centers of ellipses of best fit for chambers do not pass through or close to the center of the proloculus because the inflated chambers become slightly evolute and the b-axes of the ellipses are not the same as the radius vector. To express the area of chambers in axial sections it is necessary to measure the b-axis. In a sagittal section chamber height increases abruptly about 2 3/4 volutions before termination of growth and continues to a point about 2 volutions before termination of growth. Later chambers gradually decrease in height. Superimposed on this general trend are minor fluctuations of the same kind and magnitude as observed in the other two species studied. Graphs of radius vectors and b-axes plotted to the nearest half volution from axial sections can be adjusted to fit on the outer 2 to 2½ volutions of the growth curve for the sagittal section and it is possible to approximate a value for the b-axis. This assumes that the ontogenetic history and life span of each specimen are the same after the initiation of the inflated chamber stage.

Interpretations

Megalospheric individuals dominate the populations of most species of fusulinaceans as they also do in most populations of living foraminifers (Myers, 1942; Hedley, 1965; Ross, 1972a). The range in size of megalospheric proloculi of fusulinaceans from one sample suggests that if they are about the same size they arose from a single parent, but if they have a great size range they probably arose from several parents. Megalospheric proloculus and the microspheric juvenarium are commonly about the same size and are followed by a change in growth (or a change in axis of coiling) that the individual retains for the adult shell. This form is analogous with *Marginopora vertebralis,* which adopts a new mode of shell construction after the embryonic apparati are released.

The chambers of the fusulinacean shell provide more data for interpretations. Differences in volume of individual chambers commonly reflect on the availability of nutrients, as indicated by growth in living foraminifers. Similar variations in chamber volume in fossil foraminiferal shells should be a gauge of seasons of growth if nutrient is seasonal as it usually is in the ocean. Chambers that have less volume in comparison to adjacent chambers indicate that nutrient supply was limited, and a grouping of chambers produced during different growth seasons can be identified. These trends in chamber volume are seen also in variation of chamber depth and wall thickness. In the specimens of fusulinaceans measured and studied four to seven major growth periods are commonly present, and each major growth increment is subdivided into an initial growth phase of about 8–15 chambers of relatively uniform growth followed by 5–8 chambers of markedly greater volume before the end of the growth season.

Conclusions

Study of the shell construction and its relationships to the life history and adaptation of living large calcareous foraminifers provides data for comparison with fossil foraminiferal shells and permits biological interpretations of some fossil shell features, particularly growth rates, variations in growing seasons, and age at reproductive maturity. In living foraminifers variations in height, depth, and volume of individual chambers and thickness of calcareous walls relate to variations in available nutrients and usually correlate with seasonal variations in temperature and sunlight. Recent *Marginopora vertebralis* commonly lives 2 to more than 5 years before undergoing reproduction (Ross, 1972b).

Comparison of Recent shell morphological data with extinct fusulinaceans indicates that three species of early Permian schwagerinid fusulinaceans lived 4 to more than 7 years before reaching reproductive maturity (Ross, 1972b). The size range of megalospheric proloculi and microspheric juvenaria of fusulinaceans suggests that these structures were formed before being released from the parent shell and may compare with embryonic apparati of other large calcareous foraminifers.

REFERENCES

Blainville, Henri M. D., de

1830. Mollusques, vers et zoophytes. Dictionnaire des Sciences Naturelles, vol. 60, p. 377. F. G. Levrault, Paris.

1834. Manuel d'actinologie ou de zoophytologie, 644 pp., illus. F. G. Levrault, Paris.

Bradshaw, John S.

1955. Preliminary laboratory experiments on ecology of foraminiferal populations. Micropaleontology, vol. 1, pp. 351–358.

1957. Laboratory studies on the rate of growth of the foraminifer "*Streblus beccarii* (Linné) var. *tepida* (Cushman)." Journ. Pal., vol. 31, pp. 1138–1147.

1961. Laboratory experiments on the ecology of Foraminifera. Contr. Cushman Found. Foram. Res., vol. 12, pp. 87–105.

Buchner, P.

1965. Algal symbiosis. Chap. 1 (pp. 3–22) *in* "Endosymbiosis of Animals with Plant Microorganisms." Wiley (Interscience), New York.

Bütschli, O.

1886. Beitrage zur Kenntnis des Flagellaten und einiger verwandter Organismen. Morph. Jahrb., vol. 11, pp. 78–101.

Collins, A. C.

1958. Foraminifera. Great Barrier Reef Exped., Sci. Rpts., vol. 6, no. 6, pp. 335–437. British Museum (Natural History), London.

Doyle, W. L., and Doyle, M. M.

1940. The structure of the zooxanthellae. Carnegie Inst. Washington, Pap. Tortugas Lab., vol. 32, pp. 127–142.

Droop, M. R.

1963. Algae and invertebrates in symbiosis. Pp. 171–199 *in* "Symbiotic Associations," Nutman and Mosse, eds. Cambridge University Press.

DUNBAR, CARL O., and SKINNER, J. W.
1937. Permian Fusulinidae of Texas: The geology of Texas, vol. 3, pt. 2. Univ. Texas Bull. 3701, pp. 517–825.

FREUDENTHAL, HUGO D.
1962. *Symbiodinium* gen. nov. and *Symbiodinium microadriaticum* sp. nov., a zooxanthella: Taxonomy, life cycle, and morphology. Journ. Protozool., vol. 9, pp. 45–52.

GOREAU, T.
1959. The physiology of skeleton formation in corals: I, A method for measuring the rate of calcium deposition by corals under different conditions. Biol. Bull., vol. 116, pp. 59–75.

HEDLEY, R. H.
1965. The biology of Foraminifera. Int. Rev. Gen. Exp. Zool., vol. 1, pp. 1–47.

LEE, JOHN J.; FREUDENTHAL, HUGO D.; KOSSOY, V.; and BÉ, ALLAN W. H.
1965. Cytological observations on two planktonic Foraminifera, *Globigerina bulloides* d'Orbigny, 1826, and *Globigerinoides ruber* (d'Orbigny, 1839) Cushman, 1927. Journ. Protozool., vol. 12, pp. 531–542.

LEE, JOHN J., and ZUCKER, W.
1969. Algal flagellate symbiosis in the foraminifer *Archaias*. Journ. Protozool., vol. 16, pp. 71–81.

LOEBLICH, ALFRED R., JR., and TAPPAN, HELEN
1964. Protista 2, chiefly thecamoebians and Foraminiferida. *In* "Treatise of Invertebrate Paleontology," pt. C, 2 vols., R. C. Moore, ed. Geological Society of America and University of Kansas Press.

MAXWELL, W. G. H.
1968. Atlas of the Great Barrier Reef, 258 pp. Elsevier Publishing Co., New York.

MCLAUGHLIN, JOHN J. A., and ZAHL, PAUL A.
1957. Studies in marine biology, II: In vitro culture of zooxanthellae. Proc. Soc. Exp. Biol., vol. 95, pp. 115–120.
1959. Axenic zooxanthellae from various invertebrate hosts. Ann. New York Acad. Sci., vol. 77, pp. 55–70.
1966. Endozoic algae. Pp. 257–297 *in* "Symbiosis," S. M. Henry, ed. Academic Press, New York.

MYERS, E. H.
1942. A quantitative study of the productivity of Foraminifera in the sea. Proc. Amer. Philos. Soc., vol. 85, pp. 325–342.
1943. Life activities of Foraminifera in relation to marine ecology. Proc. Amer. Philos. Soc., vol. 86, pp. 437–458.

RAUSER-CHERNOUSOVA, D. M., and ROSOVSKAYA, S. E.
1959. Order Fusulinida. Pp. 201–215 *in* "Osnovy Paleontologii, General Part and Protozoa," Y. A. Orlov, chief ed.

RHUMBLER, L.
1909 (1911–1912). Die Foraminiferen (Thalamophoren) der Plankton-Expedition. Teil 1 and 2, Ergebnisse der Plankton-Expedition der Humbolt-Stiftung, vol. 3, 476 pp.

ROSS, CHARLES A.
1963. The standard Wolfcampian series (Permian), Glass Mountains, Texas. Geol. Soc. Amer. Mem. 88, 205 pp.

1972a. Biology and ecology of *Marginopora vertebralis* (Foraminiferida), Great Barrier Reef. Journ. Protozool., vol. 19, pp. 181–192.
1972b. Paleobiological analysis of fusulinacean (Foraminiferida) shell morphology. Journ. Pal., vol. 46, no. 5, pp. 719–728.
1974. Evolutionary and ecological significance of large calcareous Foraminiferida (Protozoa), Great Barrier Reef. Proc. 2d Int. Coral Reef Symposium, vol. 1, pp. 327–333.
1977. Calcium carbonate fixation by large reef-dwelling Foraminifera. Amer. Soc. Petr. Geol. Studies in Geol., no. 4, pp. 219–230.

ROSS, CHARLES A., and ROSS, JUNE R. P.
1978. Adaptive evolution in the soritids *Marginopora* and *Amphisorus* (Foraminiferida). Proc. Scanning Electron Microscopy/1978, vol. 2, pp. 53–60.

THOMPSON, MARCUS L.
1948. Studies of American fusulinids. Univ. Kansas Pal. Contr. Protozoa, art. 1, 184 pp.
1954. American Wolfcampian fusulinids. Univ. Kansas Pal. Contr. Protozoa, art. 5, 226 pp.

WINTER, F. W.
1907. Zur Kenntnis der Thalamophoren, I: Untersuchung über *Peneropolis pertusus* (Forskål). Arch. Protist., vol. 10, 113 pp.

YONGE, C. M.
1963. The biology of coral reefs. Pp. 209–260 *in* "Advances in Marine Biology," vol. 1, F. S. Russell, ed. Academic Press, New York and London.

ZAHL, PAUL A., and MCLAUGHLIN, JOHN J. A.
1957. Isolation and cultivation of zooxanthellae. Nature, vol. 180, pp. 199–200.
1959. Studies in marine biology, IV: On the role of algal cells in the tissue of marine invertebrates. Journ. Protozool., vol. 6, pp. 344–352.

CHARLES A. ROSS

Ecology and Behavior of High-altitude Mammals in South Asia

Principal Investigator: George B. Schaller, New York Zoological Society and Rockefeller University, New York City.

Grant Nos. 899, 998, 1135, 1235. For a study of high-altitude mammals in south Asia.[1]

Although valuable work on large mountain mammals has been done in Russia, Europe, and North America, the unique faunal assemblages in the Himalayas, Hindu Kush, and other ranges have never been studied. I began a project on high-altitude ungulates in south Asia, particularly the wild sheep and goats, on an exploratory basis in 1970 and intensively in 1972. Among the objectives of the project were, 1, to census various species in selected localities in order to elucidate their population dynamics, a point of special importance with respect to species threated with extinction; 2, to study distribution, with emphasis on the physical, ecological, and historical factors influencing it; 3, to describe the social systems of various species and to find out if and how ecological conditions have influenced these systems; and 4, to describe and quantify behavior patterns with the hope that this may lead to a better understanding of phylogenetic relationships among members of the Caprini.

Urial Sheep and Markhor Goats in Pakistan, 1970

Mountfort (1969) and others have drawn attention to the plight of various large mammals in Pakistan, but information about these species is largely limited to hunting accounts published 30 or more years ago (e.g., Stockley, 1936). As the first stage of a study of wild sheep and goats in south Asia, we observed urial (*Ovis orientalis punjabiensis*), Kashmir markhor (*Capra falconeri*

[1]The study was financed by the National Geographic Society and the New York Zoological Society and was sponsored locally by the World Wildlife Fund Pakistan. Of the many persons who helped, I am particularly indebted to H. H. Malik Muzaffar Khan, the Nawab of Kalabagh, Princes Asad-ur-Rehman and Burhan-ud-Din of Chitral; Maj. S. Amanullah Khan, Z. B. Mirza, W. A. Kermani, Syed Babar Ali, S. M. H. Rizvi, Pervez A. Khan, and T. J. Roberts.

cashmiriensis), and the so-called Chiltan markhor (*C.f. chiltanensis*) between October and December 1970. We selected one locality in which to observe each species with the aim of gathering information upon which adequate conservation practices can be based—this with the hope of assuring the survival of these animals in at least one area of Pakistan; and of obtaining detailed quantitative data on courtship and fighting behavior for comparison with results of studies made on related species, particularly on American bighorn sheep (Geist, 1968) and Alpine ibex (Nievergelt, 1967). This report summarizes mainly those findings bearing on conservation. Most scientific data resulting from the project have been published elsewhere (see References).

Punjab Urial

The Punjab urial has a restricted distribution, being confined largely to several low, barren hill ranges between the Indus and Jhelum Rivers. The largest known population survives on the private property of the Nawab of Kalabagh whose family has protected the animals for over 30 years in the Kalabagh Wildlife Reserve. We spent October 6 to November 9 in a study of this population.

We divided the sanctuary into five blocks for census purposes and attempted to count all sheep in one block each day. A total of 410 urial were seen. As some were undoubtedly overlooked and parts of the reserve could not be censused, a total of around 500 is likely. Males and females were present in a 1:1 ratio. Eighteen percent of the population comprised large males 4½ years old and older. About three-fourths of the adult females were accompanied by young, indicating good reproduction and survival. Yearlings (18 months old) made up some 12 percent of the population in contrast to young (6 months old), which comprised 24 percent. This suggests that perhaps as many as half of the young may die between the ages of 6 and 18 months, if it is assumed that reproductive success in 1969 was as good as in 1970. Possible causes of death include disease and malnutrition, both perhaps traceable to domestic livestock. Although 20 percent of the ground is covered by grass, only one-third of this consists of species that urial like to eat. Livestock prefer the same species, and competition for food may be great at certain seasons. Herds also wander outside of the reserve, where poaching is heavy. It was our impression that the urial population had stabilized at the highest possible level that the reserve can adequately support under present conditions.

Urial associate casually in herds of 2 to 50 or more individuals. Males tend to segregate into herds of their own after they reach the age of 2½ years; one such herd we saw comprised 63 animals. On about October 20, after a sudden drop in temperature, the male herds split up and the animals began to roam widely alone or in small groups, an indication that the rut had begun. Rutting males were not territorial, nor did they attempt to collect harems: they merely searched herd after herd for an estrous female, and, when they found one, they stayed with her unless driven away by a larger male. We quantified various agonistic behavior patterns of males. Many urial patterns, such as the kick and the twist of the head, are similar to those of bighorn sheep, but both qualitative and quantitative differences exist between the two species. For example, male urial were not seen to approach one another on their hindlegs before clashing horns, common behavior among bighorns, and they nudged their opponents with the muzzle more often and mounted them less often than do bighorns (Schaller and Mirza, 1974).

The urial in the reserve receive excellent protection and as long as the domestic cattle, sheep, and goats in the area are not allowed to increase markedly the survival of this population seems assured for the present.

Kashmir Markhor

Hunting for meat and trophies has reduced this subspecies of the markhor to scattered herds throughout its range from the Pir Panjal in Kashmir through Chitral to eastern Afghanistan (Roberts, 1969). H. H. the Mehtar of Chitral has for several years protected markhor in a private shooting reserve, the Chitral Gol, a deep, narrow valley that after about 10 kilometers broadens into a basin surrounded by peaks almost 5,000 meters high. The area is about 80 square kilometers in size. We spent November 26 to December 27 in the reserve and surrounding areas.

Transects at high altitudes showed that most markhor had descended from their summer range at timberline and above to the sparse oak forests that grow at altitudes of 1,800 to 2,500 meters. Repeated contacts with the same herds in the same locality indicated that about 100 to 125 markhor were in the reserve. Of these about 10.3 percent were adult males (3½ years old and older) and 10.3 were subadult (1½ to 2½ years old). Possibly our statistic for adult males is somewhat low, for solitary individuals are less readily sighted than herds. Females comprised 39.3 percent of the population and young 40 percent. Females outnumbered males by a ratio of at least 2:1, a difference due to a paucity of large males, since yearling males (1½ years old) were as abundant as yearling females. There were 1.3 young per adult female, indicating a high twinning rate. Yearlings constituted 16.4 percent of the population, or 0.5 yearling per adult female. Thus, many animals die between the ages of 6 and 18 months. Some fall prey to snow leopards (5 out of 16 leopard droppings contained markhor remains). Starvation is also a possible mortality factor in severe winters. Although markhor graze and browse on a variety of plants (14 species were collected), preferred foods may not be available. The whole area is so heavily used by livestock that few grasses and forbs survive until autumn. Only about 5 percent of the wintering area has a ground cover, much of it *Artemisia*, which markhor rarely eat. Deep snow may cover the ground in winter. Consequently the principal available food on the markhor's winter range from late November to March consists of leathery oak leaves, which the animals sometimes obtain by climbing as high as 25 feet into the crowns of trees.

Herd size ranged from 2 to 18. In contrast to urial, females and subadults formed fairly cohesive social units that confined their activity to definite ranges. Males, 2½ years old and older, tended to travel widely, either alone or in groups of two or three, but prior to the rut some of them joined the female herds. A few males joined the females by late November, but some herds remained unattended until early December. The first estrous female was seen on December 17, and the peak of the rut was in late December. Males showed no evidence of being territorial; they merely chased subordinate males to the periphery of the herd or from the vicinity of an estrous female (Schaller and Mirza, 1971).

Three snow leopards—a female, a subadult (?), and a cub—frequented the reserve intermittently during the period of study. The female and sometimes also her cub were observed daily for a week as they fed on and rested by their domestic goat kills.

The Chitral Gol, now officially a sanctuary of the Northwest Frontier Province, is excellent for that purpose. Not only does the area encompass the winter and part of the summer range of a markhor population, and contains a representative sample of the local fauna, but also it is conveniently located for visitors, being near a city and airfield. The area can, however, maintain its full potential only if: 1, direct protection of the animals is continued and preferably increased; 2, excessive disturbance to the habitat in the form of livestock grazing and wood cutting is curtailed or eliminated, particularly in the markhor's winter range; and 3, the valleys adjoining the reserve are protected from indiscriminate hunting, to preserve the widely roaming snow leopards.

Chiltan Goat

Several authors (e.g., Roberts, 1969) have suggested that the Chiltan markhor is a hybrid between *Capra falconeri jerdoni* and *C. hircus*. However, various morphological characters, such as the shape of the horns, suggest to me that the Chiltan goat is not a subspecies of markhor but a wild goat (*Capra hircus*) with distinctly shaped horns. The animal is extremely local in distribution, being found only in the Chiltan Range and on a few other hills near Quetta in Baluchistan. We visited the Chiltan area between November 14 and 20 to obtain an impression of the status of the animal.

We divided the southern half of the Chiltan Range into blocks and attempted to count all goats in six of them. A total of 107 different markhor were seen. Taking into account the preferred habitat of the animals and the areas we did not visit, we estimate that the Chiltan Range supports around 200 markhor. Even though a few herds are said to survive elsewhere, these goats are obviously rare.

Ten percent of the population consisted of adult males and 14 percent of subadult ones; females outnumbered males by a ratio of almost 2:1. These figures are similar to those noted for the Kashmir markhor. However, the Kashmir markhor population contained 1 young per female (adult and yearling combined), whereas the Chiltan population had only 0.6 young per female, suggesting a lower reproductive rate, a higher death rate, or both.

The Chiltan Range which is under the jurisdiction of the Forest Department, is closed to shooting, except under special permit, but poaching is common according to several informants. We recommended that the southern half of the Chiltan Range be maintained as a strict sanctuary. This would entail more effective protection against poaching and elimination of the intensive grazing pressure from livestock, to which the area is subjected for part of the year. To achieve the latter it might be advantageous to build a fence along the lower slopes as has already been done to protect some other areas in the province.

High-altitude Ungulates in Pakistan and Nepal, 1972

Several species of wild goat and sheep were studied in Nepal and Pakistan during 1972. Originally my plan had been to spend the whole year in Pakistan, but the Indo-Pakistani war made it advisable to delay work in that country until conditions improved. Instead, I spent January to April in Nepal in a preliminary study of Himalayan tahr and blue sheep. Then, after picking up a Land-Rover in London in May, I drove to Pakistan and carried on research there from June through December. In this report only certain topics concerning a few species are included. More detailed accounts of the various species can be found in my scientific papers (see References).

HIMALAYAN TAHR

Most observations were made on some 50 tahr (*Hemitragus jemlahicus*) inhabiting a huge cliff in the Bhota Kosi Valley of Nepal. The animals were divided into two herds, one on the northern part of the cliff, the other on the southern. Groups were unstable in composition, as members joined and parted singly and together. About 20 percent of the population consisted of adult males and 40 percent of adult females, 22 percent were young animals (55 young to 100 adult females), and 18 percent were yearlings (44 yearlings to 100 adult females).

Tahr are morphologically intermediate between the rupicaprids, also known as goat-antelope, and the true goats of the genus *Capra*. My observations revealed that in some aspects of behavior tahr show affinities to both. For example, the American mountain goat, a rupicaprid, may stand head-to-tail beside an opponent during a fight and jab at its abdomen and thighs, a pattern also typical of tahr but not of true goats. Yet tahr resemble true goats in other forms of combat, particularly in their manner of rearing up on the hindlegs and lunging downward to clash horns with an opponent (Schaller, 1973b).

BLUE SHEEP

Blue sheep (*Pseudois nayaur*) live above timberline at altitudes of 4,000 meters and above. A small population of no more than 75 animals inhabited a ridge at the edge of the Tibetan plateau near the headwaters of the Kang Chu Valley in Nepal, and these animals were studied intensively for two weeks (see also p. 471). In March, at the end of winter, blue sheep were concentrated on snow-free slopes, subsisting on dry grass and various dead or dormant shrubs, forbs, and ferns (*Polygonum, Ephedra, Berberis*, and others). The adult sex ratio was about equal. Good survival of young in 1970 and 1971, as well as occasional twinning, had resulted in a good annual increment to the population, there being 87 young and 82 yearlings to 100 adult females.

Blue sheep have puzzled taxonomists for years because they possess physical characters typical of both goats and sheep. This study revealed that in their forms of combat, such as in their manner of rearing up and then clashing horns, and in certain courtship displays, blue sheep closely resemble goats (Schaller, 1973a).

KASHMIR MARKHOR

In late 1970 I had visited Pakistan to census Punjab urial (*Ovis orientalis*

punjabiensis) in one locality (see p. 462) and Kashmir markhor (*Capra falconeri cashmiriensis*) in another (see p. 463). Both study sites were revisited several times in 1972. By checking certain populations at all seasons over a period of years it may be possible to detect trends in number, factors affecting birth and death rates, and so forth. Some data for Kashmir markhor are illustrative.

Markhor concentrate during winter in the oak forests below an altitude of 8,500 feet, making it fairly easy to census them. As the tabulation below shows, the animals had increased slightly in number since 1970 (see also p. 472).

	1970	*1972*
Total in reserve	100–125	125–150
Percent adult males (4½ yrs. +) in population	6.1	9.5
Young per adult female	1.3	1.3
Yearlings per adult female	0.5	0.6
Average herd size	8.5	9.0
Largest herd seen	18	35

This increase is particularly evident among adult males. In 1970 only small-horned adults, 4½ years old, were with the females, even at the height of the rut, whereas in 1972 courting was done by large-horned males, 5½ and 6½ years old. This suggests that hunting pressure on males had been reduced, allowing at least some animals to reach full maturity. Reproductive success and survival of young were similar in the two years, as was average herd size.

In December 1972, the animals spent about 63 percent of their feeding time on grasses and forbs, 34 percent on acorns, of which there was an unusually big crop, and 3 percent on oak leaves. Later, in January 1973, when snow covered the ground, the animals apparently found it uneconomical to dig for the scattered grasses and forbs and concentrated on acorns instead. In a typical year, such as in 1970, the main winter forage of markhor consists of oak leaves, which the animals obviously do not much like yet are forced to take because their preferred grasses and forbs have been eaten up by domestic stock. Dependence on poor food for several months may help explain the fact that half the young die between the ages of 6 and 18 months.

WILD GOAT

The behavior of the wild goat (*Capra hircus*) has never been observed in detail even though it is the probable progenitor of the domestic goat.

With the assistance of A. Laurie, one population of this species was studied. Courtship behavior was one focus of our work. Results comparing the behavior of wild goat with that of domestic goats and other *Capra* are given in Schaller and Laurie (1974). In the Karchat Hills, which the government of Sind Province has now turned into a national park, we were asked to collect information about wild goat that would assist in the conservation effort. This provided the other focus of research. The following samples indicate the type of data collected:

1. Intensive work in the southeastern quarter of the Karchat Hills (see also p. 470) showed that usually no more than 150 wild goats frequented that part of the range. Visits to the northern and western part revealed, on the whole, a lower population density than in the main study area. This suggests that 400–500 wild goats inhabit the Karchat Hills.

2. The preferred food of wild goat is grass, at least during September. Of the common grasses the animal favored *Cenchrus, Dichanthium*, and *Eriochloa*, and they largely disdained *Cymbopogon*. Although *Acacia, Leptadenia, Capparis*, and other shrubs and trees were browsed, observations on feeding animals showed that 80 percent of their time was devoted to grazing. At that season grasses are fairly scarce in the hills. Vegetation transects along the plateau, where grass is most abundant and wild goats prefer to feed, revealed a grass cover of 5 percent. Domestic goats also favor grass and their competition with wild goats for the available food may become severe at certain seasons. A large and healthy wild-goat population can be maintained on a long-term basis only if domestic animals are eliminated, both to avoid food competition and to prevent the transmission of disease from domestic to wild forms. Domestic animals are now (1976) prohibited from grazing on the Karchat Hills.

3. The number of young and yearlings (1–2 years old) per adult female is a measure of reproductive success. One to two young per adult female can be expected per year. The actual figures were 0.4 young and 0.7 yearling per adult female. This shows that few young were born or survived in 1972 but that the 1971 season was fairly good. The availability of nutritious green forage during the rut is known to have an influence on conception rates in domestic stock. The wild goat ruts in September-October, and rainfall records show that there was probably ample forage during the 1970 rut but that 1971 was a drought year. Striking yearly fluctuations in the crop of young can thus be expected.

4. Of 21 sets of leopard droppings examined, 63 percent contained wild goat, 21 percent domestic stock, and the rest porcupine and grass. Although wild goat is the leopard's principal food, the prey population is large enough to support the few resident predators.

High-altitude Ungulates in Pakistan and Nepal, 1973

Research on high-altitude ungulates of south Asia continued throughout 1973 with the same plan and purposes as previously outlined. I spent January to mid-September in Pakistan and the rest of the year in Nepal. The work was divided into two broad categories: 1, wildlife surveys to ascertain the distribution and status of various species and to discover areas which might make good additions to the system of sanctuaries of the countries; and 2, intensive studies of certain species in selected areas.

Survey methods include driving along roads and interviewing villagers about wildlife in the adjoining hills, transecting extensive mountain tracts on foot, and making censuses in particular localities. The first two methods are useful for obtaining general information on the distribution and abundance of species, essential knowledge if effective conservation measures are to be taken. In Pakistan, road surveys were made in parts of Baluchistan, the Northwest Frontier province, the Gilgit area, and Hunza. A foot survey in the high mountains took me up the 140-mile Yarkhun River in Chitral and from there southward as far as Swat, a trip that lasted 5 weeks. The wildlife situation in that area was dismal, with, for example, markhor (*Capra falconeri*) having disappeared from large tracts, brown bear (*Ursus arctos*) almost exterminated, and ibex (*Capra ibex*) reduced to scattered remnants. Another foot survey was made in Nepal, from the town of Pokhara westward through the Himalayas to Jumla, with a detour northward to Dolpo District, which lies just to the south of the Tibetan border. This journey required nearly 3 months, including a 5-week stay in one locality, the Shey Gompa area. The purpose of this lengthy halt was to study the rut of blue sheep and to make an intensive wildlife survey of a 200-square-mile block of mountains, which, it is hoped, the Nepal Government will set aside as a wildlife reserve. The Shey area today, in 1976, is considered to be a reserve, although not officially gazetted as such. The survey showed that at least 500 and possibly 600 to 700 blue sheep (*Pseudois nayaur*) occurred in that tract. Musk deer (*Moschus moschiferus*) were rare, a not surprising status when one musk pod may bring $500 on the Kathmandu market. Evidence for 6 snow leopards (*Panthera uncia*) was found, a fairly high density when compared to other parts of the Himalayas I have visited. Wolves (*Canis lupus*), singly and in small packs, passed through the survey area sporadically.

A special effort was made during the survey trips in Pakistan to ascertain the status of various subspecies of markhor goat, several of which are threatened with extinction. The surveys helped to clarify the confusing taxonomy of the markhor. Five subspecies are generally recognized as occurring in Pakistan. One of these, the so-called Chiltan markhor (see p. 465) was found to be not a markhor but a wild goat (*Capra hircus*) with distinctly shaped horns, as noted earlier. Neither the Sulaiman and Kabul markhors nor the Kashmir and Astor markhors seem to be subspecifically distinct. Taxonomists once based their classification mainly on horn shape without realizing the large amount of variation in this trait that may occur within a population. Thus, instead of dealing with 5 subspecies one is dealing with 2. While this may see a trivial academic quibble, taxonomy is important from the standpoint of conservation and comparative behavior.

Intensive observations, particularly during the birth season and, in the case of blue sheep, during the rut, were made on populations of Punjab urial, Kashmir markhor, wild goat, and blue sheep. As an indication of the kind of information collected, some data on wild goat and blue sheep are summarized below.

WILD GOAT

One population of *Capra hircus* in the Karchat Hills, Sind, first observed in 1972 (see pp. 467-468), was again studied. The onset of the main rut had been on September 19, 1972, and reached a peak around the end of that month. The first young were born in late February 1973 and births reached a peak in early March 1973. By March 18 only 11 percent of the females were still pregnant. The gestation period was thus a little over 5 months. Although yearling females (1½ years old) took part in the rut, most did not give birth. An estimated 15–20 percent of the adult females (3 + years old) did not give birth either. One young per female was the rule, in contrast to data from Iran where multiple births in this species are common. Survival of young was poor too. At least 80 percent of the adult females were pregnant in early March, yet only 35 percent were accompanied by small young in late March, indicating that roughly half died shortly after birth. By September 1973 only 19 percent of the females still had young. It seems likely that most young died just after birth because of the poor nutritional state of the females. If the available forage is of low quality, such as during the drought that existed in 1972 and 1973, females may not only produce weak young but also lack enough milk to support them. The tabulation opposite shows that survival of young in 1973 was much poorer than in 1972 and 1971. Not enough young were produced to maintain the population, for the few survivors cannot compensate for the mortality of adults, owing to poaching, leopard predation, and other causes.

	Young born in March		
	1971	*1972*	*1973*
Adult females heavily pregnant (Pct.)	—	—	80–85
Newborns per 100 adult females	—	—	35
6-month-olds per 100 adult females	—	44	19
Yearlings (18 months old) per 100 adult females	62	42	—

BLUE SHEEP

The Shey Gompa population of *Pseudois nayaur* contained more adult males than adult females, at a ratio of 1.3:1, a discrepancy from the expected 1:1 ratio for which I have no explanation. Another population, studied in Nepal in 1972 (see p. 466), also had more males. Young animals (those born in 1973) comprised 13 percent of the population (40 young to 100 adult females), and the yearling percentage was 9.5 (28 yearlings to 100 adult females), adequate but not good survival. These figures compare unfavorably with the 87 young and 82 yearlings per 100 adult females in the population studied in 1972. It may be conjectured that the low proportion of young at Shey is due to a combination of quite high predation pressure and poor winter range conditions, the latter the result of heavy livestock grazing. The large predators—snow leopard and wolf—subsist to a large extent on blue sheep, as is apparent from the following tabulation:

Food item	*Snow leopard*	*Wolf*
Blue sheep	8	13
Livestock	2	10
Marmot	5	11
Hare	—	1
Vegetation	6	—
Unidentified hair	1	—
Total food items	22	35
Total droppings studied	16	34

Although blue sheep are, in fact, goats, their rutting behavior revealed a fascinating array of behavioral traits showing affinities to both sheep and goats. Some of these traits no doubt have been shaped by their habitat, the preferred one of blue sheep being grassy slopes near cliffs, much like the habitat of North American sheep, rather than the rugged cliffs preferred by typical goats. Rutting males, such as those of the wild goat, tend to attach themselves to certain herds of females for lengthy periods in contrast to males of the urial sheep, which, in their open, rolling habitat, restlessly wander from herd to herd in search of estrous females. The extent of roaming by blue sheep males is intermediate. Certain traits, however, are not under strong ecological influences, yet the behavior of blue sheep again seems intermediate between sheep and goats. For example, rutting *Capra* males may extend their penis and spray themselves with urine, behavior not observed in *Ovis*. Blue sheep expose the penis but do not douse themselves. Instead, they use the penis as a threat symbol when attempting to intimidate an opponent. The blue sheep probably split early from the ancestral goat stock, soon after the goat and sheep lineages diverged.

Snow Leopard, Markhor Goat, and Marco Polo Sheep in Pakistan, 1974

During the first 4 months of 1974 I made several research trips within Pakistan to round out the study prior to my leaving the country. I returned to the United States in June, then revisited Pakistan in October, remaining through December.

1. With the assistance of M. Sunquist an attempt was made between January and March to trap and place a radio collar on a snow leopard. In this we were unsuccessful. An extensive foot survey covering about 1,200 square miles of mountains revealed that only 4 or 5 snow leopards survived in that area. At least 7 of the cats had been killed by local people near Chitral town since 1971, reducing a viable population to the vanishing point. Data on wolf and ibex numbers were also collected during the survey.

2. Observations on markhor goats in the Chitral Gol reserve, Hindu Kush, had been made during the winters of 1970 (see p. 463). 1972–73 (see p. 467), and were made again in 1974. For the past two years the population has remained stable at about 125 animals (see p. 467). Reproduction and survival are relatively constant from year to year, probably a reflection on the general predictability of the food supply in spite of its seasonal variation. In contrast, the wild goat, which I studied in the desert environment of Sind (see p. 468), shows marked annual fluctuations in the numbers of surviving young and yearlings:

	Date	*Young per 100 adult females*	*Yearlings per 100 adult females*
Markhor	December 1970	130	50
	December 1972	130	56
	January 1974	137	54
Wild goat	September 1972	44	62
	September 1973	19	42
	March 1974	49	17

The amount of rainfall, and hence nutritious forage, just before the rut seems to have a profound influence on wild-goat reproduction. Since rainfall in the desert is erratic, the number of surviving young also fluctuate considerably. In contrast to 1972, the summer rains of 1973 were reasonably good, and so was young survival the following spring. The 1973 rut reached its peak two weeks earlier than in 1972.

As shown by the population statistics, the death rate of young markhor was greatest between the ages of 6 and 18 months (about 60 percent) whereas young wild goats showed little mortality after they survived to the age of 6 months. The wild-goat data, in particular, are useful from the standpoint of management of the species in heavily hunted areas, for it should be possible to predict the sizes of the coming young and yearling crops from the amount of summer rainfall.

A visit was also made to a Punjab urial sheep population which I have checked repeatedly since 1970 (see p. 462). As a comparison with the goat data, young survival of urial is shown here:

Date	*Young per 100 adult females*
October 1970	75
July 1971	69
July 1972	63
July 1973	56
(April 1974	53)

The 1974 figure is biased, for the population was sampled at the end of the birth period when some young were still hidden.

The urial live in an area in which availability of nutritious forage is less predictable than in the range of Chitral markhor but more so than in the Sind wild-goat habitat. The annual variation in the urial young crop reflects this.

3. One purpose of the project was to ascertain the distribution and status of markhor and other species by making road and foot surveys. One such survey was conducted during spring 1974 in the range of the rare Kabul markhor, which, it was found, still survive in low numbers scattered from the Safed Koh Range northward beyond the Khyber Pass.

4. In spring 1972, Himalayan tahr were observed for a month in Nepal. To obtain more data on this species in a different habitat and at a different phase in its reproductive cycle, I studied the animals briefly during May in New Zealand, where the species was introduced in 1904. Observations on pre-rutting behavior of tahr were made and various displays of chamois were also seen, usefully supplementing earlier work by myself and others.

5. Information on the status and population dynamics of wildlife species is of value to Pakistani officials who are responsible for conserving the

country's resources. To assist the officials, I visited many and gave them my data, and I wrote reports in which suggestions for suitable sanctuaries and national parks were made. While this activity does not come under "research," it is an essential part of a project in a country which has no wildlife biologists. The following paragraphs present portions of one such report, submitted to the Pakistani Government in December 1974.

The Marco Polo Sheep in Pakistan, 1974

The Marco Polo sheep (*Ovis ammon polii*) is one of the rarest animals in Pakistan, being found only around the Khunjerab and Kilik passes in northern Hunza. The appearance of many sheep trophies in private homes within the past 10 years indicates that these two small populations have been heavily hunted, and interviews with persons that know the areas suggest that the number of sheep has greatly declined in recent years. To ascertain the status of the Marco Polo sheep and to devise means of preserving this spectacular member of Pakistan's fauna, I visited the two passes in November 1974, and my recommendations for Kunjerab were as given in the following paragraphs.

Marco Polo sheep prefer flat to rolling terrain devoid of precipitous slopes and cliffs. Such habitat occurs in the Khunjerab Valley only for about 30 square kilometers at Khunjerab Pass (4,875 meters) bordering the People's Republic of China.

Several hundred sheep once frequented the Khunjerab Pass area according to villagers. An American hunter saw there a herd of 65 rams in November 1959 (see Clark, 1964). At least some of the sheep seemed to remain in Pakistan throughout the year. For instance, G. M. Beg, a member of the 1964 boundary commission, observed sheep at Khunjerab every month between May and October. However, sheep were shot indiscriminately during the late 1960's and early 1970's especially by crews who surveyed and later constructed the Karakoram Highway. One military officer shot about 50 animals for meat in 1968. With hunting restrictions obviously not enforced, villagers also began to kill extensively. About a dozen sheep were shot as recently as 1973, but killing seems to have ceased in 1974, except for two sheep shot in April by a foreigner and his guide. Because of this persecution, the remaining sheep now spend much of the year in China where they are protected. Villagers say that sheep at present visit the Khunjerab mainly in April and May, attracted there by the first green grass. When in late June the domestic sheep, goats, and yak are brought to the area most Marco Polo sheep retreat into China.

I found no sheep in late November, and the lack of tracks in the snow indicated that none had been there all month. Good grazing was available, south-facing slopes being largely free of snow. This, together with the fact that in years past sheep were often seen at Khunjerab in November, suggests that the animals have changed their habits because of being hunted.

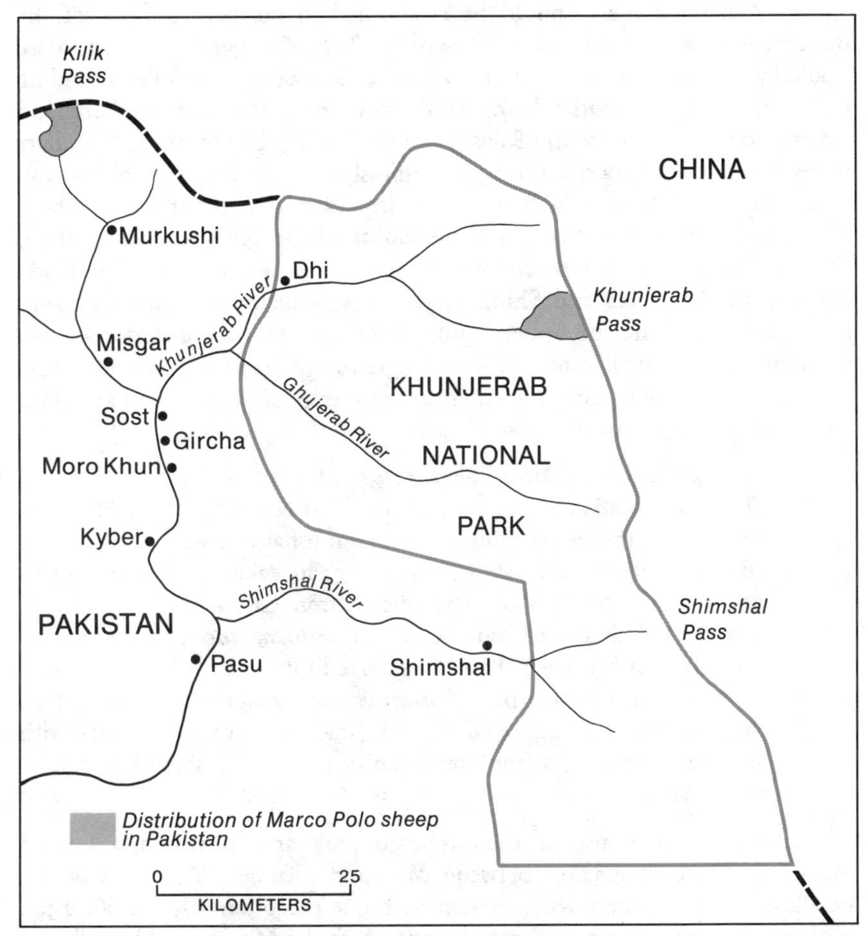

FIG. 1. Map showing recommended boundaries of Khunjerab National Park and surrounding territory. The Park, which includes an area of some 3,000 square kilometers, was officially established in April 1975 and provides protection to five species of large mammals threatened with extinction in Pakistan: Marco Polo sheep, blue sheep, Tibetan wild ass, snow leopard, and brown bear.

The Marco Polo sheep is the only animal in Pakistan that could in itself become a tourist attraction, especially since the Karakoram Highway makes them readily accessible. However, Pakistan is in danger of losing this sheep unless immediate measures are taken to protect the remnants and to induce them to remain in the Khunjerab Pass area. The following conservation measures are proposed.

1. A national park should be established in northern Hunza for the protection of all wildlife and its habitat. This Khunjerab National Park would include not only the Khunjerab Pass but also a large tract of surrounding mountains, the boundaries being as follows (see map): The northern and eastern boundaries follow the Pakistan-China border. The southern boundary traces the divides between the upper Shimshal Valley and the Hispar and other glaciers. The western boundary is irregular; starting at the northern end, it includes the Dhi Valley and the mouth of the Ghujerab Valley; then, after heading south a few kilometers, it runs eastward along the divide between the Ghujerab and Shimshal drainages. Finally, the boundary dips southward to include the upper Shimshal Valley. The park includes an area of about 3,000 square kilometers. Not a single village lies within its boundaries.

The park would offer protection to five species of large mammals which are threatened with extinction in Pakistan:

a. The population of Marco Polo sheep at Khunjerab.
b. The only populations of blue sheep (*Pseudois nayaur*) in Pakistan, occurring in the upper Ghujerab and Shimshal valleys.
c. The only Tibetan wild ass (*Equus kiang*) in Pakistan. A few animals visit the Shimshal Pass area sporadically from China.
d. A small population of snow leopard (*Panthera uncia*), a cat now so rare that possibly fewer than 250 survive in Pakistan.
e. A number of brown bear (*Ursus arctos*), a species threatened in Pakistan because cubs find a ready market as dancing bears with itinerant entertainers (the possession of these bears should be legally banned).

2. Local human use of the proposed park area is currently limited mainly to livestock grazing between May and October. This activity can be allowed to continue for the present with one exception. Over 2,000 head of domestic sheep, goats, and yak, belonging to the Mir and to the villagers of Moru Khun, Khyber, Sost, and Gircha, are taken to the Khunjerab Pass area for the 3 summer months. The herdsmen create constant disturbance and the livestock competes with the wildlife for forage. Large herds of domestic stock also have no esthetic appeal to tourists. Livestock grazing

should be prohibited at Khunjerab Pass within 10 kilometers of the border. The removal of this disturbance, coupled with a ban on shooting, might stimulate the Marco Polo sheep to remain in Pakistan again.

3. In return for not grazing at Khunjerab Pass the villagers should be compensated in some way. One means of doing this would be to set up a check post at Dhi and charge all vehicles not on official duty a park entrance fee. Most or all of this money could be given to the village councils to improve schooling, health services, etc. A fee of 100 Rs per car containing foreigners and 50 Rs per car containing solely Pakistanis would seem appropriate. Local villagers should also be given preference with park jobs.

4. Along the Khunjerab Valley grow patches of birch and willow. These groves are attractive, for they break the monotony of the barren cliffs and scree slopes, and they offer visitors delightful retreats in which to rest and have picnics. Military contractors have cut down most trees for firewood within the past 2 years. If the present rate of cutting continues, all the trees will be gone within 2 years. Aside from the fact that the military has alternative means of heating and cooking, such destruction is short-sighted, creating esthetic damage that will take nature over 100 years to repair. I feel it imperative that all cutting of wood in the Khunjerab and adjoining valleys upstream from the scout post at Dhi be prohibited immediately.

Prime Minister Zulfikar Ali Bhutto accepted these recommendations and the Kunjerab National Park was officially established in April 1975.

REFERENCES

CLARK, JAMES L.
1964. The great arc of the wild sheep, 247 pp. University of Oklahoma Press, Norman.

GEIST, V.
1968. On the interrelation of external appearance, social behaviour and social structure of mountain sheep. Zeitschr. für Tierpsych., vol. 25, pp. 199–215.

MATTHIESSEN, PETER
1978. The snow leopard. New Yorker, March 27, pp. 39–94; April 3, pp. 41–92.

MOUNTFORD, GUY
1969. The vanishing jungle, 285 pp., illus. William Collins Sons & Co., London.

NIEVERGELT, B.
1967. Die Zusammensetzung der Gruppen beim Alpensteinbock. Zeitschr. für Säugetierk., vol. 32, no. 3, pp. 129–144.

ROBERTS, T.
1969. A note on *Capra falconeri* (Wagner, 1839). Zeitschr. für Säugetierk., vol. 34, no. 4, pp. 238–249.

SCHALLER, GEORGE B.
1971. Imperiled phantom of Asian peaks. Nat. Geogr. Mag., vol. 140, no. 5, pp. 702–707, illus.
1972. On meeting a snow leopard. Animal Kingdom, vol. 75, no. 1, pp. 7–13.
1973a. On the behaviour of blue sheep. Journ. Bombay. Nat. Hist. Soc., vol. 69, no. 3, pp. 523–537.
1973b. Observations on Himalayan tahr. Journ. Bombay. Nat. Hist. Soc., vol. 70, no. 1, pp. 1–24.
1973c. Chitral Gol Reserve. Pp. 136–138 *in* "World Wildlife Yearbook, 1972–73." World Wildlife Federation, Morges, Switzerland.
1975a. A walk in the Hindu Kush. Animal Kingdom, vol. 78, pp. 8–19.
1975b. The valley of blood. Animal Kingdom, vol. 78, pp. 20–21.
1975c. Stalking the wild sheep of Kalabagh. Int. Wildlife, vol. 5, pp. 42–47.
1976a. Pakistan: status of wildlife and research needs. Pp. 133–143 in "Ecological guidelines for the use of natural resources in the Middle East and South West Asia." International Union for the Conservation of Nature (I.U.C.N.), Morges, Switzerland.
1976b. Large mammals of northern Pakistan, Oryx, vol. 13, no. 4, pp. 351–356.
1977a. Aggressive behaviour of domestic yak. Journ. Bombay Nat. Hist. Soci., vol. 73, no. 2, pp. 385–389.
1977b. A note on a population of *Gazella gazella bennetti.* Journ. Bombay Nat. Hist. Soc., vol. 73, no. 1, pp. 209–211.
1977c. Mountain monarchs: wild sheep and goats of the Himalaya, 425 pp., illus. University of Chicago Press.
1977d. The sheep that isn't. Animal Kingdom, vol. 80, no. 1, pp. 4–13.

SCHALLER, GEORGE B., and KHAN, A.
1975. Distribution and status of markhor. Biol. Cons., vol. 7, pp. 185–198.

SCHALLER, GEORGE B., and LAURIE, A.
1974. Courtship behaviour of the wild goat. Zeitschr. für Säugetierk., vol. 39, pp. 115–127.

SCHALLER, GEORGE B., and MIRZA, ZAHID BEG
1971. On the behavior of Kashmir markhor (*Capra falconeri cashmiriensis*). Mammalia, vol. 35, pp. 548–567.
1974. On the behavior of Punjab urial (*Ovis orientalis punjabensis*). Pp. 306–323 *in* "The Behaviour of Ungulates and Its Relation to Management," vol. 1, V. Geist and F. Walther, eds. Publ. (new ser.) no. 24, I.U.C.N., 511 pp., illus. Morges, Switzerland.

SIMON, NOEL, *compiler*
1966. Red data book, vol. 1: Mammalia, I.U.C.N., Morges, Switzerland.

STOCKLEY, CHARLES H.
1936. Stalking in the Himalayas and northern India, 254 pp., illus. Herbert Jenkins, Ltd., London.

GEORGE B. SCHALLER

Feeding, Spacing, and Growth in the Four Species of Bimini *Anolis* Lizards

Principal Investigator: Thomas W. Schoener, University of Washington, Seattle, Washington.

Grant No. 830: For a continuing study of the *Anolis* lizards of the West Indies.

This report covers field work performed on the island of South Bimini, Bahamas, from March 2 to May 15, 1970, most of which was supported by the National Geographic Society. Four species of *Anolis—sagrei*, *carolinensis*, *distichus,* and *angusticeps*—were studied in depth. The major purposes of the investigation were to gain information on (1) the growth in body size of the four species, and how that relates to population density; (2) the foraging behavior of the species as it varies by sex and age; (3) the spatial relationships of individuals, specifically home-range size and overlap; and (4) the percentage of time spent in inter- versus intraspecific interaction.

Field Procedure

While visiting Bimini during 1969 (with National Geographic Society support) we located three study sites judged ideal for measuring home range, parameters of foraging behavior, and population density. These areas were:

(1) The *Short-blackland* site (150 square meters), containing small-to-medium hardwood trees as well as 2–4-meter *Coccothrinax* palms, with a fairly open understory (the area is intermediate between Howard's (1950) "*Coccothrinax* Shrub" and "Blackland" vegetation types);

(2) The *Forest-path* site (95 square meters), encompassing the trees on either side of a partially overgrown, about a 3-meter path bulldozed through tall (up to about 15 meters) blackland forest; and

(3) The *Terminalia* site (68 square meters), consisting primarily of huge trees of that genus surrounded by *Bursera* saplings. (To enable us to concentrate better on the other species, *A. sagrei* was not studied at this site.)

Immediately upon arrival in 1970 we began to "mark out" populations of the four species in the first two study sites. Animals were marked permanently by toe-clipping (one front and one back toe, or this plus another toe) and temporarily by painting four or five dots in permutations of three easily distinguishable colors along the dorsal surface. The former is necessary because the lizards shed their skins every 3–4 weeks and therefore must be repainted to be observable at a distance. In 5–6 days we marked most individuals in these areas. Observations on these lizards kept us occupied for about a month, after which we felt we could safely extend our study to the third area. In all, about 300 lizards were marked during the course of the study.

We measured growth of animals by recording size at initial and subsequent captures, pressing the animal flat against a millimeter rule. Home-range size and overlap were measured after we put down a grid of 4-by-4- or 5-by-5-foot quadrats. Coordinates on this grid were recorded, as were perch height and diameter. Statistical methods of treating these data are given elsewhere (Schoener, 1978; Schoener and Schoener, 1978), and they will be briefly mentioned in the next section.

Results

1. *Population density and relative abundance of the species.* By far the most abundant species on Bimini is *A. sagrei* (table 1). Abundances ranged from 0.31 to 0.45 individual per square yard. (These abundances are slightly lower than estimated preliminarily, because of a change in procedure. We included in the counts only those lizards whose geometric center of the home range fell within the predetermined boundaries of the study site.) The next-most-abundant species, *distichus*, achieves only about half this density at most. The other two species range in density from 0.016 per square yard to 0.004 per square yard. Thus *sagrei* is about as abundant as all the other species combined, and abundances, while not perfectly geometrically distributed, come fairly close in some sites.

Combining data from all four species, we conclude that densities of anoles range from 0.53 to 0.66 lizard/square yard in optimal habitats during early spring. Our data, of course, refer only to a single year and season; densities of anoles in other localities can vary by as much as 30–40 percent between years (Schoener and Schoener, 1976), and juveniles are not abundant during spring in these seasonal breeders.

In the abundant species males and females are almost equally numerous. In the rare species males if anything have the edge. These results should be viewed as typical only of certain vegetation types; later studies have shown that the sex ratio and proportion of the various age classes are very much related to the type (and presumably favorableness) of habitat.

2. *Growth in body size.* To describe growth in these lizards we tested three growth models—the Von Bertalanffy, the logistic-by-length, and the

logistic-by-weight models. We developed some new mathematical methods for handling these models especially suitable for the field data we collected. Combining the Bimini data with data from a later field trip to Great Abaco, Bahamas, we concluded that the logistic-by-weight model fits the data by far the best. Application of this model showed:

a. Males and females have the same characteristic growth rate (rate of approach to the maximum, asymptotic size) but differ greatly in the growth asymptote. This results in males growing absolutely more rapidly than females over nearly all body sizes common to both. We have also tentatively observed (data not yet compiled) that subadult males of some species spend a greater proportion of their time in active feeding than do females; if confirmed, this behavior is what allows their faster growth. Moreover, a previous study (Schoener, 1968) showed that during the nonbreeding season males contained a considerably greater volume of food than females of the same size in at least three of the four Bimini species.

b. In six of seven possible comparisons, growth rates of lizards with low population densities were higher than rates of lizards with high population densities. We speculate that food density is higher in areas of more rapid growth and that lizards do not, and should not, diffuse sufficiently to such places to compensate exactly for their greater resources

c. Male *A. distichus*, and to a lesser extent female *carolinensis* and both sexes of *angusticeps*, all arboreal species, grow more rapidly than the trunk-ground *sagrei.* Unlike *sagrei*, they also grow more rapidly than several common West Indian species (Andrews, 1976), suggesting less food pressure upon these relatively low-density species.

d. Variation in growth within a site and sex is not explained by variation in home-range area.

3. *Home-range area.* Table 1 lists the median home-range areas for those lizards having this statistic estimated as of this writing. Methods of home-range estimation differed greatly from any so far reported in the literature: a regression method was employed, and estimates were somewhat lower than those of the Jennrich and Turner method (1969), the most commonly used recent previous method (Schoener, 1978).

In *A. sagrei*, male home ranges are nearly double the size of female ranges (this statistic includes subadult males, and were these deleted the difference would be much greater). In the other species measured males have home ranges more comparable in size to those of females, but they are still always larger. Both *distichus* and *angusticeps* have home ranges considerably larger than *sagrei's*, but similar in size to one another. Data from *carolinensis* are not yet compiled, but male *carolinensis* appear to have much larger home ranges than most classes of the other species. Home-range estimation is extremely sensitive to sample size, and we have been careful to compensate for differences of that sort in our methods. We are convinced our data are unbiased in that respect.

Comparison of these results with those reported under section 1 shows that there is a fairly strong inverse correlation of home-range size and population density within and, to a lesser extent, between species. Thus *A. sagrei*, with about 3.3 square yards per individual in the Short-blackland site, has a home range about half that of *distichus*, with 7.4 square yards per individual. The three arboreal species both are rarer and have larger home ranges than the more terrestrial *sagrei*.

4. *Home-range overlap*. Although all home ranges have been plotted, and overlaps computed among these, we have not yet perfected a method to estimate home-range overlap while compensating for differences in sample size. The following descriptions are therefore based on preliminary observation and are subject to change.

In *A. sagrei*, a species highly sexually dimorphic in size, adult males defend territories against other adult males, whereas other, smaller individuals occupy areas largely exclusive of one another regardless of sex. Thus there are roughly two layers of territories in this species (more may be evident once the data are treated systematically). In all cases, however, territorial defense does not result in the perfectly nonoverlapping areas that one frequently sees in the ornithological literature. Rather, overlap over a month's time is rather substantial in some places. The greatest amount of overlap in male *sagrei* occurred when a fruiting tree attracted large numbers of insects; about six males extended their ranges into this area, and while chases and fights were frequent most individuals persisted in their attempt to exploit this temporary food supply.

Other species vary considerably from *A. sagrei* in their spatial organization. Although male *carolinensis* sometimes fight viciously and in a highly stylized fashion, they overlap extensively in home range relative to *sagrei*, perhaps because their ranges are so large and in such dense foliage that they are less defendable. Female *carolinensis* overlap to some extent both among each other and with subadult males. Adult male *distichus* have fairly exclusive ranges, but these can overlap substantially, sometimes in areas of intensive feeding. In the *Terminalia* site the four largest male *distichus* had territories arranged radially about the largest trunk. No evidence of exclusion along the height dimension was found. Female *distichus* sometimes occur in nested ranges, and these are sometimes almost perfectly contained within the range of a large male. Subadult male *distichus* can have very large home ranges

TABLE 1. DENSITIES AND MEDIAN HOME-RANGE SIZES FOR THE FOUR BIMINI SPECIES OF *Anolis* (MAXIMUM IN ANY 5-DAY PERIOD)

Study site	*Species and sex*	*Number per square yard*	*Median home range (square inches)*
Short-blackland	*sagrei* female	0.163	4,562
Short-blackland	*sagrei* male	0.146	8,570
Short-blackland	*distichus* female	0.079	11,532
Short-blackland	*distichus* male	0.062	15,394
Short-blackland	*carolinensis* female	0.032	
Short-blackland	*carolinensis* male	0.021	
Short-blackland	*angusticeps* female	0.021	
Short-blackland	*angusticeps* male	0.016	
Forest-path	*sagrei* female	0.232	3,244
Forest-path	*sagrei* male	0.232	4,999
Forest-path	*distichus* female	0.036	
Forest-path	*distichus* male	0.054	
Forest-path	*carolinensis* female	0.023	
Forest-path	*carolinensis* male	0.062	
Forest-path	*angusticeps* female	0.009	
Forest-path	*angusticeps* male	0.036	
Terminalia	*distichus* female	0.208	12,703
Terminalia	*distichus* male	0.250	14,655
Terminalia	*carolinensis* female	0.015	
Terminalia	*carolinensis* male	0.059	
Terminalia	*angusticeps* female	0.080	8,330
Terminalia	*angusticeps* male	0.129	13,984

that overlap with many other individuals. Male *distichus* display to one another frequently but seldom make contact during an interaction. Female *distichus* rarely show aggressive behavior of any kind toward one another. Both sexes of *angusticeps* were too rare in most places for us to say much about intraspecific interaction. Ranges frequently do not overlap, but this may be because of rarity per se rather than because of active repulsion. The one area of fairly abundant *angusticeps* was the *Terminalia* site for males. Here, individuals overlapped broadly and more so than did *distichus*, even though population densities were somewhat less. Aggressive behavior in both sexes of *angusticeps* is uncommonly observed, and the few male-male interactions that were seen consisted primarily of display.

We also have preliminary information on the stability of home ranges. In all species males seem less stable than females in their position in the study site or permanence there. Unestablished males of *A. sagrei* and *carolinensis*, and less often *distichus*, were found briefly in the study area, whereas this was more seldom the case for adult females. This tendency for males to be more vagile can affect our long-term estimates of sex ratio, biasing them in the direction of more males than exist instantaneously in a site.

Our information on frequency of and success in aggressive encounters is not yet compiled, but we believe this will mostly show that larger individuals are more successful (as did Rand, 1967, for *A. lineatopus*) and that the percent of time spent in interspecific interaction is much less than that spent in intraspecific interaction. This latter trend would agree with other similar reports in the literature for lizards (Schoener, 1977).

5. *Feeding behavior.* Our feeding observations will be gleaned from continuous observation of individual lizards: periods ranged from ½ hour to 4 hours and were of predetermined lengths. The species differed greatly in several major ways, which I now surmise from our as yet unanalyzed data.

a. Type of search. *A. sagrei* is a classical sit-and-wait predator, perching in a stationary manner while watching for prey. The other species are to varying degrees active searchers. Male *carolinensis* will sometimes ambush prey flying to the tips of twigs, but will more frequently crawl slowly about the vegetation, inspecting it carefully for food. Female *carolinensis* favors this latter style of search, as do both sexes of *angusticeps. A. distichus* feeds most commonly on aggregated prey (ants); it searches actively for them, then sits passively in front of a trail and gobbles the ants up as they pass by.

b. Pursuit distance. Correlated with the style of search is the average pursuit distance; this is greatest in *A. sagrei* and smaller to varying degrees in the active searchers.

c. Size of food and handling-swallowing time. *A. sagrei* takes larger prey than similarly sized individuals of most of the other species (Schoener, 1968). This results in a longer handling-swallowing time, though we do not yet have the magnitude of the difference.

d. Location of food. *A. sagrei* obtains most of its prey from the ground and gets a lesser amount from the lower vegetation. The prey of the other species is gleaned almost entirely from various parts of the vegetation; only *distichus* frequently comes to the ground to eat ants in one of the study sites. Prey of *distichus* is most commonly obtained from trunks and branches, that of *carolinensis* is from leaves, and that of *angusticeps* is from twigs.

e. Feeding period. The species differ greatly in the extent and position of the feeding period. This period for the passive searcher *A. sagrei* runs more or less continuously throughout the day; under intense sun individuals will sit motionless in shady spaces but still will often dart down at a prey if the opportunity arises. The other species, active searchers to a much greater extent, have more restricted periods of feeding. *A. distichus* and especially *angusticeps* will be more active early in the day or on cloudy days than in full, hot sun. The former species, but not the latter, will also frequently be active in late afternoon and at dusk. *A. carolinensis* has its activity complementary to these two, being most active at midday during sunny days; it nearly disappears from conspicuous view during a cold wave or on very cloudy days. One seems forced to conclude that the thermal optima are different for the different species of active searchers and that climatic conditions in general are less of a consideration for a passive searcher than for an active one.

REFERENCES

ANDREWS, R. M.

1976. Growth rate in island and mainland anoline lizards. Copeia, 1976, no. 3, pp. 477–482.

HOWARD, R. A.

1950. Vegetation of the Bimini island group. Ecol. Monogr., vol. 20, pp. 317–349.

JENNRICH, R. I., and TURNER, F. B.

1969. Measurement of non-circular home range. Journ. Theoret. Biol., vol. 22, pp. 227–237.

RAND, A. STANLEY

1967. Ecology and social organization in the iguanid lizard *Anolis lineatopus*. Proc. U.S. Nat. Mus., vol. 122, no. 3598, 79 pp., illus.

SCHOENER, THOMAS W.

1968. The *Anolis* lizards of Bimini: Resource partitioning in a complex fauna. Ecology, vol. 49, pp. 704–726.

1977. Competition and the niche. Pp. 35–136 *in* "Biology of the Reptilia," vol. 3, Carl Gans, ed. Academic Press, New York.

1976. Habitat shift in widespread *Anolis* lizard species. Nat. Geogr. Soc. Res. Rpts., 1968 Projects, pp. 369–378, illus.

1978. An empirically based estimate of home range. Unpublished MS.

SCHOENER, THOMAS W., and SCHOENER, AMY

1976. The ecological context of female pattern polymorphism in the lizard *Anolis sagrei*. Evolution, vol. 30, pp. 650–658.

1978. Estimating and interpreting body-size growth in some *Anolis* lizards. Copeia, 1978, no. 3, pp. 390–405.

THOMAS W. SCHOENER

[illegible]

REFERENCES

[illegible]

THOMAS W. SCHOENER

Biology of Northern American Accipiters in Arizona and New Mexico

Principal Investigators: Noel F. R. Snyder and Helen A. Snyder, University of South Florida, Tampa, Florida.

Grant Nos. 849, 967: In support of a comparative study of North American accipiters.

During the spring and summer of 1970 the National Geographic Society supported research on the biology of three species of hawks of the genus *Accipiter* in Arizona and New Mexico. Emphasis was given to studies of comparative behavior and of the effects of organochlorine pesticides on reproductive success. This research represented a continuation of research begun during the spring and summer of 1969.

General Biology of Accipiters

Of the three species of accipiters, Cooper's hawk (*Accipiter cooperi*) is the most common and widespread in Arizona and New Mexico, and it was found nesting from the lower limits of trees in the deserts up to the Canadian Life Zone near the tops of mountains. Nests were generally located in wooded canyon bottoms, and distances between nests averaged between 1 and 1.5 miles in good habitat. In all, 53 nests of Cooper's hawk were studied during the 2-year period. Goshawks (*Accipiter gentilis*) and sharp-shinned hawks (*Accipiter striatus*) are relatively rare in the study area, and only two nests of the former and one of the latter were studied during the two years. All nests of these two species were at relatively high elevations. Of the total of 56 nests of all species, 8 of Cooper's hawks, 2 of goshawks, and 1 of sharp-shinned hawk were studied intensively from blinds.

The nesting season begins in March and April when hawks return to their territories from wintering grounds. Territories were exceedingly stable over the years, and most nests were built on top of old nests or close-by. Nest-building began promptly with the return of the hawks, and in all cases but one, the sharp-shinned-hawk nest, males performed the bulk of the gathering of nesting material. Nests were built of twigs and lined with outer bark of a variety of local tree species. Both Cooper's hawks and goshawks utilized leafy green sprigs in nest construction, but this was not observed with sharp-shinned hawks. The trait is most highly developed in goshawks. Typically, most next-building took place in mornings and was organized into bouts interspersed with periods of hunting, preening, or other activities. Actual gathering of nesting material was most leisurely in goshawks and most rapid in sharp-shinned hawks. Twigs were snapped off from standing trees with the beak or feet and were carried in flight to the nest. On onlv one occasion have we seen an accipiter (Cooper's hawk) gather nesting material from the ground. Nest-building generally took on the order of a month, during which time the male hawks did most of the hunting for the pair. Copulations were frequent and took place from the start of the nest-building period through to the laying of eggs, and in some cases partway into the incubation period. Most copulations occurred during nest-building bouts but not at nests themselves.

In Cooper's hawks the interval between eggs varied from 2 to 5 days (averaging 3.2 days), resulting in a period of about a week and a half for the completion of a clutch of 4 eggs. Clutch size averaged 3.67 eggs, significantly lower than the average of 4.22 reported for the species in New York (Meng, 1951). Incubation began partway through the laying period but was not intensive until laying of the last egg. The incubation period for the last egg laid was 34–35 days in Cooper's hawk.

During incubation, as during nest-building, nearly all food for the pair was captured by the male. Feeding of the female was similar in all three species. The male brought food to a perch near the nest and summoned its mate with a characteristic food call. The female flew from the nest immediately to take the food. While she fed, the male took over incubation in goshawk and Cooper's hawk (generally) but not in sharp-shinned hawk. Females resumed incubation as soon as they were through feeding. Nest-building continued to some extent during incubation for all three species.

Hatching of eggs was witnessed at two nests of Cooper's hawks and one of sharp-shinned hawk. The adult female gave some assistance to the young by tugging on eggshells, but the primary force in the hatching process was that of the young themselves. They hatched with their eyes open and took food about half a day after hatching.

During the early nestling period the females brooded their young and fed them with food brought in by the male. Transfers of food proceeded as they had during incubation. About midway through the nestling phase females also began to hunt extensively, and they continued to do so through the rest of the breeding season. The length of the nestling period was about 4 weeks for sharp-shinned hawk, 5 weeks for Cooper's hawk, and 6 weeks for goshawk. Male young tended to fledge several days ahead of females.

After fledging, young were still fed at the nest for a week or two, and adults defended nests even when young were at some distance. In time young began to take food from adults away from the nest. The length of the post-fledging dependency period was observed most accurately at one nest of Cooper's hawks and lasted 6 weeks. During this period the young made few attempts to capture prey and these were incompetent.

Vocalizations of the three species are comparable, though with some interesting differences. All three give a call in alarm, which is made up of a long series of repeated short notes and might be called a cackle. The pitch is highest in sharp-shinned hawk and lowest in goshawk. The cackle is not limited to contexts of alarm and is often heard by birds engaged in nest-building and other activities. In sharp-shinned hawk this call serves also as the food call of the male when he has prey for the female. The food call of male goshawks is the single syllable ***guck***, while that of male Cooper's hawks is the single syllable ***kik***. Both these calls are given also in other contexts. In addition, all three species have a separate solicitation-type vocalization heard frequently from females but only rarely from males. This call develops from begging calls of the young. In goshawks and sharp-shinned hawks begging calls of well-developed young and the solicitation calls of adults sound identical. In Cooper's hawk they are similar but distinguishable. In goshawks the solicitation call is a plaintive ***weer***, in Cooper's hawk a harsh ***caw***, and in sharp-shinned hawk a high-pitched ***ee***. All three species use the call in a variety of contexts and sometimes link the call to other vocalizations.

During copulations Cooper's hawks and goshawks give loud calls that appear to be intense forms of the solicitation call. Copulations in sharp-shinned hawks are sometimes silent and sometimes accompanied by weak cackles.

Diets of the three species, as determined quantitatively from observations from blinds, were as follows:

Goshawks (40 prey, 2 nests)............	100 percent birds (mostly pigeons and jays)
Sharp-shinned hawks (87 prey, 1 nest)..	100 percent birds (a great variety)
Cooper's hawks (265 prey, 7 nests)	45.1 percent mammals (mostly chipmunks)
	38.5 percent birds (a great variety)
	16.4 percent lizards (mostly *Sceloporus*)

The chief surprises here were the heavy dependence of Cooper's hawks on mammals and lizards and the complete dependence of goshawks on birds. In previous studies (Schnell, 1958; Meng, 1959; Craighead and Craighead, 1956; Storer, 1966) Cooper's hawks are reported to have taken considerably higher percentages of birds and goshawks much lower percentages of birds.

Effects of Chlorinated Hydrocarbons and Heavy Metals

The results of this study, including studies in 1971, have been published in *BioScience* (Snyder and Snyder, 1973). Emphasis was given to studies of effects of DDE, as this organochlorine has been implicated as the major stress factor for other raptorial birds in the United States. Other pollutants studied were Dieldrin, PCB, and four heavy metals (copper, lead, mercury, and cadmium). For the most part the materials analyzed were eggs that failed to hatch in nests, but we analyzed also some fertile eggs and prey species.

The concentrations of DDE found in eggs varied from low in goshawks to very high in sharp-shinned hawks. In Cooper's hawks, the species from which most materials were analyzed, levels of DDE in eggs correlated highly significantly with the extent of thinning of eggshells, and unsuccessful nests had eggs significantly more contaminated than eggs from successful nests. Stress appears to be hitting the species both through breakage of eggs (11 out of 60 clutches over the entire study) and through disturbed behavior of adults. The three cases of abnormal behavior seen in Cooper's hawks were all of birds that were highly contaminated with DDE. Although Cooper's hawks in Arizona and New Mexico are being significantly stressed by DDE, the population appears to be absorbing the stress at present, and the density of nesting adults has remained stable. More contaminated populations of Cooper's hawks in the Eastern States have been declining sharply since the introduction of this substance into widespread agricultural use.

As sharp-shinned hawks are carrying even higher levels of DDE in their eggs than are Cooper's hawks we are much concerned for the future of this species. Though no egg breakage occurred in nests observed in the Southwest, sample size was very small. In Oregon egg breakage in this species has been frequent. Levels of DDE in several Oregon sharp-shinned-hawk eggs we have analyzed are as high as the highest recently found in arctic peregrine falcons (Cade et al., 1971).

The United States has recently banned use of DDT, and we may hope for declines in levels of this material (and its common metabolite DDE) in wildlife tissues. However, this ban may do little to reduce contamination in Southwestern accipiters as these birds receive their contamination primarily from species that winter in regions south of the border where the ban is not in effect. The state of contamination in Southwestern accipiters bears continued watching.

Levels of Dieldrin, PCB, and heavy metals were uniformly low in the eggs analyzed, and the only significant correlation found was between levels of cadmium and nesting failure. Since the same correlation was found between levels of DDE and nesting failure and since cadmium levels were very low, we believe the cadmium correlation may be only a chance effect.

REFERENCES

CADE, TOM J.; LINCER, JEFFREY L.; WHITE, CLAYTON M.; ROSENEAU, DAVID G.; and SWARTZ, L. G.

1971. DDE residues and eggshell changes in Alaskan falcons and hawks. Science, vol. 172, pp. 955–957.

CRAIGHEAD, JOHN J., and CRAIGHEAD, FRANK C., JR.

1956. Hawks, owls, and wildlife, 443 pp., illus. Stackpole Co., Harrisburg, Pennsylvania.

MENG, HEINZ K.

1951. The Cooper's hawk. Doctoral dissertation, Cornell University.

1959. Food habits of nesting Cooper's hawks and goshawks in New York and Pennsylvania. Wilson Bull., vol. 71, pp. 169–174.

SCHNELL, JAY H.

1958. Nesting behavior and food habits of goshawks in the Sierra Nevada of California. Condor, vol. 60, pp. 377–403, illus.

SNYDER, NOEL F. R., and SNYDER, HELEN A.

1973. Experimental study of feeding rates of nesting Cooper's hawks. Condor, vol. 75, no. 4, pp. 461–463.

1974a. Function of eye coloration in North American accipiters. Condor, vol. 76, no. 2, pp. 219–222, illus.

1974b. Increased mortality of Cooper's hawks accustomed to man. Condor, vol. 76, no. 22, pp. 215–216.

SNYDER, NOEL F. R.; SNYDER, HELEN A.; LINCER, JEFFREY L.; and REYNOLDS, RICHARD T.

1973. Organochlorines, heavy metals, and the biology of North American accipiters. BioScience, vol. 23, no. 5, pp. 300–305.

SNYDER, NOEL F. R., and WILEY, JAMES W.

1976. Sexual size dimorphism in hawks and owls of North America. Ornith. Monogr. no. 20.

STORER, ROBERT W.

1966. Sexual dimorphism and food habits in three North American accipiters. Auk, vol. 83, pp. 425–436.

NOEL F. R. SNYDER
HELEN A. SNYDER

Sedimentological Evidence for Current Reversal at the Strait of Gibraltar[1]

Principal Investigator: Daniel J. Stanley, Smithsonian Institution, Washington, D. C.

Grant No. 915: For a study of Late Glacial to Recent hydrographic evolution of the western Mediterranean.[2]

The changes in climate, vegetation, and sea level that occurred in the Mediterranean region at the end of Pleistocene and early Holocene time are generally well documented. However, the effect of such changes on the hydrography of the Mediterranean Sea is still poorly defined. The present study focused on the problem of possible altered exchange patterns of Atlantic and Mediterranean waters at the Strait of Gibraltar.

There are two hypotheses for the circulation in the Mediterranean during Würm time. One suggests that this sea was an estuary-type basin with deep Atlantic water inflow below less dense Mediterranean outflow across the sill at Gibraltar. The other maintains that the Mediterranean was a lagoonal-type basin with net outflow of a deep layer of more saline Mediterranean water, i.e., a circulation system not drastically different from the present one, but with a somewhat lower exchange of water masses at the Strait of Gibraltar.

Of particular interest in this respect is the Alboran Sea, a partially land-locked depression in the western Mediterranean enclosed between the mountainous Spanish and Moroccan margins. Water masses in this body extend across the Strait of Gibraltar to the Atlantic on the west and through the

[1]Adapted from Huang, Stanley, and Stuckenrath (1972), which includes charts and extensive literature citations.

[2]Grateful acknowledgment is made to the SACLANT ASW Research Centre, La Specia, Italy, and the U.S. Naval Oceanographic Office Geological Laboratory for use of cores and for subbottom and bathymetric data. Bathymetric data, bottom samples, and photographs were collected also on USCGC *Rockaway* cruise $RoSm_1$ (August 1970), and appreciation is expressed to the captain, officers, and men of this ship for their help in the work at sea. Mademoiselle J. N. Valette, Université de Perpignan, provided trace-element data. In addition to the National Geographic Society, the research was supported by Smithsonian Institution grants and a travel grant to La Spezia from the Office of Naval Research.

Alboran Trough to the Balearic Basin on the east. The Western Alboran Basin is bounded roughly by the 500-fathom (914-meter) contour line with a flat basin plain (the Western Alboran Plain) in its center portion. The plain proper is defined by the 800-fathom (1,463-meter) isobath. The diamond-shaped configuration of the basin is apparently controlled by dominant NE-SW and NW-SE tectonic trends. The Gibraltar Valley links the basin plain with the Strait of Gibraltar and the Ceuta and Gibraltar Canyons to the northwest.

Present circulation patterns in this portion of the Mediterranean are reasonably well known. Three semipermanent water masses are present: (1) surface water, with a water-core depth of about 75 meters and extending to a depth of 100 to 200 meters, consisting of Atlantic water that flows into the Mediterranean through the Strait of Gibraltar with a temperature range of 15° to 25°C. and salinity of 37.0 o/oo; (2) intermediate water (200–600 meters), consisting mainly of denser Mediterranean water (Levantine Water) outflowing to the Atlantic Ocean through the Strait with a temperature of 15°C. and salinity of 38.5 o/oo; and (3) somewhat colder Deep Water (deeper than 600 meters). The velocities of inflowing currents through the Strait of Gibraltar range up to 150 cm/sec and velocities of outflowing denser water encountered at depths near 200-meter range from 100 to 300 cm/sec.

Late Quaternary Stratigraphy in the Alboran Sea

Materials examined during the course of this study include: (a) 49 large-diameter (13-centimeter) sphincter cores collected during *R/V Maria Paolina G.* cruises in the Western Alboran Basin and adjacent areas (a tight network of some 2,200 kilometers of PGR high-resolution subbottom profiles was also obtained on these cruises) (Stanley et al., 1970; Gehin et al., 1971); (b) 15 Shipek grab and dredge samples and photographs obtained at 44 camera stations in this area during USCGC *Rockaway* cruise $RoSm_1$ in August 1970; (c) sample cuts from three short cores collected from the Gibraltar Canyon area by the *R/V Zelian* cruise in 1964 and one Kullenberg piston core collected from the Eastern Alboran Basin by the *R/V Atlantic Seal* cruise in 1967. The cores serve to define the lithology of the upper 7 meters of sedimentary section observed in the PGR profiles.

The sedimentary and organic structures in the cores were examined by x-radiography. Grain-size analysis and mineralogical determination of the sand clay fractions were obtained (petrological data in Huang and Stanley, 1972). In almost all cores, at least 95 percent of the section consists of hemipelagic mud (mixture of terrigenous and pelagic components) with only a few distinct thin sand and silt layers. Three well-defined seismic reflectors noted in PGR profiles are correlated with three thin sand and silt layers retrieved in cores (Stanley et al.,

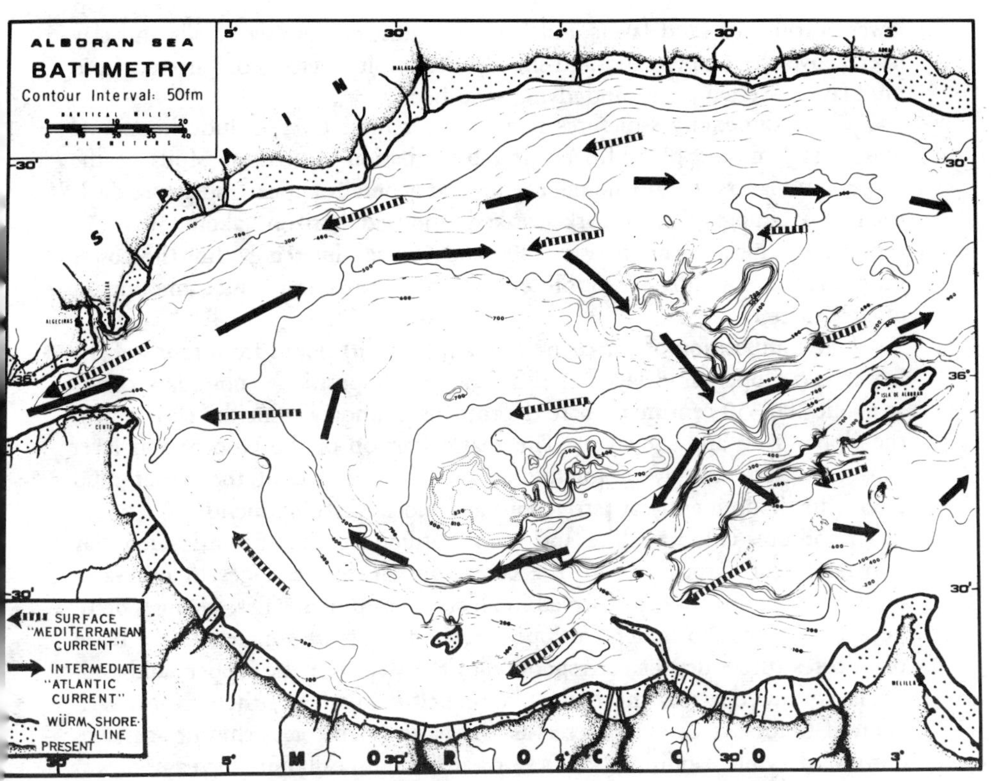

FIG. 1. Chart showing major physiographic features in the Alboran Sea. Cores studied are concentrated in the Western Alboran Basin Plain. Depth in fathoms (1 fathom = 1.8 meters).

1970; Gehin et al., 1971). Both PGR records and cores show that two of these layers extend almost continuously across most of the Western Alboran Basin plain. Excellent correlation of reflectors is possible in the basin plain, but it is difficult to correlate the thin sand layers of the basin plain with sands found occasionally in slope cores. The basin plain sequence is as follows:

(1) The *Lower-sand-and-silt layer* (L) occurs at about 450-centimeter depths; it consists of terrigenous (primarily quartz, feldspar, heavy minerals, plant remains) and bioclastic components. (2) The *Upper-sand-and-silt layer* (U) is found at about the 300–350-centimeter depth and is composed mainly of whole planktonic foraminiferal tests. (3) The *Uppermost sand-and-silt layer* occurs only sporadically at a depth of about 50 centimeters; it also contains mostly foraminiferal tests. Samples were collected from upper, middle, and

lower portions of sand layers and from an indistinct laminated silt and clay later above the Upper sand-and-silt layer. Samples were also collected from mud layers overlying and underlying sand beds.

The sedimentary structures in the Lower mud layer include horizontal and cross laminae, plant fibers, and bioturbation structures. Muds of the Upper mud layer are more homogeneous and generally appear "structureless," even in x-radiographs. A dark-streaked, mottled horizon, about 50 to 70 centimeters thick, occurs between 400 and 500 centimeters within the Lower mud layer; it contains hydrotroilite-pyrite-filled tests and minor amounts of organic matter.

The composition of the coarse fraction (>62 μ) sieved from muds of the Lower and Upper mud layers is different. A compositional boundary occurs at about 300-350 centimeter core depth; this boundary coincides closely with the Upper sand-and-silt layer). The coarse fraction of the Upper mud layer consists almost entirely of foraminiferal tests, and that of the Lower mud layer is made up mainly of terrigenous and bioclastic components.

Kaolinite, chlorite, illite and montmorillonite, and mixed-layered clay minerals occur throughout all the cores, but distinct changes in peak-area ratios of clay minerals are observed in all cores examined. These changes occur between 1.0 and 2.5 meters in slope cores and at about 3 meters in the basin plain cores (these depths correspond with the depth of the Upper sand-and-silt layer, traced across the basin plain); below this level, there is less variation of ratios. At about 3 meters in the basin plain cores, chlorite increases downward, while kaolinite increases upward; montmorillonite increases downward; and all ratios tend to diverge from one another upward. The trace element distribution also changes at about the same depths in cores, and the upward increase of boron, strontium, zinc, lead, and manganese above 3.5 meters is particularly noteworthy.

In summary, two mud sections (Upper and Lower mud layers) are distinguished on the basis of mineralogy and sedimentary structures, and the boundary between these two stratigraphic layers is the well-defined Upper sand-and-silt layer composed of Foraminifera.

Dating Stratigraphic Horizons and Sedimentation Rates

The geographic distribution of cores and the core isochrons inferred from 21 carbon-14 dates is illustrated in figure 4 of Huang, Stanley, and Stuckenrath, 1972. The sedimentation rate has been higher in the basin plain than on the slope during the late Quaternary. The rate in the plain during the past 10,000 years is 30 to 40 cm/1,000 years (values range closer

FIG. 2. Water catchment on eastern side of the "Rock" of Gibralter.

to 40 cm/1,000 years). This is about twice as fast as the rate on slope areas which range from 12 to 28 cm/1,000 years (an average of about 20/1,000 years). Comparable values were obtained independently in this region by other workers.

There is a very marked increase in sedimentation in the basin plain below a core depth of 2.5 to 3 meters, a depth corresponding to a period from about 11,000 to 9,000 years B.P. Rates average 80 cm/1,000 years during the late Würm, and values as high as 130 cm/1,000 years are recorded. The sudden increase in rate is also discernible in slope Core 111, but at a shallower depth below 2 meters. However, in some slope areas no corresponding increase in sedimentation rate is apparent, and some cores (100, 108, 107) actually reveal a slight decrease in rate in the Lower mud layer. Sedimentation near banks, ridges, and adjacent slope areas has been maintained at a lower but almost constant value during the past 20,000 years.

The time of deposition of the Upper sand-and-silt layer (dated at 9,125 ± 410 years B.P.) appears to coincide with the marked break in sedimentation occurring between 11,000 and 9,000 B.P. The Lower sand-and-silt layer was emplaced subsequently to about 12,500 years B.P. Coarse graded sand layers in two much shallower slope cores are older than the sand-and-silt layers of the basin plain; one was deposited before 13,275 years B.P. (Core 108) and the other (Core 107) before 19,055 years B.P.

Sediment Ponding

Two important features of sub-Recent sedimentation in the Western Alboran Basin emerge from stratigraphic correlation and carbon-14 age dating of cored sequences. First, the thickness of sediment separating the Upper and Lower sand-and-silt layers increases progressively from the surrounding slope areas toward the Western Alboran Basin plain. Secondly, Holocene sedimentation rates are not constant throughout the basin, but increase from about 20 cm/1,000 years in the slope areas to 40 cm/1,000 years in the basin plain. This higher deposition in a topographic low exemplifies ponding. The Western Alboran Basin, an excellent example of an enclosed sediment trap, received material eroded from topographic highs and subsequently transferred downslope toward the basin plain. Rates of erosion on the slope varied regionally during the late Quaternary. For example, the reduced thickness of the Lower mud layer (late Pleistocene) in slope Cores 100 and 114 suggests a higher rate of erosion or lower rate of deposition or both than in the slope region near Core 111 during the same period.

Ponding has resulted from several processes detailed elsewhere (Huang and Stanley, 1972): (1) cyclic motion of the surface water masses in the Alboran Sea Basin; (2) deep water masses which have eroded sediment from topographic highs and redeposited these materials and suspensates settling to the bottom in adjacent lows, thus concentrating both coarse and fine particles; and (3) low-velocity turbid flows and gravity-assisted bottom currents which transported coarser material downslope from shelf and upper slope areas. High-velocity turbidity currents, infrequent episodes in this region, also transferred some material downslope via submarine channels (Stanley et al., 1970). Subsequent studies also indicate that a large proportion of the mud sections may be attributed to mud-rich turbidity-current flows.

Sedimentation and Current Reversal in the Alboran Sea

The change in sedimentation patterns observed in the Alboran Sea cores coincides in time with the end of the Pleistocene, which workers place at approximately 11,000 to 10,000 years B.P. The sudden change of sedimentary structures and mineral suites and the concomitant reduction in rates of sedimentation reflect changing sedimentary conditions on the bottom at that time. The higher amount of hydrotroilite in the Lower mud layer suggests that reducing conditions must have prevailed during the Würm. However, the high frequency of bioturbation and lack of sapropel layers show that in late Würm time the Western Alboran Basin plain was not stagnant, as were some Mediterranean basins to the east. Moreover, the higher frequency of current-produced lamination in the Lower mud layer clearly indicates stronger bottom current activity at this time, a conclusion confirmed by the high sedimentation rate in the basin plain during the late Würm.

As Holocene time began, the decreasing rate of deposition was accompanied by a reduction of coarse terrigenous components (wind-blown quartz, coarse carbonate debris, and plant fibers) and a sudden increase of planktonic tests. The increase in content of certain trace elements such as boron indicates a return to more normal open-ocean conditions. Sedimentary structures show that dispersal by bottom and turbidity currents became relatively less important than hemipelagic deposition. The lower amount of eolian quartz points to changes in wind regime and intensity. The increase in kaolinite/chlorite ratio and decrease in montmorillonite suggest a change in weathering regime and in provenance as well. It is noteworthy that the same compositional changes have been observed in cores collected off Algeria and in the western Balearic Basin farther to the east. Moreover, a decrease in sedimentation rate similar to that in the Alboran Basin (from 67 cm/1,000 years in the period 13,000 to 11,000 B.P. to 27 cm/1,000 years in the Holocene) has been recorded in the western Balearic Basin.

Petrological changes can be attributed directly to the effect of the climatic change on weathering and drainage of the surrounding lands and partly to changes in sea level and the marine circulation system. For example, the enhanced proportions of chlorite, eolian quartz, and plant debris in the late Würm Lower mud layer probably reflect the more widespread development of vegetation and the colder, drier conditions prevailing at that time. Reliable evidence of Pleistocene permafrost is lacking in the Mediterranean region during Würm glacial time although cold climate phenomena such as solifluction, colluviation, and valley alluviation are common in the Betic and the Rif chains. Accordingly, during the early Würm, flash floods probably were more frequent and may have been capable of carrying a larger load for greater distances into the Mediterranean than at present. Also, during the Würm glacial maximum, the sea level was at least 100 meters lower than at present and rivers could thus transport sediment beyond the subaerially exposed shelf margins.

On the other hand, not all petrological changes taking place about 10,000 years ago can be attributed directly to eustatic factors alone (sea level then was only 20 meters below the present stand). More probably they reflect important changes in the circulatory system of the Alboran Sea. The presence in the Würm Lower mud layer of coarse terrigenous material derived mainly from the Strait of Gibraltar and the Spanish coast indicates, for instance, the operation of east-flowing bottom currents (an "Atlantic Undercurrent"). The relative enrichment in Würm sediments of the clay mineral montmorillonite, probably derived from volcanic areas east of the Alboran Sea, suggests transport by a west-moving surface current system (a "Mediterranean Surface Current"). The increase of boron and other trace elements at about 10,000 years B.P. reflects the change in hydrographic regime, i.e., a return to more open ocean and saline conditions.

Conclusions

Geological investigations can be used, in some instances, to help solve paleophysical oceanographic problems. In this case, we visualize a late glacial circulatory system in the western Mediterranean that was the reverse of the existing system. This conclusion accords with the theory of those workers who on the basis of other evidence have suggested that a reversal of water mass flow through the Strait of Gibraltar occurred at the end of Pleistocene time. Prior to this reversal, less saline Mediterranean water outflowed above denser Atlantic water which flowed into the Alboran Sea through the Strait of Gibraltar. The excess of lower density Würm Mediterranean surface water is attributed to the lower evaporation rates and the higher run-off from the surrounding lands, consequent upon the more temperate climatic conditions obtaining in this region during late glacial time. This hydrographic situation in upper Würm time calls to mind the present pattern of the Black Sea with its reduced exchange at the Dardanelles-Sea of Marmara-Bosporus. The Mediterranean at that time may be likened to an "estuary" of the eastern Atlantic, a phenomenon discussed at greater length by Stanley et al. (1975) on the basis of studies in both the eastern and western Mediterranean.

The sum of evidence from the Alboran Sea cores suggests that, if a reversal occurred, it did so between 11,000 and 9,000 years B.P., a time that coincides with marked changes in temperature recorded in cores of the Atlantic and other oceans (Huang and Stanley, 1974). This is also borne out by oxygen isotype analyses of foraminiferal tests in cores of this area. Hydrographic changes of the magnitude envisaged here clearly must have had profound biological consequences. A sudden decrease, followed by an upward increase, of planktonic Foraminifera in Alboran Sea cores reflects corresponding changes of productivity and is only one of the consequences of the new circulatory pattern established at the beginning of the Holocene.

REFERENCES

[See Huang, Stanley, and Stuckenrath (1972) for more extensive references.]

ERICSON, D. B.; EWING, MAURICE; WOLLIN, GOESTA; and HEEZEN, BRUCE C.
1961. Atlantic deep-sea sediment cores. Bull. Geol. Soc. Amer., vol. 72, pp. 193–286.

GEHIN, CLAUDE E.; BARTOLINI, CARLO; STANLEY, DANIEL J.; BLAVIER, P.; and TONARELLI, B.
1971. Morphology of late Quaternary fill of the Western Alboran Basin, Mediterranean Sea. SACLANT ASW Res. Centre Techn. Rpt. no. 201, 78 pp.

HUANG, TER-CHIEN, and STANLEY, DANIEL J.
1972. Western Alboran Sea: Sediment dispersal, ponding and reversal of current. Pp. 521–559 *in* "The Mediterranean Sea; A Natural Sedimentation Laboratory," Daniel J. Stanley, ed. Dowden, Hutchinson & Ross, Inc., Stroudsburg, Pennsylvania.
1974. Current reversal at 10,000 years B.P. at the straight of Gibraltar—a discussion. Marine Geol., vol. 17, pp. 1–7.

HUANG, TER-CHIEN; STANLEY, DANIEL J.; and STUCKENRATH, ROBERT
1972. Sedimentological evidence for current reversal at Strait of Gibraltar. Marine Techn. Journ., vol. 6, no. 4, pp. 25–33, charts.

STANLEY, DANIEL J.; GEHIN, CLAUDE E.; and BARTOLINI, CARLO
1970. Flysch-type sedimentation in the Alboran Sea, western Mediterranean. Nature, vol. 228, pp. 979, illus.

STANLEY, DANIEL J.; MALDONADO, ANDRES; and STUCKENRATH, ROBERT
1975. Strait of Sicily depositional rates and patterns, and possible reversals of currents in the Late Quaternary. Paleogeogr., Paleoclimat., Paleoecol., vol. 18, pp. 279–291.

DANIEL J. STANLEY

Seasonal Activity Patterns of Terrestrial Vertebrates in a Monsoon Environment (Sinaloa, Mexico)

Principal Investigator: Terry A. Vaughan, Northern Arizona University, Flagstaff, Arizona.

Grant No. 860: In support of a study of seasonal activity patterns of Neotropical vertebrates.

This project was initiated in 1970 and the research was the subject of an M.S. thesis in biology completed at Northern Arizona University in 1971 by Roger B. Smith. Additional financial support of the Northern Arizona University Department of Biological Sciences is gratefully acknowledged.

Numerous references have been made suggesting that the availability of moisture is the major climatic control in the tropics (Dobzhansky, 1950; Duellman, 1966; Richards, 1963). Seasonal events in the tropical biota seem to be directly or indirectly associated with seasonal fluctuations in rains (Owen, 1966). This report will outline a study of the relationships between seasonal rainfall and vertebrate activity, discussing briefly some of the more significant results of the research.

The study's main purpose was to gain insight into the extent of seasonal activity among small terrestrial vertebrates in a semitropical area with distinct annual dry and rainy periods. The study was further directed toward obtaining additional knowledge about the biology of each species and its habitat requirements. A secondary purpose was to investigate the applicability of an electric fence as a technique for collecting vertebrates. This technique is reported on in detail in another publication (Smith, 1971).

Study Area Description and Study Methods

The mammals, reptiles, and amphibians of Sinaloa have only recently been subjected to comprehensive studies on distribution and natural history (Armstrong and Jones, 1971; Armstrong, Jones, and Birney, 1972; Hardy and McDiarmid, 1969; Jones, Choate, and Cadena, 1972). Comparatively little is known about the habitat or life histories of many species at present.

The study area was near Panuco, a small mining village east of Mazatlán. Near the southern end of the rugged Sierra Madre Occidental Mountains, the area's topography is characterized by steeply sloping hills and rocky canyons containing rapidly descending, frequently intermittent, streams. Located on the Tropic of Cancer, the region experiences a pronounced period of monsoon rains from June to September. The rainy season is followed by a prolonged dry period during which streams dry up and the woody vegetation is largely deciduous.

Response of the vegetation to the onset of the rains is remarkable. From a dull, gray-brown desertlike landscape the countryside is shortly transformed into a dense, verdant semitropical forest. Coupled with the rains and changes in vegetative aspect is an increase in relative humidity and cooler air temperatures. The combined cloudiness, rains, and shade of the vegetative canopy produce a comparatively stable environment with minimum daily fluctuation in temperature and humidity. The behavioral responses of vertebrates to these changing seasons were the basic quest of the study.

The field activities were completed during three visits to the study area in 1970. Laboratory work and data analysis continued into 1971. A reconnaissance trip was made to the study area in March 1970. The main study period was from June 7 to August 27, 1970, covering about 2 weeks of the dry season and 8 weeks of the rainy season. During this period Roger B. Smith maintained a permanent field camp near Panuco, and I made several visits to the area. A third trip, in December 1970, was made to supplement previous dry-season collections.

The main emphasis during the summer study period was on collecting small vertebrates at different sites with a series of electric-fence transects. The fence was erected at each site and operated for a continuous 48-hour period. It was checked at 2-hour intervals to retrieve specimens. Details of capture, site description, and standard specimen measurements were recorded. Specimens were preserved for additional study and identification. The electric fence proved capable of killing animals as large as the opossum (*Didelphis marsupialis*). It was assumed that the fence provided a representative sample of active terrestrial vertebrates present at a given site at a given time. Differences in behavior, home range, and susceptibility to the capture method undoubtedly influenced the results somewhat.

Additional general collecting for reptiles and amphibians was done during the course of the field work. Many of the vertebrates were identified by Dr. William E. Duellman of the University of Kansas. A collection of principally woody plants was made and later identified by Dr. Charles T. Mason of the University of Arizona. Climatic data were gathered at a rudimentary base camp weather station.

Results and Discussion

In all, 334 vertebrate specimens were collected and positively identified in the study area in 1970 (table 1). These included 12 anuran species, 11 lizard species, 15 snake species, and 7 species of mammals. Three of the nine study sites were sampled with the electric fence during both dry and wet seasons. The vertebrate catch per lineal transect foot averaged approximately four times greater during the wet season on these sites.

Distinct seasonal patterns in some species are indicated by the electric-fence collections. Anurans were captured frequently during the early wet season but were absent from the dry-season collections. The initial flurry of activity in this group can be attributed to movements associated with breeding behavior as well as highly favorable moisture conditions in upland and riparian sites. During the dry season the anurans were largely confined to streams or wet caves and mine tunnels.

Two lizard species, *Cnemidophorus costatus* and *Sceloporus utiformis*, exhibited the most distinct seasonal periodicity. *Cnemidophorus costatus* was captured frequently prior to mid-July during the late dry season and early rainy season. During the remainder of the summer study period, it was seldom captured or observed. The cooler, shadier conditions of the rainy season apparently prevent *C. costatus* from reaching its optimal body temperature. Medica (1967) found that *Cnemidophorus* spp. in New Mexico were not active at soil temperatures below 26 °C. When it is considered that mean air temperatures recorded during the wet season at Panuco averaged only 26.7 °C., it is unlikely that soil temperatures were very often high enough for optimum activity. Another partial explanation for the apparent decrease in wet season activity may be related to a reduction in total activity and a reduction of home range size following the breeding season, which occurs during the late dry season and early wet season.

The period of maximum activity in *S. utiformis* appears to begin in about mid-July and continues at least into the early dry season. Although a single individual was collected as early as June 10, this species was not collected regularly until late July. On one electric-fence transect site, 8 specimens were caught in August, whereas none had been collected previously in June on the same site. This species must have a lower optimum temperature for activity than does *C. costatus*, which is active during the warmer dry season. Reproductive data collected indicate that breeding in *S. utiformis* occurs after the onset of the rains, an additional explanation for the activity peak.

The seasonal activity of the vertebrates studied appears to be closely linked to the abundance of food available during the rainy season. In the seven lizard species examined, breeding generally occurs during the late dry season or early wet season. Hatching occurs later in the rainy season or early dry season. *Marmosa canescens*, the most commonly collected mammal, appears to fit this reproductive pattern as well. Inger and Greenberg (1966) suggest that in lizards food supply is the ultimate factor restricting breeding season in a monsoon climate. Most of the lizards and anurans, as well as many of the mammals and snakes, found in the study area are known or suspected to be largely insectivorous. Casual observations reveal a vast increase in insect abundance during the rainy season. Janzen and Schoener (1968) documented a significant increase in insect numbers and diversity with increasing site wetness in Costa Rica. Seasonal availability of insect food presumably strongly influences the activities of the insectivorous vertebrate species in the study area.

The electric-fence collections provided some tentative insight into relative abundance and frequency of occurrence of various species. Among the major groups, approximately twice as many lizards as either anurans or mammals were collected. The numbers of anurans and mammals collected were nearly equal and snakes were the least commonly collected group. Collection frequency by species for nine transect sites shows that the lizards *Anolis nebulosus* and *C. costatus* occurred in 78 percent of the transects. The ubiquity of these species was equaled by one mammal, the mouse opossum *Marmosa canescens*. *Sceloporus utiformis* and the anuran *Eleutherodactylus occidentalis* were recorded on 55 percent of the transect sites. *Masticophis bilineatus* was the most frequently collected snake.

The composition of the terrestrial vertebrate fauna studied is primarily a product of the climatic factors determining the patterns of vegetation growth and food availability. A secondary and particularly significant factor influencing this composition is the intensive utilization of the habitat by the rural human population. Twelve families with some 60 members live within the roughly 15-square-mile study area. Small family farms and livestock raising are relied upon heavily to supplement income earned in the mines at Panuco. Fields are typically hand cultivated and many occupy slopes with over a 75 percent gradient. New fields are placed under cultivation by a combination of burning and hand clearing. The fertile life of a field is severely limited by erosion and nutrient leaching. Much of the study area has at one time been cultivated. Heavy overstocking with cows, goats, horses, and burros aggravates the erosion factor.

The direct effect of this slash-burn pattern of agriculture on vertebrates is initially a loss of habitat for some species. Herbaceous vegetation soon invades and is followed rapidly by shrubby growth. The area is therefore habitable by certain species in virtually all successional stages. The cumulative effect of this pattern of land use is the perpetual maintenance of vegetation in some seral stage. The composition of the vertebrate fauna likewise must be largely seral. Only in a few locations within the study area did tree height and composition indicate a near climax vegetation type.

The relative abundance of *C. costatus, M. canescens,* and *M. bilineatus* in the study area tends to corroborate this conclusion. Scott (1962) states that *C. costatus* prefers open, sunny areas in lowland Sinaloa. Collections and observations indicate that this species is most common on the less densely vegetated sites in early successional states. The dominant plants there are shrubs, chiefly legumes such as *Cassia* spp., *Acacia* spp., and *Mimosa* spp. *Masticophis bilineatus*, which appears to be one of the chief predators on *C. costatus*, is also common in these areas. It too prefers openings and exhibits a diel activity period similar to that of *C. costatus. Marmosa canescens,* which was found throughout the study area, appears well adapted for living in all successional stages. Its omnivorous food habits may render it a better-suited species for the rigors of seasonality than the next most common mammal, *Liomys pictus*, which is predominantly a seed eater. As the vegetative canopy becomes more dense and the climax semideciduous forest vegetation is approached, the semiarboreal habits of *M. canescens* may place it in good stead as succession advances. More arboreal lizards such as *Sceloporus clarkii* and *Ctenosaura pectinata* appear to be much more common in the more mature forest areas.

It can be tentatively concluded from this study that the seasonal activity patterns of many terrestrial vertebrates in a monsoon environment are closely attuned to the selective pressures of the annual wet-dry cycle. While annual temperature and day-length changes are important, the availability of moisture and its effect on vegetative growth and food availability are the factors, that most effectively govern the activity of some species. Invertebrates are the major food of many terrestrial vertebrates and reproduction is timed to correlate with the rainy season abundance of insects. There is partial seasonal separation of activity in some species with similar habitat requirements. Further evidence suggesting some degree of niche heterogeneity among vertebrates was found in the form of partial isolation in diel activity periods, differing spatial relationships in microhabitat, and presumed non-overlap in food requirements related to differences in body size.

TABLE 1. RESULTS OF VERTEBRATE COLLECTING IN 1970, PANUCO, SINALOA.

Species	*Specimens*
ANURANS:	
Bufo marinus	5
B. marmoreus	1
B. mazatlanensis	20
Eleutherodactylus augusti cactorum	4
E. occidentalis	26
E. vocalis	19
Hyla smaragdina	2
H. smithi	1
Rana pipiens	5
R. pustulosa	8
Smilisca baudinii	2
Tomodactylus nitidus petersi	7
Total	100
LIZARDS:	
Anolis nebulosus	26
Cnemidophorus costatus huico	37
Ctenosaura pectinata	9
Eumeces parvulus	1
Gehyra mutilata	1
Heloderma horridum horridum	1
Phyllodactylus tuberculosus saxatilis	3
Sceloporus clarkii boulengeri	6
S. nelsoni	26
S. utiformis	29
Urosaurus bicarinatus tuberculatus	7
Total	146
SNAKES:	
Boa constrictor imperator	1
Coniophanes lateritius lateritius	1
Dryadophis cliftoni	2
Drymarchon corais rubidus	1
Drymobius margaritiferus fistulosus	3
Elaphe triaspis intermedia	1
Imantodes gemmistratus latistratus	1
Leptodeira splendida ephippiata	6
Leptophis diplotropis	3
Leptotyphlops humulis dugesii	1
Masticophis bilineatus	7
M. striolatus	1
Oxybelis aenus auratus	2
Rhadinea hesperia hesperoides	3
Tropidodipsas philippii	3
Total	36
TURTLES:	
Kinostenon integrum	6
Rhinoclemys pulcherrima pulcherrima	3
Total	9
MAMMALS:	
Dasypus novemcinctus mexicanus	1
Didelphis marsupialis californica	3
Liomys pictus escuinapae	14
Marmosa canescens sinaloae	16
Notiosorex evotis	6
Reithrodontomys fulvescens tenuis	2
Spilogale pygmaea pygmaea	1
Total	43
Grand total	334

REFERENCES

ARMSTRONG, D. M. and JONES, J. KNOX, JR.
1971. Mammals from the Mexican state of Sinaloa, I: Marsupialia, Insectivora, Lagomorpha. Journ. Mamm., vol. 52, pp. 747–757.

ARMSTRONG, D. M.; JONES, J. KNOX, JR.; and BIRNEY, ELMER C.
1972. Mammals from the Mexican state of Sinaloa, III: Carnivora and Artiodactyla. Journ. Mamm., vol. 53, pp. 48–61.

DOBZHANSKY, THEODOSIUS
1950. Evolution in the Tropics. Amer. Sci., vol. 38, pp. 209–221.

DUELLMAN, WILLIAM E.
1966. The Central American herpetofauna: An ecological perspective. Copeia, 1966, pp. 700–719.

HARDY, L. H., and MCDIARMID, ROY W.
1969. The amphibians and reptiles of Sinaloa, Mexico. Univ. Kansas Publ. Mus. Nat. Hist., vol. 18, pp. 39–252.

INGER, ROBERT F., and GREENBERG, B.
1966. Annual reproductive patterns of lizards from a Bornean rain forest. Ecology, vol. 47, pp. 1007–1021.

JANZEN, DANIEL H., and SCHOENER, THOMAS W.
1968. Differences in abundance and diversity between wetter and drier sites during a tropical dry season. Ecology, vol. 49, pp. 96–110.

JONES, J. KNOX, JR.; CHOATE, JERRY R.; and CADENA, A.
1972. Mammals from the Mexican state of Sinaloa, II: Chiroptera. Occ. Papers Kansas Mus. Nat. Hist., vol. 14, pp. 145–159.

MEDICA, P. A.
1967. Food habits, habitat preferences, reproduction, and diurnal activity in four sympatric species of whiptail lizards (*Cnemidophorus*) in south central New Mexico. Bull. Southern California Acad. Sci., vol. 66, pp. 251–276.

OWEN, DOUGLAS F.
1966. Animal ecology in tropical Africa, 122 pp. Witt. Freeman & Co., San Francisco.

RICHARDS, P. W.
1963. What the Tropics can contribute to ecology. Journ. Ecology, vol. 51, pp. 231–241.

SCOTT, NORMAN J.
1962. The reptiles of southern Sinaloa: An ecological and taxonomic study, 92 pp. M.S. thesis, Humboldt State College, Arcata, California.

SMITH, ROGER B.
1971. An electric fence technique for collecting small vertebrates. Herpetologica, vol. 27, pp. 488–491.

TERRY A. VAUGHAN

From Hunter-gatherers to Pastoralists: Rock Paintings and Neolithic Origins in Southeastern Spain

Principal Investigator: Michael J. Walker, University of Sydney, New South Wales, Australia.

Grant No. 881: For continuation of archeological investigations in southeastern Spain.

Hitherto the earliest Neolithic in southeastern Spain has been best known from excavations at Coveta de l'Or (Alicante), where wheat, barley (Hopf, 1966; Hopf and Schubart, 1965), ceramics (Schubart and Pascual, 1966), and chipped-stone tools (Plá, 1961) date back to 6510 ± 160 and 6265 ± 75 B.P. (Schwabedissen and Freundlich, 1965). It has long been assumed that colonists, deriving originally from the Near East, carried agriculture westward, perhaps via North Africa (Martínez Santa-Olalla, 1946; Childe, 1950; Evans, 1958; Savory, 1968), and colonists have been held responsible also for the southern Italian Neolithic (Whitehouse, 1968). Not all prehistorians have accepted this as the whole story; thus Jordá (1953) and Fletcher (1953) drew attention to indigenous strands in the southeastern Spanish Neolithic chipped-stone tool forms, considered to be derived from pre-Neolithic traditions. One series of Neolithic assemblages with predominantly backed bladelet flints and *Cardium edule*-impressed pottery, and another with predominantly geometrical flints and plain pottery, were held to be due to autochthonous development, the first including many cave sites with shell-impressed ware from eastern Spain (Colominas and Esbona, 1925; Ballester, 1928; San Valero, 1950), and the second, cave sites such as Cueva de la Cocina or Covacha de Llatas (Pericot, 1946; Jordá and Alcácer, 1949). Nevertheless, there are drawbacks, since l'Or has shell-impressed ware but predominantly geometrical flints, while la Cocina (Fortea, 1971) does have shell-impressed ware, albeit rare. We shall see that a simpler explanation is to regard the flint forms not as mutually exclusive "cultural" traits but as functional variants within a common material cultural series of pre-Neolithic origin, and that stratigraphical and pictorial data do not contradict that view.

Following Jordá's reassessment, there was renewed interest in the possibility of an indigenous southeastern Spanish ceramic culture preceding the arrival of agricultural colonists from overseas (Martínez Santa-Olalla, 1950), reflecting "la civilització de les coves" (Bosch Gimpera, 1919). An appropriate point to emphasize is that one of the problems presented by the peninsular Neolithic, in contrast to that of the Italian Foggia plain or of Greece or the Near East, where settled village settlements demarcate the Neolithic from the preceding hunter-gatherer economic cultural complexes, is that the majority of sites are caves, just as in preceramic times; and, moreover, cereal grains are by no means common and are never in quantities that confidently proclaim predominance of cultivation in the subsistence economy. The most often cited open site, El Gárcel (Almería), with plain pottery whose pointed, nipplelike bases suggest North African parallels, and where geometrical flints with obliquely transverse retouch vaguely recall the Tunisian Capsian, has been seen as the type-site of agricultural Neolithic colonists (Siret and Siret, 1887; L. Siret, 1893; Gossé, 1941; Martínez Santa-Olalla, 1946; Childe, 1950; Savory, 1968), notwithstanding aspects of its material assemblage, which support a later, Copper Age, assignation ca. 3500–3000 B.C. (Walker, 1973a, 1977a, 1977b) that, it is hoped, material being analyzed for carbon-14 will soon confirm. Apart from this site, Andalusian megalithic tombs and their assemblages have been used in support of overseas influence in the Neolithic (Blance, 1960, 1971). Pressure-flaked bifacially worked flint arrowpoints have been interpreted as a late Neolithic acquisition in these assemblages from overseas, but not only is Blance's statistical method for separation of phases faulty (Walker, 1973a) but also such "late" arrowpoints occurring in deep levels at Coveta de l'Or suggest an early and indigenous presence in the southeastern sequence. Most of the Andalusian exotica seem contemporaneous with eastern Mediterranean cultures dated between 3500 and 2500 B.C. (Walker, 1973a, 1977b, and cf. Arribas, 1953; Tarradell, 1959; Savory, 1968) and have no claim to be early in the southeastern Spanish Neolithic. Rather, they are Copper Age sites (copper slag was even found at Gárcel), and one open Copper Age settlement, Terrera Ventura (Almería), has given a carbon-14 date of 5370 ± 350 B.P. (Walker, 1973b; Otlet and Slade, 1974; Cuenca and Walker, 1976b), in accordance with such a chronology.

There have not been sufficient attempts to correlate studies of material artifacts with those of rock art in eastern Spain. Most opinions about cultural assignation or absolute age of the paintings rely heavily on internal evidence about "styles," rather than attempting to integrate the art into prehistoric assemblage distributions and geographical patterns of human territorial exploitation, though the latter is not wholly untried (Cabré, 1915; Hernández-Pacheco, 1924, 1959). One school of thought, which has received wide publicity, stresses the Upper Paleolithic aspects of the art (Breuil, 1912; Obermaier, 1924; Burkitt 1925; Obermaier and Wernert, 1929; Bosch Gimpera, 1932,

1964). A wholly opposed view claims most of the paintings as Bronze Age (Jordá, 1964, 1967). Most authorities regard the art as Epi-Paleolithic and perhaps Neolithic, i.e., Holocene rather than Upper Pleistocene, on internal faunal grounds (Cabré, 1915; Hernández-Pacheco, 1924, 1959; Pericot, 1942a, 1950; Martínez Santa-Olalla, 1946; Almagro, 1947a, 1947b, 1951, 1954, 1964; Ripoll, 1964a, 1964b; Beltrán, 1968, 1968b). Some stress its Upper Paleolithic origins, while others (e.g., Walker, 1971, 1972) emphasize later aspects of the paintings.

Presence of rock-art sites and of sites with Epi-Paleolithic and Neolithic assemblages (some dated by carbon-14), not to mention presence of data about climatic change (Cuenca, 1971; Cuenca and Walker, 1974, 1976a, 1976b, 1976c) in the southeastern Spanish river basins of the Segura and Vinalopó, renders that region suitable for an integrated study of early prehistory, notwithstanding that distributions of material representing particular peninsular assemblage categories pass beyond its geographical boundaries.

Rock-art Sites

The distribution of these sites in southeastern Spain forms an inland spread across the extensive Segura River basin (e.g., Minateda art series, Breuil, 1920, 1928a, 1933–35; Cieza series, López, 1968, Beltrán, 1968c, 1969, Walker, 1971, 1972; Nerpio series, Sánchez Jiménez, 1961–62, García, 1961–62, 1962, García and Krapovickas, 1958–59, Walker, 1969, 1971; Sabinar series, Martínez Sánchez, 1969, Beltrán, 1968a, Walker, 1969, 1971, Carbonell, 1970). They are found both among the headwaters of and around the middle reaches of the Segura and its tributaries. From the middle reaches they extend across the rolling uplands interrupted by endorrheic basins (Cueva del Peliciego at Jumilla, Fernández de Avilés, 1939–40; Monte Arabí series near Yecla, Cabré, 1915, Breuil and Burkitt, 1915, Breuil, 1933–35) toward the middle reaches of the Júcar drainage basin (Cuevas de la Araña near Bicorp, Hernández-Pacheco, 1924, Breuil, 1933–35; the Dos Aguas series, Jordá and Alcácer, 1951, 1952, Plá, 1966; Cueva del Sordo, Sánchez, 1947; Cueva de la Tortosilla, Breuil et al., 1912, Cabré, 1915) and the uplands to its south (Alpera and Mugrón series, Breuil et al., 1912, Breuil and Obermaier, 1912, Breuil, 1915, Cabré, 1915). Northward from Valencia, they are found in Cuenca, Castellón, Teruel, and Catalonia. South of the Segura, rock paintings occur along its tributary the Guadalentín (Cueva del Tío Labrador, Cueva de los Paradores, Breuil, 1933–35) to its headwaters and surrounding uplands (Vélez Blanco series, Breuil and Obermaier, 1914, Cabré, 1915, Breuil and de Motos, 1915, Breuil, 1935). Apart from the Nerpio series already cited, the mountains of the Segura system headwaters have paintings of lesser importance (e.g., Collado del Guijarral near Parolís, Sánchez, 1956, Walker, 1971; Solana del Molinico near Socovos, Sánchez Jiménez, 1961–62), while on the Andalusian side of the high mountains there are paintings also (Cueva de la Zarza, Cabré, 1915; Almaciles, Breuil and de Motos, 1915; Aldeaquemada and Santa Elena, Cabré, 1915). However, most of the Andalusian art is less obviously representational than that of the Levantine provinces, and apart from the sites just mentioned portrays men and animals as conventionalized "stick-men" motifs. From Estremadura there are possible representations of wheeled carts and swords, suggesting a late date (cf. Breuil, 1933–35; Acosta, 1968), as do halberds and daggers depicted in northwestern Spanish rock art (Walker, 1977c). Conventionalized representations do occur in eastern Spain (Breuil, 1933–35), especially in the Alicante-Valencia mountains, where there are examples not painted together with naturalistic figures, viz., paintings and carvings near Navarrés (La Labor del SIP . . ., 1935; Plá, 1966), 3 sites near Benasal (La Labor del SIP . . ., 1942), 3 near Culla (ibid.,), near Rótova (Plá, 1966), Beniatjar (Breuil, 1933–35), the Cueva del Pernil (Breuil, 1928b), and Peña Escrita (Breuil, 1935). This region has relatively few naturalistic paintings, viz., Barranc dels Covarjos (La Labor del SIP . . ., 1942), Barranc de Ullets (Gurrea, 1956), Cueva de la Sarga (Rey, 1952), Cueva del Barranco de las Cañas (Plá, 1966). However, conventionalized motifs are frequent among the naturalistic figures of Murcia and Albacete, and so perhaps not too much should be made of that. A characteristic "Andalusian" motif is a rayed sun, found at Cañaíca del Calar in the Sabinar series (Walker, 1969, 1971); it is well known from Copper Age pottery on which it is incised, as are conventionalized cervines, and it has now been found painted on a sherd from Cueva de los Tiestos near Jumilla dated by carbon-14 at ca. 3790 ± 115 and 3600 ± 80 B.P. (Otlet and Slade, 1974; Cuenca and Walker, 1976b), confirming the late date of conventionalized motifs, at least in some instances. The naturalistic art has been termed expressionist in its capture of movement. By contrast, some southeastern representations, especially Collado del Guijarral, have "wooden" figures, which, while showing more details than do conventionalized anthropomorphs, perhaps indicate a stage intermediate between naturalistic and conventionalized painting.

How old is the naturalistic art? Elsewhere arguments have been offered contrasting it against Upper Paleolithic cave paintings (Walker, 1971). Suffice it here to stress that although many of the painted wild quadrupeds are not found today in the Segura basin, being confined to the highest ranges on its periphery (*Cervus elaphus; Capra ibex; Sus scrofa*), and some live no nearer than the distant Pyrenean or Cantabrian ranges (*Rupicapra rupicapra; Ursus arctos*),[1] nevertheless there are few, if any, wholly extinct peninsular species represented. Unconvincing as is Breuil's identification of a painted rhinoceros at Minateda, particularly given its absence in eastern Spanish naturalistic rock art,[2] his elk there and at Alpera with palmate antlers are paralleled at Solana de las Covachas in the same river system (Walker 1969, 1971), an identification which, however, is offered tentatively because no bones of *Alces* or *Megaceros* are known from the region.[3] Even elk, however, being a "parkland or savannah" species (Kurtén, 1968), suggests postglacial conditions, and similar conditions prevailed in layer b at Còva del Toll, to judge from its "nonsylvan" fauna, which included *Capra ibex*, and was contrasted against underlying, extinct, cold-adapted fauna at the Catalan cave (Donner and Kurtén, 1958), which is probably upper pleniglacial (but see also Butzer and Freeman, 1968; Rosselló, 1970). Open scrub seems implied by fauna similar to that of Levantine art depicted in the Upper Paleolithic Còva de El Parpalló carvings (cf. Pericot, 1942b) from the Valencian coastal mountains; but whereas Upper Paleolithic sites were in mild, coastal locations during the upper pleniglacial (Cuenca and Walker, 1976c), conditions were very different at that time in the upper reaches of the Segura, Taibilla, and Mundo rivers, where mountains rising to 2,000 meters show periglacial phenomena and perhaps even glacial vestiges (López Bermúdez, pers. comm.) and were severely eroded by (a) meltwaters, (b) hillwash that was caused by predominantly anticyclonic winds generated by the European ice-cap and which consequently bore Mediterranean rainstorms to the eastern Spanish mountains, and (c) following in-filling of river trenches with derived

---

[1] Painted in the upper Taibilla Valley at Solana de las Covachas and Cañaíca del Calar, respectively, though the *Ursus* is unconvincing notwithstanding osteological evidence for it at southeastern Neolithic and Bronze Age sites (Siret and Siret, 1887; Blance, 1960, 1971).

[2] Breuil claimed to see it in the Cueva de la Pileta paintings in Málaga, the art of which is most certainly Upper Paleolithic, and at Valdejunco in Portugal, where there are conventionalized signs of a type usually attributed to the Neolithic or metal age (see below).

[3] Certainly there are two eastern Spanish examples of Upper Paleolithic art portraying extinct species whose bones are absent in the region, viz., from Guadalajara *Gulo gulo* in a cave painting (Ucko and Rosenfeld, 1967), and reputedly from Teruel *Rangifer tarandus* engraved on bone (Breuil, 1964). Moreover, *Equus hydruntinus* was identified in Levantine rock art early (Breuil and Cabré, 1911), though its bones have only recently been found in eastern Spain (Boessneck, 1969; Davidson pers. comm.) It is not beyond the bounds of possibility that a few Upper Pleistocene faunal atavisms survived in the eastern Spanish mountains (Almagro, 1956).

sediment by sheetwash over *glacis*-terrace deposits. The result was a denuded landscape hardly capable of supporting large mammal herds. On the inland slopes of the Baetic range, sheltered from the devastation caused by rainstorms, alpine pine forest developed in the last glacial, as demonstrated at Padul (Menéndez Amor and Florschütz, 1964; Vogel and Waterbolk, 1972).

As the following table shows, the sites around the headwaters of the Segura basin have more representations of cervines and caprines, whereas the rolling uplands around the middle reaches of the Segura and Júcar basins have depictions of bovines and equines as well:

Site	Wild mammals					Domes-	Anthropomorphs		
	Cerv.	Capr.	Bov.	Equ.	Other	ticates	Archers	Skirted	Other
Solana de las Covachas	23	19		1	21	1?	16	3	2
Fuente del Sabuco	3	1		1	8		8	2	30
Cañaíca del Calar	3	1			5		2		
Barranco de los Grajos	2	3			2	4?	1?	15	14
Minateda	39	27	7	10	64		59	9	71
Monte Arabí	6	4	12	9	30				8
Alpera (Cueva de la Vieja)	18	11	4		16		28	2	35

Wide grasslands, especially in the endorrheic basins of the uplands, doubtless favored establishment of bovine and equine herds, which seem to have lasted till the second millennium B.C., judged from the large quantities of their bones excavated at Cabezo Redondo (Dreisch and Boessneck, 1969) in the former Villena endorrheic basin (Cuenca and Walker, 1976a), where there also occurred bones of both red (*Cervus elaphus*) and roe (*Capreolus capreolus*) deer.[4] The cattle are probably *Bos primigenius,* whose bones have been found in Portugal (Murray, 1971) at an Epi-Paleolithic-Neolithic site (Moita do Sebastão) where there were also bones of a smaller bovine (perhaps similar to Western European mesolithic cattle of reduced size.[5] Two

[4]Fallow deer (*Dama dama*) was identified by Breuil at Alpera (Breuil et al., 1912), and its bones have been found in Upper Paleolithic contexts at Parpalló (Davidson, pers. comm.). Given the patchiness of faunal collection at southeastern prehistoric sites, it could have lingered on much later.

[5]Bison occurrence, identified by Breuil at Roca dels Moros (Lérida), has few adherents: the animals are *Bos primigenius.*

equine species are known from the Parpalló bones (*Equus hydruntinus* and *E. caballus*), and the former has been identified at a metal-age site (Cerro del Real, Boessneck, 1969), while its portrayal was claimed at Fuente del Cabrerizo in Teruel (Breuil and Cabré, 1911). Feral asses (*E. asinus*) occurred in the Middle Ages (Hernández-Pacheco, 1959). It is impossible to say when equines were domesticated in Spain, though if they were domesticated in prehistoric times it would most likely have been for meat. Nevertheless, possible horse-rider portrayals occur at Fuente del Sabuco in Murcia (Walker, 1969, 1971) and El Mortero in Teruel (Beltrán, 1968a; Savory, 1968), while men leading horses are depicted in Cuenca at Boniches de la Sierra and in Jaén at Canjorros de Peñarrubia (Breuil, 1933–35; Hernández-Pacheco, 1959; Beltrán, 1968a; Savory, 1968). Possibly sheep are portrayed at El Mortero in Teruel (Beltrán, 1968a; Savory, 1968) and Barranco de los Grajos in Murcia (Walker, 1971, 1972), where a human being is painted grasping a goat by the horn. Sometimes these "domesticates" seem conventionalized in depiction, suggesting their possible addition at later date; nor can taming be distinguished pictorially from domestication in eastern Spanish art. Spanish wild caprines have been assigned to various taxonomic categories (Miller, 1912; Ellerman and Scott, 1951; Huerta y Ramírez and Palaus, 1967), but, granted some interfertility among wild caprines (Zeuner, 1963),[6] they may all belong to one species, *Capra ibex.*[7] Nevertheless, wild caprines, unlike domesticates, have heteronymous horn spirals (Harris, 1960–61), and so it cannot be assumed that peninsular caprines played a major role in domestication of the goat, and importation of domestic goats (*C. hircus*), derived ultimately from the eastern Mediterranean bezoar (*C. hircus* (*aegagrus*)) must have been involved. Wild sheep are not native to the peninsula,[8] but sheep bones have been found in levels deep to those in which pottery first appears at Còva de les Mallaetes (Valencia).[9] It may be concluded, since most mammals are wild species depicted in situations of the chase or in isolation, that the artists were not concerned to paint domesticated herds. The Anatolian

---

[6] But see Payne, 1968.

[7] I am indebted to discussions with Dr. Michael Ryder of the Animal Breeding Research Organization of the U.K. on this matter.

[8] Mouflons in the Sierra Cazorla were imported in the 18th century for the hunt.

[9] I am obliged to I. Davidson for this information, who also informs me that sheep bones claimed for Balma de Sant Gregori in Catalonia are NOT to be accepted (*pace* Vilaseca, 1939). Sheep bones occur at French mesolithic sites (Murray, 1971). It is unknown whether there were wild indigenous sheep in Mediterranean France and Spain, much less whether the bones and representations refer to wild or domesticated animals.

Çatal Hüyük temple frescoes testify to predominance of the chase in the art of a wholly Neolithic township, and its importance as an artistic topic in centuries down to our own should not be overlooked. Nonetheless, absence of domestication from Spanish paintings suggests most of the beasts were wild or at most tamed occasionally.

Paintings of artifacts, too, represent the materials of hunters. Bows and arrows are widespread. Arrows may have tips with twin barbs (Solana de las Covachas; Alpera). This type of flint arrowpoint first appears in the stratigraphical record in the Neolithic at Coveta de l'Or, ca. 6000 B.P. and continues in use into the second millennium B.C. Another type of painted arrowpoint at Alpera looks microlithic (Walker, 1971). We shall see later that microlithic battered back flints, crescents, and geometrical forms all continue in use until well into the Neolithic as defined by contemporaneity with pottery and polished stone tools. Bows include simple arcs and recurved forms, as in Saharan depictions of the fourth and third millennia B.C. (for dates, see Delibrias et al., 1964, 1966), a region in contact with Egypt, since a bulbous stone axhead of Egyptian type is painted at Sefar in the Sahara. Bifacial arrowpoints reached Egypt from the Sahara about 6000 B.P., and recurved bows doubtless also spread to Egypt, where three types were known.

Jordá (1967) has compared those of Spanish rock art with composite laminated Egyptian bows, but these were not introduced into Egypt until Hyksos times (McLeod, 1962), whereas pre- and early-dynastic periods knew of another type made of a working arm with hand-grip to which were attached endpieces of oryx antlers (Wolf, 1926), giving a recurved outline. Both these and the laminated bows are short, however. The third type, like bows shown in Saharan and Spanish rock art, is a long recurved bow, known from Egypt certainly by 1750 B.C. (*vide* one preserved in the Royal Scottish Museum at Edinburgh). This type is a self bow made from a single wooden shaft like a longbow, with the ends treated by steam or boiling water so as to be recurved, making the bow more manageable in the hunt.[10] There was no direct link between the Sahara and Spain, however; Epi-Paleolithic stone tools in the two regions have different forms and origins (Vaufrey, 1933; Almago, 1947a; Balout, 1955), and physical anthropological data on Spanish and Saharan painted figures demonstrate differences of physique,[11] while

---

[10] A recurved bow carved on a megalithic construction at Göhlitzsch of the Corded Ware–Single Grave complex shows that recurved bows were known in central Europe by 2000 B.C. (Clark, 1963).

[11] Spainish art: *Brachial index*—males 16, females 10, *Lower limb index*—males 48½, females 47. Tassili art: *Brachial index*—males 20, *Lower limb index*—males 51. Thick lips, prognathism, and steatopygy all characterize Saharan rock art, unlike

the sea-crossing between North Africa and Spain presents difficulties for sailors with a primitive nautical technology (Jáuregui, 1949), and no land bridge seems to have existed during the upper pleniglacial. Climatic and environmental conditions were similar, however, and may have determined developments in material cultures in similar ways. Possible hafted stone axes are portrayed at Barranco de los Grajos and Solana de las Covachas, baskets at Cuevas de la Araña and Dos Aguas and also ladders or ropes for climbing cliffs, while clothing is commonly depicted—knee-length skirts, short breeches, head-dresses, and arm or leg bands with streamers. Metal weapons are unusual in the art (swords at Calapatá and Tivisa in the north of the eastern Spanish art distribution) and are possibly second-millennium additions.

Epi-Paleolithic and Neolithic

What relationship is there between the naturalistic paintings and Epi-Paleolithic or Neolithic assemblages? Jordá (1954) derived his two indigenous Neolithic flintworking traditions from two Epi-Paleolithic ones, characterized, respectively, by backed bladelets and geometrical flints, representing a continuation of Upper Paleolithic Gravettian (Perigordian) techniques on much smaller blades, and therefore termed by him "Epigravettian IIIA" and "Epigravettian IIIB." Previously the emphasis had been on North African resemblances for both backed bladelets ("Ibero-Mauritanian," Pallary, 1909—nowadays called "Oranian") and geometrical forms ("Capsian," Obermaier, 1924), the latter persisting into the Neolithic ("Hispano-Mauritanian," Martínez Santa-Olalla, 1946), though, as mentioned earlier, there are differences in tool-types and frequencies when Spanish and North African lithic industries are compared.

Jordá's view of autochthonous development of backed bladelets and geometrical flints in Holocene eastern Spain was a distinct advance. However, it raised a matter that has been evaded by prehistorians, namely, if there are two cultural entities in eastern Spain, does the rock art relate to one or both, and if one, then to which? Jordá himself views the art as metal age; so for him the question does not arise. Geographical distribution of naturalistic painting reflects that of Epi-Paleolithic-Neolithic transitional sites, defined by continuity of stone tool-types from nonceramic into ceramic stratigraphical

eastern Spanish art. Spanish art values for *antebrachial index* (males 13, females 10) were also very low—unlike any modern known population, but Tassili values (males 14) were also low. While there seems to be a Negro element in the Saharan population, lower limb index is low in contrast with that of modern Negroes. In the Spanish art it is also low, compared with modern Europeans and Africans.

levels at those sites. The distribution differs from that of metal-age settlements, and, while it is true that conventionalized rock paintings spread even farther away from the latter, namely, across the northern Andalusian uplands and into Estremadura, that is explicable if deforestation of earlier resource zones led to development of ever-farther-afield pastoral transhumance from southeastern Spain. Regardless of whether the conventionalized art depicts domesticated herds as well as wild species, the naturalistic art predominantly portrays the latter, which accords with stratigraphical evidence for continuity of Epi-Paleolithic tool kits, presumably reflecting a hunting and gathering economy, into higher levels with pottery, and hence supports persistence of that life-style into the "Neolithic" as defined by occurrence of new artifacts (pottery, polished stone tools) alongside the earlier tool types. Nor can we say hunting was abandoned when cereal cultivation commenced ca. 6500-6000 B.P. Far from it. The development of bifacially flaked flint arrowpoints in a variety of shapes (foliate, stellate, rhomboidal, hollow-based, barbed, and tanged), and their popularity until the mid-second millennium B.C., testify to the chase, and we believe the pictorial evidence can be interpreted in terms of gradual conventionalization of motifs representing fundamentally similar preoccupations with man and mammal activities.

Not many caves have both rock art and stratified artifacts. Cueva de la Cocina (Valencia) had a red painting of an animal on one wall (Pericot, 1946). Its two nonceramic phases are characterized by geometrical triangular and trapeziform flints made by the microburin technique, with merely 2.6 percent backed bladelets (Fortea, 1971). Geometrical flints continued into the ceramic phases, Cocina III and IV, the former with Cardium-impressed sherds, the latter with incised, channeled, combed, and relief-ornamented sherds, as well as a flat quern, polished stone ax, and a rhomboidal bifacial flint arrowpoint. Discoidal and end-scrapers occurred among the implements. Red ochre and 38 skeuomorphically engraved plaques were found, 12 with traces of paint. They call to mind Cueva del Filador (Tarragona), where an engraved skeuomorphic plaque occurred but where levels with backed bladelets and triangles made by the microburin technique were interstratified (Vilaseca Anguera, 1949) in a way that would necessitate several cultural comings and goings if Jordá's "Epigravettian IIIA" and "Epigravettian IIIB" attributions are made. Even at Cocina, however, steepness of flint retouch led Fortea to remark on difficulties attendant on comparing geometrical implements there with French Tardenoisian artifacts, and he suggested some influence exerted by battered back flint-knapping. In other words, Cocina is perhaps not as good a type-site for geometrical traditions as is often claimed. Mention must be made of Covacha de Llatas (Valencia), where another geometrical assemblage also containing backed bladelets continued from non-ceramic to ceramic levels with incised and relief-ornamented sherds (Jordá and Alcácer, 1949). Although the site provided neither paintings nor carved plaques, it is important because of the continuity of Epi-Paleolithic flint-working traditions into ceramic-using times.

There are a number of painted rock shelters farther north that have yielded up artifacts: e.g., Cocinilla del Obispo (Teruel), where the microburin technique was practised and a polished stone ax found (Almagro, 1944, 1947a); El Navazo (Teruel), where discoidal and end-scrapers occurred (ibid.); Doña Clotilde (Teruel), with geometrical and backed bladelet flints (ibid.); and from the Valltorta canyon (Castellón), where there are several painted shelters and others without paintings, among which last-mentioned the Cueva de la Rabosa provided bifacial flint arrowpoints and a segmented bone pinhead that is almost certainly Chalcolithic in age (Pallares, 1923; Almagro, 1947a).

Now in support of deriving Holocene pre-Neolithic lithic assemblages from Upper Paleolithic precursors there are sites where microlithic flints occur in an early context. Còva de El Parpalló (Valencia) has a well-known Upper Paleolithic sequence, and following Magdalenian IV levels there is an industry with geometrical triangles, shouldered points, discoidal and end-scrapers, awls, including *zinken*-like pieces, and burins among which are possible parrot-beak forms, and similar artifacts occur in the lowest level of Hoyo de la Mina (Málaga), except that backed rods and bladelets take the place of geometrical shapes (cf. Such, 1920). These assemblages have much in common with later French Magdalenian VI material and the Magdalenian-derived Federmessergruppen of Germany. Magdalenian influence, too, is seen clearly at Cueva del Volcán del Faro (Valencia) where a deep level contained a Magdalenian III perforated spear-thrower and the level above a single-bevel Magdalenian III (or perhaps IV) bone point, notwithstanding a somewhat atypical flint assemblage, which did contain, however, a shouldered blade, tanged bladelets, burins, awls, and backed bladelets (Aparicio, 1974; Fletcher and Aparicio 1969, 1970). In another area of this cave calcrete flows seem to separate the Upper Paleolithic levels from one with geometrical scalene triangles, though above these there occur levels with pottery, backed bladelets, burins, and scrapers. A similar hiatus at Còva de les Mallaetes (Valencia) has been found in recent excavations there (Fortea, 1973). Previous excavations (Jordá, 1954; Fletcher, 1956, 1956a) had suggested a long continuous sequence from a Solutreo-Gravettian via Epi-Paleolithic to ceramic layers (Neolithic). The reassessment throws much doubt on that interpretation, one reinforced by the calcrete separation below ceramic-bearing levels and by the observation that pottery extended much farther down into so-called Epi-Paleolithic (backed bladelet) layers than had been stated in earlier accounts (Fortea, 1973). The upper ceramic layers contained decorated pottery, a bifacial foliate arrowpoint, and geometrical and backed bladelet flints, while in the deeper ones *Cardium*-impressed pottery and backed flints predominated, as well as plain sherds. It is unnecessary to comment at length on similar backed bladelet assemblages with pottery stratified above Upper Paleolithic backed blade industries at the Valencian Còva de les Maravelles, Còva de les Rates Penaes, and Covacha del Barranc Blanc, where another possibly Magdalenian bone point occurred in the largely backed blade industry. Those sites were poorly excavated and stratigraphical layers not adequately separated. However, at both the Verdelpino (Cuenca) rock shelter (Fernández-Miranda and Moure, 1974) and at Abrigo Grande (Murcia) the predominant flint industry associated with pottery is one of backed bladelets.

Abrigo Grande (Walker, 1972) is crucial to the transition to ceramic use in the southeast in the same way that are Cueva de la Cocina and Covacha de Llatas, notwithstanding their geometrical flints, namely, in that there is a continuity of the flint assemblage from lower layers without pottery into upper layers with it. Moreover, occurrence of red ochre in all layers at the Abrigo, of a sinuous "expressionistic" anthropomorph painted on the rear wall, and of conventionalized paintings on another wall,[12] not to mention its proximity in the Barranco de los Grajos to a richly decorated rock shelter (Walker, 1971, 1972), combined with absence in the vicinity of archeological material of different periods, strongly suggests the assemblage is contemporaneous with the art. The Abrigo is carbon-dated for its ceramic phase to 7200 ± 160 B.P. (Otlet and Slade, 1974), and although this is earlier by about 800 years than the Coveta de l'Or Neolithic, and than preceramic/ceramic transition in Portuguese middens (cf. Walker, 1972), it is later than one of the dates for an early ceramic phase at Verdelpino (7950 ± 150 B.P.), though other dates there are not much older than 5000 B.P. (Fernández-Miranda and Moure, 1974).[13] Nor is Abrigo Grande the only site with firm evidence of continuity of preceramic lithic types into layers with pottery. Apart from Cocina and Llatas, mention should be made of Cueva del Lagrimal (Soler, 1968–69) in Alicante on the border with Murcia, where

---

[12] Probably some of these are very late, since letters of the alphabet occur.

[13] A 5120 ± 620 B.P. date from preceramic levels at Abrigo Grande is unreliable because of the "insufficient sample" (Otlet and Slade, 1974), as indicated by the very large standard error.

both geometrical and backed bladelet flints (as well as a keeled knife paralleled at Abrigo Grande[14]) occurred in a preceramic level, continuing into the one above with pottery, above which, in turn, was Copper Age material. At Hoyo de la Mina, too, the next to the lowest layer containing a nonceramic assemblage of awls, backed points, rods, bladelets, and bones (including dog) was followed by one that contained not only geometrical flints, awls, and backed points but also plain sherds, stratified below a level with a rich collection of decorated pottery and a stone "idol" the Aegean parallels for which are dated 3500–2500 B.C. At Còva d'En Pardo (Alicante), however, a deep layer with backed bladelets but without pottery was separated from overlying layers commencing with *Cardium*-impressed ware and bifacial flint arrowpoints, by a sterile layer (Pascual, pers. comm.).

The Abrigo Grande excavations have been detailed elsewhere (Walker, 1972, 1977a). Retouched pieces comprised a very small number of the total lithic assemblage: 71 out of almost 6,000 items—largely backed bladelets, end-scrapers, a discoidal scraper, pyramidal pieces, and occasional awls, notched and serrated pieces, a crescent, as well as two microburin spalls and one unretouched roughly triangular spall, which might testify to knowledge of geometrical flint-knapping also. No convincing burins were found. The pottery was sparse but included *Cardium*-impressed sherds, as well as a plain bowl with a strap handle which was sun-baked or fired at a very low temperature. A decorated bone tube was found, and also pierced sea-shells, notwithstanding a distance of some 60 kilometers from the coast. Apart from rabbit, bones of *Sus scrofa* and *Cervus elaphus* occurred in all layers, equine bones in the lower layers, and caprine and bovine bones in the ceramic layers. All layers had land mollusks in profusion.

Early Holocene Culture and Environment

Not only do the faunal remains from Abrigo Grande reflect the species painted in eastern Spanish rock art, but, moreover, most of the preceramic implements came from a thick layer of eolian sand underlying the ceramic layers, so that the sand must be pre-7200 B.P. Somewhat unusually among eastern Spanish painted rock shelters, Abrigo Grande faces north, which, apart from affording much-needed shade in summer and consequent suitability for domestic or industrial activities, indicates the direction whence the sand had been blown. Eolian sand occurs in the upper part of the 10-meter terrace

[14] And several other southeastern sites, e.g., Cueva de la Palica (cf. Fortea, 1970).

of the River Vinalopó (glacis-terrace A) and derives from Tertiary sandstones to the north-northwest on the fringe of the Meseta (Cuenca, 1971). This sand unit has been carbon-dated to 8920 ± 180 and 8190 ± 130 B.P. (Cuenca and Walker, 1976a); so perhaps the Abrigo Grande sand can be regarded as broadly contemporaneous. Eolian sand has been identified at other stations in southeastern Spain, notably in the Segura River system (Cuenca and Walker, 1976b, c) in the same chronostratigraphical formation, glacis-terrace A. A sand layer occurred in the north-facing Cueva del Gato near Moratalla (Murcia) where it lay beneath a burnt layer but above a darker layer which contained microlithic flints (including three backed pieces) and three potsherds (Cuadrado, 1947). Given the antiquity of the Verdelpino ceramic assemblage, it is quite possible that there could be overlap between the earliest ceramic culture and the eolian sand depositional phase.

Caves not facing between west and north are not described as containing sand. Thus Cueva Grande and Cueva Pequeña near Villena (Alicante), with backed bladelet and geometrical flints, respectively (Soler, 1956, 1968–69), contained thermoclastic soils, nor is mention made of sand at Cantos de la Visera near Yecla (Murcia), another shelter not facing between west and north, which contained naturalistic rock paintings and flints which must have comprised many backed bladelets.[15] Outside our area, it is interesting that the Cocinilla del Obispo painted shelter contained artifacts, including a polished stone ax, but not pottery, below a sandy deposit (Almagro, 1944, 1947a).

Moreover, surface collections of microliths have been made from sandy deposits lacking pottery, such as at Fuente de la Zarza near Jumilla (Murcia) (Walker, 1973a) and Pinar de Tarruella near Villena (Alicante) (Soler, 1968–69), though other sandy deposits near Villena with microlithic flints, such as Arenal de la Virgen and Casa de Lara, have yielded up also bifacial arrowpoints, pottery, and even metal artifacts, the reason for which must be sought in prolonged marshy sedimentation in a fundamentally endorrheic basin with disturbance of the original eolian sand and addition of later material by hunters, fowlers, and fishermen (Cuenca and Walker, 1976a).

[15]The article citing the discovery (Breuil and Burkitt, 1915) compared the assemblage to one from Burgos, which had been defined (Breuil and Obermaier, 1913) as Gravettian. One blade, however, was "retouchée à la manière d'une feuille de saule solutréenne" (Breuil and Burkitt, 1915). This is reminiscent of another bifacial point he found at Cueva Chiquita in Almería, "une jolie flèche de taille probablement solutréenne; elle pourrait être néolithique" (Breuil and Obermaier, 1914), which, Breuil's caution notwithstanding, have both been taken as showing the rock art to be Solutrean in age (Pericot, 1961). The point is that foliate points are found in early Neolithic assemblages (Fortea, 1973) with backed bladelets.

The Abrigo Grande stratigraphy demonstrates that the eolian sand was deposited between two phases of thermoclastic sedimentation, the second of which coincided with appearance of pottery and therefore cannot have begun much after 7200 B.P. and probably began before that date. Carbon-14 dates from the Vinalopó Valley also point to partial erosion of eolian sand, and deposition of calcrete thereupon by 5000 B.P. derived from dry limestone scree, which had begun to develop over the sand before that date. Many Copper Age remains come from surface scree in powdery soil, often cut through by subsequent fluviatile incision, which over the past 2,500 years has excavated 10-meter-deep canyons, exposing the earlier sediments, including massive scree beneath the eolian sand (doubtless associated with torrential precipitation in the late glacial), and thick underlying microrhythmically bedded sands and clays with occasional pebble lenses, which correspond to the upper pleniglacial (Cuenca and Walker, 1974, 1976a,b,c). This sequence is everywhere in the Segura and Vinalopó basins and in the Almanzora and Antas valleys of northern Almeria. Quite striking is the lack of large plant roots or trunks from lower parts of the succession, not to mention the upper ones, so that it may be inferred that the landscape presented an open vegetation and had been repeatedly ravaged by episodic torrential storms, sheetwash over alluvial in-filling of valley systems, the latter having been particularly marked in the lower pleniglacial, and hillwash, due to the coastal slopes receiving the effect of predominantly anticyclonic winds in consequence of the southward extension of the circumglacial anticyclonic pressure system. Latterly, as that receded, cyclonic wind predominance led to eolian deposition, only to recede northward in its turn, as southeastern Spain entered the Sahelian anticyclonic belt. If that is so, then the eolian deposition and aridity both occurred under conditions of relatively mild temperatures, though lack of surface water prevented establishment of substantial vegetative cover. The subsequent scree development occurred as temperatures rose as southeastern Spain entered the Sahelian system, though only later did its effect become so pronounced as to cause flash floods and trenching, maybe in part aided by man's denudation of such vegetation as theretofore existed.

What has all that got to do with rock art and stone tools? Perhaps the answer lies in the art itself. Large mammals are a recurring theme on the Upper Paleolithic stone plaques of Còva de El Parpalló (Pericot, 1942b) and are largely the same groups as shown on eastern Spanish rock paintings—caprines, cervines, equines, bovines, suines, though the bony remains, as at Abrigo Grande, contained many bones of rabbit, an animal absent from art of all periods. Davidson (1972) stresses the importance of cervines at Cueva del Volcán del Faro, not far from Parpalló in Valencia. It is interesting that despite proximity to the sea, mammal remains predominated and marine fauna was virtually absent. The material from Volcán is largely Magdalenian in age but characterized by predominance of Gravettoid flintwork, though it is possible that some occupation continued into the Holocene. Shellfish did occur in lower, perhaps Magdalenian VI, layers at Hoyo de la Mina in Málaga (Such, 1920), though large mammals were also represented, and, interestingly, dog. It seems clear that large mammals were an important economic resource in the late Upper Paleolithic and early Holocene of the southeast. Unfortunately, there are few sites of the early Holocene that have yielded quantities of bone sufficient for site catchment analysis of faunal material and reconstruction therefrom of population numbers of huntsmen.

But there is an interesting sidelight offered by Abrigo Grande. If it be admitted that cervines were important, and they are represented, at least, in the faunal remains and art of the neighboring rock shelter, then we can ask how many deer the land could have supported by analogy with British data on red deer. Taking maximum and minimum adult red-deer weights of 200 and 150 kilograms, respectively (Harris and Duff, 1970), and maximum and minimum densities of 0.2 and 0.12 animal per square kilometer, with the further assumptions of an annual cull of one-sixth of herd sizes (so as to maintain herds at constant size, cf. Lowe, 1966), of two-thirds edibility of carcasses of deer, of a daily intake of 0.25 kilogram of venison per man per day (lower than the 0.377 kilogram + 0.162 kilogram fat ingested by Eskimos, cited in Weiner 1964, p. 416), and of a one-hour site exploitation territory from Abrigo Grande of 73 square kilometers, we can calculate four values of numbers of men capable of being supported at the site, viz., 148, 89, 111, and 67, with a mean of 104. Now, the rock painting with several "dancing" figures in the neighboring painted rock shelter shows about 30 anthropomorphs, some of whom are wearing skirts, and none of whom bears bow and arrows; so it is likely they are female. They form a "scene," and it is likely that most were painted at the same time. Thirty women would be about right for a total population of both sexes, plus children, of 104.

Other rock paintings suggest a proximity between anthropomorphs and large mammals such as can on occasion be reached by gamekeepers and red deer in northwest Scotland (Darling, 1956); indeed, I have approached them near enough to offer fodder in winter. Whereas Upper Paleolithic sites by and large are near the coast, indicating choice of milder conditions when periglacial conditions embraced the high mountains, Holocene sites and the rock art shelters are at higher altitude farther inland, which, apart from precluding pleniglacial age, throws light on paleoeconomy. Today, *Quercus rotundifolia,* often associated withe *Pinus halepensis,* occurs only over 700 meters and where rainfall exceeds 305 millimeters per annum (López Bermúdez, 1973). Early Holocene aridity is unlikely to have permitted wider extension than today, though density may have been greater before human interference, given that cyclonic winds would have limited precipitation to the higher mountains and excluded coastal ranges somewhat. Watercourses would have been more active upstream, as today, contrasted against their lower reaches. Endorrheic basins with retention of water in swamps would have favored the climax flora and concomitant large mammalian herds. This intermediate upland and inland zone is the one where we find both early Holocene assemblages of lithic material and shelters with rock paintings, distinguishing both from Upper Paleolithic tools and art.[16] The reconstruction of early Holocene environments, using present land-use and what we know of sedimentary relocation in later Holocene times, suggests that most rock-art sites were on land not predominantly arable without irrigation, e.g., the upper Taibilla sites and those of Cañaíca del Calar and Fuente del Sabuco, as well as Barranco de los Grajos with its Abrigo Grande; while other sites with art, such as Cueva del Peliciego near the Jumilla basin, or with stone tools, such as Cueva del Lagrimal, which overlooks a small endorrheic basin, or the Huesa Tacaña and Pinar de Tarruella sites near that of Villena (see maps, figs. 1–6), underline the important role of such natural drainage basins where streams from neighboring hillsides and springs fed swamps capable of supporting game, that at Villena remaining important to huntsmen even in the Middle Ages. Moreover, the location of the art and habitation sites recalls that of Upper Paleolithic ones vis-à-vis possible reindeer pastures in Germany (cf. Sturdy, 1975) near vantage points whence herd movements could be scrutinized or maybe controlled.

We suggest that the geographical factor and the unity of Levantine art demand that early Holocene stone-tool assemblages be regarded as functional facies of one culture, the more so since there are few sites with backed bladelets that lack all traces of geometrical workmanship, and *vice versa mutatis mutandis*. Climatic necessity and consequent distribution of pasture restricted man-mammal relationships geographically. Maintenance of human group numbers demanded greater control of the faunal and thus of the floral environments, though whether full domestication was reached is uncertain. Perhaps a relationship not unlike that between Lapps and reindeer was reached, with the herds being directed toward suitable pasture and selective

[16]One exception is Cueva Ambrosio, an inland Upper Paleolithic site. Middle Paleolithic sites, perhaps mainly interpleniglacial, do occur in inland situations (Cuenca and Walker, 1976*c*).

slaughter practised to ensure that herd size did not get out of control. Perhaps a gradual increase in human population occurred such that other ancillary food sources had to be introduced. The putative conventionalized sheep painted at Barranco de los Grajos might have been one such, and the cereals of Coveta de l'Or another, slightly later on. The chronological and typological data of material assemblages suggest basic continuity between early Holocene preceramic assemblages and those of the early Neolithic, reinforced by Fortea's reassessment of the Còva de les Mallaetes sequence in Valencia (Fortea, 1973), which underlines the role of backed bladelets in that continuity, just as Cocina does that of geometric flint-knapping.

Conclusion

New light is shed on the origins of the southeast Spanish Neolithic and the relevance of Levantine rock paintings and early Holocene material assemblages and paleoenvironmental change in determining the material assemblages and subsistence economy of the early Neolithic. Indigenous development is emphasized, rather than alternative views that attribute it to an influx of foreign cultivators.

REFERENCES

ACOSTA, PILAR

1968. La pintura rupestre esquemática en España. Monografías del Seminario de Prehistoria y Arqueología 1, 250 pp. Universidad de Salamanca.

ALMAGRO BASCH, MARTÍN

1944. Los problemas del epipaleopolítico y mesolítico en España. Ampurias, vol. 6, pp. 1–38.

1947a. El paleolítico español. Pp. 243–485 *in* "Historia de España," R. Menéndez Pidal, ed., vol. 1, no. 1. Madrid.

1947b. El arte prehistórico español. Pp. 13–122 *in* "Ars Hispaniae," A. García Bellido, ed., vol. 1. Madrid.

1951. La cronología del arte levantino de España. Pp. 67–80 *in* "Crónica, VI Congreso Arqueológico del Sureste Español, Cartagena 1951." Cartagena.

1954. Las pinturas rupestres levantinas. Pp. 5–38 *in* "IV Congreso Internacional de Ciencias Prehistóricas y Protohistóricas, Madrid 1954," vol. 1. Madrid.

1956. Las pinturas rupestres del Bajo Aragón. Pp. 41–95 *in* "Prehistoria del Bajo Aragón," M. Almagro Basch, A. Beltrán Martínez, and E. Ripoll Perelló, eds. Zaragoza.

1964. El problema de la cronología del arte levantino español. Pp. 103–111 *in* "Prehistoric Art of the Western Mediterranean and the Sahara," L. Pericot García and E. Ripoll Perelló, eds., Viking Fund Publication in Anthropology, no. 39. Chicago.

Aparicio Pérez, José
1974. La cueva del Volcán del Faro (Cullera) y el paleomesolítico valenciano. Quartär, vol. 25, pp. 71–91.
Arribas, Antonio
1953. El ajuar de las cuevas sepulcrales de los Blanquizares de Lébor (Murcia). Memorias de los Museos Arqueológicos Provinciales, vol. 14, pp. 78–126.
Ballester Tormo, Isidro
1928. Unas cerámicas interesantes en el valle de Albaida. Cultura Valenciana, vol. 3, pp. 89–100, 170–182.
Balout, Lionel
1955. Préhistoire de l'Afrique du Nord, vi + 543 pp. Paris.
Beltran Martínez, A.
1968a. Arte rupestre levantino. Monografías Arqueológicas, no. 4, 256 pp. Universidad de Zaragoza.
1968b. El arte rupestre levantino: Cronología y significación. Caesaraugusta, vol. 31–32, pp. 7–43.
1968c. La cueva de los Grajos, y sus pinturas, en Cieza (Murcia). Caesaraugusta, vol. 31–32, pp. 45–88.
1969. La cueva de los Grajos y sus pinturas, en Cieza (Murcia). Monografías Arqueológicas, no. 6, 87 pp. Universidad de Zaragoza.
Blance, Beatrice
1960. The origin and development of the early Bronze Age in the Iberian Peninsula. Ph.D. thesis, Edinburgh University, published in 1917 as: Die Anfänge der Metallurgie auf der iberischen Halbinsel *in* "Studien zu den Anfangen der Metallurgie, IV," K. Bittel, S. Junghans, H. Otto, E. Sangmeister, and M. Schröder, eds., 204 pp. Romanisch-Germanisch Zentralmuseum, Berlin.
Boessneck, J.
1969. Die Knochenfunde, vom Cerro del Real bei Granada (Prov. Granada). Studien über frühe Tierknochenfunde von der iberischen Halbinsel, vol. 1, pp. 3–42. Universität München and Deutsches Archäologisches Institut Abteilung, Madrid.
Bosch Gimpera, Pedro
1919. Prehistòria Catalana, xvi + 300 pp. Barcelona.
1932. Etnología de la Península Ibérica, xxiv + 711 pp. Barcelona.
1964. The chronology of the rock-paintings of the Spanish Levant. Pp. 125–132 *in* "Prehistoric Art of the Western Mediterranean and the Sahara," L. Pericot García and E. Ripoll Perelló, eds., Viking Fund Publication in Anthropology, no. 39. Chicago.
Breuil, Henri
1912. L'âge des cavernes et roches ornées de France et d'Espagne. Revue Anthropologique, vol. 19, pp. 193–234.
1915. Les peintures rupestres d'Espagne VII: Les roches peintes de la région d'Alpera (Albacete). L'Anthropologie, vol. 26, pp. 329–331.
1920. Les peintures rupestres de le péninsule ibérique XI: Les roches peintes de Minateda (Albacete). L'Anthropologie, vol. 30, pp. 1–50.
1928a. Station moustérienne et peintures préhistoriques de "Canalizo el Rayo," Minateda (Albacete). Archivo de Prehistoria Levantina, vol. 1, pp. 15–17.

1928b. Vestiges de peintures préhistoriques à "La Cueva del Pernil," Játiva (Valence). Archivo de Prehistoria Levantina, vol. 1, pp. 19–21.

1933–1935. Les peintures rupestres schématiques de la péninsule ibérique, I-IV, 559 pp. Lagny.

1964. Un grabado de reno posiblemente procedente del Bajo Aragón, Pp. xvii–xix *in* "Miscelánea en Homenaje al Abate Henri Breuil (1877–1961)," E. Ripoll Perelló, ed., vol. 1. Barcelona.

BREUIL, HENRI, AND BURKITT, MILES C.

1915. Les peintures rupestres d'Espagne VI: Les abris peints du Mont Arabí près Yecla (Murcie). L'Anthropologie, vol. 26, pp. 313–328.

BREUIL, HENRI, AND CABRÉ AGUILÓ, JUAN

1911. Les peintures rupestres d'Espagne III: Los Toricos de Albarracín. L'Anthropologie, vol. 22, pp. 641–648.

BREUIL, HENRI, AND DE MOTOS, FEDERICO

1915. Les peintures rupestres d'Espagne VIII: Les roches à figures naturalistes de la région de Vélez-Blanco (Almería). L'Anthropologie, vol. 26, pp. 332–336.

BREUIL, HENRI, AND OBERMAIER, HUGO VON

1912. II Travaux sur les peintures rupestres d'Espagne. L'Anthropologie, vol. 23, pp. 16–26.

1913. Travaux exécutés en 1912. L'Anthropologie, vol. 24, pp. 1–16.

1914. II Travaux en Espagne. L'Anthropologie, vol. 25, pp. 233–253.

BREUIL, HENRI; SERRANO GÓMEZ, P.; AND CABRÉ AGUILÓ, JUAN

1912. Les peintures rupestres d'Espagne: IV, Les abris de Bosque à Alpera (Albacete); V, Tortosilla à Ayora (Valence). L'Anthropologie, vol. 23, pp. 528–562.

BURKITT, MILES C.

1925. Prehistory, viii + 458 pp. Cambridge.

BUTZER, K. W., AND FREEMAN, L. G.

1968. Pollen analysis at the Cueva del Toll, Catalonia: A critical re-appraisal. Geologie en Mijnbouw, vol. 47, no. 2, pp. 116–120.

CABRÉ AGUILÓ, JUAN

1915. El arte rupestre en España (regiones septentrional y meridional). Comisión de Investigaciones Paleontológicas y Prehistóricas, Memoria 1, xxxiii + 229 pp. Madrid.

CARBONELL ESCOBAR, JAIME

1970. Dos nuevos abrigos con pinturas rupestres en El Sabinar (provincia de Murcia). Archivo de Prehistoria Levantina, vol. 12 (1969), pp. 19–26.

CHILDE, V. GORDON

1950. The dawn of European civilization, xviii + 362 pp. London. (First ed., 1925.)

CLARK, JOHN GRAHAME D.

1963. Neolithic bows from Somerset, England, and the prehistory of archery in northwestern Europe. Proceedings of the Prehistoric Society, new ser., vol. 29, pp. 50–98.

COLOMINAS ROCA, JOSÉ, AND ESBONA, B. M.

1925. Prehistòria de Montserrat. Analecta Montserratensia, vol. 6, pp. 225–352.

CUADRADO DÍAZ, E.
1947. La cueva del Gato. Pp. 115–125 *in* "Crónica del II Congreso Arqueológico del Sureste Español Albacete 1946." Albacete.
CUENCE PAYÁ, ARTEMIO
1971. El cuaternario del valle de Elda. Revista del Instituto de Estudios Alicantinos, vol. 6, pp. 23–56.
CUENCA PAYÁ, A., AND WALKER, MICHAEL JOHN
1974. Comentarios sobre el cuaternario continental en el centro y sur de la provincia de Alicante (España). Pp. 15–38 *in* "Actas de la I Reunión Nacional del Grupo de Trabajo del Cuaternario, Madrid, 8–11 Octubre 1973," T. Aleixandre, J. Gallardo, and A. Pérez Gonzales, eds., Trabajos sobre Neogeno-Cuaternario 2. Madrid.
1976a. Pleistoceno final y holoceno en la cuenca del Vinalopó (Alicante). Estudios Geológicos, vol. 32, pp. 95–104.
1976b. Nuevas fechas por ^{14}C de la zona del Vinalopó y del Segura, SE. de España. *In* "Actas de la II Reunión Nacional del Grupo de Trabajo del Cuaternario Jaca 15–20 Septiembre 1975," T. Aleixandre and J. Gallardo, eds., Trabajos sobre Neogeno-Cuaternario 9. Madrid.
1976c. Paleogeografía humana. *In* "Actas de la II Reunión del Grupo de Trabajo del Cuaternario Jaca 15–20 Septiembre 1975," T. Aleixandre and J. Gallardo, eds., Trabajos sobre Neogeno-Cuaternario 9. Madrid.
DARLING, FRANK FRASER
1956. A herd of red deer: A study in animal behaviour, xiv + 226 pp. London.
DAVIDSON, IAIN
1972. The animal economy of La Cueva del Volcán del Faro, Cullera, Valencia, Spain. Transactions of the Cave Research Group of Great Britain, vol. 14, no. 1, pp. 23–31.
DELIBRIAS, G.; GUILLIER, M. T.; AND LABEYRIE, J. T.
1964. Saclay natural radiocarbon measurements I. Radiocarbon, vol. 6, pp. 233–250.
1966. Gif natural radiocarbon measurements. Radiocarbon, vol. 8, pp. 74–95.
DONNER, J. J., AND KURTÉN, BJÖRN
1958. The floral and faunal succession at the "Cueva del Toll," Spain. Eiszeitalter und Gegenwart, vol. 9, pp. 72–82.
DRIESCH, A. VON, AND BOESSNECK, J.
1969. Die Fauna des "Cabezo Redondo" bei Villena (Prov. Alicante). Studien über frühe Tierknochenfunde von der Iberischen Halbinsel, vol. 1, pp. 43–87 (Universität München and Deutsches Archäologisches Institut Abteilung Madrid).
ELLERMAN, J. R., AND SCOTT, T. C. S. MORRISON
1951. Checklist of Palearctic and Indian mammals, 1758 to 1946, 810 pp. London.
EVANS, JOHN D.
1958. Two phases of prehistoric settlement in the western Mediterranean. London University Institute of Archaeology, Thirteenth Annual Report and Bulletin for 1955–56, pp. 49–70.
FERNÁNDEZ DE AVILÉS, A.
1939–40. Las pinturas rupestres de la cueva del Peliciego, en término de Jumilla (Murcia). Boletín de Trabajos del Seminario de Estudios de Arte y

Arqueología (Facultad de Historia, Universidad de Valladolid), vol. 6, fasc. 22., pp. 37–46.

FERNÁNDEZ-MIRANDA, F., AND MOURE, A.

1974. Verdelpino (Cuenca): Nuevas fechas de C-14 para el neolítico peninsular. Trabajos de Prehistoria, vol. 31, pp. 311–316.

FLETCHER VALLS, DOMINGO

1953. Avances y problemas de la prehistoria valenciana en los últimos veinticinco años. Anales del Centro de Cultura Valenciana, new ser., vol. 14, pp. 8–36.

1956. Problèmes et progrès du paléolithique et du mésolithique de la région de Valencia (España). Quartär, vols. 7–8, pp. 66–90.

1956a. Estado actual del estudio del paleolítico y mesolítico valenciano. Revista de Archivos, Bibliotecas y Museos, vol. 62, pp. 841–876.

FLETCHER VALLS, D., AND APARICIO PÉREZ, JOSÉ

1969. Bastón de mando procedente de Cullera (Valencia, España). Quartär, vol. 20, pp. 189–193.

1970. Noticia de las excavaciones efectuadas en la cueva del Volcán del Faro (Cullera, Valencia). Archivo de Prehistoria Levantina, vol. 12 (1969), pp. 7–18.

FORTEA PÉREZ, JAVIER

1970. La cueva de la Palica, Serrón (Antas). Trabajos de Prehistoria, vol. 27, pp. 61–91.

1971. La cueva de la Cocina. Servicio de Investigación Prehistórica, Trabajos Varios 50, xii + 88 pp. Valencia.

1973. Los complejos microlaminares y geométricos del epipaleolítico mediterráneo Español, 504 pp. Memoria no. 4, Seminario de Prehistoria y Arqueología, Universidad de Salamanca.

GARCÍA GUINEA, MIGUEL ANGEL

1961–62. Nuevos abrigos con pinturas rupestres en las proximidades de Nerpio (Albacete). Pp. 397–415 *in* "Homenaje at Profesor Cayetano de Mergelina." Murcia.

1962. Los recientes descubrimientos de las pinturas levantinas en Nerpio (Albacete). Las Ciencias, vol. 27, pp. 458–469.

GARCÍA GUINEA, MIGUEL ANGEL, AND KRAPOVICKAS, P.

1958–59. Nuevos hallazgos de pinturas rupestres en España: Los abrigos de "El Prado de Tornero" (Nerpio Albacete). Quartär, vols. 10–11, pp. 253–265.

GOSSÉ, G.

1941. Aljoroque, estación neolítica inicial, de la provincia de Almería. Ampurias, vol. 3, pp. 64–84.

GURREA CRESPO, V.

1956. El hombre emplumado del "Barranc de Ullets" (Gandía). Pp. 317–320 *in* "Actas de la IV Sesión del Congreso Internacional de Ciencias Prehistóricas y Protohistóricas, Madrid 1954." Zaragoza.

HARRIS, DAVID R.

1960–61. The distribution and ancestry of the domestic goat. Proc. Linnean Soc. London, vol. 173, pp. 79–91.

HARRIS, R. A., AND DUFF, K. R.
1970. Wild deer in Britain. Newton Abbott, London.
HERNÁNDEZ-PACHECO Y ESTEVAN, EDUARDO
1924. Las pinturas prehistóricas de las cuevas de Araña (Valencia). Comisión de Investigaciones Paleontológicas y Prehistóricas, Madrid, Memoria 34, 221 pp.
1959. Prehistoria del solar hispánico: Orígenes del arte pictórico. Real Academia de Ciencias Exactas, Físicas, y Naturales, Serie Ciencias Naturales, Memoria 20, xv + 767 pp. Madrid.
HOPF, MARIA
1966. *Triticum monococcum* L. y *Triticum dicoccum* Schübl. en el neolítico antiguo español. Archivo de Prehistoria Levantina, vol. 11, pp. 53–73.
HOPF, M., and SCHUBART, HERMANFREID
1965. Getreidefunde aus der Coveta de l'Or (Prov. Alicante). Madrider Mitteilungen, vol. 6, pp. 20–38.
HUERTA Y RAMÍREZ, P., AND PALAUS, X.
1967. Pp. 49–73 *in* "Enciclopedia de la Caza," vol. 1. Barcelona.
JÁUREGUI, J. J.
1949. Influencia de los vientos y corrientes de la cuenca occidental del Mediterráneo en las relaciones ibero-africanas. Pp. 96–104 *in* "Crónica IV Congreso Arquelógico del Sureste Español," Elche 1948. Cartagena.
JORDÁ CERDÁ, FRANCISCO
1953. Notas sobre los comienzos del neolítico en nuestra península. Archivum, vol. 3, pp. 259–271.
1954. Gravetiense y epigravetiense en la España mediterránea. Caesaraugusta, vol. 4, pp. 7–30.
1964. Sobre posibles relaciones del arte levantino español. Pp. 467–472 *in* "Miscelánea en Homenaje al Abate Henri Breuil (1877–1961)," E. Ripoll Perelló, ed. Barcelona.
1967. Zur Zeitstellung der Levantekunst. Madrider Mitteilungen, vol. 8, pp. 11–29.
JORDÁ CERDÁ, FRANCISCO, AND ALCÁCER GRAU, J.
1949. La covacha de Llatas (Andilla). Servicio de Investigación Prehistórica, Valencia, Trabajos Varios 11, 41 pp.
1951. Las pinturas de Dos Aguas (Valencia). Servicio de Investigación Prehistórica, Valencia, Trabajos Varios 15, 39 pp.
1952. Las pinturas rupestres de Dos Aguas (Valencia). Archivo Español de Arqueología, vol. 25, pp. 103–105.
KURTÉN, BJÖRN
1968. Pleistocene mammals of Europe, 317 pp. Wiedenfeld and Nicolson, London.
La Labor del S.I.P. y su Museo en el Pasado Año 1934, 1935, Valencia.
La Labor del S.I.P. y su Museo en los Años 1935–1939, 1942, Valencia.
LÓPEZ-BERMÚDEZ, FRANCISCO
1973. La vega alta del Segura (clima, hidrología y geomorfología), 288 pp. Muncia.
LÓPEZ PASCUAL, EDUARDO
1968. El testimonio rupestre: Nota acerca de las pinturas rupestres de Cieza (Murcia). Geo y Bio Karst, vol. 5, pp. 468–469.

LOWE, V. P. W.
1966. Observations on the dispersal of red deer on Rhum. Pp. 211–228 *in* "Play, Exploration and Territory in Mammals," P. A. Jewell and C. Loizos, eds. Symposia of Zoological Society of London, vol. 18. London.
MARTÍNEZ SÁNCHEZ, J. J.
1969. Las pinturas rupestres de "El Sabinar" en Moratalla (Murcia). Instituto de Estudios del Sur de España, 1 semestre 1969, pp. 10–13. Barcelona.
MARTÍNEZ SANTA-OLALLA, JULIO
1946. Esquema paleontológico de la península hispána, 156 pp. Madrid.
1950. Cuadernos de Historia Primitiva, vol. 5, no. 2.
MCLEOD, WALLACE E.
1962. Egyptian composite bows in New York. American Journal of Archaeology, vol. 66, pp. 13–19.
MENÉNDEZ AMOR, J., AND FLORSCHÜTZ, F.
1964. Results from the preliminary palynological investigation of samples from a 50 metres boring in S. Spain. Boletín de la Real Sociedad Española de Historia Natural, no. 62 (G), pp. 251–255.
MILLER, GERRIT S.
1912. Catalogue of mammals of western Europe in the collection of the British Museum, xv + 1,019 pp. London.
MURRAY, JACQUELINE
1971. The first European agriculture, vii + 380 pp. Edinburgh.
OBERMAIER, HUGO VON
1924. Fossil man in Spain, xxviii + 495 pp., London.
OBERMAIER, HUGO VON, AND WERNERT, PAUL
1929. La edad cuaternaria de las pinturas rupestres del Levante español. Memorias de la Real Sociedad de Historia Natural, vol. 15, no. 2, pp. 527–537.
OTLET, ROBERT L., AND SLADE, B. S.
1974. Harwell radiocarbon measurements I. Radiocarbon, vol. 16, no. 2, pp. 178–191.
PALLARES, M.
1923. Exploració dels jaciments prehistórics de la Valltorta. Annuari, Institut d'Estudis Catalans, no. 1 (1915–1920), pp. 454–457.
PALLARY, P.
1909. Instructions pour les recherches préhistoriques dans le nord-ouest de l'Afrique. Mémoires Société Historique Algérienne, vol. 3, pp. 45–46, 96–97.
PAYNE, SEBASTIEN
1968. The origins of domesticated sheep and goats—a reconsideration in the light of the fossil evidence. Proceedings of the Prehistoric Society, new ser., vol 34, pp. 332–367.
PERICOT GARCÍA, LUIS
1942a. Historia de España I: Épocas primitiva y romana. Barcelona.
1942b. La cueva de Parpalló (Gandia), ix + 351 pp.. Madrid.
1946. La cueva de la Cocina (Dos Aguas). Archivo de Prehistoria Levantina, vol. 2 (1945), pp. 39–71.
1950. El arte rupestre español, 56 pp. Barcelona.

1961. The social life of the Spanish Palaeolithic hunters as shown by Levantine art. Pp. 194–213 *in* "Social Life of Early Man," S. L. Washburn, ed., Viking Fund Publication in Anthropology, no. 31. Chicago.

PLÁ BALLESTER, ENRIQUE
1961. Actividades del Servicio de Investigación Prehistórica (1956–1960). Archivo de Prehistoria Levantina, vol. 9, pp. 211 ff.
1966. Actividades del S.I.P. Archivo de Prehistoria Levantina, vol. 11, pp. 284–285.

REY PASTOR, A.
1952. Jijona (Alicante): La cueva de la Sarga. Noticiario Arqueológico Hispánico, vol. 1, p. 25.

RIPOLL PERELLÓ, EDUARDO
1964a. Problemas cronológicos del arte paleolítico. Pp. 83–100 *in* "Prehistoric Art of the Western Mediterranean and the Sahara," L. Pericot García and E. Ripoll Perelló, eds., Viking Fund Publication in Anthropology, no. 39. Chicago.
1964b. Una pintura de tipo paleolítico en la Sierra de Montsía (Tarragona) y su posible relación con los orígenes del arte levantino. Pp. 297–305 *in* "Miscelánea en Homenaje al Abate Henri Breuil (1877–1961)," E. Ripoll Perelló, ed., vol. 2. Barcelona.

ROSSELÓ VERGER, VICTOR M.
1970. Clima y morfología pleistocena en el littoral mediterráneo español. Papeles del Departamento de Geografía, Universidad de Murcia, vol. 2, pp. 79–108.

SAN VALERO APARISI, J.
1950. La cueva de la Sarsa. Servicio de Investigación Prehistórica, Valencia, Trabajos Varios 12, 99 pp.

SÁNCHEZ, J.
1947. Pinturas rupestres en la Sierra de Enguera. Saitibi, vol. 7, pp. 53–59.

SÁNCHEZ CARRILERO, JULIA
1962. Avance al estudio de las pinturas rupestres de Solana de las Covachas, pedanía de Río-Moral (Nerpio—Albacete). Noticiario Arqueológico Hispánico, vol. 5 (1956–1961), pp. 1–12.

SÁNCHEZ JIMÉNEZ, J
1956. Pinturas rupestres de "Collado del Guijarral," Segura de la Sierra (Jaén). Noticiario Arqueológico Hispánico, vol. 3–4 (1954–1955), pp. 5–8.
1961–62. Pinturas rupestres de Socovos (Albacete). Pp. 782–783 *in* "Homenaje al Profesor Cayetano de Mergelina." Murcia.

SAVORY, HUBERT N.
1968. Spain and Portugal: The prehistory of the Iberian Peninsula, 324 pp. London.

SCHUBART, HERMANFRIED, AND PASCUAL PÉREZ, VICENTE
1966. Datación por el carbono 14 de los estratos con cerámica cardial de la Coveta de l'Or. Archivo de Prehistoria Levantina, vol. 11, pp. 45–51.

SCHWABEDISSEN, H., AND FREUNDLICH, J.
1965. Köln radiocarbon measurements I. Radiocarbon, vol. 8, pp. 239–247.

SIRET, HENRI, AND SIRET, LOUIS
1887. Les premiers âges du métal dans le sud-est de l'Espágne, iii+437 pp. Antwerp.
SIRET, LOUIS
1893. L'Éspagne préhistorique. Revue des Questions Scientifiques, ser. 2, vol. 4, pp. 489–562.
SOLER GARCÍA, JOSÉ MARÍA
1956. La cueva grande de Huesa-Tacaña. Pp. 121–131 *in* "Libro Homenaje al Conde de la Vega del Sella." Oviedo.
1968–69. La "Cueva Pequeña" de la Huesa Tacaña y el "mesolítico" villenense. Zephyrus, vol. 19–20, pp. 33–56.
STURDY, DAVID A.
1975. Some reindeer economies in prehistoric Europe. Pp. 55–95 *in* "Palaeoeconomy," E. S. Higgs, ed. Cambridge.
SUCH, MIGUEL
1920. Avance al estudio de la caverna "Hoyo de la Mina." Boletín Sociedad Malagueña de Ciencias, ser. 3, vol. 3, pp. 23–54.
TARRADELL, MIGUEL
1959. El estrecho de Gibraltar. ¿Puente o frontera? (Sobre relaciones post-neolícas entre Marruecos y la Peninsula Iberica). Tamuda, vol. 7, pp. 123–138.
UCKO, PETER J., AND ROSENFELD, ANDRÉE
1967. Palaeolithic cave art, 256 pp. London.
VAUFREY, R.
1933. Notes sur le capsien. L'Anthropologie, vol. 43, pp. 457–483.
VILASECA ANGUERA, S.
1939. L'estació taller de sílex de St. Gregori (Falset, Baix Priorat). Memorias de la Academia de Ciencias y Artes de Barcelona, vol. 23. (1932–1934), pp. 415–439.
1949. Avance al estudio de la cueva del Filador, de Margalef (provincia de Tarragona). Archivo Español de Arqueología, vol. 23, pp. 347–361.
VOGEL, J., AND WATERBOLK, H. T.
1972. Groningen radiocarbon dates X. Radiocarbon, vol. 14, no. 1, pp. 6–110.
WALKER, MICHAEL J.
1969. The naturalistic animal art of eastern Spain. Transactions of the Cave Research Group of Great Britain, vol. 11, no. 2, pp. 121–132.
1971. Spanish Levantine rock art. Man, new ser., vol. 6, no. 4, pp. 553–559.
1972. Cave dwellers and cave artists of the neothermal period in southeastern Spain. Transactions of the Cave Research Group of Great Britain, vol. 14, no. 1, pp. 1–22.
1973a. Aspects of the Neolithic and Copper Ages in the basins of the rivers Segura and Vinalopó, south-east Spain. D. Phil. thesis, Oxford University. (Unpubl.)
1973b. T-tests on prehistoric and modern charred cereal grains. Science and Archaeology, vol. 10, pp. 11–32.
1977a. The persistence of Upper Palaeolithic tool-kits into the early S.E. Spanish and Neolithic. Pp. 354–379 *in* "Stone Tools as Cultural Markers: Change,

Evolution, and Complexity," R. V. S. Wright, ed. Australian Institute of Aboriginal Studies, Canberra.

1977b. Spanish Neolithic and Chalcolithic pottery. Australian Studies in Archaeology, vol. 2.

1977c. 'Schematized' rock carvings as archaeological markers. *In* "Form in Indigenous Art: Schematisation in the Art of Australia and Prehistoric Europe," P. J. Ucko, ed. Australian Institute of Aboriginal Studies, Canberra.

1978. Archeological investigations at El Castillico, near El Sabinar, Mucia, Spain. Nat. Geogr. Soc. Res. Rpts., 1969 Projects, pp. 573–591, illus.

WEINER, J. S.

1964. Part V: Human ecology. Pp. 399–506 *in* "Human Biology, an Introduction to Human Evolution, Variation and Growth," G. A. Harrison, J. S. Weiner, J. M. Tanner, and N. A. Barnicot, eds. Oxford.

WHITEHOUSE, RUTH D.

1968. Settlement and economy in southern Italy in the neothermal period. Proceedings of the Prehistoric Society, new ser., vol. 34, pp. 332–367.

WOLF, W.

1928. Die Bewaffnung des altägyptischen Heeres, vi + 108 pp. Leipzig.

ZEUNER, FRIEDRICH E.

1963. A history of domesticated animals, 560 pp. Harper & Row, New York and London.

MICHAEL J. WALKER

Figures 1–6 on the following pages show the six areas of investigation and, for each site territory, three different aspects as follows: *a*, topography and 1,5, and 10 kilometer radii; *b*, present exploitation pattern; and *c*, probable exploitation pattern or potential in prehistoric times (see individual legends).

Land below 700 meters above sea-level (on *a* only).

Land between 700 and 1000 meters above sea-level.

Land between 1000 and 1500 meters above sea-level.

Land between 1500 and 2000 meters above sea-level.

Land over 2000 meters above sea-level.

Irrigation agriculture via channels from rivers.

Cultivation by rainwater or sporadic inundation only.

Olive groves.

Vineyards.

Rough pasture.

Montane scrub, or, above 1000 meters, woodland.

Fruit trees.

Swamp.

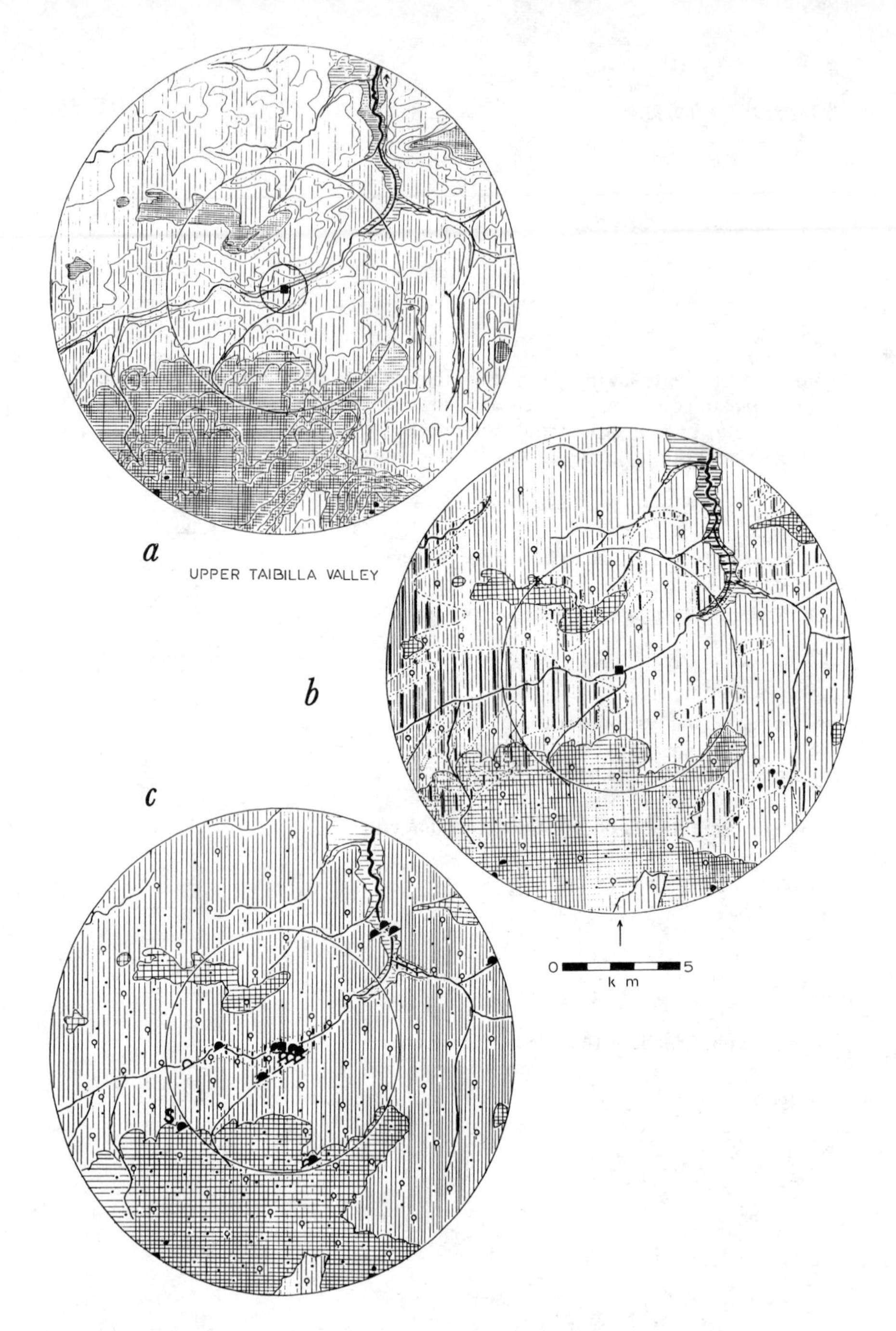

FIG. 1. Upper Taibilla Valley. Center of map is Nerpio (Albacete). In *c*, ▬ = naturalistic paintings in rock shelters and ⌂ = conventionalized paintings. S = Solana de las Covachas.

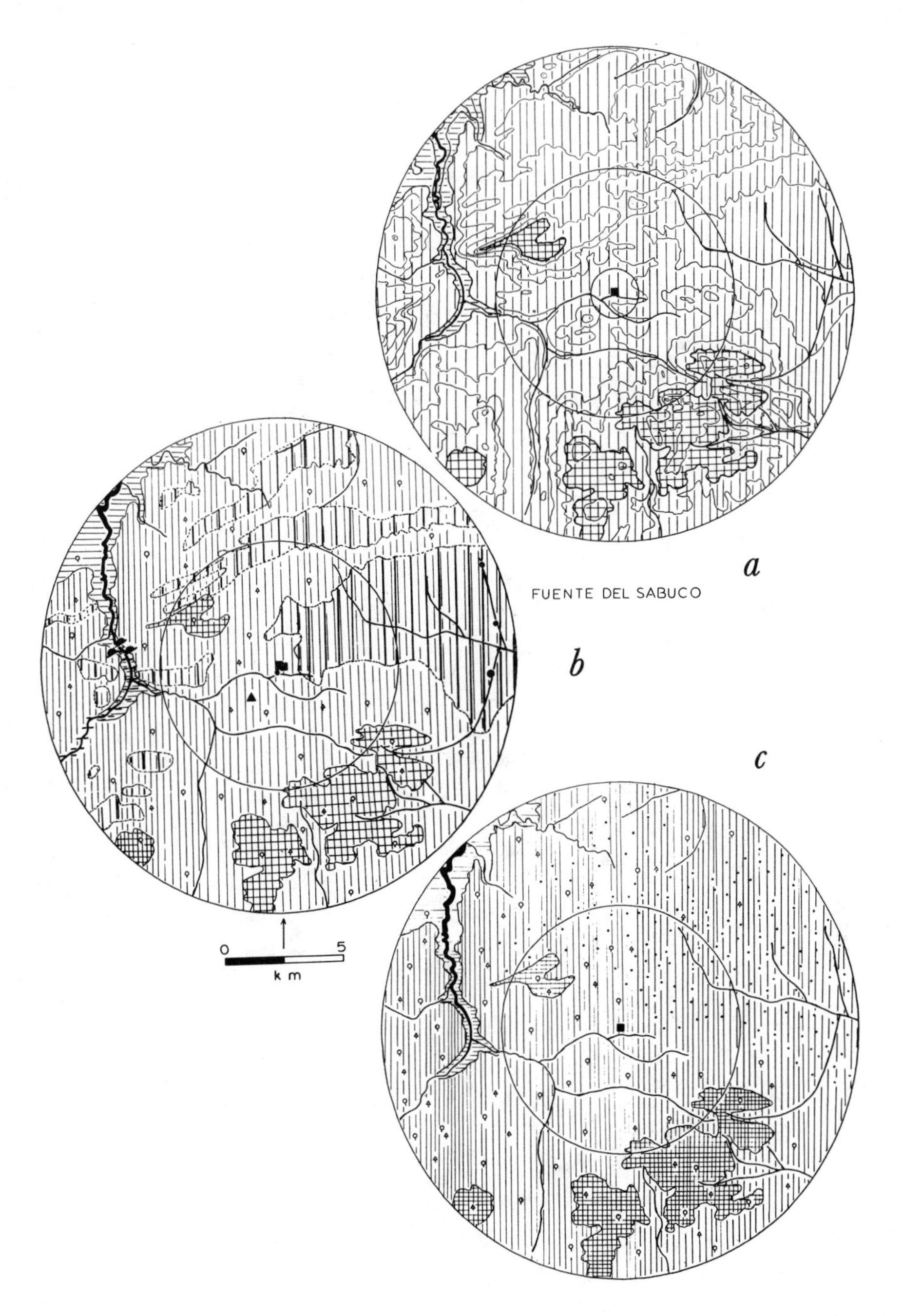

FIG. 2. Fuente del Sabuco and Cañaíca del Calar (see center of map *b*). This map overlaps with map 1. Solid triangle in *b* refers to a Copper Age settlement, solid dots are active springs, and dots in circles are springs now dry.

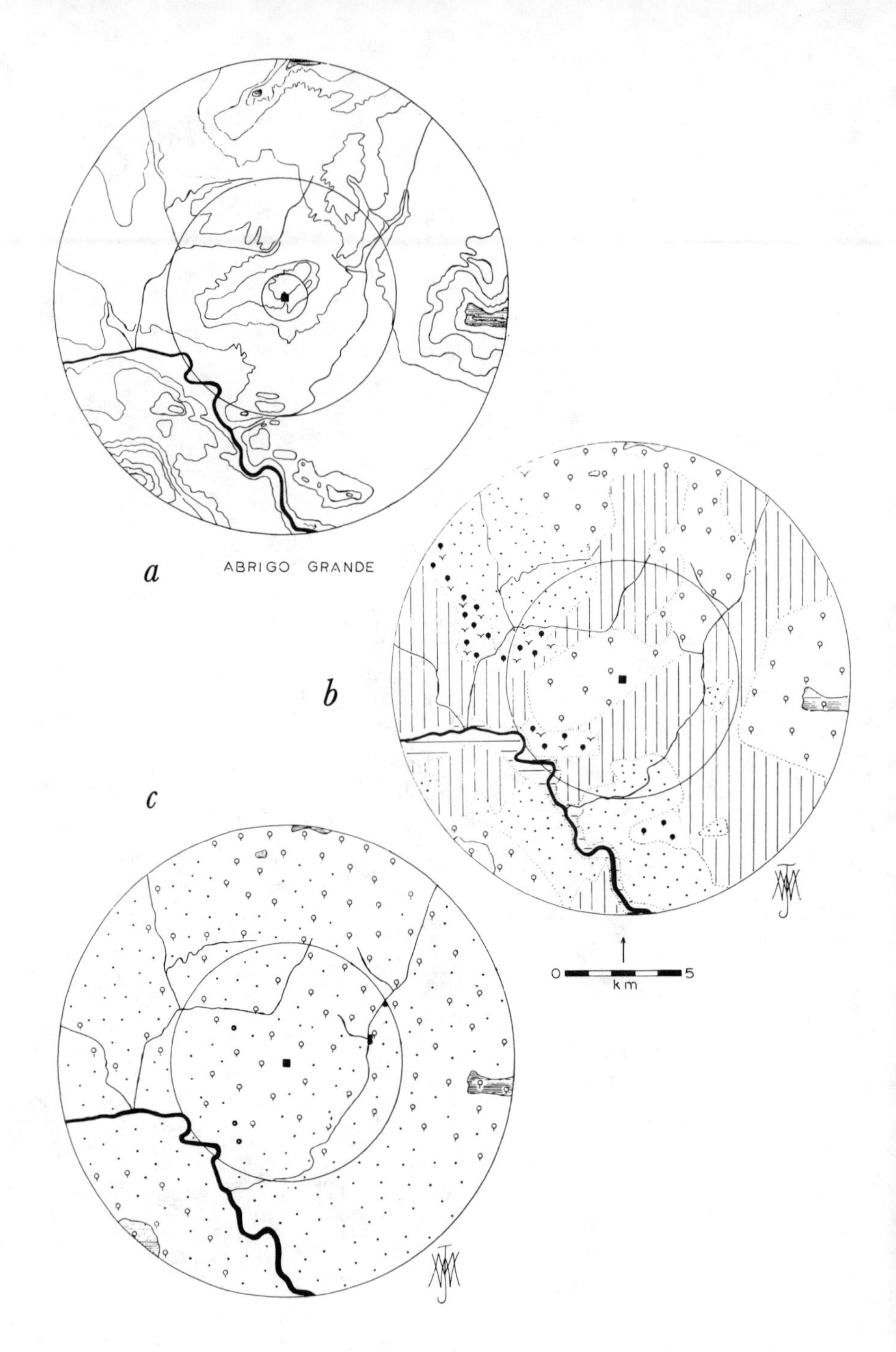

FIG. 3. Abrigo Grande (in center of map). Dots in circles in map *b* refer to springs which have dried up; open circles to wells.

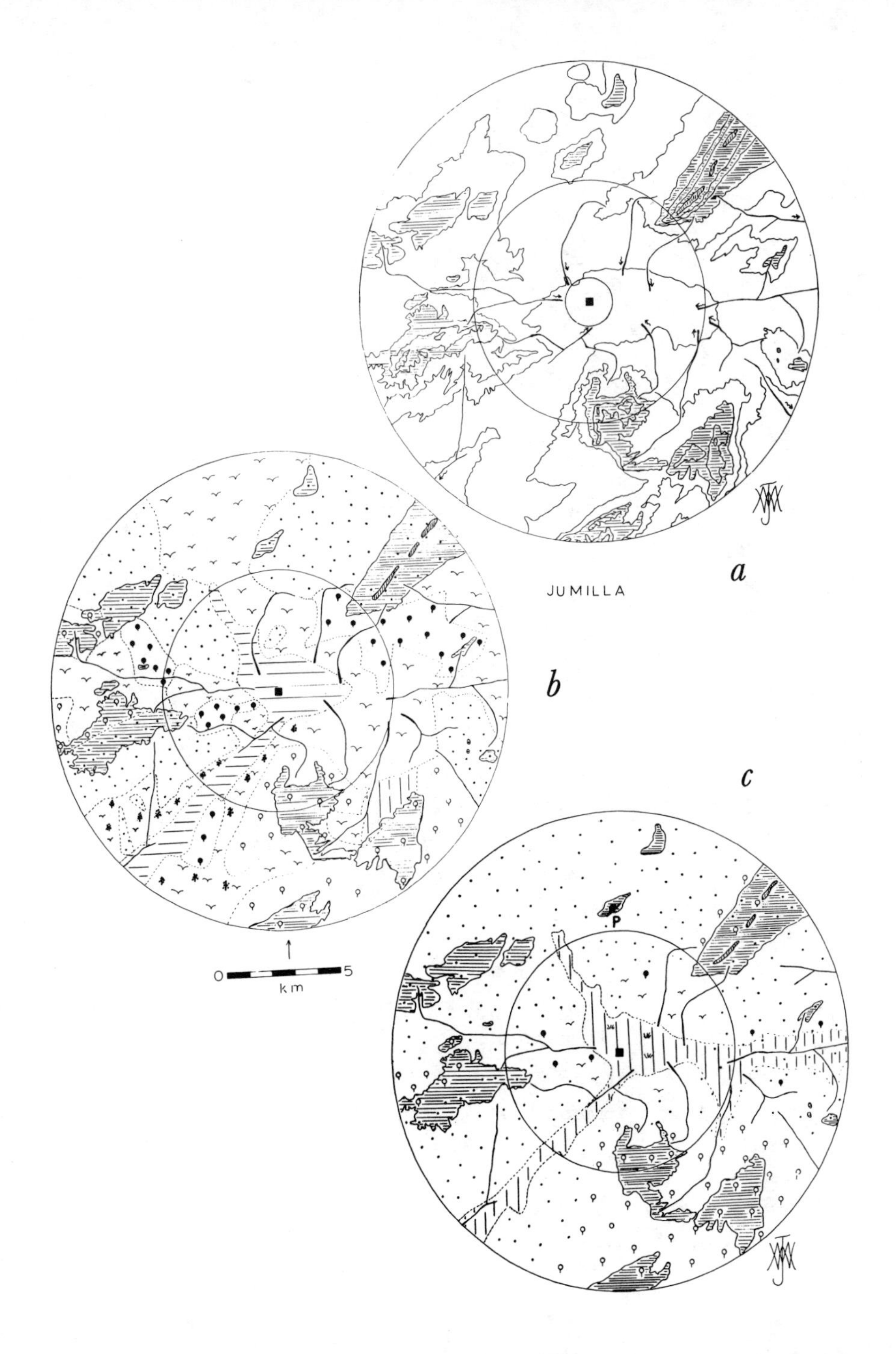

FIG. 4. This map is centered on Jumilla and its endorrheic basin. The south edge of this map almost touches the north tip of map in figure 3. P = Cueva del Peliciego.

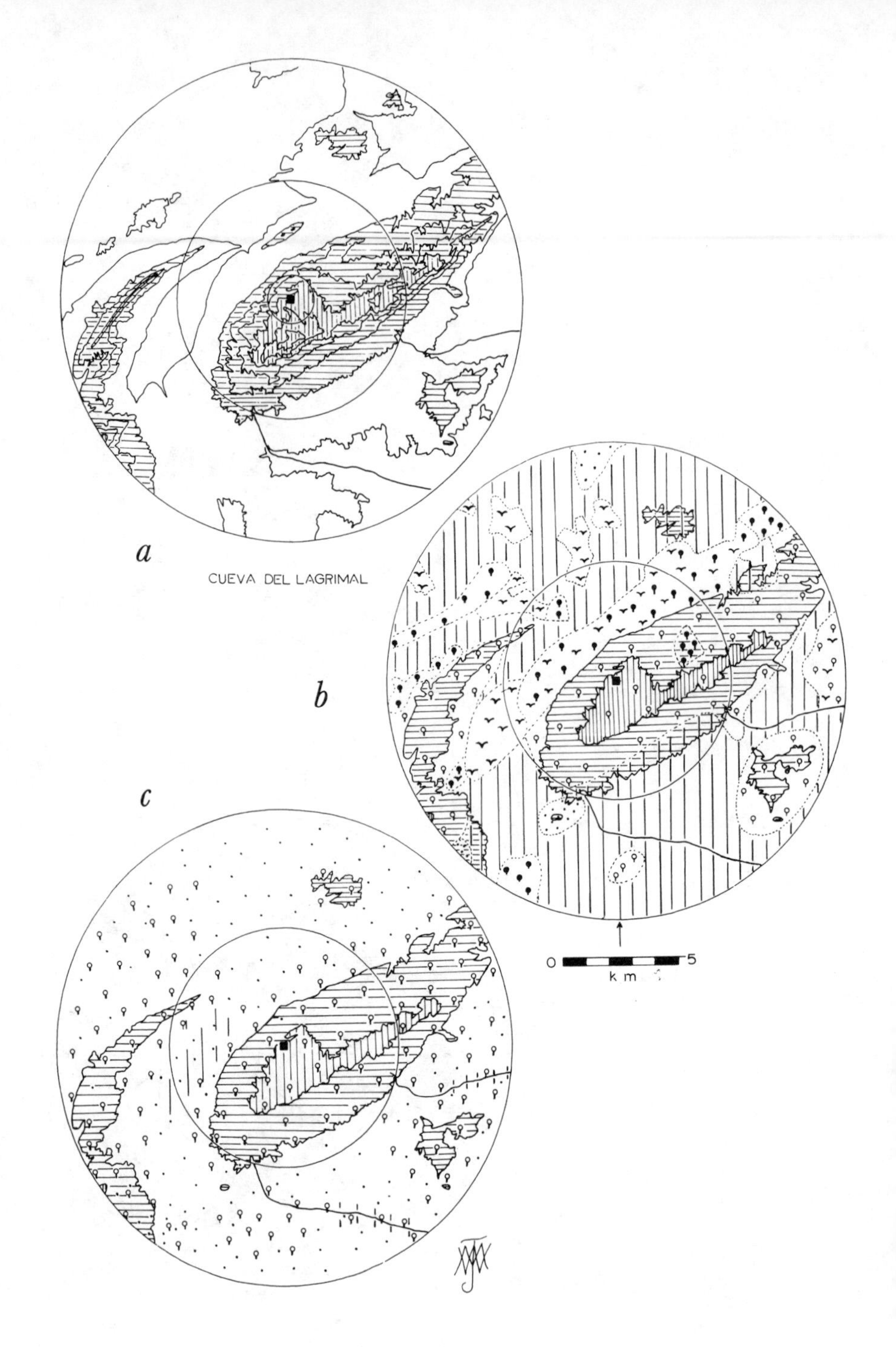

FIG. 5. Cueva del Lagrimal. Note endorrheic basin to west. This map is just northeast of map in figure 4.

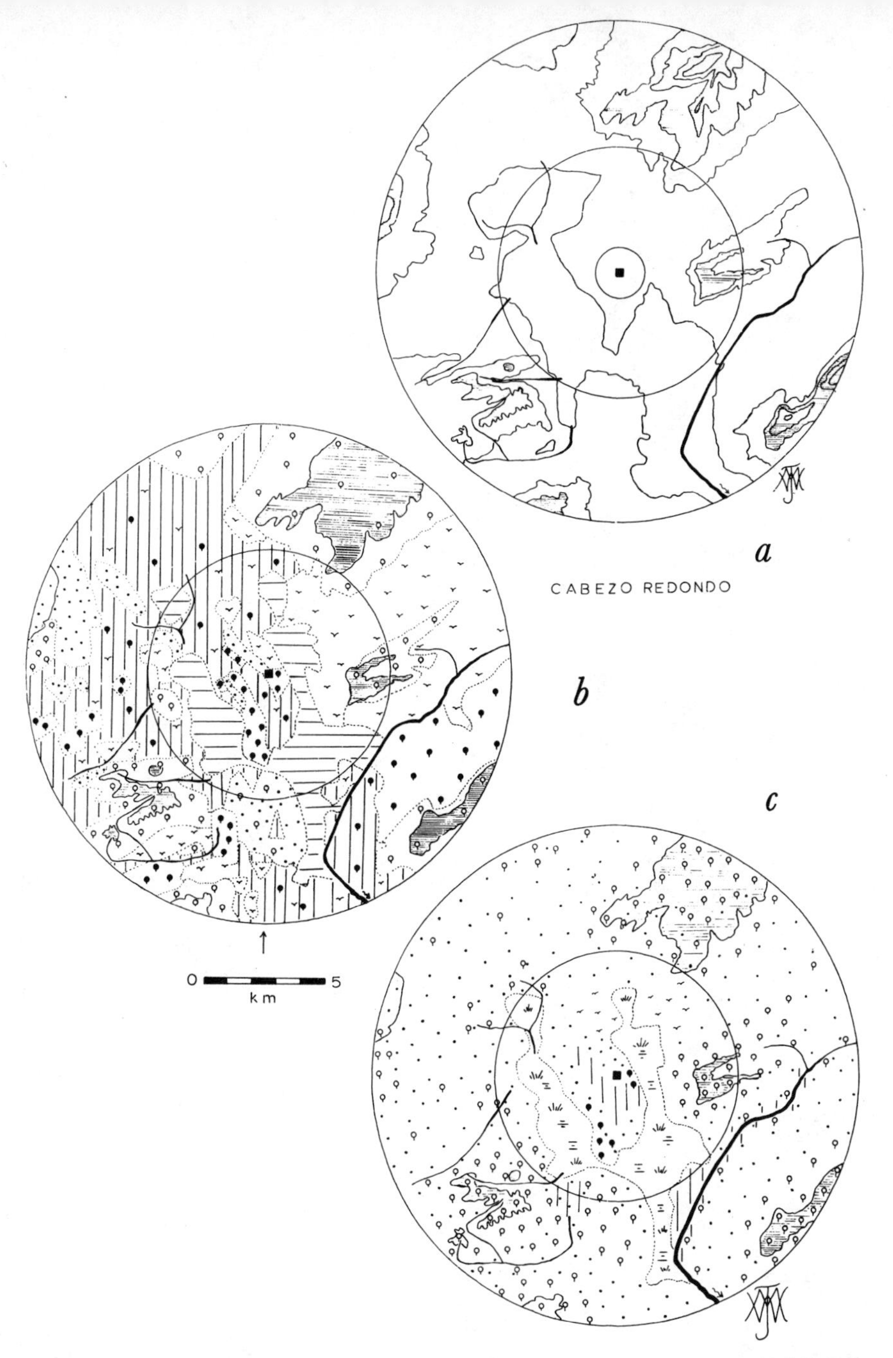

FIG. 6. Cabezo Redondo. This map is centered on the Bronze Age site of Cabezo Redondo in the Villena endorrheic basin. Many finds of flint arrowpoints and *Cardium*-impressed pottery come from the sands exposed near the site. The map is continuous with map in figure 5 at the northeast sector of the latter and southwest sector of map in figure 6.

Vision and Orientation in Aquatic Animals

Principal Investigator: Talbot H. Waterman, Yale University, New Haven, Connecticut.

Grant Nos. 868, 982, 1196, 1307, 1653. For continuation of research on sensory information processing and visual behavior in aquatic animals.

The research summarized here is part of an ongoing program to demonstrate the correlation between visual physiology and oriented behavior in aquatic animals. We have been particularly interested in studying the mechanisms of polarization sensitivity (PS) and discovering the ways in which this sensory capacity may be useful in the orientation and migration of the various animals possessing it.

Strong basic support for much of the laboratory research at Yale has been provided by continuing grants from the National Eye Institute of the National Institutes of Health. Field work and long-term collaboration with biologists mainly in Japan have been made possible by a series of National Geographic Society grants whose results are briefly reviewed here. Detailed reports and reviews of the work so far published are cited in the references.

Although the over-all program is conceived as unified and coherent, it does in fact comprise a rather wide range of subprojects requiring a variety of techniques and levels of analysis. These range from microspectrophotometry and electron microscopy to field experiments on behavior.

The components of the work supported by the National Geographic Society fall mainly into two categories determined in part by the experimental animals used, by the specific kinds of experiments required, and by the location of appropriate collaborators. One category involves the study of visually oriented behavior of fishes both in the field and in the laboratory (grants 868, 1196, 1307, and 1653). The 1969 volume of Research Reports contains a summary of the work accomplished under an earlier grant (788) in this area (Waterman, 1978). The second category relates to the molecular, fine structural and celluar bases of visual-information processing in rhabdom-bearing eyes particularly in crustaceans (grants 982, 1307, 1653). The results of an earlier grant in this category (709) have already been recorded in the 1968 Research Reports (Waterman, 1976).

Field Work on Fishes

With regard to fish orientation in polarized light we have continued underwater and other field experiments begun in 1969 both in 1970 and in 1974. Again the site was Palau in the Western Caroline Islands and the experimental animals almost exclusively the halfbeak fish *Zenarchopterus*. For this work some research associates and assistants had to be selected for their established experience in SCUBA as well as their other necessary skills. In 1970, in addition to myself, Dr. Richard Forward, Dr. Kenneth Horch, Mrs. Mabelita Campbell, and William Corell comprised the team in Micronesia. In 1974 Werner Eheim and George Boehlert worked with me.

The results of these two additional Palau expeditions were at the same time gratifying yet somewhat disappointing. They were exciting in fact because they reinforced the preliminary evidence obtained in 1969 (Waterman and Forward, 1970) that *Zenarchopterus* indeed can show PS and will spontaneously orient its longitudinal axis accordingly (Forward, Horch, and Waterman, 1972; Waterman and Forward, 1972). However, by the end of the extensive 1974 experiments it was disappointing that a protocol for reliably evoking strong PS behavior had not so far been discovered. Weak but significant PS orientation could be frequently evoked and occasionally strong responses to *e*-vector were obtained experimentally. Yet the kind of consistent sharply distinct behavioral pattern needed to analyze both the sensory mechanisms involved as well as their adaptive significance in the everyday life of these animals had not been found. A full review of the 1974 data has not yet been completed, so that a more optimistic final conclusion may well emerge. Meanwhile the findings to date may be summarized below. For details and more extensive discussion see three resulting research papers (Forward, Horch, and Waterman, 1972; Waterman and Forward, 1972; Forward and Waterman, 1973), and several relevant reviews (Waterman, 1972, 1974, 1975a).

EXPERIMENTS IN 1970

1. *Underwater.* Most of the effort during this expedition (10 weeks) was devoted to underwater experiments testing *Zenarchopterus*'s oriented responses to linearly polarized light. Such work is relatively difficult to execute, as four SCUBA divers (2 teams of 2) were needed to run through the protocol carried out with a series of untrained fishes. However, as a result of using a new greatly improved underwater camera case and control system much more could be accomplished than in the initial experiments of this sort in 1969.

The main coherent set of experiments comprised photographic measurement of the azimuth orientation of 36 juvenile *Zenarchopterus* swimming spontaneously in a covered underwater experimental vessel. These results were obtained in a series of six successive mornings. Orientation to the underwater irradiance from the sun and sky was different in these experiments with or without clouds over the sun as well as in the presence or absence of a linear Polaroid filter placed over the experimental vessel.

The total data (n = 2135) without polarizer demonstrate that significant preference for the axis 60°–240° relative to the sun's bearing was shown and that orientation in this axis was also unsymmetrical relative to the sun since of the 12 30° sectors analyzed those centered at 210°, 240°, 270° to the solar bearing were preferred to a significant extent (fig. 1A). Hence the fishes oriented as if they were using a sun compass of some sort. The direction involved was close to that of the channel where the experimental animals had been caught, but the necessary control experiments were not done to prove an unequivocal causal relation.

With linearly polarized light imposed on the underwater experimental vessel significant axial orientation was again found (n = 2135), this time

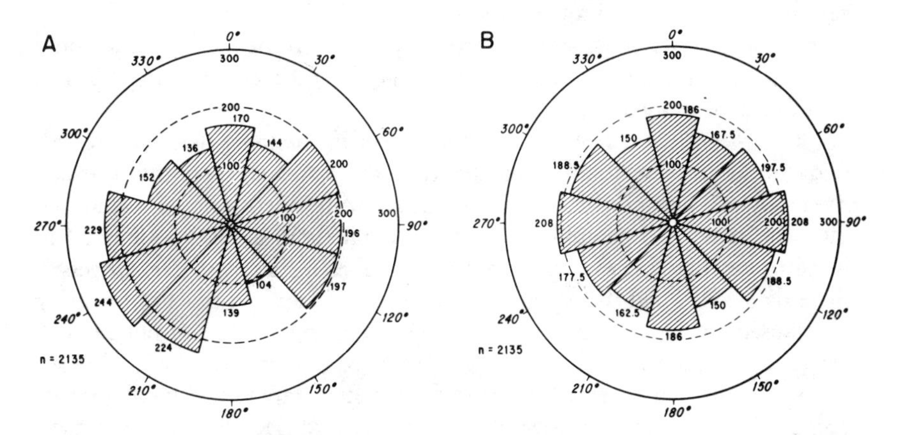

FIG. 1. Spontaneous azimuth orientation underwater of the halfbeak fish *Zenarchopterus* to sun and sky (A) without and (B) with a Polaroid filter covering the experimental vessel. Observations are recorded for 12 30° sectors around the circle although *e*-vector symmetry in 180° imposes itself on plot (B). In (A) 0° is the sun's bearing; significant orientation preference was shown for the 210°. 240°, and 270° sectors. In (B) 0° is the *e*-vector direction; here the 0° (+180°) and 90° (+270°) sectors were significantly preferred by the fish. n = total number of observations on 36 fish included in each distribution. (From Waterman and Forward, 1972.)

systematically related to *e*-vector orientation. Thus the four 30° sectors at 0° and 90° to the *e*-vector direction were significantly preferred, as were consequently the axes perpendicular and parallel to the polarization plane (fig. 1B).

More detailed analysis of this substantial batch of data showed that two factors were intermittently prominent in decreasing the polarotactic response of the fishes. One was the occasional presence of a cloud over the sun (even though this would scarcely alter the *e*-vector pattern established by the Polaroid over the experimental vessel). The other was the result of or at least correlated with too rapid a spontaneous turning rate in the swimming behavior of certain fish.

When analysis was limited to the runs in which these disturbing elements were absent or below criterion level, stronger polarotaxis is found (fig. 2A). Here the mean orientation of 15 fishes ($n = 646$) was predominatly normal to the *e*-vector and much stronger than in the total data. Further selection of data suggested that at times *Zenarchopterus* may systematically show oblique rather than perpendicular and parallel orientation to an imposed *e*-vector.

However, the reality of this four-peaked response to linear polarization well documented in arthropods and cephalopods (Waterman, 1973) has not yet been further demonstrated in vertebrates. If it can be confirmed it would indicate a striking parallelism despite the quite different visual systems of the animals concerned.

2. *Other field experiments.* Since *Zenarchopterus* normally spends much of its time swimming just beneath the water surface (the air-water interface), we performed some experiments with this species on land but using the same photographic and experimental setup as under-water. Here the fish swam just beneath the air-water interface in the experimental vessel. These data confirmed the earlier evidence for polarotaxis in this fish orienting to imposed linear polarization. It also provided one of the strongest such responses obtained in fishes (fig. 2B). These experiments were of additional interest because they yielded evidence for a time-compensated light compass reaction and possibly a negative phototaxis (Forward, Horch, and Waterman, 1972).

Experiments in 1974

Encouraged by the strong responses and interesting correlations obtained at the water surface (fig. 3) in 1970, the 1974 expedition (2 months) concentrated exclusively on this type of experiment, as well as on laboratory experiments when the Palau weather was unsuitable, which was often the case that year. Extensive series were run (on *Zenarchopterus* again) not only with and without imposed polarization but also with screens blocking out the direct sunlight and with mirrors transposing the bearing of the sun apparent to the fishes.

As mentioned, exact replication of the 1970 experiments of figure 2B was attempted from the very beginning. But comparable strong polarotaxis was only occasionally observed even though extensive variations made in experimental protocol as well as any other conceivably involved parameter were tested in the course of a long series of experiments. Sporadic but often weak polarotactic responses were in fact obtained, but the right combination of conditions to evoke readily analyzable high level responses was not achieved.

As a result, the final analysis of these data searching for the important variables has been protracted and is still not finished. Consequently firm conclusions about this aspect of our program should not yet be considered

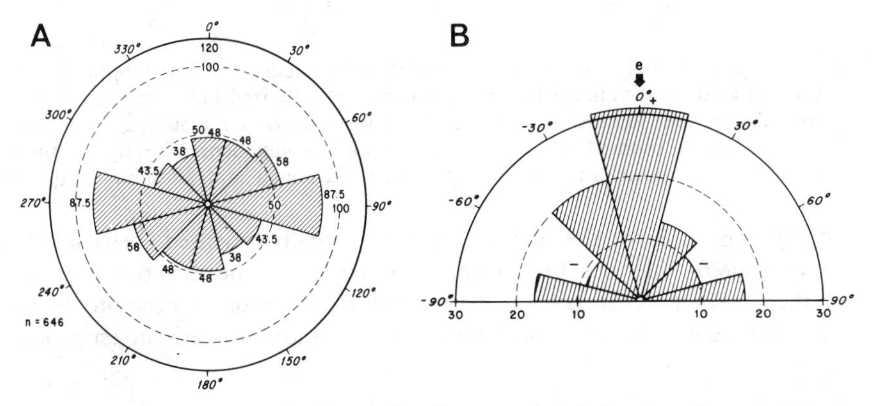

FIG. 2. Azimuth orientation of *Zenarchopterus* to sun and sky plus a linear polarizer covering the experimental vessel. The *e*-vector was parallel to the 0-180° axis. A, Selected underwater data from the totals plotted in figure 1B. Here 15 fishes were chosen from 36 in figure 1 because these were not spontaneously turning too rapidly and because they were recorded with the sun shining continuously without interference by temporary cloud cover. Note that the polarotaxis for the selected fish while still 90° to the *e*-vector was considerably stronger than for the total data (figure 1B) although both show statistically significant directional preferences. B, Similar spontaneous orientation data for six fishes orienting at the air-water interface of the experimental vessel and exposed to the sun, sky and imposed *e*-vector at 0°. Here 31 percent of the headings are within ±15° of the *e*-vector. n = 348. (From Waterman, 1975a.)

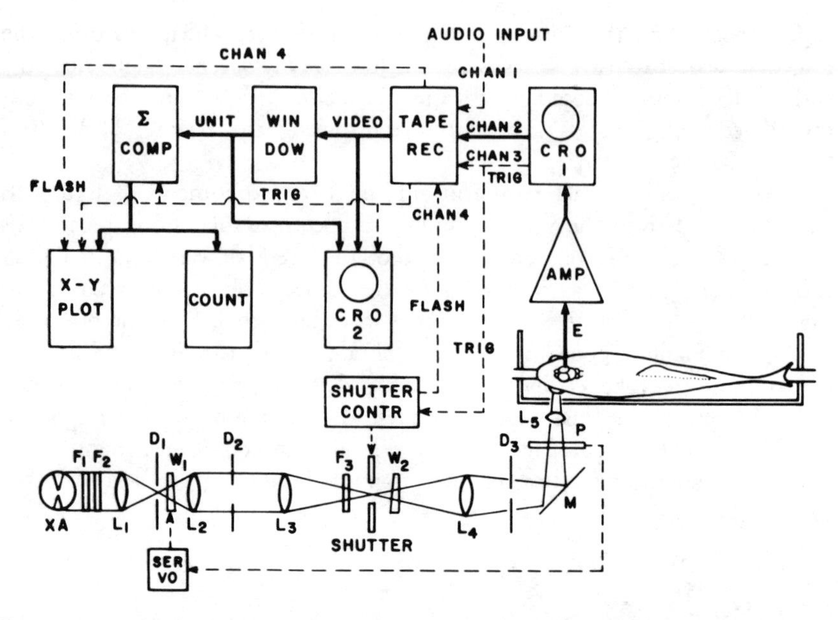

FIG. 3. Experimental setup used for studying spike responses of single optic tectum units in goldfish stimulated by 500-msec flashes of polarized light presented to the contralateral eye. Results were ultimately recorded by an x-y plotter and the constituent spikes counted for the various response components. Nearly all units showed strong polarization sensitivity. (From Waterman and Hashimoto, 1974.)

appropriate. Clearly the investigation of visually oriented behavior by *Zenarchopterus* has not been completed. However, the effective outcome of these 1974 experiments has to be determined before a decision should be made about the most profitable way of continuing this investigation.

Laboratory Work on Fishes

Meanwhile a number of laboratory studies of PS in fishes have been undertaken. Some have been completed at least pro tem; others are still active and being currently pursued.

EXPERIMENTS ON *Dermogenys*

After the 1969 and 1970 field experiments in Palau similar laboratory experiments were undertaken at Yale with a commercially available freshwater relative of *Zenarchopterus*. Although we again were unable to find the right conditions to evoke a strong polarotaxis in *Dermogenys*, we could prove polarotactic orientation was present predominantly parallel to the *e*-vector in a vertical beam of linearly polarized light (Forward and Waterman, 1973).

Of itself, just adding another fish to the list with PS was not so important, but under laboratory conditions we were able to make a worthwhile advance. Thus it was found that the observed polarotaxis involved the perception of polarized light per se and was not just a phototaxis induced by some concomitant intensity pattern. Actually this is the only case (before or since) where this crucial control has been carried out successfully. To do so we compared the oriented responses of *Dermogenys* to black and white sectors in the wall of the experimental vessel. These were found to be incompatible with the hypothesis that differential scattering of polarized light might be providing the clue for the apparent PS (Jander and Waterman, 1960; Waterman, 1960). Hence we could conclude that the orientation of *Dermogenys* to the *e*-vector was not a phototaxis induced by dark and light patterns but must involve a distinct submodality of the fish's visual capacity.

Although the *Dermogenys* experiments were productive in the sense reported above, they still did not disclose a fish species or a protocol that would provide a reliable PS strong enough to be readily useful in analyzing mechanisms and their consequences. We have continued our search for such a preparation and are still optimistic about finding one. Our major assays in this field since *Dermogenys* have been as follows:

Experiments on Goldfish

1. *Collaboration with Professor Kleerekoper.* In 1973 a promising possibility was offered by the fish orientation research under way in Prof. Herman Kleerekoper's laboratory at Texas A & M University. Stimulated by our work that group had quantitatively analyzed swimming patterns of goldfish in a vertical beam of linearly polarized light (Kleerekoper, Matis, Timms, and Gensler, 1973). *Carassius* was shown to orient primarily parallel to the *e*-vector when swimming about a 2-meter circular tank with 16 freely accessible peripheral compartments. Changing the plane of polarization also induced alterations in the fishes' behavior patterns from the unpolarized control.

National Geographic Society grant 1196 allowed me to initiate some joint research on this system, and a subsequent National Science Foundation grant to Professor Kleerekoper with myself as co-principal investigator on that grant subsequently permitted a year's program to be carried out. Many interesting experiments suggested themselves for tests with this highly automated large-scale behavior-measuring system. Unfortunately, however, difficulties began to appear from the beginning. As discussed above, it seemed important and probably routine to establish, as had been done for *Dermogenys*, that the goldfish behavior recorded was not just a response to light intensity patterns produced by differential scattering of PL in the water. Measurements showed this was substantial in the original setup.

It turned out that changing the side walls of the tank from black to an off-white, which would reduce the likelihood of such an intensity pattern being seen, induced quite different swimming behavior in the fish. Similarly, using adjustable light sources in each of the various compartments to equalize the horizontal irradiance in polarized light also gave rise to quite different swimming patterns. Later it also became clear that individual goldfish differed quite sharply in their polarotactic responses; whether this was because of their origins or season or individual variability was not clearly determined.

The outcome of about two years of work on this project was that significant differences in behavior pattern could be readily recorded in polarized and unpolarized light (Dorn, 1976). Yet it was difficult to repeat on order the strong positive results obtained earlier (Kleerekoper et al., 1973). In this regard our behavioral experience with goldfish has been rather similar to that with halfbeaks.

2. *Experiments by James Brandt.* Aided by a summer National Science Foundation Undergraduate Research Fellowship attempts were made to train goldfish to respond to polarized light stimuli and also to utilize unconditioned responses in their electrocardiogram as evidence of PS. Probably because of the brief research period involved as well as the skill and experience required to apply such tests effectively no conclusive results were obtained. However, more successful cichlid conditioning experiments were carried out later as described below.

3. *Electrophysiological experiments.* As soon as the first Palau polarotactic responses in *Zenarchopterus* were obtained an experimental program was initiated at Yale to determine the mechanism of fish PS. This was carried out primarily with National Institutes of Health funds and in collaboration with Dr. H. Hashimoto and Dr. K. Aoki from 1970 to 1974 (Waterman and Hashimoto, 1974; Waterman and Aoki, 1974). However, note that (1) our research interest in fish PS was due to the National Geographic Society supported work in Palau and (2) our ongoing collaboration with various Japanese biologists has also been stimulated and supported by major financial help from the Society.

Of course, we already knew that the vertebrate eye generally lacked the direct dichroic polarization analyzer present in rhabdom-bearing eyes of arthropods and cephalopods. So it remained to find out how fishes could nevertheless behave as if they could perceive *e*-vector orientation. Starting first with intracellular recordings of isolated fish photoreceptor we attempted to localize the required ocular analyzer. None was found, however, by this relatively direct approach. This was of course frustrating because it meant that we had a behavioral response without an identifiable sensory mechanism!

To analyze this further a long series of experiments on the goldfish optic tectum was initiated. In response to 550-msec flashes of PL, spikes were recorded extracellularly from the contralateral tectum in the goldfish (fig. 3). Surprisingly, in the light of our failure to record retinal PS, all (or nearly all) the tectal units recorded were sensitive to *e*-vector direction.

Control tests with a depolarizer very close to the cornea proved that these responses were due to intraocular discrimination of *e*-vector orientation and not to some differential extraocular mechanism that modulated the intensity of the light entering the eye. It became clear that unlike the crustacean systems we had found to have two orthogonal PS channels (Waterman and Horch, 1966; Waterman, Fernández, and Goldsmith, 1969; Waterman and Fernández, 1970) whatever mechanism was functioning in the goldfish PS has various elements with maximum sensitivities distributed evenly around 180°.

The level of PS in tectal cells is about 6:8 (ratio of max/min sensitivity) with occasional records yielding much higher ratios. Testing with equal quantum flashes of narrow spectral band width in red, green, and blue light showed no evidence of λ selectivity in the fish PS. This is quite unlike the insects where only λ's below 500 nm are effective, and according to some recent analyses significant PS occurs only in the near UV in the honeybee (Menzel and Snyder, 1974).

Similarly, no consistent effect of intensity on the PS of goldfish tectal units could be demonstrated over a 4–5 log unit range; nor did light or dark adaptation have much effect on PS. The latter finding is inconsistent with Snyder's (1973) hypothesis to account for the disorienting effect of cloud cover over the sun in our Palau field experiments (Waterman and Forward, 1972).

Study of the relation between the distribution of tectal cells' PS indicated that the anatomical location of the corresponding receptor units in the retina was not responsible for the orientation and degree of the PS. Instead these were proved to be dependent on the photoreceptors' location in the stimulating beam (fig. 4).

On the basis of these variable properties of the system it was concluded that when illuminated with a uniform field of linearly polarized light the fish would perceive a large (up to 50°–60° angular subtent) entoptic image with two light sectors oriented perpendicular to the *e*-vector. This image thus shares some but clearly not all of the properties of Haidinger's brushes and of Boehm's brushes in man (Waterman, 1975a). The most likely hypothesis to explain this in the fish eye is differential scattering of light within the retina itself. But some features of the response particularly its wide angular extent seem hard to explain with such a model. In any case, direct proof of this hypothesis remains to be achieved.

EXPERIMENTS ON OTHER FISHES

1. In collaboration with me and Dr. Ken McKaye, Michael Davitz, a Yale undergraduate, carried out some successful training experiments to *e*-vector in juveniles of a species of African cichlid. Here a small school of fishes in an aquarium was conditioned to be fed on presentation of a linearly polarized light stimulus consisting of an illuminated square with a horizontal *e*-vector located behind the feeding area. After the training period these fishes were tested for 20 days (20 trials each) in the circumstance that two polarized light squares were presented at the same time in diagonal corners of the experimental tank. In a randomized sequence one or the other was horizontally polarized (the trained orientation) while the other square was vertically polarized. Feeding reinforcement was given only when the horizontally polarized signal was chosen.

For the first several days choices were random, but from days 6–20 a clear trend toward correct choices occurred and was maintained. The performance plateaued at a rather low but statistically significant level. As far as it goes this is an interesting positive result. It is again disappointing, however, in that the performance level associated with the PS was not strong. Also the possibility of differential scattering in the light beam being the functional clue was not directly ruled out although precautions were taken in the design of the experimental setup to minimize the likelihood of such an artifact.

2. In collaboration with Dr. Robert S. Wilson, supported by a National Institutes of Health Postdoctoral Fellowship, we are beginning to use a closed-circuit TV setup to record oriented behavior and use a video-digital converter to process the resulting record through appropriate computer programs. This work is only partly directed toward fish orientation, but we have already

continued some explorations for suitable species and experimental conditions. It is hoped that this procedure, which potentially can handle large amounts of data, will provide us with the sort of quantitative system for which we have been searching for a long time.

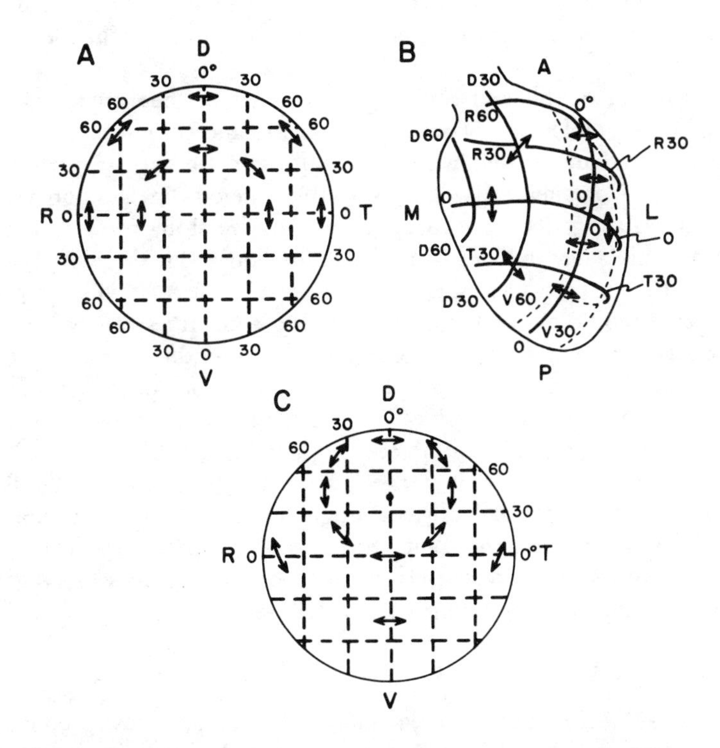

FIG. 4. Polarization sensitivity in the goldfish. A, Preferential retinal responses to axial stimulation of the eye inferred from the projections onto the optic tectum recorded as shown in B. The double-headed arrows in the latter represent the directions of maximum *e*-vector response actually observed. Those in A show the apparent directions of maximal response by the retinal receptors giving rise to the tectal spikes recorded. Note these are all perpendicular to the stimulus *e*-vector. C, Result of changing the PL stimulus from axial to oblique centered at 45° above the coordinate origin in the retina. This shows that the PS is not due to receptor cell location in the retina *per se* but to its location relative to the stimulating light beam. (From Waterman and Aoki, 1974.)

Work with Crustaceans

Our research on PS in crustaceans and its molecular, fine structural and cellular basis (as well as its behavioral implications) has an even longer history than that with fishes. Stimulated by the results (already recorded in the 1968 Report) obtained in Professor Tomita's laboratory at Keio Medical School in Tokyo (Waterman and Fernández, 1970) we have continued to work on the problem of information channeling in the decapod visual system.

As a result of this and earlier work we have become interested in the more general problem of photoreceptor membrane turnover. The stability of this key structure, as well as the effects of light and dark adaptation on it and associated organelles, is of considerable interest. In addition we have been accumulating EM material for a comparative study of compound eye structure. This serves as a reservoir of information about the most favorable species to use for particular aspects of the over-all project. It will also become particularly significant if such differences and similarities can be correlated with special environments like epipelagic, bathybenthic, etc., where light conditions may induce quite special adaptations. Work recently initiated at the Woods Hole Oceanographic Institution and the Bermuda Biological Station is partly directed to this objective (grant 1653, 1976).

Finally we anticipate that in the long term our comparative study may shed new light on the polyphyletic origin of arthropods (Manton, 1973) and the degree to which the compound eyes of various groups involved can be ascribed to evolutionary convergence as some have proposed. Progress in these various areas may be summarized as follows:

INFORMATION CHANNELING

1. In 1971 the research in Japan (grant 982) was most productive in demonstrating the retinal basis for *e*-vector and λ discrimination (Eguchi, Waterman, and Akiyama, 1973). We had learned in 1968 that both the blue sensitive and yellow sensitive units in the crayfish retina showed strong PS in intracellular recordings (Waterman and Fernández, 1970). But those electrophysiological results did not identify the cellular pattern of these two photoreceptor submodalities.

To accomplish this Professor Eguchi and I carried out selective light-adaptation experiments to induce differential fine structural changes in the retinular cells of the *Procambarus* retina. Extensive quantitative study of EM's showed that on the average two of the regular retinular cells in each ommatidium were violet receptors and the other five were yellow receptors. Again on an average the two violet cells could be identified as R_3 and R_4, whereas the yellow cells were usually R_1, R_2, R_5, R_6, and R_7. We had previously shown (Eguchi and Waterman, 1968) that R_1, R_4, and R_5 were maximally sensitive to a horizontal *e*-vector whereas R_2, R_3, R_6, and R_7 responded most strongly to vertical polarization. Hence there appears to be a complete overlap of the polarization and color channels.

2. Relevant to this information channeling problem is the presence in mysid, decapod, and stomatopod crustacean eyes of a curious 4-lobed R_8. This has its rhabdomere distal to the regular rhabdom (Waterman, 1977) and its axon terminating in the medulla externa instead of in the lamina ganglionaris where all the other retinular cells (R_1-R_7) terminate (Nässel, 1976, a,b). Eguchi and I had observed the cross retinular cell R_8 some time ago but refrained from publishing on it as Kunze independently discovered it in *Ocypode* and published several reports (Kunze, 1967; Kunze and Boschek, 1968).

However, in EM's of the retinula of the rock crab *Grapsus* we discovered a novel feature of its R_8 rhabdomere namely that it comprised two sets of orthogonal microvilli in alternating layers (Eguchi and Waterman, 1973). Presumably this would cancel out any PS due to dichroism of the regularly arranged microvilli. These are usually strictly parallel to one another for a given cell and perpendicular to the optic axis in decapod eyes (Eguchi and Waterman, 1966).

Furthermore, this curious rhabdomere of R_8 occupies 20 percent of the total rhabdomere length, and so the function of this kind of receptor cells is a newly emerging question of some importance. This seems particularly pertinent relative to PS because recent evidence (Menzel and Snyder, 1974; Menzel and Blakers, 1975; Wehner, Bernard, and Geiger, 1975) indicates that R_8 in the honeybee (previously largely ignored) plays a key role in PS in this insect, which was the first animal found to make use of natural polarized light (von Frisch, 1948).

While the rhabdomere of R_8 in the spiny lobster *Panulirus* like *Grapsus* has two sets of orthogonal microvilli (Meyer-Rochow, 1975), the crayfish R_8 (Krebs, 1972) has only horizontal ones (therefore parallel to R_1, R_4, and R_5) as found by Nässel (1976a) and Eguchi and Waterman (unpublished). For such reasons the function of R_8 is now an important item on our agenda and will be approached from the point of view of comparative fine structure and electrophysiology. Currently the former is under study in collaboration with D. R. Nässel (Lund), and the latter will start soon with Prof. T. Yamaguchi

(Okayama), both of whom are research associates on my National Institutes of Health grant.

Further progress is being made on the information channeling problem by studying the connectivity of the receptor cells in the crayfish lamina ganglionaris (Nässel, 1976a; Nässel and Waterman, 1977). Three different

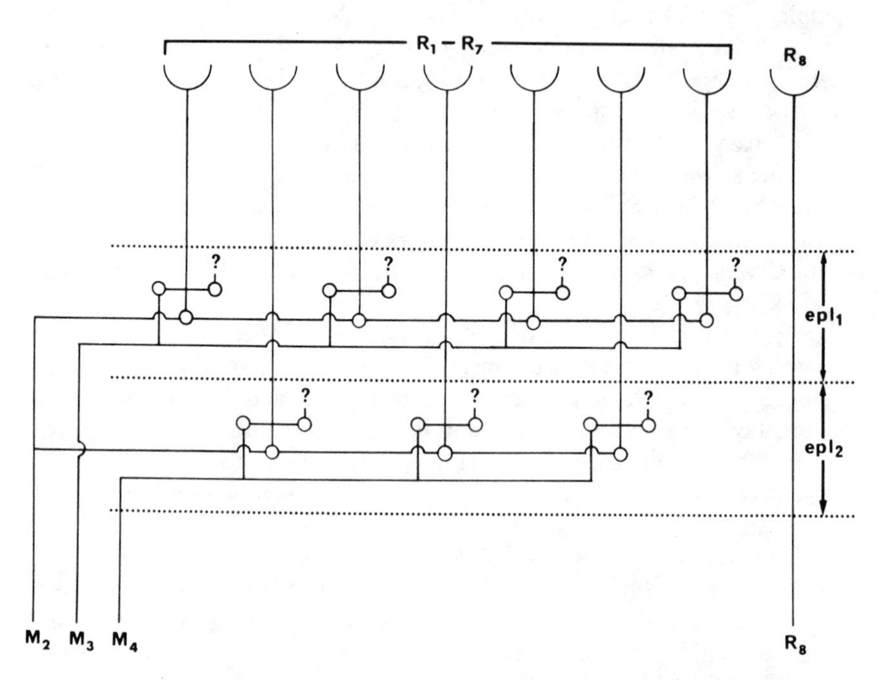

FIG. 5. Visual input channeling in the crayfish eye schematically summarizing current knowledge. R_1 - R_7 represent the seven regular retinular cells which form triadic synaptic connections in the outer and inner plexiform layers (epl_1 and epl_2) of the first optic ganglion the lamina ganglionaris. Input from all seven of these receptor units is received by one of three types of primary interneurons shown (monopolar neuron type M_2). This could be the same as neuron I previously hypothesized (Waterman, 1966, 1975b). Two types of monopolars (M_3 and M_4) synapse, respectively with four and three regular retinular cells as shown; these may turn out to be polarized light discriminating channels previously hypothesized (Waterman, 1975b, PH and PV). Note that the third profile of the postsynaptic triads (labeled with question marks) has not yet been identified although the mechanism of wavelength discrimination has yet to be assigned. The 4-lobed distal R_8 whose function also remains speculative does not synapse in the lamina ganglionaris but terminates instead in the next more proximal optic ganglion, the medulla externa. (From Nässel and Waterman, 1977).

types of first-order interneurons have been identified, and these may be similar to some hypothesized earlier (Waterman, 1966). Each photoreceptor synaptic terminal contacts a triad of postsynaptic elements (fig. 5). The three types of interneuron mentioned above comprise two of these, but the third remains to be identified. Probably it should be related to color discrimination but direct evidence for this is lacking. Clearly the still unknown input contribution of R_8 and its terminal connections may also be important in this regard.

PHOTORECEPTOR MEMBRANE

Our earlier efforts to trace the information channels in the retinula demonstrated a wide range of fine structural changes induced in the photoreceptor cells by light and darkness (Eguchi and Waterman, 1967, 1968). While we continued to use this information as originally intended (Eguchi, Waterman, and Akiyama, 1973) it became clear to us that these phenomena were also of considerable interest in relation to turnover and stability of the photoreceptor membrane. Consequently Professor Eguchi and I have been pursuing this aspect of the work, also.

1. *Research in Japan 1974* (grant 1307). Major progress was made in studying the photoreceptor membrane by initiating our use of freeze-fracture techniques on the crayfish rhabdom. This procedure cleaves apart the two lamellae of plasma membranes and often reveals details quite invisible in conventional transmission EM. It proved particularly fruitful for us because it demonstrated a clear structural difference between the ordinary plasma membrane of retinular cells and that of their microvilli (Eguchi and Waterman, 1976).

The latter actually are seen to have a dense array of ca.90A particles on the hydrophobic face of the protoplasmic leaflet (PL). These particles, which apparently can be identified with the visual pigment molecules, are rare or absent in plasma membrane away from the photoreceptive organelle. However, they are abundant and have a characteristic location in the membranes of pinocytotic vesicles, coated vesicles, multivesicular bodies, and other elements believed to be related to photoreceptor membrane turnover.

These 1974 results supported an earlier hypothesis that light strongly accelerated photoreceptor membrane turnover in the rhabdom and that this was reflected in the substantial changes in fine structure induced by light and dark adaptation. Direct demonstration of membrane transport by molecular labeling of intercellular spaces in the rhabdom and pinocytotic vesicles has been repeatedly attempted, but no positive results have been obtained as yet (collaboration with Dr. Eguchi and with Stanley Poole, research associate at Yale on the National Institutes of Health grant).

2. *Research in New Haven, 1976.* In addition to continuing to study the turnover problem Professor Eguchi and I in 1976 extended the work into the area of receptor membrane stability, in particular to determine the effects of long-term dark adaptation. Since Eguchi had shown in his thesis at Kyushu University (1964) that severe disturbance of rhabdom organization resulted in many arthropods from extended periods in darkness, this had become a controversial field. Some people attributed the finding to some sort of supposed fixation artifact and others failed to confirm it. Now we can not only confirm and extend it but also suggest why some researchers failed to find it (Eguchi and Waterman, 1977, in preparation).

For these experiments different groups of crayfishes were kept in constant darkness for periods of 2, 4, 8, 12, and 16 weeks. Both transmission EM and freeze-fracture EM preparations were studied and quantitative measurements were made of four parameters: *a*, fraction of the rhabdom having the normal regular microvillus pattern; *b*, number of lysosomes in adjacent retinular cytoplasm; *c*, spatial density of photoreceptor membrane particles (presumably representing rhodopsin molecules); *d*, diameter of these particles.

Only the last of these four was apparently unaffected by prolonged darkness. There was no significant difference in the PF particles' diameter from normal to those light-dark exposed crayfish kept 4 months in the dark. However, the number of such particles per unit membrane surface area fell from a normal count of about $5000/\mu^2$ to about half that after one month in the dark and somewhat fewer still after 4 months in the dark.

The perirhabdomal lysosome count in contrast dropped precipitously during the first 2 weeks of darkness but showed a partial (20 percent) but significant recovery after remaining 2 months or more in the dark. The disruption of the regular pattern of microvilli in the rhabdom followed a different curve.

Thus some degree of disturbance of the regular pattern had begun during the first 2 weeks, but a major part of the deterioration occurred in the second half of the first month. Thereafter continuing but smaller-scale disruption continued through the fourth month period in darkness. A notable point about the dark-induced microvillus disruption was its specific distribution in different regions of the retinula. Five were recognized.

Thus quite different sensitivities to darkness are shown by R_8, the distal neck region (DN), and the distal (D), middle (M), and proximal (P) thirds of the regular rhabdom region. Least affected by protracted darkness were R_8 and P, where the ratio of disruption in dark vs. normal eyes were 2.4 and

3.6, respectively. Most affected was D with a ratio of 14.7 and M at 5.5. Actually DN had the highest degree of irregular mvl arrangement in the dark, but as this region was also less regular than the others even in normal eyes its ratio was only 4.2 for dark over normal and hence lower than both D and M.

While it remains to be discovered why there is such a range of sensitivities to darkness in different retinular regions, it is clear that if sample sections happened to be taken only through P or R_8 considerably more careful measurements would be needed to detect significant differences than if they were in DN, D, or M. This could be a source of discrepancies in the literature.

COMPARATIVE DATA

In the more than 10 years we have been collaborating Professor Eguchi and I have been gradually assembling knowledge about the fine structure of many different kinds of crustacean eyes with several objectives in view. Occasionally, as in the case of *Grapsus* reported above, some striking new relationship will become obvious because of special qualities of that particular organism (the Krogh Principle).

Also it is likely that as such material is organized new generalizations and relationships will become obvious where they were obscure or doubtful before. See, for example, tabular data for various species already known 10 years ago (Eguchi and Waterman, 1966) and those now known in regard to the nature of R_8 (Waterman, 1977). Recently, aided by grant 1653, we have been obtaining for study eyes of species of particular evolutionary interest (e.g., *Nebalia*) or those from habitats with special light regimes (pelagic amphipods, the deep-water crab *Geryon,* deep-water mysids). These specimens were obtained alive in Bermuda or at Woods Hole through the collaboration of staff members of the Woods Hole Oceanographic Institution. A number of interesting findings promise important leads for our future program.

Conclusion

While nearly all phases of this research program still pose challenging unanswered questions, one can nevertheless conclude that a substantial amount of worthwhile progress has been achieved with the support granted by the National Geographic Society. It is to be hoped that we and others will continue to explore the relevance of this research area of biology to various fundamental aspects of vision and its relation to the oriented behavior of aquatic animals.

REFERENCES

DORN, P.

1976. Several aspects of the orientation of some fish to light: Response to polarized light in goldfish, and response of shark to light, chemical stimulus and their combination. Ph.D. dissertation, Texas A & M University.

EGUCHI, EISUKE

1964. The structure of rhabdom and action potentials in single retinula cells in crayfish. Ph.D. dissertation, Kyushu University.

EGUCHI, EISUKE, and WATERMAN, TALBOT H.

1966. Fine structure patterns in crustacean rhabdoms. Pp. 105–124 *in* "The Functional Organization of the Compound Eye," C. G. Bernhard, ed. Pergamon Press, Oxford.

1967. Changes in retinal fine structure induced in the crab *Libinia* by light and dark adaptation. Zeitschr. Zellforsch., vol. 79, pp. 209–229.

1968. Cellular basis for polarized light perception in the spider crab, *Libinia.* Zeitschr. Zellforsch., vol. 84, pp. 87–101.

1973. Orthogonal microvillus pattern in the eighth rhabdomere of the rock crab *Grapsus.* Zeitschr. Zellforsch., vol. 137, pp. 145–157.

1976. Freeze-etch and histochemical evidence for cycling in crayfish photoreceptor membranes. Cell Tiss. Res., vol. 169, pp. 419–434.

EGUCHI, EISUKE; WATERMAN, TALBOT H.; and AKIYAMA, JIRO

1973. Localization of the violet and yellow receptor cells in the crayfish retinula. Journ. Gen. Physiol., vol. 62, pp. 355–374.

FRISCH, KARL VON

1948. Gelöste und ungelöste Rätsel der Bienensprache. Naturwiss., vol. 35, pp. 38–43.

FORWARD, RICHARD B., JR.; HORCH, KENNETH W.; and WATERMAN, TALBOT H.

1972. Visual orientation at the water surface by the teleost *Zenarchopterus.* Biol. Bull., vol. 143, pp. 112–126.

FORWARD, RICHARD B., JR., and WATERMAN, TALBOT H.

1973. Evidence for *e*-vector and light intensity pattern discrimination by the teleost *Dermogenys.* Journ. Comp. Physiol., vol. 87, pp. 189–202.

JANDER, R., and WATERMAN, TALBOT H.

1960. Sensory discrimination between polarized light and intensity patterns by arthropods. Journ. Cell. Comp. Physiol., vol. 56, pp. 137–160.

KLEEREKOPER, HERMAN; MATIS, J. H.; TIMMS, A. M.; and GENSLER, P.

1973. Locomotor response of the goldfish to polarized light and the *e*-vector. Journ. Comp. Physiol., vol. 86, pp. 27–36.

KREBS, W.

1973. The fine structure of the retinula of the compound eye of *Astacus fluviatilis.* Zeitschr. Zellforsch., vol. 133, pp. 399–414.

KUNZE, P.

1967. Histologische Untersuchungen zum Bau des Auges von *Ocypode cursor.* Zeitschr. Zellforsch., vol. 82, pp. 466–478.

KUNZE, P., and BOSCHEK, C. B.

1968. Elektronenmikroskopische Untersuchungen zur Form der achten Retinulazelle bei *Ocypode.* Zeitschr. Naturforsch., vol. 23, pp. 568b–569b.

MANTON, S.
1973. Arthropod phylogeny—a modern synthesis. Journ. Zool. London, vol. 171, pp. 111–130.
MENZEL, R., and BLAKERS, M.
1975. Functional organization of an insect ommatidium with fused rhabdom. Cytobiologie, vol. 2, pp. 279–298.
MENZEL, R., and SNYDER, A. W.
1974. Polarized light detection in the bee, *Apis mellifera.* Journ. Comp. Physiol., vol. 88, pp. 247–270.
MEYER-ROCHOW, V.
1975. Larval and adult eye of the western rock lobster *Panulirus longipes.* Cell Tiss. Res., vol. 162, pp. 439–457.
NÄSSEL, D. R.
1976a. The retina and retinal projection on lamina ganglionaris of the crayfish *Pacifastacus leniusculus* (Dana). Journ. Comp. Neurol., vol. 167, pp. 341–360.
1976b. The fine structure of photoreceptor terminals in the compound eye of *Pandalus* (Crustacea). Acta Zool., vol. 57, pp. 153–160.
NÄSSEL, D. R., and WATERMAN, TALBOT H.
1977. Golgi-EM evidence for visual information channeling in the crayfish lamina ganglionaris. Brain Res., vol. 130, pp. 556–563.
SNYDER, A. W.
1973. How fish detect polarized light. Invest. Ophthalmol., vol. 12, pp. 78–79.
WATERMAN, TALBOT H.
1960. Interaction of polarized light and turbidity in the orientation of *Daphnia* and *Mysidium.* Zeitschr. vergl. Physiol., vol. 43, pp. 149–172.
1966. Polarotaxis and primary photoreceptor events in Crustacea. Pp. 493–511 *in* "The Functional Organization of the Compound Eye," C. G. Bernhard, ed. Pergamon Press, Oxford.
1972. Visual direction finding by fishes. Pp. 437–456 *in* "Animal Orientation and Navigation," S. R. Galler, K. Schmidt-Koenig, G. J. Jacobs, and R. E. Belleville, eds. National Aeronautics and Space Administration, Washington, D.C.
1973. Responses to polarized light: Animals. Pp. 1272–1289 *in* "Biology Data Book," ed. 2, vol 2, P. L. Altman and D. S. Dittmer, eds. Federation of American Societies for Experimental Biology, Bethesda, Maryland.
1974. Underwater light and the orientation of animals. Pp. 415–443 *in* "Optical Aspects of Oceanography," N. G. Jerlov and E. Steemann Nielson, eds. Acadamic Press, London.
1975a. Natural polarized light and *e*-vector discrimination by vertebrates. Pp. 305–335 *in* "Light as an Ecological Factor: II," G. C. Evans, R. Bainbridge, and O. Rackham, eds. Blackwell Scientific Publications, Oxford.
1975b. The optics of polarization sensitivity. Pp. 339–371 *in* "Photoreceptor Optics," A. W. Snyder and R. Menzel, eds. Springer-Verlag Berlin, Heidelberg, New York.
1976. Information channeling in the crayfish retina. Nat. Geogr. Soc. Res. Rpts., 1968 Projects, pp. 467–472.

1977. The bridge between visual input and central programming in crustaceans. Pp. 371–386 *in* "Identified Neurons and Behavior in Arthropods," G. Hoyle, ed. Plenum Press, New York.

1978. Submarine polarized light and the behavior of aquatic animals. Nat. Geogr. Soc. Res. Rpts., 1969 Projects, pp. 621–623.

WATERMAN, TALBOT H., and AOKI, K.

1974. *E*-vector sensitivity patterns in the goldfish optic tectum. Journ. Comp. Physiol., vol. 95, pp. 13–27.

WATERMAN, TALBOT H., and FERNÁNDEZ, HECTOR R.

1970. *E*-vector and wavelength discrimination by retinular cells of the crayfish *Procambarus.* Zeitschr. vergl. Physiol., vol. 68, pp. 154–174.

WATERMAN, TALBOT H.; FERNÁNDEZ, HECTOR R.; and GOLDSMITH, TIMOTHY H.

1969. Dichroism of photosensitive pigment in rhabdoms of the crayfish *Orconectes.* Journ. Gen. Physiol., vol. 54, pp. 415–432.

WATERMAN, TALBOT H., and FORWARD, RICHARD B., JR.

1970. Field evidence for polarized light sensitivity in the fish *Zenarchopterus.* Nature, vol. 228, pp. 85–87.

1972. Field demonstration of polarotaxis in the fish *Zenarchopterus.* Journ. Exp. Zool., vol. 180, pp. 33–54.

WATERMAN, TALBOT H., and HASHIMOTO, H.

1974. *E*-vector discrimination by the goldfish optic tectum. Journ. Comp. Physiol., vol. 95, pp. 1–12.

WATERMAN, TALBOT H., and HORCH, KENNETH W.

1966. Mechanism of polarized light perception. Science, vol. 154, pp. 467–475.

WEHNER, R.; BERNARD, G. D.; and GEIGER, S.

1975. Twisted and non-twisted rhabdoms and their significance for polarization detection in bee. Journ. Comp. Physiol. A, vol. 104, pp. 225–243.

TALBOT H. WATERMAN

National Geographic Society - Cave Research Foundation Salts Cave Archeological Project, 1971–1975

Principal Investigator: Patty Jo Watson, Washington University, St. Louis, Missouri.

Grant Nos. 897, 1283: For a study of the prehistoric cave miners and horticulturists of west-central Kentucky.

As noted in my previous Research Report (Watson, 1976a), this project has two major goals: To describe and explain the aboriginal utilization of portions of the world's longest cave, the Flint Mammoth System in Mammoth Cave National Park; and to use the well-preserved botanical material from the cave interiors (especially the abundant remains of desiccated human paleofecal matter), together with charred plant remains recovered by flotation from sites inside and outside Mammoth Cave National Park, to document prehistoric subsistence in this time and place. The time span in question—the last two millennia B.C.—is that when plant cultivation was beginning in this part of the New World, and the botanical material referred to reflects this transitional economic phase. By analyzing this material, we hope to gather data bearing on the development of horticulture in this region that may help answer some of the important questions anthropologists and historians pose about the origin of food production and its role in cultural evolution. More specifically, we want to know what sort of local economy gave rise to horticulture and whether it developed essentially indigenously or was a result of ideas (and seeds) ultimately derived from Mexico.

Results 1971–1975

Present knowledge about the activities of the aboriginal cave miners and spelunkers has been summarized in detail in earlier publications (Watson et al., 1969; Watson, 1974) and is outlined in a previous National Geographic Society Research Report (Watson, 1976a). There is no need to repeat that information here, except to say that we are concentrating on detailed recording in Mammoth Cave in remote lower-level canyons and also in the large rooms and passages (like Wright's Rotunda and Chief City) where—in spite of 160 years of commercial activity—the prehistoric debris is still relatively abundant, scattered among rocks off the tourist trail.

In Salts Cave similar recording continues in one part of Upper Salts near the north end of the main trunk passage where prehistoric cultural debris is especially abundant in side passages and rooms off the main route.

A 1-by-2-meter trench (K) was excavated in Salts Cave Vestibule to supplement and complement information from the flotation square in an earlier trench (J; see Watson, 1974, chapter 11). All deposit from Trench K was floated during the summer of 1975 and the material recovered is now in the hands of the specialists.

Other field work has been and is being carried out above ground inside Mammoth Cave National Park in nearby areas outside the Park boundaries (under the supervision of Kenneth Carstens), as well as in the Big Bend region of the Green River some 40 to 50 miles west of the Park (the field supervisor here is William Marquardt).

Work in and Near Mammoth Cave National Park

In the immediate area of the Park, our concern is to locate above-ground sites that will reveal the cultural historic sequence: What total time span is represented by aboriginal occupation here, and what is the general cultural context of the prehistoric cave-mining? Since January 1974 we have recorded some 28 sites not previously known and have revisited 13 sites that had been noted earlier. Besides the cave interiors already noted above, there are three main categories of sites representing two main cultural horizons: rock shelters; surface scatters of chipped stone tools and flaking debris; and surface chert outcrops (there are chert outcrops inside some of the caves, also).

The cultural horizons for which we have radiocarbon dates or typological grounds for relative placement are Late Archaic/Early Woodland and Late Woodland. (In addition, we have found Paleo-Indian points at two locales near the Park; hence, a third major cultural period is represented in the region.)

Following is a thumbnail sketch of our present understanding of the prehistory of the Mammoth Cave National Park region, integrating the information from above-ground survey and test excavation so far with our knowledge of the below-ground activities of the ancient spelunkers:

Beginning about 2000 B.C., inhabitants of the Central Kentucky Karst region began to explore some of the big caves. During the first millennium B.C., these people removed large quantities of minerals (gypsum, mirabilite, some epsomite, and possibly other sulphate minerals as well) from the caves and they quarried chert from outcrops in the cave interiors. During this long period, the cave exploring/mining groups camped and lived in the entrances of caves suitable for such occupation, in open sites, and probably in sandstone rock shelters, although none of the shelters test-excavated by us so far (a total of three) has revealed definite evidence of early horizon occupation.

During the first millennium A.D., the local inhabitants stopped using the interiors of Mammoth, Salts, and Lee Caves but continued to occupy rock shelters in what is now the Park.

The diet of the prehistoric cave explorers is well documented in flotation and paleofecal remains from the big caves (see Yarnell's chapters in Watson et al., 1969, and Watson, 1974; see also chapters by Bryant, Marquardt, and Stewart, respectively, in Watson, 1974). These people were at least part-time horticulturists who grew squash, gourds (these are both tropical species first domesticated in Mexico or farther south in the 6000–8000 B.C. period), sunflower, and one or two other plant species (sumpweed—a relative of sunflower—and chenopod) as well as using a series of forest products, especially hickory nuts. They also hunted and ate deer, rabbit, turkey, and lesser animals (fish and turtle), but—at least while in the cave—were much more dependent on plant foods than on animals.

The Late Woodland users of the rock shelters certainly continued to rely on hickory nuts and some of the same faunal species (such as deer, turkey, turtle, and fish) as the earlier caving Indians, but we are at the moment uncertain about the status of the cultigens used by the caving Indians: Were these plant species also tended by the Late Woodland folk, or did they depend entirely on wild plant and animal foods? We have a large series of flotation samples from the shelters tested but are still in the process of recovering the charred botanical material from them. Hence, we cannot answer these questions now, but hope to be able to do so soon.

Work in the Big Bend Region of the Green River

During the spring and early summer of 1975, William Marquardt (director of our archeological activities in this area) supervised survey and test excavations in the Big Bend region of the Green River some 40 miles west of Mammoth Cave National Park. This work developed from our earlier (spring, 1972, and summer, 1974) excavations at two of the Archaic period Green River shellmounds where we had gone in search of antecedents for the subsistence economy revealed in Salts and Mammoth Cave flotation and paleofecal remains (Marquardt, 1972; Marquardt and Watson, 1974). Yarnell and his students at the University of North Carolina are working on the botanical material from these shellmounds, and have recently reported finding fragments of cucurbit shell there which date to approximately the mid-third millennium B.C., and are 1,500 years older than any previously known cultigens from this part of North America.

Rockshelters in the uplands near the riverside shellmounds so far all seem later in time (Middle to Late Woodland) than the mounds, and are comparable to shelters investigated by Carstens inside the Park.

Future Work

Plans for the future include continuation of recording in Mammoth Cave (and in a few parts of Salts Cave), continuation of survey and test excavation in and near Mammoth Cave National Park, investigation of the paleoenvironment in this area and in the Big Bend by means of pollen and snail analysis as well as analysis of macrofloral and macrofaunal remains, continuation of survey and test excavation in open and rock shelter sites in the Big Bend region. The highest priority, immediate research goal is to document fully the context of the early cultivated cucurbit (presumably some kind of squash) in the Green River shellmounds, to pin down its time of introduction (cucurbits were originally domesticated in Latin America, then diffused north), and to see whether the prior Middle Archaic subsistence pattern included use of native North American cultigens (such as sunflower and sumpweed) eaten in abundance by the Late Archaic/Early Woodland horticulturists and cave miners of Salts and Mammoth Caves.

Project Personnel

DAVID A. BAERREIS: Department of Anthropology, University of Wisconsin, Madison, Wisconsin; analysis of snails from archeological sites.

VAUGHN BRYANT: Department of Sociology and Anthropology, Texas A and M University, College Station, Texas; pollen analysis of paleofecal specimens from Salts and Mammoth Caves.

KENNETH C. CARSTENS: Department of Anthropology, Washington University, St. Louis, Missouri; director of surface survey and test excavations above ground in Mammoth Cave National Park and vicinity.

GARY W. CRAWFORD: Department of Anthropology, University of North Carolina, Chapel Hill; Identification and analysis of charred plant remains from the Green River shellmounds. Kentucky; analysis of macrofauna from Salts Cave Vestibule and the shellmounds.

LATHEL P. DUFFIELD: Department of Anthropology, University of Kentucky, Lexington, Kentucky; analysis of macrofauna from Salts Cave Vestibule and the shell mounds.

ELIZABETH DUSSEAU: Department of Epidemiology, School of Public Health, University of Michigan, Ann Arbor, Michigan; parasitological analyses of human paleofecal specimens from Salts Cave.

ADOLF FALLER: Department of Life Sciences, Indiana State University, Terre Haute, Indiana; Consultant on present-day vegetation of Mammoth Cave National Park.

GARY FRY: Department of Sociology and Anthropology, Youngstown State University, Youngstown, Ohio; parasitological analyses of human paleofecal specimens from Mammoth Cave.

MARY ELIZABETH KING: University Museum, University of Pennsylvania, Philadelphia; analysis of textiles from Salts and Mammoth Caves.

WILLIAM H. MARQUARDT: Department of Anthropology, University of Missouri, Columbia, Missouri; statisical analyses of constitutents in Salts Cave and Mammoth Cave human paleofecal specimens, director of survey and excavation in the Big Bend area of the Green River.

HAROLD MELOY: Attorney-at-law, Shelbyville, Indiana; consultant on Mammoth Cave history and the history of the various Indian "mummies."

STEPHEN MOLNAR: Department of Anthropology, Washington University, St. Louis, Missouri; analysis of dental-wear patterns and microstructure of prehistoric human jaws and teeth from Salts Cave Vestibule.

DIANA C. PATCH: Department of Anthropology, University of Pennsylvania, Philadelphia; analysis of mussel shell from Green River shellmounds and from rockshelters in Mammoth Cave National Park (in consultation with David H. Stansbery).

SHARON PATTON: Department of Parasitology, School of Veterinary Medicine, University of Kentucky, Lexington, Kentucky; parasitological analyses of human paleofecal specimens from Salts Cave.

L. GREER PRICE: Micropaleontologist, Offshore/Alaska Division, Exxon Corp., Houston, Texas; microfaunal analysis of sediments from Salts Cave Vestibule excavations.

LOUISE M. ROBBINS: Department of Anthropology, University of North Carolina, Greensboro, North Carolina; analysis of human remains (bones and "mummies") from Salts Cave, Mammoth Cave, and the Green River shellmounds.

WILLIAM ROBERTSON: Environmental Studies Board, National Academy of Engineering, Washington, D.C.; flotation specialist.

JAMES SCHOENWETTER: Department of Anthropology, Arizona State University, Tempe, Arizona; analysis of pollen in Salts Cave paleofecal specimens, in archeological deposits in Salts Cave Vestibule and rockshelters in Mammoth Cave National Park, and from the Green River shell mounds.

STANLEY SIDES: Medical doctor, Cape Girardeau, Missouri; consultant on history of Salts Cave and Colossal Cave.

DAVID H. STANSBERY: Director, Ohio State University Museum of Zoology, Columbus, Ohio; consultant on analysis of mussel shell from archeological sites.

ROBERT B. STEWART: Department of Biology, Sam Houston State University, Huntsville, Texas; wet analysis and quantification of Salts Cave and Mammoth Cave human paleofecal specimens.

STEVEN WARD: Department of Anthropology, Kent State University, Kent, Ohio; analysis of dentition of prehistoric human remains from Salts Cave and from the Green River shellmounds.

RICHARD A. YARNELL: Department of Anthropology, University of North Carolina, Chapel Hill, North Carolina; dry analysis of Salts Cave paleofecal specimens, identification and quantification of charred botanical remains from excavations in Salts Cave Vestibule and the Green River shellmounds.

REFERENCES

(In addition to those listed in Watson, ed., 1974, pp. 251–252)

CARSTENS, KENNETH C.

1974. Archeological surface reconnaissance of Mammoth Cave National Park, Kentucky. Master's thesis, Department of Anthropology, Washington University, St. Louis, Missouri.

1975. Surface archeology in Mammoth Cave National Park, Kentucky. Paper presented at 40th annual meeting of Society for American Archaeology, Dallas, Texas, May 8–10, 1975.

CHAPMAN, JEFFERSON; STEWART, ROBERT B.; and YARNELL, RICHARD A.

1974. Archaeological evidence for Precolumbian introduction of *Portulaca oleracea* and *Mollugo verticillata* into eastern North America. Econ. Bot., vol. 28, pp. 411–412.

MARQUARDT, WILLIAM H.

1972. Recent investigations in a western Kentucky shell mound. Research report presented to 38th annual meeting of Society for American Archaeology, Miami Beach, Florida, May 4, 1972.

MARQUARDT, WILLIAM H., and WATSON, PATTY JO

1974. The Green River, Kentucky, Shellmound Archeological Project. Paper presented at 73d annual meeting of American Anthropological Association, Mexico City, November 10–24, 1974.

WATSON, PATTY JO

1973. Prehistoric miners of the Flint Mammoth Cave System, Mammoth Cave National Park, Kentucky, U.S.A. Paper presented at 6th International Congress of Speleology, Olomouc, Czechoslovakia, August 31–September 18, 1973. (Subsequently published in the Proceedings of the Congress, vol. VI, subsect. Eb, pp. 147–149, 1977.)

1976a. National Geographic Society—Cave Research Foundation Salts Cave Archeological Project, 1969–1971. Nat. Geogr. Soc. Res. Rpts., 1968 Projects, pp. 473–478.

1976b. In pursuit of prehistoric subsistence: A comparative account of some contemporary flotation techniques. Midcont. Journ. Archaeol., vol. 1, no. 1, pp. 77–100.

1976c. The Greater Salts Cave Archeological Project, 1974–1975: Summary report. Cave Res. Found. Ann. Rpt. for 1974, pp. 61–65.

1977. Central Kentucky Karst archeology project. Cave Res. Found. Ann. Rpt. for 1976, pp. 46–47.

1978. Cave Research Foundation Archeological Project and Shellmound Archeological Project. Cave Res. Found. Ann. Rpt. for 1977, pp. 40–45.

WATSON, PATTY JO, ed.

1974. Archaeology of the Mammoth Cave area, xxi + 255 pp., illus. Academic Press, New York.

WATSON, PATTY JO, et al.

1969. The prehistory of Salts Cave, Kentucky. Illinois State Mus. Rpts. Invest., no. 16, 86 pp. Springfield, Illinois.

WATSON, PATTY JO, and CARSTENS, KENNETH C.

1975. Archeological resources of Mammoth Cave National Park: A brief summary. Report prepared for the National Park Service, July 1975.

YARNELL, RICHARD A.

1976. Early plant husbandry in eastern North America. Pp. 265–273 *in* "Cultural Change and Continuity: Essays in Honor of James B. Griffin," Charles E. Cleland, ed., Academic Press, New York.

____. Cultigen prehistory in the Southeast. Pp.— *in* "Handbook of North American Indians," William C. Sturtevant, ed. (In press.)

PATTY JO WATSON

The Metallurgical Trail of Homer and Strabo in Northern Turkey

Principal Investigator: Theodore A. Wertime, Research Associate, Smithsonian Institution, Washington, D.C.

Grant No. 878: In support of a study of the metallurgic zones in northern Turkey described by Homer and Strabo.

From September 1 to 7, 1970, and April 15 to 25, 1971, I returned to Turkey to carry on metallurgical explorations along the Black Sea. The region was that from Samsun to Trabzon, made famous by Homer in the *Iliad* as the birthplace of silver, and by Aeschylus, Xenophon, and Strabo as the birthplace of iron. Also included in my purview was the pre-Hittite and Hittite metallurgical domain encompassing the bronze-, gold-, and iron-producing centers of Alaça Hüyük, Eskiyopar, and Mahmatlar in Çorum, Yozgat, and Tokat provinces.

I served as the team leader of the study. In September I was accompanied by Constantinos Conophagos, professor of metallurgy at the Polytechnic University in Athens and expert on lead at Lavrion in Greece, and in April by Ahmet Coşkun, promising young Turkish metallurgist trained at the Massachusetts Institute of Technology. For various reasons it was impossible for Radomir Pleiner, Czech expert on the history of iron, to accompany our team.

We are much indebted to the Turkish Embassy in Athens, the American Embassy in Athens, and the Turkish Foreign Ministry for their help and to the National Geographic Society for its financial assistance. Special thanks go also to Dr. Sadrettin Alpan, director of the Maden Tetkik Arana Enstitusi (MTA), and to Dr. Raçi Temizer, director of the Hittite Museum, for their many kindnesses and favors, without which this exploration could not have succeeded. Messrs. Alpan and Kirağli of the MTA placed every facility at our disposal, including the services of metallurgist Coskun. Also of great value to us was the work of James Dengate, Department of Classics at the

University of Texas, who has been identifying the metals found in association with the Greek and pre-Greek colonies along the Black Sea. We owe a debt of thanks of Dengate for pointing out to us the works of the several 19th-century travelers—such as William J. Hamilton—who saw the last gasp of the traditional metallurgies along the Black Sea. With their help we found slag heaps giving important clues as to mineral resources anciently exploited.

September. In September we visited the sites of Alaça Hüyük, Bogazköy, Yazilikaya, and Eskiyopar, examining the latter in the company of Raçi Temizer, its excavator. The three most salient features of that short stay in Hittite country were: (1) Our discovery in the museum at Alaça Hüyük of probable proof of the matte smelting of sulphide copper about 1800 B.C., using iron as an agent; (2) our discovery in the Hittite Museum in Ankara of probable proof of the cupelling of silver at Mahmatlar in the mid-third millennium B.C.; (3) our examination of the artifacts at the excavations of Eskiyopar, which show tentatively the evolution from bronze to iron age in one pre-Hittite and Hittite center.

We call particular attention to the Alaça evidences, since they come from a nearly intact copper-smelting furnace called "Maden Cürufu," exhibiting copper slags and pieces of iron interrupted in the middle of a heat. Nearby were copper billets of the Kültepe type. I am seeking experimental samples.

Also of note were our meetings with Nahid Kirağli, versatile director of technical services for the MTA, who identified for us the sites we should visit in April. He not only described a large number of resources for us, including the richest areas of the Black Sands, but also arranged to have samples of slags and furnaces available for me on my return in April.

April. In April Coşkun and I followed the trail of Homer and Strabo from Samsun to Trabzon on the Black Sea. Homer says that silver was born between Unye and Trabzon. Aeschylus, Xenophon, and Strabo also identify this as the home of the Chalybs, the discoverers of iron. The birth of these two metals together is technologically believable. Especially is this true along the Black Sea, where black magnetite sands are in prominence for 100 miles or more—now under consideration for metallurgical exploitation by the Turkish Government; and lead and copper mines occupy the mountain passes leading to the coast.

On the basis of the pattern of contemporary finds of metal objects, set against maps of resources, one can begin to speculate about the incidence of early metallurgy in northern Turkey and its relationship to the coming of the Assyrian colony at Kültepe, the rise of the Hittites, and the later immigration of the Phrygians and Greeks:

(1) The Black Sea was attractive metallurgically for its woods, ores, and black sands; indeed its resources commanded visible attention.
(2) Early bronze making seems to have stretched along the small copper deposits of Çorum and Tokat, reaching the upper mountain passes of Amasya and Niksar. Dengate has reported a number of flat axes and adzes from the Yeçilirmak Valley above Samsun.
(3) Lead making based on high silver ores was concentrated in the Niksar-Akkuş-Beybart areas, stretching later to the areas above Ordu and about Gümüshane.
(4) I do not know enough about the migration of early metal-working peoples such as the Chalybs or Pamphalgonians to offer judgments about the pattern of movement, beyond noting that by the time of the first advent of the Greeks—and possibly even in Hittite and Assyrian times—metallurgy stood astride the mountain passes leading from the Pontic Highlands to the coast. One can be sure that the transition from bronze to iron as a producer's good had one base in this region and another in Hittite and Phrygian centers on the plateau.

General Findings and Conclusions

The two surveys have been increasingly valuable in consolidating my evidences on the coming of both bronze and iron ages in Anatolia. These evidences I have incorporated in two articles, one each on "Metallurgy" and "Pyrotechnology." Another, "How Metallurgy Was Born," was presented at the International Congress in Pre- and Proto-history in Belgrade (September, 1971). I shall not attempt to precis these articles, beyond saying that they draw heavily on the two surveys for the technical evidence of the rise of metals. Of particular importance is our discovery that the black sands 28 kilometers west of Ordu amount to more than 70 percent magnetite. Unfortunately we have not yet located definitive sources of tin for the early bronze age; the sands do not appear to contain tin, which probably lay in higher places.

One can begin to surmise that:

(1) Especially in the light of the new discoveries at Varna, Bulgaria, northern Anatolian copper was important in the beginning of the bronze age; and by the period of the old Assyrian colony in 1900–1800 B.C., sulphide ores were being used. We must presume that some tin lay in the granites well above the Black Sea but was quickly exhausted. We must also look for the shipments down the Danube. Of equal importance in establish-

ing bronze in this area, however, were the deposits of native arsenic and the presence of high arsenic coppers, as well as some stannite.

(2) If copper smelting was a discovery of the plateau, it probably occurred at those junctures where iron and lead were also found, not least the upper Black Sea passes. The smelting belt in pre-Hittite and Hittite times seems to have been concentrated along the ridge from Çorum and Alaça through Amasya to Niksar, Tokat, and beyond.

(3) Gold bowls appear in some profusion at early third millennium Alaça and Eskiyopar. Gold inlays are also found in early bronzes, and gold evidently was common in the river basins, such as the ancient Halys. The Jason story does reflect an early Greek search for metals. By Greek times metallurgy had diversified; a piece of platinum has been found as well as brass Amazon coins.

(4) One cannot draw any inferences as to the relative abundance of silver and gold. Lead and silver pieces appear at Eskiyopar. Silver seems to have been an Anatolian export from a very early period, continuing at the hands of the Greeks of the Pontus. Silver buttons at third century Mahmatlar are the first major indication of cupelling of lead for silver.

(5) The MTA in 25 years has not located tin ores except for spectrographic traces. Yet from the earliest period, Anatolian bronzes have evidenced ample tin as well as arsenic. Starting about 1600, Gordion produced very high tin or "black" bronzes like the Chinese. The Kültepe bronzes of an earlier period also have their fair proportion of tin. The earliest sources of tin remain a mystery, except for the speculations noted in (1).

(6) The iron age in Turkey had its roots in both meteoric iron and bronze, the latter especially after the advent of sulphide copper ores. At site after site one sees the gradual advent of iron objects—beginning with nails, pins, and ornamental objects. Judged from the Assyrian motifs of iron statues found near Samsun and appearing in the antique shops, iron had gained artistic uses before the advent of the Greeks. At Gordion in the Phrygian period, 800–600 B.C., one finds a complete workshop of iron tools (raw material sources unknown).

REFERENCES

WERTIME, THEODORE A.

1973a. Pyrotechnology: Man's first industrial uses of fire. Amer. Sci., vol. 61, no. 6, pp. 670–782, illus.

1973b. The beginnings of metallurgy, a new look. Science, vol. 182, no. 4115, pp. 875–887, illus.

1973c. How metallurgy began: A study in diffusion and multiple innovation. Actes du VIII[e] Congres Int. des Sci. Prehist. et Protohist. Belgrade.
1976. National Geographic Society—Smithsonian pyrotechnological reconnaissance of Afghanistan, Iran, and Turkey. Nat. Geogr. Soc. Res. Rpts., 1968 Projects, pp. 483–492, illus.

THEODORE A. WERTIME

Archeological Surveys in Southwest Mississippi

Principal Investigator: Stephen Williams, Peabody Museum, Harvard University, Cambridge, Massachusetts.

Grant Nos. 914, 1082: To conduct an archeological survey in southerwestern Mississippi, starting in 1971.

Archeological Survey, 1971

The Lower Mississippi Survey, Peabody Museum, conducted a summer field session of 11 weeks (June 15–September 1) in the southwestern corner of Mississippi between Vicksburg and the Louisiana State line. The expedition was headquartered in Cannonsburg, near Natchez, Mississippi, and consisted of Jeffrey P. Brain (field director), Robert S. Neitzel (assisant field director), and four student crew member (Ian Brown and James LeMoyne, Harvard University; Gilman Parson, Williams College; and Mike Reckard, Louisiana State University. Additional unskilled personnel were hired from the local labor pool.

The primary objective of the expedition was to conduct an archeological survey of the left bank of the Mississippi River (fig. 1). Special attention was to be directed to the prominent bluffs that define the eastern margin of the alluvial valley of the river, since they represent a major ecotone between the rich but unstable valley floor and the poorer but physically dominant upland hills. It was hypothesized that a considerable prehistoric occupation would be evidenced in these bluffs as the local population took advantage of the natural benefits of the diverse environments from an intermediate position. In brief, archeological data from the narrow strip of bluff zone were expected to encapsulate the entire span of man's occupation of the valley, as well as test current theories regarding the importance of transitional ecological zones in sociocultural development.

An extensive survey of the designated region was carried out by the core crew in order to discover and record as many of the remaining archeological sites as possible. This was accomplished by vehicle (more than 20,000 miles were logged) and on foot. Promising areas were intensively covered and additional locations were explored on the basis of information developed in the field. Some 130 actual new sites were recorded, including a most important string of mound ceremonial centers constructed about 1,000 years ago. Numerous other pieces of information were also integrated into the over-all study. As a preliminary statement, it appears that the expectation of a relatively complete outline of the prehistoric and early historic occupation of the valley will be fulfilled (see table 1). Furthermore, although this requires considerably more evaluation, it would seem that while the bluffs may well have been a preeminent occupation locus at certain periods, the ecotonal hypothesis is subject to some qualification.

The secondary objective of this summer's investigations, beyond the basic archeological survey, was the reconstruction of particular events in the late prehistoric and early historic period of the region, and the relating of these events to the over-all archeological record. In preparation for the next summer's investigations, special emphasis was directed toward the development and interrelationships of the principal historic occupants of the area, the Natchez and Tunica Indians. The latter tribe is of interest because it was a recent newcomer to the region and because its importance had recently been documented by the discovery of a large cache of burial furniture of native and European manufacture (the "Tunica Treasure"). However, no additional sites certainly relating to the Tunica were recorded this summer, and this clearly indicates their late and restricted impact upon the region.

By contrast, the Natchez were the true heirs of the in situ prehistoric development, and their remains were found throughout most of the region. A number of new sites definitely attributable to the Natchez and their forebears were recorded, and, at seven of these, brief test excavations were conducted toward the end of the season in order to determine their suitability for intensive excavation during the summer of 1972. Three of these sites gave ample indication that further work would be well rewarded with information relating to the development of the Natchez. Combined with existing data on the Natchez and Tunica, this information would firmly establish the later end of the chronology for the aboriginal occupation of this region of the valley, as well as provide some insight into the development of the Natchez Indians, the single most important tribe in the Lower Mississippi Valley at the time of historic contact.

Archeological Investigation, 1972

The Survey completed its second field season (June 15–September 1) of research centering on the southwestern corner of the state of Mississippi. Emphasis was on the excavation of preselected sites, with supplementary surveys as necessary to complete the study of the region. Most of the excavation

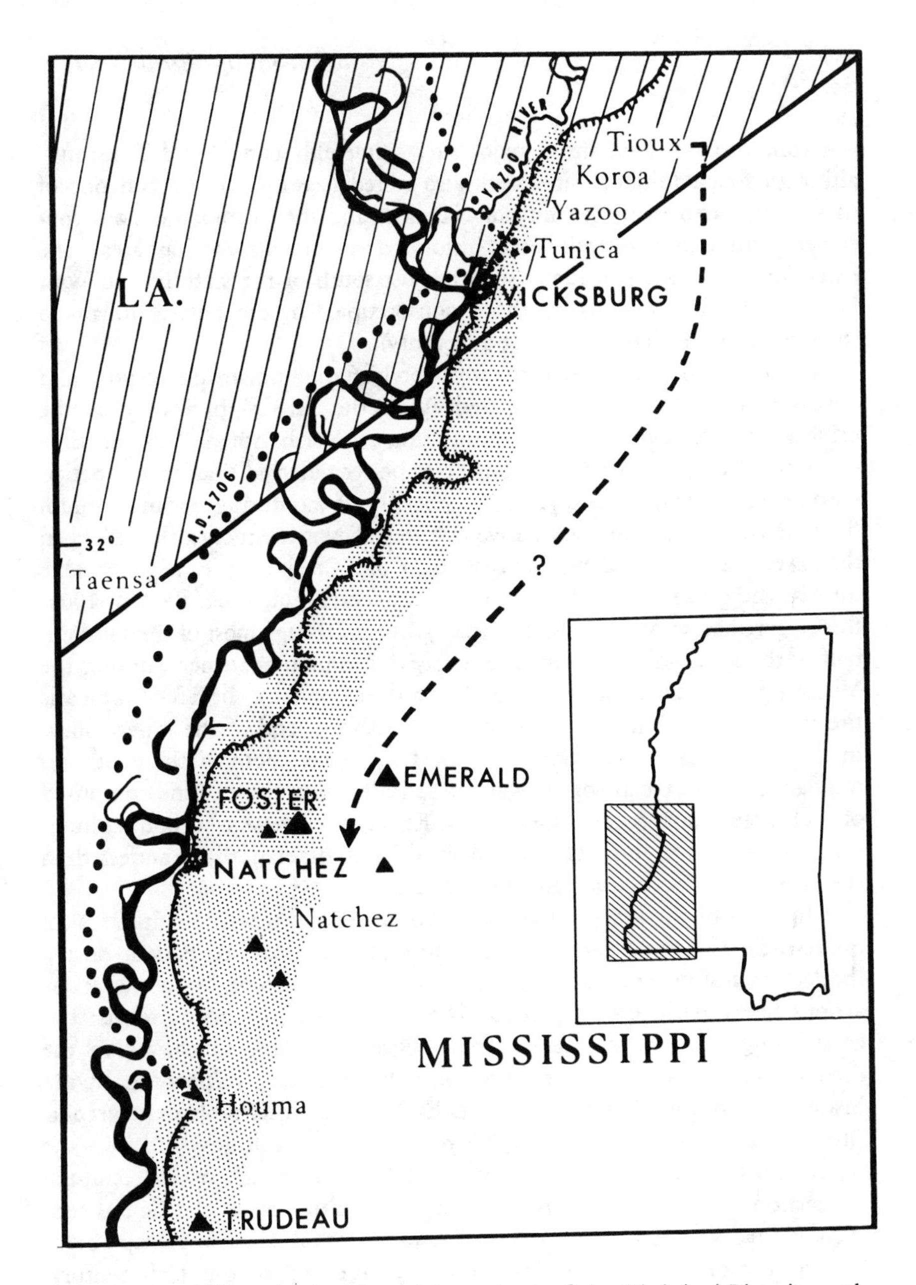

FIG. 1. Area of investigation along the east bank of the Mississippi River in southwestern Mississippi. Stippling represents the region surveyed intensively in 1971, and the triangles indicate sites excavated in 1972. Culture-historical information includes the intrusion of the Mississippian culture (hatched area) and movements of tribal groups in the early historic period.

was concentrated upon three major sites—Emerald, Foster, and Trudeau—although four additional sites were also tested (see fig. 1). All but one of these are located in the vicinity of Natchez, and their exploration was concerned with late-prehistoric / early-historic developments in that area. The exception, Trudeau, is actually situated just south of the state line in West Feliciana Parish, Louisiana, in the region occupied by the Tunica Indians in the late historic contact period (18th century).

In our continuing concern with prehistoric human interaction and development, we have concentrated upon the Mississippi Valley as the principal natural avenue of communication in North America. At no time is the significance of the Mississippi River better reflected than in the period encompassing the last 1,000 years of prehistory. It was during this millennium that the two most developed native cultures of North America flourished in the lower Mississippi Valley. The first, the Coles Creek culture, began to take form at the beginning of this period in east-central Louisiana. By A.D. 1000, this culture had so succeeded that it had grown to occupy most of the southern half of the lower valley. At approximately this same time, a new culture, the Mississippian (named after its cradle of development), began a dramatic rise from seemingly humble origins at the northern end of the lower valley, in the vicinity of the junction with the Ohio River. Both of these cultures were agricultural, technologically and artistically sophisticated, and comprised of highly structured sociopolitical units. Religious expression in both cultures centered around a form of sun worship, most dramatically manifested in the construction of mound ceremonial centers.

In spite of these superficial similarities, these two viable cultures were quite distinct, and the remaining centuries of aboriginal occupation, during the late prehistoric and early historic periods, were marked by various interactions between these protagonists. The interactions took many forms, but as the aggressive Mississippian culture began expanding southward in the direction of the Coles Creek culture conflict is increasingly apparent. By the historic period, population movements had created an unstable demographic situation at the point of contact between these two cultures, and it is the study of this situation and what it can tell us about the over-all cultural interaction that brings us to the Natchez, the in situ heirs of the Coles Creek cultural tradition, and the Tunica, the vanguard of Mississippi expansion.

At the onset of the historic period, at the end of the 17th century, the Natchez were found to be scattered around the vicinity of the modern Mississippi city of that name. In this position they were on what was then the northern frontier of the old Coles Creek culture sphere. At this same time the Tunica were found in a position immediately to the north, near Vicksburg,

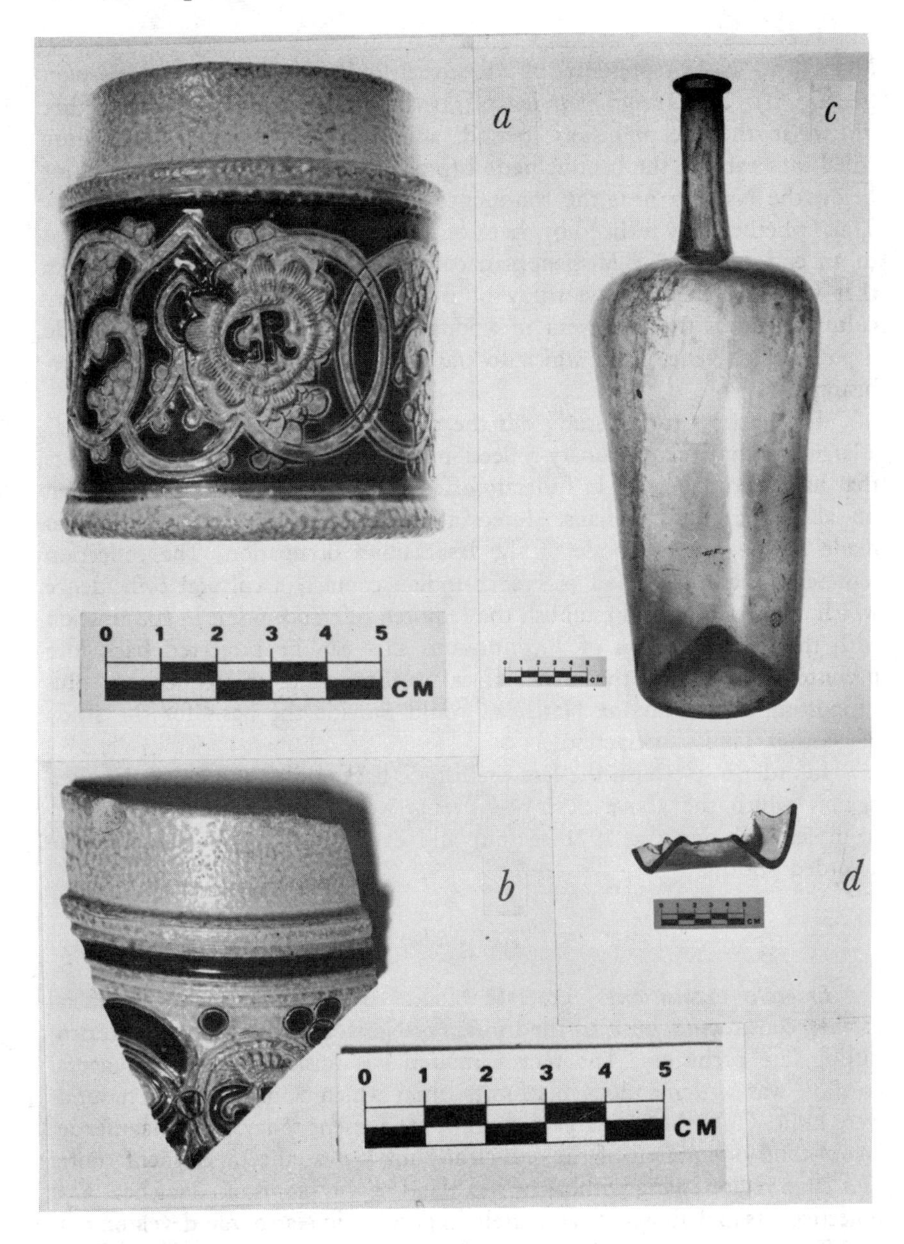

FIG. 2 Distinctive artifacts from the "Tunica Treasure" and fragments of similar artifacts from the excavations at Trudeau. *a-b*, Westerwald "GR" mug; *c-d*, unusually large blue-green glass bottle.

Mississippi, which represented the southern limit of Mississippian expansion (see fig. 1). The Tunica had moved to this location from a point farther upriver in the late prehistoric period, and then moved again as an entire tribal unit early in the historic period (probably in the year 1706) to a point below the Natchez near the confluence of the Red and Mississippi Rivers. Thus, whether fully realized by them or not, the Natchez had been subjected to an end run by the Mississippian culture. It was this known occurrence that was to present a case study of interaction between the two primary cultures, and as the last event in a long sequence was expected to provide a point of reference from which to trace developments backward into prehistory.

The impetus to the study was the discovery of the "Tunica Treasure," a large and quite extraordinary collection of European and aboriginal artifacts that had been deposited as funerary offerings in what could only have been burials of the Tunica Indians. Moreover, the find was reported to have been made in the general locale of the last Tunica occupation. The collection represents a crucial period of French-Indian contact, a cultural coincidence which, if proved, would establish the required reference point in conjunction with the last expression of a continuum that can be projected back into prehistory. Therefore, the archeological verification of this collection, plus supporting data from the Natchez, would provide the basis for the study of Natchez-Tunica interaction.

In order to establish the late prehistoric background and cultural milieu against which the above described events were to be played out, survey (completed during the 1971 season) and excavation of the Natchez were accorded priority.

The Natchez

Emerald Excavations. Emerald Mound is the second-largest artificial earthen construction built by the Indians of North America (north of Mexico) during late prehistory. The term "mound" is misleading, for the actual creation was a tremendous platform, upon which 8 or 10 lesser mounds were built. Only the two largest mounds are present today. The magnitude, layout, and orientation of the site clearly mark it as the preeminent center of a large region, lying within the heartland of the prehistoric Natchez. Our objective was to define more accurately its position in Natchezan development.

The excavations revealed that the platform and mounds had been built during the last phases of prehistory and that altogether this mighty construction represented the Natchez climax. Although a similar site plan and

TABLE 1. REGIONAL CHRONOLOGY FOR THE NATCHEZ BLUFFS

Era	Chronology		Culture	
	Period	Time	Phase	Tradition
	VI	Historic 1600	Natchez	Plaquemine
	V	Protohistoric Prehistoric	Emerald Anna	Plaquemine
		1200		
	IV		Gordon Balmoral Ballina Sundown	Coles Creek
		600		
Neo-Indian	III		Hamilton Ridge	Deasonville
		400		
	II		Issaquena Grand Gulf	Marksville
			Panther Lake	Tchefuncte
		1000	Frasier	Poverty Point
		2000		
	III		Barksdale	
		3000		
Meso-Indian	II	4000	Bryandale	Eastern Archaic
		5000		
	I	6000	Brown's Folly	
Paleo-Indian	IV ?	7000	Mammoth Bayou ?	Plano

orientation were to be reflected at the slightly later Foster and then the historic Natchez sites, their much less impressive size marks a clear decline.

Foster Excavations. The Foster site is the largest mound site on the banks of St. Catherine Creek, the prime geographic point of the historic Natchez. As such, the question was what part it had played in the development of the Natchez. It was found that, although the initial occupation was slightly later, Foster was largely contemporary with Emerald. Thus, at least two major ceremonial centers were constructed and occupied in the immediate vicinity of Natchez during the late prehistoric / protohistoric period. Evidence for a large population supportive of such extensive ceremonial activity at these periods was found throughout the countryside.

Miscellaneous Excavation and Survey. Four additional small mound or hamlet sites were tested in the vicinity of Natchez. Three of these, all on tributaries of St. Catherine Creek, were found to have been occupied contemporaneously with Emerald and Foster. So also were another dozen small sites located on survey but not excavated. Together with dozens more plotted during the previous year's survey, a comprehensive picture of the proto-Natchez settlement pattern has begun to emerge.

Interpretation and Summary. The Natchez development was established to have been an in situ phenomenon with a long history. In the late prehistoric period the precedent culture was viable, centralized, and oriented along the Mississippi River. This florescence was followed into the historic period by an increasing localization and turn-away from the river toward the interior drainages, e.g., St. Catherine Creek. The full reasons for these trends cannot now be ascertained, but undoubtedly a large part of the explanation may be found in external demographic pressures, as exampled by the case of the Tunica.

The Tunica

With the in situ cultural background established, attention could then be focused upon the introduction of the Tunica, representatives of the rather distinct Mississippian cultural tradition, who had recently moved into the area from farther upriver (see fig. 1). The interest here was in the historically documented case of cultural contact among the Indians themselves, as well as the Europeans. As already noted, impetus to the investigation was provided by the "Tunica Treasure," a very impressive collection of aboriginal and European artifacts, which could have come only from a historic Tunica site. The collection itself was a wealth of information, but it was necessary to locate the site and firmly establish the archeological context.

At first, the collector was reluctant to reveal the location of the site. This reluctance was understandable as it became clear after considerable negotiation that there was some irregularity in the manner by which the collection was acquired. Eventually, however, the collector found himself in a position increasingly distasteful, if not untenable, and during the summer he was persuaded to reveal the general location of the site. Land ownership was researched, and permission gained to conduct a survey of the location. When we were satisfied that the site was in the vicinity, we returned to the land owners and apprised them of the situation. After their initial surprise at the discovery—for they had had no intimation of the historical importance or content of the land—the owners permitted us to conduct test excavations in order to confirm our suspicions and specifically to establish the provenience of the "Tunica Treasure."

We were thus able to devote the last four weeks of the field season to the excavation of the Tunica site. This site, recorded as Trudeau (29-J-1) in the Lower Mississippi Survey files, was found to be a rich, tightly nucleated, single-component village occupation, which contained within it numerous graves. It was from these latter, buried at depths ranging from 2 to 6 feet, that the original collection had been derived. Additional undisturbed graves were located, as well as plundered ones. Artifactual material proved beyond doubt that the site was indeed the provenience of the "Tunica Treasure" (see fig. 2). Ample evidence of the village occupation was also recorded, although no definite house structures were isolated.

With the site thus pinpointed, it was then possible to date it through cartographic research. Two contemporary French maps, one prepared by Broutin, de Vergés, and Saucier in 1740 and the other by de Mandeville in 1763 from earlier sources (ca. 1740), show an occupation at this location around 1740. Negative evidence from other maps suggests that the village was founded soon after 1731 and abandoned by 1764. Allowing for a reasonable lapse between acquisition and deposition, we see that these dates coincide very satisfactorily with the age of the European artifacts in the "Tunica Treasure," most of which were probably manufactured between 1720 and 1740, with a few earlier than and some as late as ca. 1760. The collection and its archeological context, then, could be given a very tight absolute dating, which invaluably increases it utility as a prime point of reference.

Conclusion and Summary

As a result of our researches within the ancient territories of the Natchez and Tunica Indians we are better able to understand the major events that seem to have occurred during the terminal aboriginal occupation of the Lower Mississippi Valley. The cultural background from which the Natchez sprang, and upon which the Tunica came to act, has been given greater substance as the spatial, temporal, and cultural parameters were more closely defined. The Tunica, especially, have become an archeological reality and not just a vague historical reference. And, guided by the extraordinary "Tunica Treasure," a case study of human development and interaction in the Lower Valley is now possible in greater detail than ever before.

Within the proto-Natchez sphere, there has emerged a clear pattern of cultural withdrawal and breakdown that was certainly caused at least in part by the pressures exerted by various late Mississippian groups. In the early historic period, then, the Tunica migration seems a logical extension of the preexisting trend. To this aboriginal background, the catalyst of French intervention added a new dimension that increased the complexity of the situation, but provided an important datum for the illumination and interpretation of the foregoing events.

By way of over-all summary it must be noted that the principal objectives, as originally laid forth, were met. However, this statement does not represent a conclusion, for the satisfactory completion of this first stage has inevitably led to the recognition of a host of new problems and to the formulation of new objectives.

The construction of a regional chronology (table 1) has created a spatial-temporal framework, a context within which certain events may now be measured. The events that have generated the most attention are those relating to the transitional late prehistoric / protohistoric-historic contact periods. The knowledge of how earlier groups have exploited the same region has provided a comparative basis in which these later groups are placed in greater perspective.

But additional perspective may also be brought to bear. We are privileged, in dealing with the latest aboriginal occupation of the valley, in having a quantitatively larger sample of archeological data to consider. There is also a qualitative difference. The data are amenable to much wider manipulation because of other possible sources of investigation. Theories and methodologies appropriate to such research situations have recently been set forth elsewhere (Brain et al., 1974). It is our intention to follow through with a new research design to implement these procedures relative to the data base and special concerns described above.

REFERENCE

BRAIN, JEFFREY P; TOTH, ALAN; and RODRIQUEZ-BUCKINGHAM, ANTONIO
1974. Ethnohistoric archaeology and the De Soto entrada into the lower Mississippi Valley. Conference on Historic Sites Archaeology, Papers, vol. 7, pp. 232–289.

STEPHEN WILLIAMS

Studies of the Systematics, Evolution, and Ecology of Pleurodiran Turtles in South America

Principal Investigator: Roger Conant Wood, Faculty of Science and Mathematics, Stockton State College, Pomona, New Jersey.

Grant Nos. 831, 900: In support of continued research on the pleurodiran turtles of the world, both fossil and Recent.

During the summer and early fall of 1970 I spent nearly four months in South America studying fossil and living pleurodiran (side-necked) turtles. While there I visited every museum and research facility that I knew contained (or was suspected of containing) relevant collections. In addition, I was able to carry out a small amount of field work. Subsequently I visited most of the major natural history or paleontological museums in the United States that house South American chelonian material. These travels have enabled me to obtain a comprehensive overview not only of pleurodires but also of other types of turtles from that continent.

Living pleurodiran turtles are confined to the continents of Africa (and also the island of Madagascar), Australia, and South America. Members of this suborder are divided into two families, the Pelomedusidae and the Chelidae. The former are presently found only in Africa, Madagascar, and South America, while the latter are restricted to South America and Australia. South America is thus the only continent upon which both families now coexist. Published accounts of fossil pleurodirans are sufficient to show that this suborder formerly had a much more cosmopolitan distribution, occurring in Asia, Europe, and North America as well on as the continents in which they are presently found. My South American research was undertaken in the hope of resolving several problems relating to these facts: 1, Why are pleurodires now limited to the Southern Hemisphere; 2, where and when did the two pleurodiran families originate; 3, why do pelomedusids have a reasonably good fossil record whereas chelids do not; 4, what is the actual nature of the relationship between the African and South American pelomedusids, some of which are generally considered to be congeneric; and 5, how did the present disjunct distribution of the Australian and South American chelids arise? These lines of inquiry were the outgrowth of earlier research on African pelomedusids supported in part by the National Geographic Society (Wood, 1974).

My South American itinerary included visits to the following institutions: Escuela de Geología y Minas, Universidad Central de Venezuela, Caracas; Instituto Nacional de Investigaciones Geológico Mineras, Bogotá, and Instituto Robert Franco, Villavicencio, both in Colombia; Instituto Miguel Lillo, Tucumán, Museo Municipal de Ciencias Naturales, Mar del Plata, Museo de la Plata, La Plata, and Museo Argentino de Ciencias Naturales, Buenos Aires, all in Argentina; and in Brazil, the Museo de Zoologia do Universidad de São Paulo, São Paulo, the Departamento de Geografia da Faculdade de Filosofia, Ciencias e Letras de Presidente Prudente (Estado de São Paulo), and the Brazilian Geological Survey, Rio de Janeiro. In the United States, I examined fossil and/or Recent specimens at the Museum of Comparative Zoology, Harvard University; the American Museum of Natural History, New York; the National Museum of Natural History, Smithsonian Institution, Washington, D.C.; the Field Museum of Natural History, Chicago; and the University of California Museum of Paleontology, Berkeley. To the directors, curators, and staff of these various institutions, too numerous to mention individually, I am enormously indebted for their cordial hospitality and helpfulness. Without their cooperation it would have been impossible to carry out my research successfully. I wish in addition to express my particular appreciation to the following individuals: Profs. B. Patterson and E. E. Williams; and Drs. M. A. Freiberg, W. D. Sill, and P. E. Vanzolini.

Scientific Results

Venzuela. A number of partial and complete pelomedusid shells were the basis for describing a new species, unusual in its complete lack of carapacial neural bones, as *Podocnemis venezuelensis* (Wood and Diaz de Gamero, 1971). These specimens were from the middle Pliocene Urumaco Formation, which outcrops in a restricted area of the state of Falcón. Remains of other types of vertebrates had also been collected from this same formation, mostly by oil-company geologists some years ago, but no intensive paleontological field work had ever been undertaken in these beds up to the time of my Venezuelan visit. It was obvious that systematic prospecting of the Urumaco Formation might result in the discovery of an important new vertebrate fauna and so, in cooperation with Venezuelan colleagues, the Museum of Comparative Zoology sent a paleontological expedition[1] to explore exposures of the

[1]Members of the expedition included Prof. Bryan Patterson, Arnold Lewis, Dan Fisher, Bob Repenning, Michael Stanford, and me.

FIG. 1. One of the two known shells of *Stupendemys geographicus,* the world's largest fossil turtle, a gigantic pelomedusid of Pliocene age from northern Venezuela. Because of its enormous size and the impossibility of getting a vehicle to the locality where the specimen was discovered, it was necessary to break the shell into a number of pieces small enough to be carried out on back packs. Before doing so, the one-half meter grid shown here was set up to enable a detailed and accurate photographic record which later facilitated reconstruction of the shell in the laboratory.

Urumaco Formation during the summer of 1972. Funds for this expedition were provided by the National Science Foundation, but the expedition itself would never have been possible had not support from the National Geographic Society previously enabled me to assess the potential importance of the existing collection and, equally important, to discuss logistical problems and cooperative arrangements with the appropriate Venezuelan scientists. Among the discoveries of this highly successful expedition were: 1, the world's largest fossil turtle, which proved, most unexpectedly, to be a gigantic pelomedusid (this species was named *Stupendemys geographicus* in honor of the National Geographic Society; figs. 1 and 2, and Wood, 1976b); 2, the first authenticated remains of trionychid (soft-shelled) turtles from the continent (Wood and Patterson, 1973); 3, a quarry yielding a large quantity of well-preserved turtle shells and skulls that clearly represent an entirely new pelomedusid genus; and 4, the remains, in varying abundance, of several other types of chelonians including still another type of pelomedusid, a tortoise, and a new species of the bizarre and previously monotypic matamata, *Chelus* (Wood, 1976a). In terms of species diversity, the Urumaco Formation is certainly one of the richest fossil turtle localities in the world. Because of the enormous quantity of material recovered and the large amount of time required for its preparation, however, it will be several years before all the specimens can be properly described.

Colombia. Several publications (Royo y Gómez, 1945–46; Stirton, 1953; Medem, 1966, 1968) had mentioned the existence of chelonian material from the mid-Tertiary beds of Colombia (associated with the Coyaima and La Venta faunas) but, except for some fossil tortoises now in collections of the University of California Museum of Paleontology (Auffenberg, 1971), none have yet been formally described. From my examination of specimens, both at Bogotá and Berkeley, it is clear that a number of new taxa are represented. One of these is another new species of *Chelus* (Wood, 1976a). There are also several types of pelomedusids, as yet undescribed, all probably referable to the genus *Podocnemis*. Giant tortoises, considerably larger than those described by Auffenberg, are also present in the collections and may represent still another new taxon. Thus, in terms of their chelonian fauna, the Colombian deposits are nearly as rich as those of the Urumaco Formation in Venezuela. They are somewhat older in age and are derived from a different type of facies; the sediments of the Urumaco Formation were evidently deposited in near-shore marine and brackish deltaic environments, whereas the vertebrate-bearing Colombian formations are largely fresh-water fluvial deposits. Quarry samples are lacking from the Colombian Tertiary, as are well-preserved skulls. Nevertheless, the Colombian localities unquestionably provide the second best occurrence so far reported of South American fossil turtles, both in terms of their diversity and abundance.

Probably the best assemblage of Recent chelonian skeletal material in the entire continent is housed at the Instituto Roberto Franco. Among the specimens I examined there was a suite of shells of the pelomedusid *Podocnemis lewyana*. These were of particular interest in their lack of suprapygal bone, as all other living pelomedusids possess one (Wood and Diaz de Gamero, 1971). Some years ago, pelomedusids from the early Tertiary of Europe, however, were described as a new genus, *Elochelys*, in large measure on the basis of lacking a suprapygal (Nopsca, 1931). The discovery of *Podocnemis lewyana*'s aberrant shell structure will necessitate a redefinition of *Elochelys* on the basis of characters other than the absence of a suprapygal,

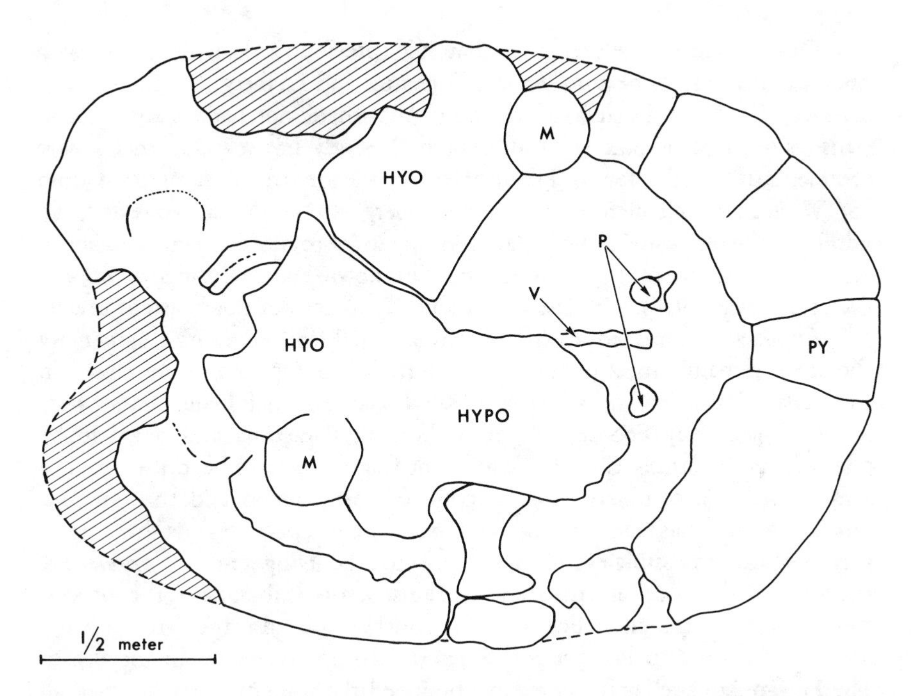

FIG. 2. Sketch, based on photographs taken in the field, of the shell shown in figure 1. The shaded areas represent missing portions of the carapace. The left hyoplastron and mesoplastron were discovered at a distance of about a meter from the rest of the shell and have been restored to their proper position with respect to the remainder of the plastron. Abbreviations: HYO, hyoplastron; HYPO, hypoplastron; M, mesoplastron; P, pelvic fragments attached to carapace; PY, pygal; V, dorsal vertebrae fused to underside of carapace.

since the presence or absence of such a bone clearly falls within the limits of variation of a modern pelomedusid genus.

Argentina. The vertebrate fossil record of Argentina is better known than that of any other part of South America. One reflection of this fact is that probably more fossil turtle material has been described from here than from the rest of the continent combined. For this reason I had not expected to discover much new chelonian material during my visit to Argentina; rather, I had largely anticipated an examination of previously described fossil chelonians which would then serve as a basis for comparison with specimens from elsewhere in South America. Therefore, I was pleasantly surprised during the course of my Argentinian travels to find new material of considerable interest.

One example is a specimen that had previously been described in a one-page note as *Notoemys laticentralis* (Cattoi and Freiberg, 1961). No illustrations of this specimen had ever been published, nor had extensive comparisons with other taxa been attempted. Restudy has revealed that it is a representative of the family Plesiochelyidae, the first to be recognized from the Western Hemisphere (Wood and Freiberg, 1977). *N. laticentralis* is, in addition, the oldest fossil turtle (late Jurassic) so far to be described from South America, the next oldest being the poorly known pelomedusid *Apodichelys lucianoi* (Price, 1954) from the Cretaceous (Turonian) of northeastern Brazil.

Another unexpected discovery was a small collection of fragmentary chelonian remains, most of them apparently belonging to a single taxon, in the Museo Municipal de Ciencias Naturales at Mar del Plata. These were found in the early Eocene Casamayor beds of Patagonia and prove to be referable to the family Chelidae. Sufficient fragments have been preserved to make possible a complete reconstruction of the plastron and this, in conjunction with a diagnostic nuchal bone from the carapace, reveals that a form very close to, or possibly even congeneric with, the living genus *Hydromedusa* is represented. Not only do these remains occur well outside the present distributional limits of chelids in South America, but also they are evidently the oldest known chelids yet to be described from anywhere in the world. The Patagonian shell fragments have provided the impetus for a study of all the fossil chelids of South America, now in progress, which includes the description of additional new material as well as a review of all previously described specimens. My work on South American fossil chelids, moreover, led me to study the osteology of their living relatives; some of these investigations had surprising results (Wood and Moody, 1976).

A collection of undescribed Argentinian fossil turtles belonging to the American Museum of Natural History is also of unusual interest. This includes several relatively small but virtually complete shells, some shell fragments, and a single nearly complete skull. All were recovered from a single early Tertiary locality in the province of Juyjuy. The specimens appear to fall into two discrete size classes; the larger fragments, which are few in number, are probably referable to the poorly known species *Podocnemis argentinensis* (Cattoi and Freiberg, 1958), while the smaller specimens probably represent a new pelomedusid genus.

Much additional chelonian material besides that already mentioned was also examined during my visit to Argentina. Through the kind of offices of Dr. Marcos A. Freiberg I was able to photograph living examples of most of the extant species of Argentinian turtles. I also attempted to locate the types of a number of fossil forms that had been described by Ambrosetti,

Ameghino, Rovereto, Rusconi, and other early Argentinian paleontologists. These efforts were largely unsuccessful, as many of the specimens I was searching for have been lost or, in one case, damaged beyond recognition. While attempting to locate the specimens in question, however, I did come across a variety of undescribed material which I hope eventually to be able to incorporate into future publications.

Brazil. In the western part of the state of São Paulo, near the municipality of Presidente Prudente, lies one of the most incredible fossil turtle localities in the world. A railroad cut through a small hill has exposed, for a length of roughly 80 meters along each side of the track, a layer varying from 10 to 15 centimeters in thickness which consists of almost nothing but turtle shells and skeletons. This ancient chelonian charnel was discovered in 1968 by Prof. José Martín Suarez while carrying out investigations on the geology of the late Cretaceous Bauru Formation, within which the bone bed occurs. The preponderance of the specimens, although somewhat compacted dorsoventrally, are otherwise well-preserved and complete shells, many of which have associated with them skulls and elements of the appendicular skeleton. All the specimens so far recovered from this locality appear to be referable to a single relatively small species of pelomedusid turtle, which has been named *Podocnemis elegans* (Suarez, 1969). I estimate that 80 cubic meters of bone-rich sediment were removed in the course of digging out this railroad cut, and further that the average number of shells in a cubic meter of this matrix was probably somewhat in excess of 500. Thus, something in the excess of 40,000 shells were evidently destroyed in the process of building this particular segment of the railroad line! How many specimens still remain buried on each side of the railroad cut is a matter for conjecture—certainly thousands, I would guess. What accounts for such a tremendous concentration of a single species at one small locality is a mystery. I am currently in the process of trying to analyze a number of biological and geological factors in an attempt to arrive at some kind of reasonable explanation for this extraordinary occurrence.

Much undescribed Brazilian fossil turtle material exists in the collections of the Geological Survey at Rio de Janeiro. These specimens, representing in many cases new taxa of both chelids and pelomedusids, are being studied by L. I. Price, who kindly permitted me to examine and photograph the material under his care. The fossils are from a variety of localities throughout Brazil and range from late Cretaceous to Pleistocene in age. They will add considerably to our knowledge of specific lineages and, in addition, indicate a heretofore unsuspected diversity of South American pleurodiran turtles in the past.

Conclusions

From my travels and subsequent correspondence, it is evident that much has already been discovered in South America that still needs to be described and, happily, more is turning up all the time. The fossil record of South American turtles is much richer than the published record indicates, and as more becomes known it is increasingly possible to formulate hypotheses about the evolution of and relationships among side-necked turtles. For example, the discovery of pelomedusid remains from the Oligocene of Puerto Rico (Wood, 1972) lends strong support to the idea that the living, fresh-water pelomedusids may have achieved their present disjunct distribution as the result of derivation from marine ancestors. The occurrence of the extinct genus *Taphrosphys* in coastal sediments of three continents (Africa, North America, and South America) serves to reinforce this belief (Wood, 1975). The early Tertiary chelid remains from Argentina seem to indicate that members of this family have undergone little fundamental change over a long period of time. So few fossil chelids are known, however, that all conclusions regarding their origins and evolution must still be treated with extreme caution. Very little useful information even exists for living chelids, and our lack of knowledge about their morphology and ecology hampers interpretation of their meager fossil record. In fact, the necessary data do not yet exist to answer many of the questions I had hoped to resolve at the outset of my research program, but the recent spate of discoveries in South America and elsewhere encourages me to believe that resolution of at least some of these is not far distant.

REFERENCES

AUFFENBERG, WALTER

1971. A new fossil tortoise, with remarks on the origin of South American testudinines. Copeia, 1971, no. 1, pp. 106–117.

CATTOI, NAOMI AND FREIBERG, MARCOS A.

1958. Una nueva especie de "*Podocnemis*" del Cretaceo Argentino. Physis, vol. 21, pp. 58–67.

1961. Nuevo hallazgo de chelonia extinguidos en la República Argentina. Physis, vol. 22, p. 202.

MEDEM, FEDERICO

1966. Contribuciones al conocimiento sobre la ecología y distribución geográfica de *Phrynops* (*Batrachemys*) *dahli* (Testudinata, Pleurodira, Chelidae). Caldasia, vol. 9, no. 45, pp. 467–489.

1968. El desarrollo de la herpetología en Colombia. Revista Acad. Colombiana Ciencias Exactas, Físicas y Naturales, vol. 13, no. 50, pp. 149–199.

NOPSCA, F.
1931. Sur des nouveaux restes de tortues du Danien du Midi de la France. Bull. Soc. Geol. France, ser. 5, no. 1, pp. 223–235.

PRICE, L. I.
1945. Um quelônio pleurodiro no calcário da série Apodi, Cretáceo do Estado do Rio Grande do Norte. Nosta Preliminaires e Estudias, Divisão de Geologia e Mineralogia, no. 85, 12 pp.

ROYO Y GÓMEZ, J.
1945–46. Los vertebrados del terciario continental Colombiano. Revista Acad. Colombina Ciencias Exactas, Físicas y Naturales, vol. 6 no. 24 pp. 496–512.

STIRTON, RUBEN A.
1953. Vertebrate paleontology and continental stratigraphy in Colombia. Bull. Geol. Soc. Amer., vol. 64, pp. 603–622.

SUAREZ, JOSÉ MARTÍN
1966. Um quelônio da formação Bauru. Dept. Geogr. Fac. Filos., Cienc. e Letras Pres. Prudente, no. 2, pp. 35–54.

WOOD, ROGER CONANT
1972. A fossil pelomedusid turtle from Puerto Rico. Breviora, no. 392, 13 pp.
1974. The systematics, ecology, evolution, and zoogeography of African turtles. Nat. Geogr. Soc. Res. Rpts., 1967 Projects, pp. 301–306.
1975. Redescription of "*Bantuchelys*" *congolensis*, a fossil pelomedusid turtle from the Paleocene of Africa. Rev. Zool. Africaine, vol. 89, no. 1, pp. 127–144.
1976a. Two new species of *Chelus* (Testudines, Pleurodira) from the late Tertiary of northern South America. Breviora, no. 435, 26 pp., illus.
1976b. *Stupendemys geographicus,* the world's largest turtle. Breviora, no. 436, 31 pp., illus.

WOOD, ROGER CONANT, AND DIAZ DE GAMERO, MARÍA LOURDES
1971. *Podocnemis venezuelensis,* a new fossil pelomedusid (Testudines, Pleurodira) from the Pliocene of Venezuela and a review of the history of *Podocnemis* in South America. Breviora, no. 376, 23 pp., illus.

WOOD, ROGER CONANT, AND FREIBERG, MARCOS A.
1977. Redescription of *Notoemys laticentralis,* the oldest fossil turtle from South America. Acta Geológica Lilloana, no. 14, pp. 187–204.

WOOD, ROGER CONANT, AND MOODY, RICHARD THOMAS JONES
1976. Unique arrangement of carapace bones in the South American chelid turtle *Hydromedusa maximiliani* (Mikan). Zool. Journ. Linn. Soc., vol. 59, pp. 69–78.

WOOD, ROGER CONANT, AND PATTERSON, BRYAN
1973. A fossil trionychid turtle from South America. Breviora, no. 405, 10 pp., illus.

ROGER CONANT WOOD

APPENDIX

List of Grants for Research and Exploration Made by the National Geographic Society, 1975 and 1976

1975

No. 1422: To Dr. Henry S. Robinson, Case Western Reserve University, Cleveland, Ohio, for an analysis of skeletal biology of Corinth from prehistoric through Byzantine times, based on remains recovered from burials.

No. 1423: To Dr. Barbara N. Aziz, City University of New York, New York City, for anthropological explorations of religious centers in the eastern Himalayas.

No. 1424: Dr. Charles W. McNett, Jr., American University, Washington, D.C., in further support of the Upper Delaware Valley Early Man Archeological Project.

No. 1425: To Dr. Arthur G. Miller, Center for Pre-Columbian Studies, Dumbarton Oaks, Washington, D.C., in further support of archeological investigations at Tancah, Quintana Roo, Mexico.

No. 1426: To Dr. Dennis A. Powers, Johns Hopkins University, Baltimore, Maryland, for a cooperative research project to study the foundations of genetic variability in Atlantic and Pacific fish communities.

No. 1427: To Dr. Donald E. Vermeer, Louisiana State University, Baton Rouge, Louisiana, to study the practice and effects of geophagy among the Yoruba of Nigeria.

No. 1428: To Dr. John A. Van Couvering, University of Colorado Museum, Boulder, Colorado, for research on vertebrate paleontology in the Lower Eocene of South-West Africa.

No. 1429: To Dr. David R. Robertson, Smithsonian Tropical Research Institute, Balboa, Canal Zone, in support of a study of social systems and sex change in labrid fishes.

No. 1430: To Dr. W. Grainger Hunt, Chihuahuan Desert Research Institute, Alpine, Texas, for time-lapse photograph studies of nesting golden eagles in western Texas.

No. 1431: To Dr. Paul E. Simonds, University of Oregon, Eugene, Oregon, to study social networks in wild bonnet macaques, south India.

No. 1432: To Dr. Craig G. MacFarland, Estación Charles Darwin, Galápagos, Guayaquil, Ecuador, for a study of the behavior, population, and ecology of the Pacific green turtle in the Galápagos.

Nos. 1433, 1487: To Peter A. Metcalf, Harvard University, Cambridge, Massachusetts, to film a secondary burial ritual in central North Borneo—death rites of a fast-disappearing ancient culture.

No. 1434: To Dr. S. Jeffrey K. Wilkerson, University of Florida, Gainesville, Florida, in further support of an investigation of the ecology and early cultures of the Mexican Gulf Coast.

Nos. 1435, 1493: To Dr. Kenan T. Erim, New York University, New York City, in continuation of the Society's support of the Aphrodisias Archeological Project, in Turkey.

No. 1436: To Dr. Edmund D. Brodie, Jr., Adelphi University, Garden City, New York, in aid of research on antipredator mechanisms of Neotropical salamanders.

No. 1437: To Dr. Willem Meijer, University of Kentucky, Lexington, Kentucky, for botanical explorations for the establishment of research forests in Celebes.

No. 1438: To Dr. George M. Haselton, Clemson University, Clemson, South Carolina, for a study of the late Wisconsin and neoglacial history of northwestern Glacier Bay, Alaska.

Nos. 1439, 1515: To Dr. John A. Wilson, University of Texas, Austin, Texas, for silicone-rubber casting of endangered Oligocene footprints in Presidio County, Texas.

No. 1440: To Dr. Charles C. Porter, Fordham University, Bronx, New York, in further support of research on the systematics and zoogeography of Neotropical Ichneumonidae (Hymenoptera).

Nos. 1441, 1520: To Dr. Tim W. Clark, University of Wisconsin, Madison, Wisconsin, for a study of the behavior and population ecology of martens in Grand Teton National Park, Wyoming.

No. 1442: To Dr. Wolfgang P. J. Dittus, National Zoological Park, Smithsonian Institution, Washington, D.C., to study the influence of genealogy on socioecology and social evolution among Ceylonese macaques.

No. 1443, To Dr. François Vuilleumier, American Museum of Natural History, New York City, for research on zoogeography and speciation of high-Andean birds.

No. 1444: To Miss Dagmar I. Werner, Estación Charles Darwin, Galápagos, Guayaquil, Ecuador, for a study of the life history and conservation of the Galápagos land iguanas (*Conolophus pallidus* and *C. subcristatus*).

No. 1445: To Dr. Mary D. Leakey, National Centre for Prehistory and Palaeontology, Nairobi, Kenya, for exploration of the Laetolil beds and continuation of dating and paleoecology studies at Olduvia Gorge, Tanzania.

No. 1446: To Richard E. Leakey, National Museums of Kenya, Nairobi, Kenya, for continuation of the East Rudolf Research Project, Africa.

No. 1447: To Dr. David Sanger, University of Maine, Orono, Maine, in continued support of archeological operations at the Hirundo site, Maine.

No. 1448: To Dr. David H. Thomas, American Museum of Natural History, New York City, for a study of the prehistoric demography and paleoecology of Gatecliff Shelter, Nevada.

No. 1449: To Dr. Memory P. Elvin-Lewis and Dr. Walter H. Lewis, Washington University, St. Louis, Missouri, to study the kinds of native plants used by indigenous populations as chewing sticks, particularly in west Africa, Egypt, and Pakistan, and to obtain ethnologic data about the practice and specimens for laboratory analysis.

No. 1450: To Dr. John W. Terborgh, Princeton University, Princeton, New Jersey, for a census of primates in Manu National Park, Peru, and a study of their behavior and ecology.

No. 1451: To Dr. David E. Sugden, University of Aberdeen, Old Aberdeen, Scotland, for a study of glacial erosion on Baffin Island, Canada.

No. 1453: To Dr. Craig C. Black, Texas Tech University, Lubbock, Texas, to continue his research on the systematics and paleoecology of small vertebrates from the Plio-Pleistocene deposits east of Lake Rudolf, Kenya.

No. 1454: To Dr. William A. Calder, Jr., University of Arizona, Tucson, Arizona, for continuation of grantee's study of the biophysical ecology of the rufous hummingbird.

No. 1455: To Hugh A. Freeman, Hillcrest High School, Dallas, Texas, in support of his continuing researches on the Hesperiidae (Lepidoptera) of Mexico.

No. 1456: To Dr. Kenelm W. Philip, University of Alaska, Fairbanks, Alaska, in support of the Alaska Lepidoptera Survey (1975 field season), Victoria Island expedition.

No. 1457: To Dr. Richard J. Elzinga, Kansas State University, Manhattan, Kansas, for research on species and distribution of army-ant mites and leafhoppers, Paraguay.

No. 1458: To Dr. Paul K. Anderson, University of Calgary, Calgary, Alberta, Canada, to study the behavior, herd structure, feeding ecology, and interspecies relationships of dugongs on the eastern coast of Cape York Peninsula, Queensland, Australia.

No. 1459: To Dr. Eugenie Clark, University of Maryland, College Park, Maryland, to study the behavior of sharks and their teleost symbionts.

No. 1460: To Dr. James Richard Karr, Purdue University, West Lafayette, Indiana, for a study of species stability in tropical bird communities.

No. 1461: To Dr. Paul F. Healy, Rutgers University, New Brunswick, New Jersey, for an archeological study of cultural change on a Pre-Columbian Mesoamerican frontier: Northeast Honduras.

No. 1462: To Mrs. Susan W. Katzev, Athens, Greece, for assembling a complete documentary motion-picture record of the Kyrenia Ship Project, Cyprus.

No. 1463: To Dr. Edward B. Kurjack, Western Illinois University, Macomb, Illinois, for completing a study of Pre-Columbian settlement patterns in northwestern Yucatán.

No. 1464: To Dr. Nancy M. Farriss, University of Pennsylvania, Philadelphia, Pennsylvania, in support of a search by electronic equipment for remains of Maya vessels in likely areas along the east coast of Yucatán.

No. 1465: To Dr. George F. Bass, American Institute of Nautical Archeology, College Station, Texas, in further support of an investigation of an Iron Age shipwreck off the Turkish coast.

Nos. 1466, 1557: To Dr. George E. Stuart, National Geographic Society, Washington, D.C., in further support of the Cobá Archeological Mapping Project, Yucatán Peninsula.

No. 1468: To Dr. Ronald D. Garst, University of Maryland, College Park, Maryland, for a study of the population, migration, and communication in Kisii district, Kenya.

No. 1469: To Dr. Paul O. McGrew, University of Wyoming, Laramie, Wyoming, in support of his investigation of a new fossil flamingo nesting locality in Wyoming.

No. 1470: To Dr. Margery C. Coombs, University of Massachusetts, Amherst, Massachusetts, for excavation of a Late Arikareean vertebrate assemblage in northwestern Nebraska.

No. 1471: To Dr. James A. Jensen, Earth Sciences Museum, Brigham Young University, Provo, Utah, for collection and study of new Jurassic dinosaurian fauna from Colorado.

No. 1472: To Dr. Farish A. Jenkins, Jr., and Dr. A. W. Crompton, Museum of Comparative Zoology, Harvard University, Cambridge, Massachusetts, for continuing research in Early Cretaceous mammals of North America.

No. 1473: To Dr. J. David Ligon, University of New Mexico, Albuquerque, New Mexico, for a field study of the social systems found in two African bird families—the wood hoopoes (Phoeniculidae) and colies, or mousebirds (Coliidae).

No. 1474: To Gary L. Nuechterlein, Colorado State University, Fort Collins, Colorado, to study the breeding biology and social behavior of western grebes.

No. 1475: To Dr. Ralph M. Wetzel, University of Connecticut, Storrs, Connecticut, for a study of the mammals of the Chaco Boreal, South America.

No. 1476: To Dr. Fred N. White, University of California, Los Angeles, California, for research on the physiological and ecological significance of colonial nesting in the European bee-eater (*Merops apiaster*).

No. 1477: To Dr. Bruce J. Bourque, Maine State Museum, Augusta, Maine, for continuing research at the Turner Farm archeological site, North Haven, Maine.

No. 1478: To Dr. John A. Eddy, High Altitude Observatory, Boulder, Colorado, for a study of astronomical alignment of Canadian Indian cairns and medicine wheels.

No. 1479: To Dr. Marian E. White, State University of New York, Buffalo, New York, for archeological investigations of an Early Man site in the western Finger Lakes region, New York.

No. 1480: To Dr. Gus W. Van Beek, National Museum of Natural History, Smithsonian Institution, Washington, D.C., in support of archeological investigations at Tel Jemmeh, Israel.

No. 1481: To Alexander Marshack, Peabody Museum of Archeology and Ethnology, Harvard University, Cambridge, Massachusetts, for an analysis of Paleolithic symbol systems in east Europe and the Soviet Union.

No. 1482: To Dr. Dennis J. Stanford, National Museum of Natural History, Smithsonian Institution, Washington, D.C., for continued archeological investigations of the Jones-Miller Paleo-Indian bison-kill site, northeastern Colorado.

No. 1483: To Dr. Lowell J. Bean, California State University, Hayward, California, for an ecological analysis of southern California Indian ethnobotany.

No. 1484: To Dr. Judith C. Lang, University of Texas, Austin, Texas, for a study of intraspecific and interphyletic interactions on Jamaican coral reefs.

No. 1485: To Dr. John J. Craighead, University of Montana, Missoula, Montana, for computer-assisted wildlife-habitat classification using satellite imagery.

No. 1486: To Dr. Robert W. Mitchell, Texas Tech University, Lubbock, Texas, to continue his survey of cave fauna of the Yucatán Peninsula.

No. 1488: To Dr. E. Richard Sorenson, National Anthropological Film Center, Smithsonian Institution, Washington, D.C., for a research film study of traditional Cook Island Polynesian dances.

No. 1489: To Dr. Robert F. Heizer, University of California, Berkeley, California, for a study of prehistoric rock art of Nevada caves.

No. 1490: To Dr. Trevor F. Watkins, University of Edinburgh, Edinburgh, Scotland, for excavation of a prehistoric archeological site, and associated environmental studies, in northeast Syria.

No. 1491: To Dr. A. Colin Renfrew, University of Southampton, Southampton, England, and Dr. Curt W. Beck, Vassar College, Poughkeepsie, New York, for an analysis of patterns of trade in prehistoric amber.

No. 1492: To Dr. C. Vance Haynes, and Dr. Emil W. Haury, University of Arizona, Tucson, Arizona, for continuing archeological studies at the Paleo-Indian (Clovis) Lehner site, Arizona.

No. 1494: To Dr. Ian D. Hume, University of New England, Armidale, N.S.W., Australia, to study the nutritional ecology of the brush-tailed possum (*Trichosurus vulpecula*).

No. 1495: To Dr. Mason E. Hale, National Museum of Natural History, Smithsonian Institution, Washington, D.C., to study methods of controlling lichen growths on Mayan archeological ruins.

No. 1496: To Dr. Vaughn M. Bryant, Jr., Texas A. & M. University, College Station, Texas, for ethnobotanical investigation of Hinds Cave, Val Verde County, Texas.

No. 1497: To Dr. Stanley S. Frissell, University of Montana, Missoula, Montana, for research on the ecology of the spruce grouse (*Canachites canadensis*) in western Montana.

No. 1498: To Dr. Bonham C. Richardson, Rutgers University, New Brunswick, New Jersey, to study labor migration and land-use intensity on St. Kitts and Nevis, Leeward Islands.

No. 1499: To Henry W. Posamentier, Rider College, Trenton, New Jersey, in continuation of grantee's studies of the chronology of glaciation of the Austrian Alps during the past millennuim.

No. 1500: To Dr. Peter Dodson, University of Pennsylvania, Philadelphia, Pennsylvania, in continuation of his studies of the Morrison Formation dinosaur fauna of the Western United States.

No. 1501: To Dr. Lionel A. Stange, National University of Tucumán, Tucumán, Argentina, in continuation of his field studies of the insect order Neuroptera in South America.

No. 1502: To Mrs. Birute Galdikas-Brindamour, University of California, Los Angeles, California, in support of her continuing research on the behavior and ecology of the wild orangutan of Tanjung Puting, Borneo.

No. 1503: To Dr. Frederick A. Urquhart, University of Toronto, Toronto, Canada, in support of his continuing research on the monarch butterfly.

No. 1504: To Dr. David M. Schaffer, Oxford University, Oxford, England, in further support of his study of the Mandinko of Pakao, southern Senegal—the history, social structure, and ethnobotany of a Manding people.

No. 1505: To Dr. Anthony G. Coates, George Washington University, Washington, D.C., for a comparative study of European and Caribbean Cretaceous reef-coral faunas.

No. 1506: To Dr. James S. Mellett, New York University, New York City, for a study of predation and formation of fossil-mammal accumulations.

No. 1507: To Dr. José Fernando Bonaparte, National University of Tucumán, Tucumán, Argentina, in support of his research on Jurassic and Cretaceous terrestrial vertebrates of South America.

No. 1508: To Dr. Anna K. Behrensmeyer, University of California, Santa Cruz, California, for her study of mammal bones from Amboseli National Park, Kenya, as a key to east African paleoecology.

No. 1509: To Peter Throckmorton, Hellenic Institute of Marine Archaeology, Athens, Greece, in support of a search for ancient Mediterranean shipwrecks.

No. 1510: To Dr. Donald J. Johanson, Case Western University, Cleveland, Ohio, for paleoanthropological research in Hadar, central Afar, Ethiopia.

No. 1511: To John F. Hansman, University of London, London, England, in further support of archeological excavations of Shahr-i Qūmis, the Lost Capital of Parthian Iran.

No. 1512: To Dr. Yosihiko H. Sinoto, Bernice P. Bishop Museum, Honolulu, Hawaii, in further support of archeological excavation of an Archaic habitation site on Huahine, Society Islands.

No. 1513: To Dr. Walter Alvarez, Lamont-Doherty Geological Observatory of Columbia University, Palisades, New York, for geological exploration of newly recognized alpine chain in southern Italy.

No. 1514: To Dr. Rockne H. Johnson, University of Hawaii, Honolulu, Hawaii, for exploration of submarine volcanoes near Samoa.

No. 1516: To Dr. Patricia D. Moehlman, Austin, Texas, for motion-picture film in connection with her studies of the black-backed jackal in East Africa.

No. 1517: To Dr. Richard D. Estes, Academy of Natural Sciences of Philadelphia, Philadelphia, Pennsylvania, in further support of Dr. Estes's long-term study of the sable antelope in the Shimba Hills National Reserve, Kenya.

No. 1518: To Dr. Charles Walcott, State University of New York, Stony Brook, New York, for his continuing studies of the behavior of the dusky porpoise and southern common dolphin (*Lagenorhynchus obscurus* and *Tursiops* sp.) in Argentina.

No. 1519: To Mrs. Julie C. Webb, University of California, Los Angeles, California, in further aid of her ecological studies of the western lowland gorilla in south-central Cameroon.

No. 1521: To Dr. Charles H. Southwick, Johns Hopkins University, Baltimore, Maryland, for his study of the ecology and behavior of rhesus monkeys in Nepal.

No. 1522: To Mrs. Mary Eubanks Dunn, Southern Methodist University, Dallas, Texas, to investigate ceramic evidence for the spread of prehistoric races of maize in Peru.

No. 1523: To Mrs. Christine Elvera Sharpe, Cambridge, Massachusetts, for an expedition to study the art sanctuary in Koonalda Cave, South Australia.

No. 1524: To Hamo Sassoon, Fort Jesus Museum, Mombasa, Kenya, for a preliminary underwater survey of a Portuguese frigate sunk in Mombasa Harbor in 1697.

No. 1525: To Dr. James N. Douglas, University of Texas, Austin, Texas, in further support of the project "Mapping the Radio Sky."

No. 1526: To Dr. William A. Weber, University of Colorado Museum, Boulder, Colorado, to compute an inventory of the lichens and bryophytes of the Galápagos Islands.

No. 1527: To Dr. John J. Engel, Field Museum of Natural History, Chicago, Illinois, for botanical exploration and collection of bryophytes in southern Chile.

No. 1528: To Dr. Kevin C. Kearns, University of Northern Colorado, Greeley, Colorado, for a study of depopulation and cultural change in the islands of western Ireland.

No. 1530: To Dr. Peter Moller, American Museum of Natural History, New York City, for a study of the ecology and ethology of mormyriform fishes.

No. 1531: To William W. Cochran, Illinois State Natural History Survey, Urbana, Illinois, for a study of orientation, navigation, and other migratory behavior of the peregrine falcon from Greenland to the southern border of the United States, and the migratory behavior of this falcon in South America.

No. 1532: To Dr. E. Wyllys Andrews V, Middle American Research Institute, Tulane University, New Orleans, Louisiana, in aid of the Institute's archeological publication program.

No. 1533: To Dr. Henry P. Schwarcz, McMaster University, Hamilton, Ontario, Canada, for development of absolute radiometric dating of Paleolithic sites in Israel and Hungary.

No. 1534: To Dr. William R. Coe, University of Pennsylvania, Philadelphia, Pennsylvania, for continuing archeological investigations of the ruins of Quirigua, Guatemala.

No. 1535: To Dr. Geoffrey M. O. Maloiy, University of Nairobi, Nairobi, Kenya, in further support of his research on ionic and osmotic regulation in East African vertebrates: the lungfish (*Clarias*) and *Tilapia grahami.*

No. 1536: To Dr. Raymond B. Huey, Museum of Vertebrate Zoology, University of California, Berkeley, California, for studies of the ecology of lizards of the Kalahari Desert, Africa.

No. 1537: To Dr. James L. Newman, Syracuse University, Syracuse, New York, for a survey of food accessibility among the Mijikenda of Kenya.

No. 1538: Dr. C. Vance Haynes, University of Arizona, Tucson, Arizona, in further support of geological-anthropological surveys in the Libyan Desert.

No. 1539: To Dr. William J. Zinsmeister, Institute of Polar Studies, Ohio State University, Columbus, Ohio, for a study of Tertiary molluscan biostratigraphy of Tierra del Fuego and Patagonia.

No. 1540: To Dr. Stuart H. Hurlbert, San Diego State University, San Diego, California, to study comparative behavior, distribution, and movements of flamingos in the high plains of Chile and Bolivia.

No. 1541: To Dr. Fred G. Thompson, University of Florida, Gainesville, Florida, for research on the evolution and systematics of Hispaniolan urocoptid land snails.

Nos. 1542, 1568: To Dr. John A. Graham, University of California, Berkeley, California, for archeological investigations at Abaj Takalik, Guatemala.

No. 1543: To Dr. Herman A. Bankoff, Brooklyn College, Brooklyn, New York, for archeological investigations at Popov Salas, northeastern Yugoslavia.

No. 1544: To Dr. Krzysztof Serkowski, Lunar and Planetary Laboratory, University of Arizona, Tucson, Arizona, in aid of a study for detecting other planetary systems in the universe.

No. 1545: To Dr. Knut Norstog, Northern Illinois University, DeKalb, Illinois, for a cytological and morphological study of arborescent species of the cycad genus *Zamia*.

No. 1546: To Dr. John J. Gaudet, University of Nairobi, Nairobi, Kenya, to study nutrient relationships between plants and the ecosystem in Lake Naivasha, Kenya.

No. 1547: To Dr. Thomas R. Soderstrom, National Museum of Natural History, Smithsonian Institution, Washington, D.C., for studies of bamboos and bambusoid grasses in Bahian Brazil.

No. 1548: To Dr. E. Earl Willard, University of Montana, Missoula, Montana, for continued research on the ecology of the Nez Perce Creek bighorn-sheep herd, Idaho.

No. 1549: To Dr. Maurice G. Hornocker, University of Idaho, Moscow, Idaho, for continued research on the ecology of the wolverine in northwestern Montana.

No. 1550: To Dr. Nigel M. Wace, Australian National University, Canberra City, Australia, to study the plants and landforms of Tristan da Cunha and St. Helena Islands.

No. 1551: To Dr. S. K. Gangwere, Wayne State University, Detroit, Michigan, for a study of the distribution and behavior of orthopteroid insects of Madeira.

Nos. 1552, 1565: To Dr. Charles A. Woods, University of Vermont, Burlington, Vermont, in further support of research on the status and biology of the Haitian hutia.

No. 1553: To Dr. Robert W. Storer, University of Michigan, Ann Arbor, Michigan, for a study of the behavior and relationships of the hooded grebe (*Podiceps gallardoi*) of Patagonia.

No. 1554: To Dr. Dian Fossey, Ruhengeri, Rwanda, Africa, for her continuing program of research on the mountain gorilla in Rwanda.

No. 1555: To Anthony P. Andrews, University of Arizona, Tucson, Arizona, for an analytical history of the Maya salt trade.

No. 1556: To Bruce H. Dahlin, Catholic University of America, Washington, D.C., for investigations of agronomic potentials in Bajo de Santa Fe, El Petén, Guatemala.

No. 1558: To Robert C. Wheeler, Minnesota Historical Society, St. Paul, Minnesota, in aid of the Fort Charlotte Underwater Archeology Project at Grand Portage National Monument, Minnesota.

No. 1559: To Dr. Peter J. Mehringer, Jr., Washington State University, Pullman, Washington, for a study of Libyan Desert Holocene environments and chronology.

No. 1560: To Dr. J. Alan Holman, Michigan State University, East Lansing, Michigan, for research on Upper Miocene amphibians and reptiles from northeastern Nebraska.

No. 1561: To Dr. Larry D. Agenbroad, Chadron State College, Chadron, Nebraska, for excavation of a Late Pleistocene mammoth locality in South Dakota.

No. 1562: To Dr. Thomas H. Rich, National Museum of Victoria, Melbourne, Australia, to investigate the origin and early history of Australia's unique vertebrates.

No. 1563: To Douglas A. Lawson, University of California, Berkeley, California, for studies of giant pterosaurs from Texas.

No. 1564: To Dr. Julia M. Shepard, Laboratory of Ornithology, Cornell University, Ithaca, New York, in further support of her study of the behavioral differences among lekking male ruffs (*Philomachus pugnax*).

No. 1566: To Dr. Paul J. Spangler, National Museum of Natural History, Smithsonian Institution, Washington, D.C., for biosystematic and zoogeographic studies of aquatic insects of Ecuador.

No. 1567: To Dr. Masakazu Konishi, California Institute of Technology, Pasadena, California, for research on the ecology and neuroethology of the oilbird (*Steatornis caripensis*).

1976

No. 1569: To Dr. Roger C. Green, University of Auckland, Auckland, New Zealand, for a study of Lau Island, Fiji, archeology.

No. 1570: To Dr. Margaret A. Alexander, University of Iowa, Iowa City, Iowa, to complete field studies leading to a publication on the corpus of the mosaics of Tunisia.

Nos. 1571, 1646: To Dr. Kenan T. Erim, New York University, New York, City, for further support of archeological investigations at Aphrodisias, Turkey.

No. 1572: To Dr. Philip B. Tomlinson, Harvard University, Cambridge, Massachusetts, for research on the evolutionary mechanisms in mangroves of the genus *Rhizophora* and related Rhizophoraceae.

No. 1573: To Jan G. Reese, St. Michaels, Maryland, for a study of population ecology of feral mute swans in Chesapeake Bay.

No. 1574: To Dr. W. Gary Sprules, Erindale College, University of Toronto, Mississauga, Ontario, Canada, for a study of invertebrate predation, competition, and the structure of crustacean zooplankton communities in the English Lake District.

No. 1575: To Dr. William L. Franklin, Iowa State University, Ames, Iowa, for research on the socioecology of the South American guanaco.

Nos. 1576, 1687: To Dr. William L. Graf, University of Iowa, Iowa City, Iowa, to study landscape change in the Green River area, Utah/Colorado.

No. 1577: To Dr. Joyce R. Richardson, National Museum of Victoria, Melbourne, Victoria, Australia, for a study of marine environments of Recent brachiopod faunas.

No. 1578: To Dr. Douglas M. Lay, University of North Carolina, Chapel Hill, North Carolina, for a study of Plio-Pleistocene fossils in tar pits in southwestern Iran.

No. 1579: To Dr. Walter F. Heilgenberg, Scripps Institution of Oceanography, La Jolla, California, for field studies on electrolocation and communication in electric fishes.

No. 1580: To Dr. G. Causey Whittow, University of Hawaii, Honolulu, Hawaii, to study the physiological ecology of the Hawaiian monk seal (*Monachus schauinslandi*).

No. 1581: To Dr. Thomas B. Thorson, University of Nebraska, Lincoln, Nebraska, to study in Colombia the evolution of fresh-water adaption in stingrays.

No. 1582: To Miss Francine G. Patterson, Stanford University, Stanford, California, for research on linguistic and behavioral development of a juvenile lowland gorilla.

No. 1583: To Dr. Georgio P. Morpurgo, University of Rome, Rome, Italy, for anthopological studies on Sherpas: High-altitude adaptation and genetic parameters.

No. 1584: To Dr. James M. Adovasio, University of Pittsburgh, Pittsburgh, Pennsylvania, for archeological and geomorphological studies of Meadowcraft Rockshelter and the Cross Creek Drainage, southwestern Pennsylvania.

No. 1585: To Dr. Michel Pichon, James Cook University of North Queensland, Australia, for a comparative analysis of coral-reef community structure in the vicinity of Lizard Island, Australia.

No. 1586: To Dr. Tod F. Stuessy, Ohio State University, Columbus, Ohio, for a study of fish poisons in the sunflower family (Compositae).

No. 1587: To Dr. Gordon L. Kirkland, Jr., Shippensburg State College, Shippensburg, Pennsylvania, for a faunal survey of the mammals of the Uintah Mountains, Utah.

No. 1588: To Dr. K. A. Kershaw, McMaster University, Hamilton, Ontario, Canada, to study the lichen *Sterocaulon paschale* as fodder in the winter range of the caribou.

No. 1589: To Galen B. Rathbun, University of Nairobi, Nairobi, Kenya, for research on territorial, pair-bonding, and scent-marking correlates in captive elephant shrews (*Elephantulus rufescens*).

No. 1590: To Richard E. Leakey, National Museums of Kenya, Nairobi, Kenya, for continuation of interdisciplinary studies of the prehistory of Lake Turkana (formerly Lake Rudolf).

No. 1591: To Dr. Mary D. Leakey, National Centre for Prehistory and Palaeontology, Nairobi, Kenya, for further exploration of the Laetolil beds, Tanzania.

No. 1592: To Dr. Raymonde Bonnefille, Laboratoire de Géologie du Quaternaire, Meudon, France, for palynological studies related to paleoecology and evolution of early hominids at Olduvai and Laetolil, Tanzania.

No. 1593: To Dr. Richard L. Hay, University of California, Berkeley, California, for studies of the stratigraphy of the Laetolil beds, Tanzania.

No. 1594: To Dr. Marvin J. Allison, Medical College of Virginia, Richmond, Virginia, for continued support of studies of Pre-Columbian American disease.

No. 1595: To Dr. Paul F. Healy, Rutgers University, New Brunswick, New Jersey, for an archeological study of cultural change on a Pre-Columbian Mesoamerican frontier: northeast Honduras.

No. 1596: To Dr. Joseph O. Vogel, Northern Illinois University, De Kalb,

Illinois, for the survey of an Iron Age settlement, Upper Zambezi Valley, Zambia.

No. 1597: To Dr. William R. Powers, University of Alaska, Fairbanks, Alaska, for archeological and paleoenvironmental research at Dry Creek, central Alaska.

No. 1598: A 3-year grant commitment for the cooperative project "Exploration of Early Man Sites in Alaska."

No. 1599: To Dr. Walter R. Siegfried, University of Cape Town, Cape Town, South Africa, in support of studies relating to the conservation of the jackass penguin in South Africa.

No. 1600: To Dr. Mary R. Dawson, Carnegie Museum, Pittsburgh, Pennsylvania, and Dr. Robert M. West, Milwaukee Public Museum, Milwaukee, Wisconsin, for research on the affinities and environment of Paleogene terrestrial vertebrates in the Canadian high Arctic.

No. 1601: To Gary L. Nuechterlein, Delta Waterfowl Research Station, Delta, Manitoba, Canada, in further support of a study of the breeding biology and social behavior of the western grebe.

No. 1602: To Dr. Charles Walcott, State University of New York, Stony Brook, New York, in aid of research on vocalizations and behavior of the southern right whale.

No. 1603: To Allen Zagarell, Freie Universität Berlin, Berlin, West Germany, for an archeological survey of routes through the Baxtiari Mountains of southwest Iran.

No. 1604: To Dr. Ray A. Williamson, St. John's College, Annapolis, Maryland, and Dr. Florence H. Ellis, University of New Mexico, Albuquerque, New Mexico, for a study of the towers of Hovenweep National Monument near Mesa Verde: Are they astronomical observatories?

No. 1605: To Dr. Charles W. McNett, Jr., American University, Washington, D.C., in further support of the Upper Delaware Valley Early Man Project.

No. 1606: To Dr. Gus W. Van Beek, National Museum of Natural History, Smithsonian Institution, Washington, D.C., for archeological investigations at Tel Jemmeh, Israel.

No. 1607: To Dr. George F. Bass, American Institute of Nautical Archaeology, College Station, Texas, for excavation of a Late Byzantine shipwreck carrying cargo of glass, near Serçe Liman, Turkey.

No. 1608: To Dr. David H. Thomas, American Museum of Natural History, New York City, for further support of a study of prehistoric demography and paleoecology of Gatecliff Shelter, Nevada.

No. 1609: To Dr. Charles R. Taylor, Harvard University, Cambridge, Massachusetts, to study general principles of vertebrate locomotion utilizing East African animals.

No. 1610: To Dr. Masakazu Konishi, California Institute of Technology, Pasadena, California, for research on the ecology and neuroethology of the oilbird (*Steatornis caripensis*).

No. 1611: To Dr. William Meijer, University of Kentucky, Lexington, Kentucky, in support of a botanical expedition in Bali and Celebes.

No. 1612: To Dr. John J. Terborgh, Princeton University, Princeton, New Jersey, to study the group structure and feeding ecology of peccaries in Peru.

No. 1613: To Dr. Fred Barker, U.S. Geological Survey, Denver, Colorado, for research on volcanic rocks of Micronesia.

No. 1614: To Dr. Arthur M. Shapiro, University of California, Davis, California, for a study of photoperiodism and physiological ecology of a relict equatorial alpine butterfly (*Reliquia santamarta*), Colombia.

No. 1615: To Dr. James E. Böhlke, Academy of Natural Sciences of Philadelphia, Philadelphia, Pennsylvania, for further collecting and ichthyological exploration of the Río Nichare, Venezuela.

No. 1616: To Dr. Robert H. Dyson, Jr., University of Pennsylvania, Philadelphia, Pennsylvania, for archeological explorations at Tal-i Malyan, Fars, Iran.

No. 1617: To Alexander Marshack, Peabody Museum of Archaeology and Ethnology, Harvard University, Cambridge, Massachusetts, for an analysis of Paleolithic symbol systems in the USSR.

No. 1618: To Dr. Dennis J. Stanford, National Museum of Natural History, Smithsonian Institution, Washington, D.C., for archeological investigations of the Selby and Dutton mammoth-kill sites, Colorado.

No. 1619: To Dr. Eric R. Craine, Stewart Observatory, University of Arizona, Tucson, Arizona, for a deep near-infrared photographic sky survey.

No. 1620: To Dr. John D. Kraus, Ohio State University, Columbus, Ohio, for preparation of transparent overlay maps for the Palomar–National Geographic Society sky survey.

No. 1621: To Dr. Robert R. Warner, University of California, Santa Barbara, California, for a study of behavioral ecology of sex change in tropical reef fishes, Secas Islands and San Blas Islands.

No. 1622: To Dr. Nicholas C. Collins, Erindale College, Mississauga, Ontario, Canada, to study life-history variations in organisms from simple environments.

No. 1623: To Dr. Michael Norton-Griffiths, Oxford University, Oxford,

England, in support of the project "Ecological Surveying in East Rudolf, Kenya."

No. 1624: To James A. Baldwin, University of California, Davis, California, to study the pig complex of New Guinea in relation to culture and ecology.

No. 1625: To Reed F. Stewart, Bridgewater State College, Bridgewater, Massachusetts, to study West African settlement geography along a linguistic and environmental transect.

No. 1626: To Dr. Bernard Nietschmann, University of Michigan, Ann Arbor, Michigan, for research on the exploitation and ecology of sea turtles and dugongs, Torres Strait, northern Australia.

No. 1627: To Dr. William C. Mahaney, Atkinson College, York University, Downsville, Ontario, Canada, to study the Quaternary history of Mount Kenya, East Africa.

No. 1628: To Dr. Fred H. Behnken, Texas Tech University, Lubbock, Texas, for a study of Permian conodont paleoecology, Wyoming Shelf region.

No. 1629: To Dr. Gale A. Bishop, Georgia Southern College, Statesboro, Georgia, for research on the paleobiogeography and evolution of Late Cretaceous crabs of North America.

No. 1630: To Donald W. Sparling, Jr., University of North Dakota, Grand Forks, North Dakota, for a study of behavioral isolating mechanisms between greater prairie chickens and sharp-tailed grouse.

No. 1631: To Dr. Ralph M. Wetzel, University of Connecticut, Storrs, Connecticut, in further support of his researches on the mammals of Paraguay.

No. 1632: To John N. Postgate, Cambridge, England, in support of archeological excavation of the Sumerian city of Abu Salabikh, Iraq.

No. 1633: To Dr. Ronald A. Nussbaum, University of Michigan, Ann Arbor, Michigan, for research on the origin and evolution of the amphibian fauna of the Seychelles Islands, Indian Ocean.

No. 1634: To Dr. David L. Pearson, Pennsylvania State University, University Park, Pennsylvania, for a pantropic comparison of lowland-forest bird-community structure.

No. 1635: To Dr. Jared M. Diamond, University of California, Los Angeles, California, for a study of distributional patchiness in birds of Tropical Pacific islands.

No. 1636: To Dr. Frank C. Craighead, Jr., Environmental Research Institute, Moose, Wyoming, for continued research toward tracking raptors by satellite.

No. 1637: To Dr. Patricia D. Moehlman, University of Wisconsin, Madison, Wisconsin, to continue her studies of the social organization and ecology of jackals on the Serengeti Plain, Tanzania.

No. 1638: To Dr. Christopher J. Feare, U.K. Pest Infestation Control Laboratory, Worplesdon, Surrey, England, to study sea-bird ecology and tick distribution in the Indian Ocean.

No. 1639: To Dr. John J. Craighead, Montana Cooperative Wildlife Research Unit, University of Montana, Missoula, Montana, for an analysis of grizzly-bear habitat using LANDSAT multispectral imagery and computer science.

No. 1640: To Dr. James A. Casada, Winthrop College, Rock Hill, South Carolina, for a history of American exploration in Africa.

No. 1641: To Dr. Reuben J. Ross, Jr., Denver, Colorado, for fission-track dating of Lower Paleozoic bentonites in British stratotypes.

No. 1642: To H. Paul Buchheim and Dr. Ronald C. Surdam, University of Wyoming, Laramie, Wyoming, for a paleoecologic study of new fossil catfish localities in the Green River Formation, Wyoming.

No. 1643: To Dr. Anna K. Behrensmeyer, University of California, Santa Cruz, California, for continued analysis of mammal bones from Amboseli National Park, Kenya, as a key to East African paleoecology.

No. 1644: To Dr. Bernice Tannenbaum, University of Washington, Seattle, Washington, for a radiotelemetric study of the oilbird in Venezuela.

No. 1645: To Mrs. Birute M. F. Galdikas-Brindamour, University of California, Los Angeles, California, for her continuing studies of orangutan adaptation in Tanjung Puting Reserve, Borneo.

No. 1647: To Dr. C. Vance Haynes, University of Arizona, Tucson, Arizona, in further support of research on the Quaternary geology of the Libyan Desert.

No. 1648: To Dr. Donald H. Menzel, Center for Astrophysics, Cambridge, Massachusetts, for observation of total solar eclipse of October 23, 1976, southeast Australia.

No. 1649: To Dr. Eldon E. Ball, Australian National University, Canberra City, Australia, in further support of a study of biological colonization of Motmot, a recently formed volcanic island, Papua New Guinea.

No. 1650: To Dr. Harald A. Rehder, National Museum of Natural History, Smithsonian Institution, Washington, D.C., for a study of the marine mollusks of the Tokelau Islands, central Pacific Ocean.

No. 1651: To Dr. James L. Patton, University of California, Berkeley, California, for a study of the biochemical genetics of the Galápagos tortoises.

No. 1652: To Dr. John R. Bockstoce, Old Dartmouth Historical Society, Whaling Museum, New Bedford, Massachusetts, to study the bowhead-whale population of the western Arctic.

No. 1653: To Dr. Talbot H. Waterman, Yale University, New Haven, Connecticut, in continuing support of his research on vision and orientation of marine animals.

No. 1654: To Dr. Douglas W. Marshall, University of Michigan, Ann Arbor, Michigan, for a study of military map sources of the American Revolution.

No. 1655: To Dr. Carl L. Johannessen, University of Oregon, Eugene, Oregon, to study the distribution and uses of black-boned chickens in Middle America.

No. 1656: To Dr. Joel R. Gat, Weizmann Institute of Science, Rehovot, Israel, for a study of the limnology and ecology of the Dead Sea system.

No. 1657: To Miss Diane P. Gifford, University of Nevada, Reno, Nevada, for a follow-up taphonomic check on wild-herbivore carcasses, Kenya.

No. 1658: To Dr. William D. Turnbull, Field Museum of Natural History, Chicago, Illinois, in support of a search for Cenozoic fossil vertebrates in Australian Pilbara and Canning Basin Areas.

No. 1659: To Dr. Charles Walcott, State University of New York, Stony Brook, New York, to study the behavior of dusky and southern bottle-nosed dolphins.

No. 1660: To Dr. Donald C. Johanson, Cleveland Museum of Natural History, Cleveland, Ohio, for paleoanthropological research in Hadar, Central Afar, Ethiopia.

No. 1661: To Dr. Jefferson Chapman, University of Tennessee, Knoxville, Tennessee, for early site location and testing in the proposed Tellico Reservoir, Tennessee.

No. 1662: To Dr. Robert J. Sharer, University of Pennsylvania, Philadelphia, Pennsylvania, for archeological investigations at Quirigua, Guatemala.

No. 1663: To Dr. William B. Hubbard, Jr., University of Arizona, Tucson, Arizona, for photometric observations of the Uranus occultation on March 10, 1977.

No. 1664: To Dr. Fred N. White, University of California, Los Angeles, California, for a study of nesting energetics of African hornbills.

No. 1665: To Dr. Dagmar I. Werner, Charles Darwin Research Station, Galápagos, Guayaquil, Ecuador, in further support of her study of the population ecology and social behavior of the Galápagos land iguanas.

No. 1666: To Dr. Craig G. MacFarland, Charles Darwin Research Station, Galápagos, Guayaquil, Ecuador, to study the population ecology of the East Pacific green turtles in the Galápagos Islands.

No. 1667: To Dr. José F. Bonaparte, Universidad Nacional de Tucumán, Tucumán, Argentina, for research on Jurassic and Cretaceous terrestrial vertebrates of South America.

No. 1668: To William Belton, Smithsonian Institution, Washington, D.C., for a survey of the birds of Rio Grande do Sul, Brazil.

No. 1669: To Dr. Frederick A. Urquhart, University of Toronto, Toronto, Canada, to study the northward migration of the monarch butterfly from its overwintering site in Mexico.

No. 1670: To Dr. John R. Krebs and Malcolm L. Hunter, Jr., Oxford University, Oxford, England, for a study of geographical variation in bird song.

No. 1671: To Dr. Ofer Bar-Yosef, Hebrew University, Jerusalem, Israel, to study the origins of pastoralism in southern Sinai.

No. 1672: To Elizabeth L. Meyerhoff, Cambridge University, Cambridge, England, to study the role of women among the agricultural and pastoral Pokot, Kenya.

No. 1673: To Dr. John A. Graham, University of California, Berkeley, California, in further support of his archeological investigations at Abaj Takalik, Guatemala.

No. 1674: To Drs. Joseph S. Balsano and Ellen M. Rasch, University of Wisconsin-Parkside, Kenosha, Wisconsin, for an ichthyological study of competitive interaction in bisexual/unisexual complexes of *Poecilia* in northwestern Mexico.

No. 1675: Dr. Lytton J. Musselman, Old Dominion University, Norfolk, Virginia, to study log-fern hybrids (*Dryopteris*) in the Great Dismal Swamp, Virginia.

No. 1676: To Dr. John M. Legler, University of Utah, Salt Lake City, Utah, for research on the biology of sympatry in eastern Australian chelid turtles.

No. 1677: To Dr. Thomas R. Howell, University of California, to study reproductive adaptations of the Egyptian plover (*Pluvianus aegyptius*).

No. 1678: To Mrs. Nicole Duplaix-Hall, New York Zoological Society, New York City, for field study of the giant Brazilian otter in Surinam.

No. 1679: To Dr. Ian Tattersall, American Museum of Natural History, New York City, for a study of the ecology and behavior of the lemurs of the Comoro Archipelago, Indian Ocean.

No. 1680: To Dr. Frederick W. Lange, National Museum of Costa Rica, San José, Costa Rica, for archeological investigations, Bay of Culebra, Costa Rica.

No. 1681: To Dr. Marcio Veloz Maggiolo, University of Santo Domingo, Dominican Republic, for archeological investigations of caves and rock shelters in the Dominican Republic.

No. 1682: To Dr. Kenneth L. Brown, East Carolina University, Greenville, North Carolina, for an archeological-ethnohistoric study of the development of Central Quichuan civilization, Guatemala.

No. 1683: To Dr. Krzysztof Serkowski, Lunar and Planetary Laboratory, University of Arizona, Tucson, Arizona, in furtherance of a study for detecting other planetary systems in the universe.

No. 1684: To Dr. Ralph A. Lewin, Scripps Institution of Oceanography, La Jolla, California, to collect prochlorophytic algae for biochemical and physiological study.

No. 1685: To Dr. Roger S. Payne, New York Zoological Society, New York City, to study singing and other behavior in humpback whales.

No. 1686: To Dr. Jack B. Fisher, Fairchild Tropical Garden, Miami, Florida, for field study and collection of rattan palms in Asian rainforests.

No. 1688: To Dr. Carl D. Hopkins, University of Minnesota, Minneapolis, Minnesota, to study the ecology and ethology of the Gabon mormyroids.

No. 1689: To Dr. Lionel A. Stange, Universidad Nacional de Tucumán, Tucumán, Argentina, to continue field studies of South American Neuroptera.

No. 1690: To Dr. Archie F. Carr, University of Florida, Gainesville, Florida, to study nest-site selection in the green turtle (*Chelonia mydas*) at Ascension Island.

No. 1691: To Dr. George B. Schaller, New York Zoological Society, New York City, for a study of the ecology and behavior of the jaguar in Mato Grosso, Brazil.

No. 1692: To Dr. Owen S. Rye, Australian National Museum, Canberra, Australia, for a study and recording of the work of Arab potters in Israel.

No. 1693: To Dr. Ivor Noël-Hume, Colonial Williamsburg Foundation, Williamsburg, Virginia, for an archeological investigation of 17th-century settlement sites at Carter's Grove, Virginia.

No. 1694: To Dr. J. David Ligon, University of New Mexico, Albuquerque, New Mexico, to study the adaptive significance of communality in the green wood hoopoe in Kenya.

No. 1695: To Dr. Ronald E. Chardon, Louisiana State University, Baton Rouge, Louisiana, for scientific testing of the accuracy of early historical maps.

No. 1696: To Dr. William B. Size, Emory University, Atlanta, Georgia, for a petrologic investigation of layered igneous intrusion in the Norwegian caledonides.

No. 1697: To Dr. S. David Webb, University of Florida, Gainesville, Florida, for research on fossil vertebrates of Central America and the Great American Interchange.

No. 1698: To Dr. Larry J. Marshall, Princeton University, Princeton, New Jersey, to study correlation and geomagnetic chronology of Late Cenozoic South American land-mammal ages.

No. 1699: To Dr. James R. Karr, University of Illinois, Champaign, Illinois, to study turnover rates in tropical-forest bird communities.

No. 1700: To Dr. Jane Goodall, Gombe Stream Research Institute, Dar es Salaam, Tanzania, to continue her investigations of free-living chimpanzees at Gombe, Kahama Community.

No. 1701: To Dr. Dian J. Fossey, Karisoke Research Centre, Ruhengeri, Rwanda, to continue her research on behavioral and ecological determinants of the free-ranging mountain gorilla.

Index